He
wi

Al
sin

Here is the most handsome, fascinating man—
a junior, but old enough to be a senior, and he
wants me?

But a troublesome thought wouldn't leave her
head. "Holden? What did you mean by not
wanting me to be 'involved in this mess'? Are
you saying I can't join your group?"

He looked up from her clavicle, which he was
just beginning to nuzzle. "That's exactly what
I'm saying."

"I am a scholar of sadistic serial killers, but I'm
also a
spat   Don't
bar n   me
out c   f all
of i   uest,
"N   her
pur

Other

Secret Romances

By Erin Cosgrove

THE BAADER-MEINHOF AFFAIR

by

ERIN COSGROVE

Printed Matter, Inc.

The Baader-Meinhoff Affair   Erin Cosgrove

Published in the United States of America in 2002 by Printed Matter, Inc.
535 West 22nd Street, New York, NY 10011.
Telephone: 212 925 0325, Fax: 212 925 0464.
Website: http://www.printedmatter.org

ISBN: 0-89439-101-4

Edited by Stephanie Salomon and Tracy Lakatua
Design by Ph.D, www.phdla.com and Erin Cosgrove
Fabio appears courtesy of the illustrious Eric Ashenberg.

The Baader-Meinhof Affair is an original book by Erin Cosgrove published by Printed Matter, Inc. All characters in this book have no relation to anyone bearing the same names or characteristics. Any similarity to anyone outside the author's head is purely a result of narcissistic paranoia.

Printed Matter's Publishing Program for Emerging Artists was made possible through the generous support of New York City's Department of Cultural Affairs. Additional support has also been provided by The Andy Warhol Foundation for the Visual Arts, the Elizabeth Firestone Graham Foundation, and the Heyday Foundation.

Printed Matter, Inc. is an independent 501(c)(3) non-profit organization founded in 1976 by artists and art workers with the mission to foster the appreciation, dissemination, and understanding of artists' books and other artists' publications.

Printed Matter, Inc. is not affiliated with, nor a division of, any other non-profit origination.

Printed and bound in Canada

DEDICATION AND FOREWORD

I would like to make a twofold dedication of this work: First is to my comrades and supporters, without whose help this groundbreaking manifesto of romance would not be complete. These highly esteemed Friends of Erin (FOEs) include John Baldessari, Donald Cosgrove, Tracy Lakatua, and the many other heroic fighters and urban *amour* pioneers who daily risk assassination from the Frigid Army, the Cautious Air Force, and their mundane minions—all hated instruments of the trendy and repressive anti-romance dictatorship.

Second, this work is dedicated to the brave comrades who escaped imprisonment in the medieval dungeons of apathetic, halfhearted attempts and self-defeating lies. There, they were subjected to tortures inflicted by those of shamelessly derivative imaginations. Driven by the importance of my trailblazing field guide to Eros, these brave foot soldiers of love risked their very lives to herald the glorious day of my book's publication. These souls, who earned the lofty rank of Patrons of Erin's Only Novel (PEONs), include Eric Ashenberg, Margaret Black, Terry Cosgrove, Fabio, Richard Huffman (author of the forthcoming *The Gun Speaks*), David Platzker, the freedom fighters at the Durfee Foundation, Stephanie Salomon, Michael Hodgson, Clive Piercy, Ph.D, Printed Matter, Inc., and other compatriots whose example we revere, as well as those downed in combat.

The third dedication (for there is always a third fold even when we say it's only twofold,) is to my most beloved member of the resistance, my Collaborator in Romantic Aesthetic Pursuits (CRAP), Hirsch Perlman. Paramour, confidante, brewer of morning coffee—in addition to other notorious qualities, I am eternally grateful for his tactical support and his exemplary contribution to the underground revolution.

With this romance I am embarking on a new era, an era in which no crimson lips will remain unkissed, no silky skin will linger uncaressed, and no drippy threshold to ecstasy will be left unpenetrated. I urge all who read this manifesto, and decide that they can no longer remain inactive, to follow its instructions and join the struggle now. You may start by circulating its contents; make mimeographed copies or print a booklet (although in this latter case, armed struggle itself will be necessary). A third option is to shout your newfound love from the highest hills or, if no high hills are available, you may substitute mouthing the words directly onto a lover's naked body. I ask this because, under any theory and under any circumstances, the duty of every lover is to make love and of every romantic to make romance.

Hippies of yesteryear were shortsighted with their "summer of love." We romance revolutionaries scoff at their seasonal antics and insist it is only a revolution if it is sustainable. The Hippies-*cum*-Yuppies' insignificant season has passed. Their "flower power" is nothing more than a paper tiger lily. There's no getting through to the defenders of the loveless status quo. Why? Because it isn't love or ideals that drive them—it's fear of death. Ridiculous! You have to be *alive* to die. We defy the lazy, self-involved ways of those who clog the flow of the revolution with their passionless tenure. We're young and strong. No one can tell us we're wrong. Love is a battlefield. We patriots of passion are prepared to fight on this battlefield like soldiers and to love like untamed, sweaty wildebeests.

The label "maudlin" or "bad writing" no longer has the negative connotation it once did. It has acquired a new color: purple. It is the purple of royalty and, always, purple prose. This is not the purple of bulbous dinosaurs who insist on peddling their flaccid version of love. ("I love you. You love me. We're a happy family." Indeed!) "Can't we all just get along?" they plead. No, we cannot. Our purple demands you choose a side. It is the violet that tinges the blood of violence. It is the lilac glint of sweat licked off a loved one's face. It is the puce-drenched moment you seize in toe-clenching rapture, trilling with pleasure. It is the indecent plum on the end of an impudent thumb. It is the rapid, amethyst breaths of passion and the heavy beating of an engorged, purple heart. Today, to be "maudlin" or a "romantic" is a quality that ennobles any revolutionary who is engaged in a passionate struggle against the shameful anti-romance dictatorship and its calculating, cynical atrocities.

Love is the saddle. Ride, people, ride!

Erin Cosgrove   B. 1969

PROLOGUE

As a result of her fascination with serial killers, Mara had to say goodbye to the family she barely knew. It was at times like these that Mara wished she came from a normal family.

Not Brady Bunch normal, but, you know, normal.

It was true that they were staring down on her with that obligatory look of parental pride in their bespectacled eyes. It was also true that there had been no arguments over the toaster oven, the large, blue bath towel, and the abridged Freud reader set she claimed as her own. And the ride up wasn't filled with fights, advice-giving, or endless nagging. But, as with all interactions with her parents, there was something too removed about it.

Although her parents loved their only child unconditionally, they knew no natural medium to express their love. Their ability to casually—let alone intimately—connect with anyone was effaced by years of staring at journals and research papers. Her mother was immersed in entomology, specifically the sex life and reproductive cycle of the dung beetle. Her father struggled daily with sociological applications of inertia theory as it applied to monogamous relationships. His research tracked the decline of desirability in the face of prolonged faithfulness. Consumed as they were with their academic careers, their relationship with Mara was, at best, distant.

Often Mara felt an irresistible urge to do something horrible to grab their attention, even if only for a moment. But she was a born chicken, a shirking milksop, and had no heart for acting out. Mara expressed her frustration and loneliness in much the same way her parents did theirs: through books.

In her solitude Mara consumed stacks of books. Her particular favorites were those on serial killers. Envious of their ability to take action (albeit lethal action), Mara spent much of her adolescence researching sadistic serial killers' behavior patterns.

9

It was this obsessive research displayed in a paper she submitted to *Serial Serial: A Quarterly of the Scientific Study of Serial Killers* that attracted the attention of Professor Mahler, noted abnormal psychiatrist and professor at Norden College. Professor Mahler invited Mara to leave the University of Wisconsin-Oshkosh after her freshman year to study at Norden, a very exclusive, upstate-New York college with a lavish endowment and a pricey tuition. To sweeten the deal he offered her a full scholarship and an enviable internship. So, of course, her parents were proud.

But, she thought, *there is no real real-ness to their pride.*

Mara was indeed a product of her parents, but she felt an inner turmoil they had never known. Against her restrained Midwestern upbringing and the ever-present cynicism of her generation, Mara, at heart, was a romantic: sentimental, gushy, tearing at Hallmark commercials and outraged at injustices in the newspaper. Brimming over with the milk of human kindness, she would cry at the sight of it in a spilt format.

She always struggled to hide her sentimental deviation, and this last break of the parental tether (moving clear across country) was no exception. Mara felt, with no surprise, pressure build in the back of her eyes.

I will not cry, she thought.

They had already dragged her scant belongings to her dorm room. All that was left was the goodbye.

Miserable and alone, she felt that if something didn't change now, then it would never change. Her relationship with her parents would forever be a sealed, empty container.

They stood staring at each other across a gulf of failed communication: The smiling parents, dressed with the same degree of fashion oblivion, on one side looking like a single unit; Mara on the other, feeling empty and angry. She knew nothing her parents could do would satisfy the heightened meaning she'd given to this departure.

"*Hamlet,* Act I, Scene iii, lines 59 though 87." Her mother ironically cited the hackneyed advice of Polonius to his son Laertes with an unwavering smile.

"Kahlil Gibran, *On Children*, Chapter 4, lines 4 through

10," ♪ her daughter answered, and cringed internally at the triteness of her response.

The father smiled at the two and, to any passerby, everything seemed peachy.

"Do you need some cash?" her father asked, offering the proverbial non-Oedipal stand-in for affection between fathers and daughters.

"You already gave me some."

"Here," he said as he shuffled through his wallet. "Buy yourself a new outfit."

He handed her a fifty, which she took simply to end the conversation. Mara glanced at the well-heeled students who

♪ Give thy thoughts no tongue,
Nor any unproportioned thought his act.
Be thou familiar, but by no means vulgar.
Those friends thou hast, and their adoption tried,
Grapple them to thy soul with hoops of steel;
But do not dull thy palm with entertainment
Of each new-hatch'd, unfledged comrade. Beware
Of entrance to a quarrel, but being in,
Bear't that the opposed may beware of thee.
Give every man thy ear, but few thy voice;
Take each man's censure, but reserve thy judgment.
Costly thy habit as thy purse can buy,
But not express'd in fancy; rich, not gaudy;
For the apparel oft proclaims the man,
And they in France of the best rank and station
Are of a most select and generous chief in that.
Neither a borrower nor a lender be;
For loan oft loses both itself and friend,
And borrowing dulls the edge of husbandry.
This above all: to thine ownself be true,
And it must follow, as the night the day,
Thou canst not then be false to any man.
Farewell: my blessing season this in thee!

♪ Your children are not your children.
They are the sons and daughters of Life's longing for itself.
They come through you but not from you,
And though they are with you, yet they belong not to you.
You may give them your love but not your thoughts.
For they have their own thoughts.
You may house their bodies but not their souls,
For their souls dwell in the house of tomorrow, which you cannot visit, not even in your dreams.
You may strive to be like them, but seek not to make them like you.

slouched in their flawlessly appointed casual couture and knew the bill wouldn't even remotely cut it.

Not quite five-foot-one and so petite that she had trouble buying clothes in her size, Mara often felt like a child in the world of adults. Her untamable, closely cropped hair didn't help her confidence problem. "I can never do anything with it," she would say.

At her old school, Mara never overcame a feeling of separateness from others, which was instilled in her psyche at an early age by her parents. Now here at Norden she imagined herself completely lost in a world of the well-dressed and beautiful giants.

"Okay then," said the socially inept daughter.

"Okay then," said the socially inept mother and father in unison. Mara turned on her heels and stepped away from her parents for what felt like the last time.

"We love you, dear, and are very proud of you," the mother said to her back.

But the gulf of need that separated the young adult and the parents was so deep that the phrase was like a Band-Aid over a gaping, hemorrhaging machete wound.

She walked away.

Mara headed in the direction of the dormitories, but soon realized that she had no idea which one was hers. Her campus map and official residential information was in her parents' car, heading back to Wisconsin. She kept walking forward, however, feeling it was only that motion that kept her from crying. She scanned the old, stone buildings covered with ivy and punctuated with gargoyles. None of them looked familiar. But, then again, nothing about this college was familiar to her.

Even the drive on a winding wagon road through the lush, darkened woods of upstate New York was visually jarring. Norden College, five miles from Norden Town, stood on a hill surrounded by woods. It was stately, like the mansion of a rich recluse. No, it wasn't that Norden failed to look like the fine institution its catalogue promised. Conversely, it was too much like Mara had envisioned it. It was very collegiate, but in a sort of fantastical way. In her fantasy she didn't clash with her surroundings. Now that she was here, she felt grossly out of place and tacky, like a blackhead on a prom queen.

I'll ask the next person I see where my dorm is, she thought to herself, building the nerve to make a connection with some future classmate.

Passing by her third stately, ivy-covered edifice, she saw a young man reclining between the paws of one of the two statues of lions guarding either side of the steps to the Von Trapp Memorial Library. The first thing Mara noticed about him was that he seemed somehow out of place.

Was it his dark, tousled hair? His large, hollowed cheekbones? His lean and very masculine way of casually exacting a nonchalance that runway models would kill for? She couldn't tell. But somehow, discovering him there, she could imagine a place for herself already carved out by other misfits. She could envision her smaller frame in that very spot, curled up among the claws of the lion, engrossed in a good book…or a good man?

But the handsome man, who she'd been staring at for quite some time without saying a word, interrupted her thoughts. Even more distressing was that, by his incredulous look, he seemed to know where her eyes had been fixed: on the small patch of skin showing between his thin, tattered, long-sleeved shirt and his dark-blue workman-style pants.

Amused, he raised an arching, dark brow, which disappeared in the coal-black bangs strewn haphazardly across his forehead. Jumping from his stoop to tower over her, he rubbed one sleepy eye with the knuckle of an extremely large and, by all appearances, powerful hand and said, "Is there something I should be made aware of?" in a voice filled with jest.

Mara didn't know how to respond. She scanned the question for malice or disdain. She guessed that it was clean. What next? Should she answer the question? Should she explain to him that she was off in a daydream and wasn't really staring at him? Or should she ignore his question and try to find out how to get to her dorm room once and for all?

I have no training for this, she thought.

One look in his eyes and she forgot her social inadequacies. He had the most fascinating eyes she had ever seen.

What are they? Brown? Blue? Green?

They seemed to flash in and out of all the different colors, framed by long black lashes that Mara thought must be the envy of most girls. Without even wanting to, she reassessed his appearance.

He was tall and beardless, with a magnetically appealing face. His frame was tough, lean, but relaxed. He was a full head above the other young men she saw on campus.

He must be a foot and a half taller than me, she thought.

Remarkably broad shoulders were even further accentuated by his slim hips. All of this fine musculature led to an astonishingly handsome face, which was kindled with a sort of swaggering, intense beauty.

Mara realized she wasn't making matters any better by gawking at him, mouth agape. She struggled for something to say as he regarded her, large hands loose at his sides.

"I'm sorry, I'm new here and..." she couldn't continue.

All at once the utopian daydream of fitting in was confounded by reality. She could barely ask someone for directions. Her spirits sank. Mara felt doomed to perpetual isolation.

The enticing man opened his mouth, but before he could speak, Mara ran away to spare herself the derision. Tears welled up as she ran through the unfamiliar campus. She ran to the dense forest surrounding the college and gathered her short and dainty limbs around the exposed roots of a wild oak tree. There she cried, cursing herself with each bitter tear.

CHAPTER 1

It is essential to foster an understanding between you, gentle reader, and Mara. I fear I've already failed. 🖋

Despite my patient detailing of Mara's lonely past, you scorn her poise, or lack thereof, when encountered by an attractive male. Perhaps you presume she lacks mettle or a certain spirit needed for a romance novel? You are even convinced that you could render a more suitable heroine and are already smug in your feelings of superiority to her.

I protest your hasty judgment. You have yet to see what she is made of and this first meeting with the stunning-but-mysterious hero is no litmus test for her true capabilities.

Furthermore, was it so wrong for Mara to shed a tear when faced by her demons? Is not vulnerability also strength? Which survives the hurricane? The stately oak? The brittle pier? Or is it the spineless jellyfish that better weathers the storm? While the defenseless jelly appears to waver weakly with each wave, is it not in fact exercising superior strength with its tactical nonresistance? Or perhaps you think Mara should swallow her tears and harden her exterior to more closely resemble the cruel automatons you seem to relish?

Mara may not be perfect, but she is not hardened and bitter, as some are. She bears no resemblance to those enemies of romance whose petty need to pass their frigid judgment on others is surpassed only by their ravenous appetite for entertainment.

Without restraint I lend them the wealth of my mind. I bend low that they may steal a peek at my innermost soul. I strip the vestments of artifice and pretense, exposing my nakedest flesh. I slice, marinate, and skewer myself on their salacious and capricious gaze and in return they infect me with their faultfinding and malice.

🖋 Comrades, this is the greatest obstacle of every romance revolutionary. We must appeal to the masses while still fighting the disastrous expectations within which the masses, our readership, operate.

All this torment I sustain for you…
You, my dear, dear reader.
Be fair.

When dusk came and Mara imagined that the puffiness in her eyes had abated, she eventually left the woods and found her dorm without assistance. Crossing a plushy, carpeted hallway, Mara found two girls, impeccably dressed in T-shirts, men's boxer shorts, fuzzy animal slippers, and an assortment of things that clip into strategically messy hair, lounged in front of her door. Their conversation stopped when they saw Mara approaching.

"I hope that isn't our new hall-mate," said the one whose face was that shade of orange only attained by tanning bed overexposure.

"THAT can't be our new hall-mate," said the one whose obvious cosmetic surgery, a dainty little button nose on a big-boned, handsome face, was an aesthetic disaster. "Norden has standards. I barely got in and I'm a triple leg'."

Mara fixed her gaze on the lock to her door as she tried to squeeze past the two young women who watched her with exaggerated looks of disgust.

"Look, Penny, it has a key," said the oranger one with thick ankles but perfectly white teeth.

"Maybe we should report this to the R.A.," said the taller one with the cut-and-paste nose.

Just as Mara unlocked her door, Penny-the-nose-job victim blocked it with her arm.

"Um, excuse me," Penny gave Mara an exaggerated once-over. "Aren't you going to introduce yourself?"

"She looks like a German major," said not-Penny.

"Ooo, I'm shaking," said Penny, who then attempted to shake but only managed to bounce her disproportionately ample breasts that started suspiciously at her clavicles.

The two girls broke into a fit of hysterics and fell against the wall. Mara used their momentary distraction to make a break for her room, but not-Penny put her arm out, blocking the way again. It was clear they wanted a conflict. Mara weighed her options. She didn't see a way to avoid being sucked into their miasma of immaturity, so she attempted naiveté.

"My name is Mara. I'm here to study psychology and do an internship under Dr. Mahler."

Silence.

"Um...what's your major?" asked Mara.

The girls were confused. Their object was asserting itself as subject and not a subject of prey. They tried to reestablish their dominance.

"Ooh, what's that accent?" asked Penny, who, Mara noted, did not have three legs.

"I don't know, sounds like the sticks to me," answered the orange one, still blocking her entrance.

"Yes, she looks corn-fed. I mean, look at the size of her head," said Penny, fluffing her highlighted blond-brown hair.

"What is that place between the East Coast and the West Coast?" asked not-Penny, orangely.

"Is there such a place, Tippy?" asked Penny.

The orange girl, Tippy, screwed her eyes to the ceiling and replied, "They have to grow dweebs somewhere—." She stopped midsentence and hit Penny while breaking into a smile that showed nearly all of her alarmingly white teeth.

Penny continued taunting, "Well there has to be a mistake because there is a one-dweeb-per-hallway policy and we already have our resident dweeb."

Mara followed Tippy's eyes and saw that the handsome young man whom had she fled only hours earlier was standing right behind the two girls.

He said in a tone that was hard and ruthless, "I hope you girls aren't giving this freshman a hard time," and laid a large, rough hand on each of their shoulders.

Penny turned her pug nose around to stare at the chest of the very impressive man. She immediately broke into an overly large but less-than-winning smile and threw her shoulders back to give him a better view of her gravity-defying bosom investment.

"Hi, Holden, how was your summer?" Penny said, batting her lashes.

It was clear to Mara that Holden had currency with the girls. Holden frowned and ignored her question. Instead, he looked at Mara and asked, "Are these girls harassing you?"

Mara, embarrassed by her previous behavior, couldn't speak and just shook her head.

Holden searched Mara's catlike eyes, whose stellar beauty no amount of makeup could rival. The stare lasted a beat longer than Mara's comfort level. Then he pulled his hand off Penny's shoulder and reached out toward Mara, as if to brush a hair away from her daintily pointed face. A flicker of apprehension coursed though her as she watched his hand move past her face and land firmly on the arm that blocked her entrance.

"Ow!" whined Tippy.

Holden smiled and pulled Tippy away from Mara's door.

"I don't know if you realize it, but you guys were blocking her way and you know how I feel about people messing with my friends," he said with a glimmer of humor in his kaleidoscope eyes.

He called me his friend! Mara bubbled with excitement.

Tippy nodded, causing the hair piled on her head to fall over her eyes.

Penny just stared straight ahead, her eyes like two colored hard-boiled eggs.

"Good," said Holden, and dropped her arm. "Now run along."

The two girls did as he said, but slowly, each turning their heads to get a better view of him as they retreated. They stopped four doors down and watched Holden and Mara from a safe distance.

Holden shook his manful head and said to Mara, "Don't let them ruin your impression of this place. It's all right once you settle in. And they're harmless, too. You'll see." He shot a threatening glance at the two girls that caused them to squeal and dive into their room, only to peek out a few seconds later.

"What did they mean when they said I looked like a German major?" Mara asked, trying to recover from the utter shock that such a charming man would talk to her.

As if reminded of something unpleasant, his amber-green

eyes grew remote. Holden sent one more scathing glance at the two girls down the hall and they shrieked and jumped back into their room. He then turned to Mara, clearly disturbed.

"Some friends and I have an interest in the German language and some...*aspects* of their, uh, *culture*," he said hesitantly.

Mara's eyes widened. Where she came from, if young people shared an interest in "German culture" that meant one of two things: an insatiable lust for sauerbraten, anything ending in wurst, lederhosen, and lagers—or Neo-Nazis.

"So, you like sausage, then?" Mara asked.

"I can take it or leave it," Holden responded affably.

She lowered her head and her voice unintentionally sank, "Oh, I see..."

"Oh! No!" Holden exclaimed, laughing.

Mara looked up at his extraordinary, cerulean eyes, which blazed and glowed.

"No, we're not racists, or card-carrying members of the KKK or anything, if that's what you're thinking."

Mara let out a sigh of relief. Up until that point she didn't realize that she had been holding her breath.

"Then what *is* your interest in German culture?" she asked, not accusingly, but really wanting to know.

Holden again looked off into the distance as if trying to find just the right way to describe the indescribable. "Well, without boring you, we share an interest in student movements of the mid-sixties to the early eighties."

Mara waited for him to continue.

"Really, it wouldn't interest you," he said dismissively. Then he gave her a deeper stare. "You're not a German major, are you?"

"No, psychology with a minor in communications. At least that's what I think."

Holden was genuinely relieved. "Good. You don't want to get mixed up in it."

"In...?" Mara asked.

"Never mind," Holden quickly replied, his face clouded with uneasiness.

For some reason his mysterious demeanor made Mara want

to fall into his arms right then and there, but she knew she had to keep the conversation going to keep him by her side.

"Thanks for helping me," she said.

He was suddenly buoyant. "You're welcome, or, as Jesus would say, 'Giveth of my cup and expect it to overfloweth.' Uh, say, you could pay me back if you want..."

Mara involuntarily beamed. "What exactly would this entail?" she asked.

He propped an elbow on the door fame above her head, seductively closing the charged space between them. Mara noticed that Holden was the first tall man who didn't make her feel short. She wondered how that could be and what it could mean.

"This would entail a dinner at my place," he said huskily. "Dinner...and a meeting. It's a planning meeting for our Free Mumia Benefit. Do you know who he is?"

Mara's heart was so busy singing that she could barely keep her mind on his question. She forced her mind to consider the name.

Mumia…

She had some vague recollection of seeing it on posters at the Oshkosh campus the year before.

"He's some sort of activist, right?"

"That's right," he said through slightly lowered eyelashes, his hot breath just grazing her brow. "And he was charged with murder by fascist pigs. They have him in prison to this day. And he's black, which proves I'm not a racist."

Mara couldn't believe what she was seeing.

Is he flirting with me? After I acted like such a fool?

"I'd love to, uh, help out," she uttered.

"Great. It's this Saturday at eight. Do you know Regan?"

"The former puppet president?" Mara asked with a bit of play in her voice. She was trying to flirt back but wasn't quite sure how to go about it.

He laughed appreciatively, causing Mara's heart to skip a beat.

He must be interested in me, she thought.

"No, I mean Regan Thresh. It's pronounced like the Muppet, puppet, whatever, but it's spelled like the girl in *The*

Exorcist. She's just down the hall from you."

"No, I don't know anyone here," Mara responded, slightly disappointed that he had brought up another girl.

Holden pushed off the wall and, offering his large and finely formed hand, said, "I'm sorry, I'm Holden Rife. And you are…?"

"Mara, and a sophomore, by the way."

He looked at her, not understanding.

"You told those girls that I was a freshman. I'm actually a sophomore, a transfer student."

Holden nodded sagely. "I apologize, Mara." He laughed at the smile that brightened her face. "You have a very nice smile."

Mara was dumbstruck. She had no idea what to do with a compliment. Whenever she heard one she assumed it was sarcasm. Although she was almost sure he meant it, she didn't know what it *meant.* She just continued to smile. With time, the lingering grin lost its freshness and began to feel grotesquely forced.

"Okay!" he laughed. "You can stop smiling now! Your point is well taken."

Relieved that this time her social ineptitude was interpreted as a witticism, Mara recomposed her face.

"See that door down the hall that's painted black with a red star? That's Regan's room. She's coming to the dinner meeting, too, and can give you a ride. I live off-campus. So be sure to introduce yourself to her."

"I will," she said. She looked into his volcanic eyes and knew that it was the answer to anything he could ask of her. Body? Soul? Her answer would be, "I will."

Holden stared at her for a second longer. Then he laughed and said, "I got to go. But if I don't see you around I'll look forward to seeing you Saturday."

"Yeah, thanks again!"

"Don't thank me yet. If you agree to the cause, I'm going to put you to work." He bent down and playfully touched her lightly on the cheek, causing a passionate fluttering to rise at the back of her neck. Then he walked away, knocking on the black door with the red star before disappearing behind it. A knobby, white hand with long, crimson nails pulled the door closed.

Mara's quickened pulse was beginning to quiet when the door to Tippy and Penny's room opened and the two girls rushed toward Mara in a blonde blur. She quickly jumped inside her room and almost had the door shut when a fuzzy pink kitty slipper blocked its closing.

"Ow! Open up! Yeah, open up!" demanded the two voices on the other side of the door.

Mara reluctantly opened her door.

Tippy and Penny came bouncing in like a pair of puppies. Penny took the chair, Tippy pulled up a box. They motioned for Mara to sit on her bed.

"I'm Penny, she's Tippy. So, are you and Holden, like, dating?" asked Penny as she took off her slipper and started sticking little white foam pads between her toes.

"Yeah, you two seemed kind of smoochy. What's up with that?" asked Tippy.

Mara, who still hadn't recovered from her second run-in with Holden, had no idea what to make of the social about-face of the two girls. Although she distrusted them, she felt obliged to treat their belated attempts at friendship with a reciprocal friendliness.

She answered earnestly. "I just met him today, actually."

"Mmm," said Penny to Tippy.

"Aha!" said Tippy to Penny.

Penny turned to Mara and said conspiratorially, "How on earth did you catch that hunk?"

Mara looked at Penny, simultaneously surprised at her directness and delighted that an outside observer thought that Holden liked her.

"You think he's interested in me?" Mara whispered.

Penny looked at Tippy with raised eyebrows and said, "Isn't she cute?" She turned to Mara, "Mara, dear, yes. He's interested. What did he say to you?"

Mara pursed her red lips as she thought. "He said that it's good I'm not a German major."

"That's interesting," Tippy said. "Do you know why?"

Mara shook her head.

Penny was applying pink nail polish to her left foot when she said to Tippy, "Look, she has no idea what's going on. She just got here today." Then she turned her snub nose to Mara, "'kay, here's the deal: Holden is a catch. But you're going to have your work totally cut out for you. First of all he's from money."

Tippy nodded and added, "Yeah, old money." Then she giggled.

Penny rolled her eyes at Tippy's interruption but spoke on, "He stands to inherit a fortune, but he's the black sheep in his family, a rebel. You know, idealistic and misunderstood and all that."

"Plus he's not all that bright," Tippy chimed in.

Penny looked at Mara. "See this is where Tiff and I disagree on the Holden thing. I think he's bright, but not in the regular way measured by grades and fashion sense. Tippy sees this as evidence of his stupidity. But the truth is, either way he needs guidance and he's easily sucked in by strong personalities."

"Which is how he started dating Regan," Tippy said.

Tippy must have noticed Mara clasping and unclasping her slender hands with rising dismay as she listened, because she was quick to add, "But Regan's an evil bitch and he broke up with her and went to the Funny Farm for a year, which is why he's only a junior."

Mara's glowing happiness was fading fast.

"No, Tiff, see, you tell it all wrong—let me tell her!" Penny snapped.

Tippy made a "W" sign with her hands and then proceeded to look for split-ends in her mop of brown-blonde hair.

"They met in the German program two years ago," Penny explained. "For some reason, don't ask me why, but for some reason all of the freaks at school are in the German department. Go figure."

"Which is why we thought you were in the German department. No offense or anything," Tippy voiced artlessly.

Penny gave Tippy a warning look. "'kay, so, they started

getting involved in this German cult thing or something. I
guess it requires them to bathe less and wear ratty clothes
because they all look like homeless Salvation Army rejects.
Anyway, that's what we think, but don't say anything because,
you know, the 'Co-lum-bine' thing. There are definitely some
unstable elements in their group."

Penny mostly mouthed the word "Columbine," so Mara
wasn't even sure if she said Columbine or something else like
Philistine or Golem-brine.

"Anyway, half of them are sloppy, bitter drunks and the
other half are hopelessly stuck in some fantasy world where
losers rule. But they all worship Holden. So every year this
group of drunks and losers do this weird deal where they hold
some kind of weeklong outdoor history play thingy."

"And they don't even get school credit for it. I mean, what's
the point? Duh!" Tippy supplemented Penny's narration.

"The whole town gets involved," Penny continued. "I think
people don't really like it. They're probably only involved
because they're afraid of being thought of as not 'intellectual' or
'liberal' enough or something."

"That's what happens when a town gets too many book-
stores and coffee shops," Tippy quipped.

"Or it could be that they're afraid of Holden's mother.
Anyway, some people think that Holden is in charge of the
group. But if you ask me," Penny leaned into Mara so that her
cold, hard bosom pressed against Mara's arm, "Regan is still in
charge of Holden."

Mara shivered and wondered fearfully how she compared
with the woman behind the black door with the red star.

Tippy nodded. "Yeah, it's so weird!"

Penny continued, "So it was clear to most of us that even
though Holden is a mega-fox and worth millions, he's under
Regan's control. And as big a freak as Holden is, Regan is
doubly so. I heard when they were still dating she threatened a
girl who hit on him..."

"Threatened her how?" Mara asked and gulped back the
panic rioting within her.

Penny pushed her shrunken nose right up to Mara's face.

"She threatened to have her, get this, 'taken out.'" Penny pulled away from Mara and, looking up, said, "But that was almost two years ago. I wasn't even here when that happened and I'm certainly not one to have faith in rumors."

"Still, it's super-creepy," Mara said.

Tippy and Penny, however, weren't paying attention and instead were looking at an intense young woman who stood in Mara's doorway staring with a severe glint in her eye.

Tippy and Penny excused themselves, saying they'd leave Mara to her company and trotted out the door, cringing slightly as they passed the newcomer.

The young woman waited silently until the girls left and then leveled a calculating eye on Mara.

"You're Mara?" she snapped.

"Yes?" Mara answered hesitantly.

"You…are…*Mara?*" she asked again, taking a closer look at Mara's petite figure and catlike eyes.

"Yes!" insisted Mara, now perturbed.

"Well, Mara, you need to be more discriminating about who your friends are." The young woman let herself in and had a seat on her chair.

Mara realized who the caustic woman was and looked at her with new eyes. She was skinny in an anemic way, with a mean slouch that spoke of years of studied delinquency. Long, dyed-red hair hung dryly around her neck. In a certain, more forgiving light, she could be seen as beautiful, but the cruel, dorm-provided fluorescents revealed all of the fairer sex's tricks used to achieve a semblance of beauty. And in her case, she used them poorly. Although striking, she was over-plucked, and too much makeup gave her eyes a blurry, haggard look.

Mara, however, admired the visitor's bold fashion sense. She wore combat boots that looked two sizes too big and a wardrobe of black garments accented by the occasional layer of navy blue. The blue-black *X*s marking her hands were more likely amateur tattoos than errant pen marks. Exciting and a little scary, she had something else that was very attractive to Mara: a fierce confidence that was hard to ignore.

"Do you know who I am, Mara?" the newcomer asked with

the attitude of an interviewer who knows the applicant couldn't possibly qualify for the job.

"Are you...Regan?" Mara asked timorously.

"That's right, I am Regan. Holden says I'm to escort you to his dinner on Saturday. So what exactly is between you and Holden?"

Mara didn't know how to answer. Even if she answered truthfully, she could only say how she was beginning to feel about him. She had no idea what he saw in her. Deep in the core of her innards there was an answer, but she didn't know how to interpret it. It was her head and not her heart that finally responded.

"I think he's just being nice because I'm new and I made a fool of myself in front of him this afternoon."

Regan's demeanor changed immediately. She dropped the demanding tone and sympathetically pressed Mara for information. It had been so long since Mara even had anything interesting to tell someone that she gave in to the joy of indiscretion. Mara told Regan all about how she ran into Holden, about her parents, and her neglected upbringing. The only thing she left out was how she thought Holden was flirting with her. But she was so unsure of her ability to size up male/female relations and why Regan was so interested anyway that she decided to keep that tasty morsel for herself.

Regan looked at her for a moment and then it seemed that something in her changed. It was as if all this time she had been puzzled by something in Mara and now she had it all figured out. She said with a strange smile, "Well, you're just his type."

Mara's eyes were as wide as pies.

"D-do you mean Holden's?"

"Yes, you're just his type. I can see why he fell for you," Regan said definitively.

"Really? 'Cause the other girls said that you used to date him and, well, you seem so much more savvy and confident than me."

Regan looked momentarily annoyed, but her recovery was so quick that Mara was led to believe it was only temporary indigestion.

"It's true that we *used* to go out, but that was a long time ago. We're still best friends, but I'm over him and it appears that he's finally over me."

Regan's left eye began to twitch and she held a long white finger to her pencil-thin eyebrow to stop the muscle spasm.

"But, I do know a few things about Holden Rife and I can help you with him if you're interested. Are you interested in him?" Regan asked, momentarily pulling her finger away from her brow and then immediately putting it back when she felt the unabated spasm.

Mara was about to answer, but Regan cut her off.

"Well, of course you are. He's good looking and rich and you…well you're a little bit naive, aren't you? But that's okay, sweetie, I'll help you."

With that Regan pulled her hand from her eye to touch Mara on the shoulder. Her eye began to twitch with a renewed vehemence.

"This is so embarrassing. It's my medication. Last year I had an emotional crisis. You probably know what I mean."

Mara was unwilling to speculate about people who weren't serial killers, so she shrugged her shoulders. Regan smiled a smile that was simultaneously relieved and studied. Mara read this as a good sign.

"Listen, Mara, I've got some stuff to do this evening, but I'm glad we had this chat." Regan grew deadly serious. "But, as a friend, let me give you a warning. Those two girls who were in your room? They are not to be trusted. You can talk with them about the weather and hair-care products, but that is it. Also, whatever they tell you is not to be trusted. I have no proof right now, but there's reason to believe that they're spies. So if you do come to our meeting on Saturday, anything that you hear is confidential. Don't trust anything in a banana clip or baseball cap, and especially not Penny and Tippy. Do you understand?" Regan asked with a look that left no room for dissension.

"Yes," answered Mara.

"Good!" exclaimed Regan, once again cheery. "Okay, Saturday we'll leave at seven-thirty. Just come to my room—the door has a star on it. And if you ever want to talk about classes, or cafeteria food, or, say, Holden, just knock."

"Thanks, Regan!" Mara uttered sincerely to her retreating form.

Mara hummed to herself as she started unpacking. The day was filled with so many ups and downs and conflicting viewpoints; she didn't know what to think. So she thought about Holden standing over her, so close she could smell his scent of natural musk and sunshine. She was certain that she was going to like Norden.

CHAPTER 2

It seemed as if she was always faced with the same problem: What to wear?

Clothing is a woman's only arsenal, and I'm seriously outgunned here, Mara thought. *Even if I could compete with the Daddy's-a-CEO-at-a-Fortune-500 wardrobe, what can a short girl wear to rival the natural beauty of the honey-colored long limbs that are as rampant here as roophies and Ritalin?* she pondered.

No matter how alluring, how well orchestrated her attire, Mara knew there was simply no way to dress herself five inches taller.

I look like a munchkin, she thought, surveying her dress, which, in her vulnerable eyes, was alternately too loose and too tight in all the wrong places.

Trying on her other five halfway decent outfits didn't help her mood.

"Argh!" she yelled at all the clothes that failed her, now scattered around the floor like so many corpses.

I can't hide what I am with clothes, she thought. *He knows I'm short. Either he likes me or he doesn't. Besides,* she suddenly realized, *you don't dress for the guy, you dress for his friends. Now what did Penny say about them? Oh yeah! Salvation Army rejects. So all I need to do is find some crappy clothes.*

Mara found a red T-shirt suitable only in her mind for stripping wood. It was tight on her and the picture of a smiling lion became distorted as it stretched over her rounded, perky breasts.

Perfect, she thought.

Then she put on her most raggedy, faded jeans and her old Converse sneakers, which were so stiff she had to bend the soles back and forth to loosen them up before she slipping them on. She topped off the tattered ensemble with a battered red sweatshirt. Mara looked at herself in the mirror and wrinkled her delicate brow.

Since Mara had little idea of the goldmine reflected in the mirror, it is up to me to describe her. Mara wasn't one of those petite girls who make you nervous just looking at them with their bony wrists, their hollow, drawn eyes, and their overwrought sharp edges, standing around making angles as if they were just too damn miserly to grow right. And she didn't make you want to roll up her shirtsleeves to check for track marks, or empty out her purse to find the Dexatrim. She was a natural knockout with a good-sized head and enough healthy flesh to make a dimple on her right cheek when her pillowy, red lips spread into a smile.

She also had a bit of curviness to her. Not the lazy kind of curviness that has no form or biological purpose, which idle women prefer to think of as feminine and everyone else as fat. Mara's curves were built for speed and performed their duty without aesthetic argument or excess. She was fit and wholesome. Not in a peaches-and-cream sort of way, but more like in a biftek tartare *and a fine port sort of way. She was a real, rare beauty and she didn't know it.*

In addition, Mara possessed all the necessary attributes to carry out a loving relationship expediently and forcefully based on the knowledge and use of the following elements: 1) ability to assess her object of desire; 2) keen observation and vigilance of "Said Object" (hereafter identified as "SO"); 3) exploration of SO's terrain; 4) camouflage, cover, and imprinting capabilities, including familiarity with feminine devices such as makeup, little black dresses, and thought echo; 5) careful selection of firepower (Cupid's arrow can strike SO only once); and 6) study and visualization of desired success (Mara's ability to sustain protracted fantasies involving SO).

Mara checked her watch. It was 7:20.

Time to go.

She grabbed her purse and anxiously headed down the hall to the black door with the red star. Performing a short and final hair check, she knocked on Regan's door.

An eyebrowless Regan invited her inside without a word. She plunked down in a beanbag and pulled on her combat boots, which Mara noticed were indeed too large for her feet. Regan leaned over toward a small, chipped mirror standing against the wall and applied the stub of an eyeliner pencil to her naked brow.

While Regan finished her peculiar preparations, Mara looked about the room and its bizarre disarray.

The space seemed to Mara like a police crime lab, albeit one used by disorderly detectives who never went home. The air was potent with the sharp smell of coffee grounds and faint traces of beedies—flavored tobacco from India rolled into a cone of dried tobacco leaves. Every square inch was crowded with stimuli. The walls were covered in posters, photos, papers, and copies of newspaper clippings. On the bedside table was an open jar of mayonnaise with a spoon in it, and a half-empty bottle of Pepto Bismol lay on a pile of what Mara wrongly assumed were dirty clothes. The only trace of order in the room was the whirring computer that conversed with a humming laser printer about the large file being output.

Mara was embarrassed for Regan's mess so she kept her eyes on the less embarrassing vertical chaos of the walls. One of the pictures appeared to be a wanted poster. It featured black-and-white reproductions of young men and women with German captions on the bottom. From the hairstyles and minimal makeup, Mara could tell that the photos were either an example of contemporary seventies retro or actually from the early seventies. Either way, though, the photos were starkly styled, like mug shots, and they seemed very trendy.

The poster excited Mara. She thought it was cool that there was the same number of women and men pictured.

They're like equal-opportunity bad guys, she thought.

Although she knew that it must be a new Benetton or Calvin Klein ad, Mara was impressed with its sensual, dangerous quality.

Mara decided who was the cutest guy in the poster. There was no competition once she realized one of them had the same dark, soulful looks as Holden. She stepped forward to see which fellow poster girl the Holden look-alike might sleep with.

Regan raised the brow that she still hadn't penciled in, giving her expression a built-in impotence. "You like the RAF poster?" she asked.

"Yeah, it's cool," Mara replied, "What's the R-A-F? A band? A clothing line?"

Regan, who was busy drawing an eyebrow, got caught in an eye spasm, which caused her to draw zigzags over her left eye. She wiped her brow clean and attempted the line again.

"Holden didn't tell you anything, did he? I wonder why..." Regan said more to herself than to Mara.

"Does this have something to do with the German program?" asked Mara.

"Mara, this talk requires more time than we have currently." Regan addressed her as if she were talking to a much younger sister. "While I cannot adequately condense years of research and activism into a one-minute description, I will attempt to give you a brief outline of what Holden has obviously neglected to tell you."

Mara momentarily tolerated Regan's haughty attitude.

Regan finished drawing her eyebrow a good quarter of an inch above where her brow, by nature, would be. Her mark-making lent her a surprised look that wasn't completely unbecoming and Mara admired her pluck and distinctiveness.

Regan fished through her hip pocket to retrieve a silver object that looked like a pen. She pulled at the small top knob and lengthened it into a good-sized pointing stick.

She snapped the stick just below the poster. "*This* is the official wanted poster of the RAF. I bought it off an auction on eBay for a mere 450 dollars. This poster was put out in 1971, the year of the RAF's inception."

Regan then pointed to a cheap, color copy of a book cover with a red star, the initials RAF, and a silhouette of a raised hand holding some kind of machine gun.

"RAF stands for the Red Army Faction, an amalgam of students, professionals, professors, and dropouts. In '71 the *Springer Press* erroneously dubbed them 'the Baader-Meinhof Gang.' But the Red Army Faction was their chosen name. They fought the German state the only way that fascists understand, through violence."

Mara looked upon her friend with a renewed admiration. Regan was fascinating and held strong beliefs about stuff and knew how to command attention. Mara secretly wished that she could have strong, firmly held convictions that she could boldly demonstrate with buttons or bumper stickers. She also appreciated the noisy authority of Regan's long, silver pointing stick.

Mara wanted to say something smart, something that would let Regan know that she understood her interests and would some day like to share them. She pointed to the wanted poster.

"This guy is hot," she said, causing Regan's eye to jump.

Regan stepped closer to the picture of the handsome young man with a slight beard and longish, dark hair that was cropped around the forehead. His face displayed a taste of the disdain and self-confidence that rock stars made a diet of. Holding her eyebrow down with one hand and pointing at the enticing activist with the other, Regan responded reverently, "*That* is Andreas Baader. He was loved by all in the RAF. He did much for the cause. He was the co-leader."

Wanting to show that she had been paying attention Mara asked, "With Meinhof?"

"No!" Regan's answer was short and cold. "We should go."

They walked in silence to Regan's old oxblood-colored BMW. Mara kept her questions to herself as they sped through the woods to the outskirts of town under a canopy of autumn leaves. They quickly reached Norden Town, a half-quaint and half-yuppified enclave. There was no shortage of candle stores, coffee shops, and books stores, and the centerpiece was a sprawling park with an outdoor stage. Mara drank in the view as they whirred past The Happy Muscle Day Spa, Book Nook, Coffee Corner, The Thoughtful Book, All Of Your Beeswax Candles, The Mellow Cup, Team Kaffeine Koffee Beanery, and The Bee's-Knees Candle Emporium.

As they passed the *Norden Gazette* Regan rolled down the window and yelled, "Fascists!"

Passing the Eyewitness News building Regan yelled, "Suppressive bootlicks!"

They drove by the Sunny Honeycomb Organic Food Co-op and Regan yelled, "Nazi pigs!"

Mara gave Regan a questioning look.

Regan explained that she used to work for the co-op, but the management wouldn't pay for her leave when she went to a march in Washington.

"And they call themselves progressive. The pig-dogs!"

Mara nodded in agreement. Regan, after all, was driving.

They pulled up to a small, white house on the edge of town. It had some land around it and, although there was an espresso bar next door, a slight whiff of manure suggested the proximity of farms. Mara noticed that the other cars there were also BMWs, the same model as Regan's.

"What's with the cars?"

"BMWs, Baader-Meinhof Wagons. The Baader-Meinhof Group, or as we call them, the Red Army Faction, loved the 2002 model of seventies BMWs, and, very possibly, popularized BMWs for a whole new generation. They were a middling company before the RAF, but the RAFians realized that they were fast, fuel-efficient, and easy to steal. So the car became one of their getaway vehicles of choice, second only to Mercedes. More than one BMW 2002 has been baptized with the blood of an RAF martyr."

Mara felt an excited tingle when Regan spoke of blood. Serial killers intrigued her with their ability to act, but to kill for a cause *and* be willing to die for one seemed so simultaneously remote and exhilarating. It was outmodedly romantic, and Mara hardly ever let herself indulge in her romantic side, which she saw as evidence of weak character.

Mid ponder, Mara realized that Regan had left the car and was already walking up the steps of the old wooden house. Mara ran to catch up.

Regan rapped on the door. A muffled voice was heard.

"Password?"

"Let me in!" Regan demanded.

"Password?"

"This is asinine!" Regan yelled at the door, but there was no response. "Fine. Benno Ohnesorg will be avenged!"

The door opened. A short, young man with ginger dreadlocks gestured them in.

Ick! White guy dreads, Mara thought.

Regan glared at the young man who responded with, "Oh, hello, Regan, I didn't recognize your voice."

"Like hell you didn't," she snapped.

He jumped back slightly and a jiggle in his Guatemalan pants revealed that he hadn't bothered putting on underwear that day.

"Who's your foxy friend?" he asked with his head rolling loosely on his neck.

Regan smiled. "This is Mara. Holden's invite. She's from Oshkosh, Wisconsin."

"Baraboo," said Mara softly.

"What?" shot Regan.

"I went to school in Oshkosh. I'm from Baraboo."

"Right," said Regan with an inscrutable grin at Mara. She turned her attention back on the very fit dreadlocked fellow. "Eric, where are the others?"

Eric blatantly ignored Regan and turned to Mara. "It's nice to meet you Mara. We're having mountain lion for dinner. Do you eat live food?"

"No, I don't think so..." said Mara.

Eric's eyes widened above a smattering of freckles.

"You should. It digests better you know. Do you know that there are seven pounds of undigested meat in your lower intestines right now? That is, if you're a meat eater. Are you a murderer?"

"Enough proselytizing, Eric. Come on, Mara."

Regan linked her arm in Mara's and led her into the living room. In the sparsely furnished room there were five other people: two were seated in chairs and three on large cushions. One heavy, mahogany chair remained unoccupied. Mara momentarily thought of taking it, but instead sat on the floor. Since no one corrected her, she assumed she did the right thing.

Regan fell into a large, red cushion and began introductions. There were two pale, cosmetics-free young women dressed in overalls and vintage hiking boots. They were cutting out cardboard stencils that read "Free Mumia!" with a silhouette of a fist behind it.

Mara was told the one with the newly shaved blonde hair

that made her look like a hedgehog was Apocalypse. She gave Mara a little wink as she said, "Good, we need another girl in here. The testosterone level was getting way too high."

The gangly, long-faced one with the Middle Eastern scarf was Rosa.

"I love your hair," she said to Mara.

"Really? I can never do anything with it!" Mara exclaimed.

"God! You should try having my hair," Rosa held out a long, limp brown braid to Mara. "Hey, I haven't seen you yet at the German House."

"I'm an abnormal-psychology student," Mara answered apologetically and watched as Rosa slowly drew her braid back.

Next to them a fine-boned young man dressed all in black with green hair and an impish face massaged the back of a similarly modest-sized, clean-cut young man with hair so shiny that it made Mara think of a dandruff commercial. Regan told Mara that the back rub-er was MK-Ultra.

"That's capital M, capital K, dash, capital U- L- T- 3- R- A," he told her.

"Three?" asked Mara.

"The three is silent," he said and then looked at his friend who was keeping a very straight face.

"Oh," Mara said to MK-Ultra and Apocalypse threw a cushion at him.

The back rub-ee, introduced as Ex-Pat, wore a fresh Gap T-shirt and khakis with a crisp crease. Suspiciously clean-cut in relation to the others, he responded to Mara's inquisitive examination of his attire with, "I'm undercover."

Mara nodded as if she understood.

The last in the group, a large, curly-haired man who was wiping beer foam off his densely tattooed face with a heavily tattooed hand, was introduced as Rat. Every visible square inch of his body was covered with green, yellow, and black camouflage tattoos with the exception of a spot above his left eye where an anthropomorphized, well-muscled rat was lurking in dark-blue ink.

Mara had a feeling his camouflage didn't help him to blend in.

"Hi," he said softly, and then quickly looked away.

Eric came back from the kitchen with a large platter of steaming something.

"Dinner is served!" he said setting the strange food on the floor.

Ex-Pat asked, "Where's Holden?"

"He's sending a fax to Germany," Eric answered with a quick furtive glance to Mara.

"God, I hope he's not being swindled by another bogus 'deep throat,'" Regan said.

"Don't say 'deep throat,'" Apocalypse countered. "Say 'informant.' 'Deep throat' is a sexist term derived from the porn film that exploited Linda Lovelace."

"Whatever," Regan answered yawningly and turned her attention to the food.

The meal was in the shape of some sort of roast beast, but was actually an astounding sculpture of colored and pressed tofu stuffed with seasoned vegetables.

"Oh. It even has a face. Clever, Eric," said Regan, a hint exasperated.

The others gathered around the dish of piping hot food with clay bowls and chopsticks.

Eric smiled at his peers and said, "A healthy activist is a happy activist."

Rat rolled his eyes at Mara and yanked a six-pack of Guinness from a paper bag. "Liquid meat, for those of us who aren't rabbits." He offered one to Mara. Seeing that none of the others were drinking, she shook her head.

Mara, cautiously tasted a cut from the haunches of the tofu beast. She found Eric's cooking good, if weird.

"So," Rat said with a tattooed mouthful of food, "Are you going to work on the Games this year?"

Mara looked at him questioningly, tilting her pretty head to the side.

Regan said, "I think Mara needs more information, so let's take this slowly. She just found out about the RAF this evening."

Rat eyed Mara with disbelief. "So you don't even know about Death Night?" he asked.

"Mara doesn't need any information except about the Mumia Benefit," boomed a voice from directly behind her.

Mara turned and beheld Holden. He entered the room carrying a carafe of foamy orange liquid and a series of glasses made from wine bottles with the tops cut off and sanded down so as not to cut the unsuspecting drinker. She noticed that his extra-long fingers could hold five glasses as casually as if he were only holding one.

"Carrot juice, anyone?" Holden said beaming.

He masterfully handed out the homemade glasses, stretching his rangy body to pour the orange liquid into the containers. He was so amazingly handsome that for a moment Mara forgot he was real and she examined him adoringly, as if he were a painting or an ancient Greek statue.

Holden was dressed in the same navy-blue work pants he had worn days earlier, but instead of the old cotton shirt, he had changed into a charcoal V-neck. The shirt was threadbare enough so that even though it was slightly oversized, Mara could still make out the contours of his firm body underneath. Hanging lopsided, it stretched lightly across his broad shoulders and a bit at his chest where the minutest of shadows hinted at his nipples that stood at attention. He must have recently come out of the shower because his longish black hair hung spikily around his ears.

Mara was in good company watching Holden. Of the seven other people gathered, only three didn't have their eyes glued to his commanding carriage. Apocalypse, Rat, and Eric had their eyes trained on Mara, and each registered private disappointment at how her feline eyes lit up at the sight of Holden. He gave Mara the slightest wink and knelt down before the nearly annihilated tofu carcass.

"So what was it this time? Shark? Jaguar?" Holden asked.

Eric smiled and said, "Roast mountain lion."

"Mmm... Sounds dangerous," Holden said and scooped up a large portion into a ceramic cup.

"You are what you eat," said Eric.

"I don't get it," sneered Apocalypse. "So we're a fake cougar?"

"Better than a paper tiger," Eric said.

Rosa shook her head. "You're such a dork, Eric."

Regan turned to Mara and whispered in her ear, "Some of the nonvegetarians were complaining about the tofu so Eric started making it in the form of animals and adding liquid smoke to appease their meat-lust. Since none of the carnivores actually cook, they mostly stopped complaining."

Holden scowled at Regan's whispering.

"Has everyone been introduced to our new guest?" he asked.

Murmured affirmations filled the room.

"Good, we'll start the meeting in five minutes. I'm starved!" Holden sank into the one good chair and dug into his pile of fake meat.

Rat shifted a beefy leg and turned to Mara.

"So have you been to the new anarchist Web site 'Anarchy In The UK-dot-co-dot-UK'?"

Regan rolled her eyes. "Those wannabes say that they have a training program, but my London contact said they're just a bunch of Cyber Punks who follow the 'Cookbook' verbatim."

MK-Ultra shook out his green mane and tucked it under some kind of woolen military beret. "*The Anarchist Cookbook?* How passé."

"Anything footnoted in *RE/Search* is passé to you, MK," Ex-Pat said.

"I think that's a good enough definition," MK-Ultra agreed.

Although she was pleased that she didn't have to speak, Mara felt goosey from all the banter she didn't understand.

Apocalypse finished eating, rolled on her back, and played with the one long braid that roped down Rosa's back. "Yeah," she said, "They talk Kaczynski but their biggest hit was throwing a tennis ball full of match heads into The Hall of Parliament. It was Guy Fawkes Day, so the blast didn't get noticed with all the fireworks. They didn't even get arrested until two weeks later after some guards reviewed the security tapes."

"Match heads? How lame!" said Rosa.

"Match heads? Don't mind if I do!" said Rat as he pulled some farmers' matches out of his pocket and started pulling off the heads with his teeth and swallowing the sulfur tips.

"Heinous. You are so disgusting, Rat!" cried Rosa.

Eric smiled and looked to Mara. "See, meat eaters are so removed from their civilized potential that they don't even know what to put in their mouths. Their natural biological instincts have failed them."

Rat turned a large, ugly face to Eric and said, "Bite me, rabbit! If meat's good enough for the Red Army Faction, it's good enough for me."

The spirited conversation was making Mara nervous and when she was nervous she didn't have the presence of mind to keep her mouth shut.

"Ex-Pat!" she exclaimed a little too loudly.

Ex-Pat turned two shrewd eyes on Mara.

"Why are you called Ex-Pat?" Mara queried in a quieter voice.

Ex-Pat looked at MK-Ultra, who rolled his eyes and softly answered for him.

"Ex-Pat is short for expatriate. Ex-Pat used to do computer stuff in the army. He became politicized through a friend's Web site that then directed him to us. We helped him get out of the army."

"I think *you* did that job all on your own, MK," Rat said laconically.

MK-Ultra smiled and put an arm warmly around Ex-Pat's shoulders and twisted his nipple. "Don't ask, don't tell," he said.

Ex-Pat blushed at the attention. "Now it's a new world for me," he said, wriggling away from MK-Ultra. "Thus, Ex-Pat."

Mara nodded, but, again, had no idea what they were talking about. Not only did their talk stray from her area of expertise, but she was also rattled by Holden's overwhelming nearness.

Holden finished his dinner, cleared the dishes, and brought in a large dry-erase board. On the board he wrote "Mumia Abu-Jamal."

"Okay folks, the teach-in has begun," Holden said in the calm voice of a man who is secure with his authority.

He squinted at one of Regan's yellow index cards and spoke in a voice now solemn and low, "'I remain innocent. A court cannot make an innocent man guilty. The righteous fight for life, liberty, and for justice can only continue. Mumia Abu-

Jamal, October 31, 1998.'"

He began walking back and forth on long legs as he explained the events that led to Mumia's arrest and subsequent death sentence. Holden's voice resonated with depth and authority. He made a sweeping gesture with his arms and Mara was acutely conscious of his tantalizing, athletic physique. Her green eyes froze on his long, lean form. As he scanned the notes for his lost place, she saw an inherent strength in his face.

He looked up from the notes and began to act out the alleged cop-shooting: first miming the cops, then the part of Mumia and his brother. The room grew warm with the heat of so many bodies, and drops of moisture clung to the stray wisps of hair at Holden's forehead. Black locks gleamed in the light as Holden dropped and rolled, dodging imaginary bullets. Raven tendrils of hair curled over his ears as he put up both hands innocently. One lock fell forward a little onto his brow and he pushed it back impatiently, displaying a hairline with a hint of a manly widow's peak.

Mara realized he had been talking the whole time and she had forgotten to listen. She tried to tune in to his words.

"Although he didn't harm a single hair on a cop's head, authorities acknowledged that Mumia was beaten while in custody…" Holden explained.

It was increasingly hard to pay attention to Holden's lecture while the language of the body was speaking to her as it never had before, overwhelming the insistence of the words. There was an air of isolation about his tall figure. Mara imagined him a lone soldier awaiting his orders in Paris, under a bridge, midwinter. She wondered what he might look like in French Resistance-style underwear, the strangely fitting cotton linen hanging gently from his narrow hips.

"… Sobo, a well-known hanging judge was in bed with the prosecution…"

Mara would be a French prostitute who sold her body only to keep her crippled father in coal for the winter. The air-raid sirens rang out and Holden, a dashing young rebel in a ragged Resistance uniform, threw her into a bomb shelter. They lay side by side. Panting. Waiting for the sounds of the German bombers to stop. Their hearts racing together.

"The officer was killed with a .44 caliber. Mumia's gun was a .38 caliber. This witch hunt requires our resistance..."

No, better yet, she would be a member of the Resistance, drawn in by the arrogant though charming Jean-Paul Sartre, but tossed out like so much rubbish when she refused to attend to his masculine needs. She wandered the streets, cold, vulnerable, and alone, with the Germans closing in.

Holden would drive up in a vintage motorcycle with a sidecar. He'd say in French to not be afraid, he'd help her. She'd hop in his sidecar and they'd drive past the German guards— who were really stupid just like in *Hogan's Heroes*—and make their way to the Riviera where they would live for weeks as if the war was over.

In tastefully revealing swimwear, they'd shimmy up long palms to knock down coconuts, pick passion fruit from the trees, and climb the neighboring hills to muse on the misty, golden vistas.

By day Holden would swim the ocean and bring back baskets heavily laden with fruits or treasures from the sea: squid, angelfish, conches, and small sharks, which she would cook in a mixture of coconut milk, cardamom, and sweet basil. At night they'd stretch out beneath the palms with a baguette in one hand and a wicker-bottomed jug of red wine in the other and gaze upon the heavenly bodies that dotted the Gallic sky. In the black-velvet night they would hear the sounds of a distant mandolin and they'd kiss.

And then, one evening, when the bent light of the sun cast long rosy shadows and the air was heavy with the perfume of the wild gardenias, Holden would turn to her and announce: "I must go back, my darling. For, although I love you, without mother France, there is no future for us."

Although she'd want to stop him, she'd instead bravely turn away. Slowly, he'd walk toward his uncertain fate, his inky footsteps marring the white sands that still held the impression of their mingling bodies.

Mara snapped out of her reverie and focused again on the deep timbre of Holden's voice.

"See, the deal is that they had a training video in Philadelphia that taught prosecutors how to remove by pre…per-emp-tory challenges eleven qualified African-Americans jury members."

Even though he was reading from Regan's notes and had to sound out "peremptory," Mara thought he was still a superb orator.

Holden had a monopoly on virility in the steamy room; the rapt attention he commanded proved it. At one point he looked around impatiently and grabbed the front of his moist V-neck, pulling the shirt entirely off his glistening torso. Mara heard a gasp that came from the direction of Ex-Pat or MK-Ultra. It was the same gasp she also felt deep within her, but didn't dare make audible.

"Do we stand by and watch as a brother is deprived of freedom? Can we idly sit back while the state gets away with 'legal' murder?" he implored.

Shirtless, with a casual slouch that allowed a view of his perfectly aligned abdominal six-pack, he was a vision to behold. Wildly emphatic, Holden stirred a primeval energy in the group. Mara watched his muscles shift and pop under his skin as he gyrated to the beat of an underground revolution. A drop of perspiration gathered at the cleft of his chin and edged its way down the supple contours of his muscle-bound chest. She imagined her tongue tracing its salty path, down to the hard, loiny line of his boxers.

Suddenly Mara noticed Holden had gone silent. His eyes seemed to be sending her a secret message. She smiled at him.

"Well?" Regan asked expectantly.

Regan was directing a question at her. Mara gulped. All the eyes in the room were on her.

I should have paid more attention to what Holden was saying.

Mara cleared her throat. Holden gazed down on her with so much encouragement that she was too embarrassed to ask what the question was. She opened her mouth and surprised herself with the words that came out.

"I think Holden made the answer quite clear," she said and waited for the chiding she so richly deserved.

Holden beamed. "Just as I thought. Mara agrees with the dinner fundraiser. If we can get a few celebrities, like Woody Harrelson or Maya Angelou, we're bound to raise the twelve-thousand dollars."

Rat moaned. "Come on, this is embarrassing. I don't want to dress up in some lame monkey suit and serve a bunch of rich assholes dinner. Can't we just do something cool, like, you know, rob a bank or something? The Revolutionary Anarchist Bowling League makes their money through mail fraud and robbery. They don't throw candy-ass benefits."

Holden seemed to be holding his anger in check as he answered coolly, "As you know, Rat, RABL does not donate money to the Free Mumia Fund and, even if they did, the Fund couldn't accept it. That's just what the feds are waiting for. Plus, RABL's in solidarity with no one but themselves. Their biggest claim is that they don't pay taxes. So what? Eight out of nine of them live with their parents! So if you're interested in joining the Revolutionary Anarchist Bowling League, I'd suggest you secure a bail bondsman first because *they* certainly won't come to spring you if you're in trouble."

"Well, not all of our daddies give us unlimited funds and send us to expensive private colleges," Rat grumbled. "We talk and do nothing. You know how much street cred' we got? Zero." Rat looked down at his large camouflaged hands, ashamed of his outburst.

There, on the palm of his right hand amidst the camouflage Mara spied a tattoo of Tattoo from *Fantasy Island*.

Holden leaned forward and socked his indelibly marked comrade in the arm.

"Rat, you and Ex-Pat are the base in reality we need, but we have to take the appropriate action for each task and for this task the appropriate action is getting celebrities. We'll talk more about this later, when we meet as the Reading Group. I'll see most of you on Sunday."

Rat glowered under his rat tattoo, but calmed down.

Regan suggested they shift the debate to e-mail until their next meeting.

"And remember, no stuff in the e-mail that could compromise our organization," she added.

Rat asked suddenly, "Hey! Before we go, what about Mara?"

Holden responded before Mara could divine Rat's meaning. "Mara is in our Free Mumia activities and out of everything else. I'd appreciate it if we could keep the two separate."

"Mara could help even out the boy-to-girl ratio—" Apocalypse began to argue, but Holden interrupted her.

"I know up until now we've had 100 percent crossover, which, at times, made it seem like our two groups are one. But to widen our base we need two clear and distinct entities. The vanguard is so named because they *guard* the cara*van* down the trail of enlightenment. It is the only way to reach the truth or, as they say in Russian, 'Prada.'"

"Pravda," Regan corrected.

Mara was in a huff; she knew when she was being patronized. *Vanguard, my foot!* she thought.

Mara gave Holden a caustic look and stomped toward the door on the heels of the others.

As they were leaving Apocalypse grabbed Mara's hand. "I'm taking this really awesome all-women self-defense class. Call me if you want to go," she said quietly and dashed off.

Rosa caught up with Mara and said as they walked toward the door. "Red is a good color for you," she said. "The new red isn't Nancy Reagan's red. It says 'blood,' 'passion,' and 'revolution.'"

Mara would have responded but Holden's shirtless body blocked her egress, his dark eyes probing her angrily flushed face.

"Mara, I was hoping you would stay after the meeting and we could talk."

Regan appeared just behind them and answered Holden, as Mara was slow to speak. "Mara came with me. Her ride is leaving."

Ex-Pat and MK-Ultra filed out beneath curious, raised brows.

Holden ignored Regan and turned to Mara. "I'll drive you home, Mara. Come on, we need to talk."

Before his captivating, earnest face Mara immediately acquiesced.

Regan gave Mara a strange but pleasant smile and walked out. The door shut with what could have been just an overly thorough bang.

Holden and Mara watched through the living room window as three various-colored 2002s and one BMW 1600 puttered off into the night, leaving a fully refurbished, black 2002 standing alone in the drive.

"Nice car," she said flatly.

"If it's any consolation, I was the first to get one. The rest followed my lead."

His broad shoulders shrunk slightly as if weighed down by the burdens of being a leader.

"Sometimes it's hard," he said and looked down.

Mara's eyes ambled down the length of his bare chest, past his washboard stomach, to the place where his hip bones began to vee. She turned her eyes back to his face and was entranced by its silent sadness. In her mind she reached out to his warm flesh and dreamed of being crushed within his embrace. The idea sent her spirit soaring while her body remained heavy and still.

Mara looked into his eyes, "It seems strange..." She didn't know how to continue.

Holden suspected her meaning and responded softly. "There's no mystery to it. You want there to be a mystery. But the only mystery is that you want one. It's like the Bible says, 'Look not on barren land for the mustard seed, for the seed you seek lies in thine head.'"

Mara puzzled over this cryptic quotation. She wondered what he was talking about, and, whether, through some unholy alliance, he could perceive her thoughts before she even had a chance to think them. Holden meanwhile used her silence as the lubricant with which he eased his body closer to hers.

His closeness alarmed Mara. She didn't know what to do with her body. She was acutely aware of its preposterous position: something between a step and a turn with each limb bent at its own angle away from her torso. Like a bug trapped under a child's magnifying glass, she began to burn and wonder stupidly about the heat's source.

Holden dropped his head to her upturned face and gently brushed his cleanly shaven cheek against hers. Each and every nerve attended to the moment as Mara clamored to regain full consciousness. Her brain stumbled over a multitude of racing options, but her body knew what to do, knew how to answer his gentle nudgings. And soon her arms found their way around Holden's ribbed torso.

He complimented her touch with a soft groan and threw his arms around her lithe and willing body. Years of loneliness poured out from deep within Mara's marrow. A sob caught in her throat but emerged as a low moan. Holden seized her lips in kisses both passionate and demanding and Mara answered in kind, her lips parting slightly to invite the fullness of his tongue.

Holden's kisses grew more desperate and he plunged into her mouth, exploring its sweet depth. His hands roamed freely over her aching body and under her T-shirt to her breasts. A gasp formed on her lips that he caught up with his own. She could feel his male hardness pressing against her hip, as they began to move with their bodies' ancient rhythms. He freed her of the heavy red sweatshirt and T-shirt and helped her to the large cushions scattered on the floor.

Mara couldn't object even if she wanted to. The reins of her desire were lost and it was now galloping about freely.

"Mara, you're beautiful," murmured Holden as he pulled her to his reclining body. Their bare skin touched, rousing a melting sweetness in Mara. He stoked the feeling as he crushed her breasts against the plane of his chest while kissing her hard on the mouth. She needed to see him, to see his eyes, to see if he was feeling the same ecstasy that he inflamed in her. His hazel eyes were at a sensual half-mast. Although she had been imagining this moment since he invited her to the dinner, she still couldn't believe it.

Here is the most handsome, fascinating man—a junior, but old enough to be a senior, and he wants me?

In her confusion she stiffened slightly.

Holden must have noted her change in temperament. "What's wrong?" he asked as he pulled his flushed face away from hers as if better to study her troubled beauty.

"Nothing," Mara murmured. "It's just that, well, what did you mean when you said I can't be part of the other group. Wouldn't that be for me to decide?"

Holden smiled sadly and pulled himself up on one elbow. His arousal was still apparent, but he took some patient moments to answer her question.

"Mara, I know it seems unfair, but there is a lot you don't know about our group. On the one hand, we are people bound together by years of shared interests. We have a similar, burning desire that we express through the Reading Group. Not everyone can be a part of it. You have to come to it naturally, not just because you want to hang out with us.

"On the other, more sinister hand, there are some dark elements about our group. The group may be headed toward a new phase of praxis. This phase calls for potentially violent action. If the majority of the group gets its way—and I hope it doesn't—but if it does, I don't want you to be here when the shit hits the fan."

He softly traced a line from the nape of her neck to her inner thigh.

"Trouble seems to follow me around. I want something in my life that isn't tainted by this mess. I was hoping that could be you."

Mara was wrapped in a silken cocoon of euphoria. *He wants me in his life!* she exclaimed to herself.

Holden spoke softly into her ear as she felt his masculine desire against her thigh.

"Through no fault of my own, I was born into a rich family. From a very early age it became clear that, although my parents did their best to mold me in their likeness, I was a rebel and destined to walk a wilder path. I longed to fling off wealth's oppressive shackles. At first I couldn't find examples of revolutionaries among the rich or even the upper-middle class. I thought people like me had no place in this world.

"Then I discovered the RAF. I was a fourteen-year-old outcast. Instead of yachting, collecting cars, or slumming abroad like my peers, I spent my free time researching the RAF.

I learned German to read more about them. At Norden I formed a reading group. Before I knew it people were asking me if they could join, so I became the leader.

"But now that I'm older I'm beginning to suspect that maybe the Baader-Meinhof Group didn't have all the answers. Could it be that Rudi Dutschke was right? That it's best to change the system from within? Maybe there are other ways than bombs and guns to elicit change. But now that we're close to the next phase, I don't know if I can stop it. If I'm this conflicted, how am I going to convince the group?"

He pushed himself away from her for just a moment and she could see the pain and suffering in his eyes. Then he descended on her fervently. His mouth sought out her neck while his hands brought shivers to the skin they seared.

Mara became distracted though. "What did you mean by not wanting me to be involved in this mess? What are you holding back?"

He looked up from her clavicle, which he was just beginning to nuzzle. "Mara, can't we talk about this later?"

"No. Frankly, this is important. Are you trying to protect me from something?"

Holden smiled in relief. "That's exactly what I'm doing."

"Well, thank you very much," spat Mara as she pulled out of his arms. "But I'm not a child."

"I don't think of you as a child," Holden said, now realizing this conversation could jeopardize the evening he had planned for them.

"Then tell me what's going on and let me decide if I want to be a part of it or not," she demanded as she reached for her T-shirt.

Holden sat up, "Sorry, but we have all the members we need."

"So your little baby game is locked, huh? Fine. But if you lock me out of part of your life, you lock me out of all of it. I expect to be treated like an equal!"

"That's what I'm trying to tell you. I don't think of you as an equal. I think of you as my better. You're sweet and naive and unsullied by the lesser struggles of humanity. I don't want you to lose these qualities and I certainly don't want to be the reason that you do." His voice had hardened but he held out his arms to her as she fished around for her clothes.

"That isn't respect, Holden. I don't know what it is, but it isn't respect."

Mara's lower lip began to tremble. She still wanted to be by his side or under him, but not at the cost of her self-respect. Her voice wavered with her next request, "Please take me home." Mara grabbed her purse and ran out the door.

In the passenger side of his 2002 Mara waited for Holden who eventually strode to the car and dropped beside her in the driver's seat. He banged on the steering wheel with his fists when the car didn't start immediately. Looking at him bent over the wheel with his brow of fury and his tousled hair falling into his eyes, Mara wanted to kiss him and make things better. Then she remembered his patronizing tone and set her jaw against those carnal thoughts.

Holden started the car and they drove off in silence.

Mara's head whirled with confusion. *What am I getting myself into? I hardly know this man. If his group is as dangerous, as he implies, then doesn't that also make him dangerous? And who is this Benno Ohnesorg? And how will they avenge his death? Oh, Holden, what is this secret Baader-Meinhof Group and why is it tearing us apart?* The questions tugged at her feminine insides.

She yearned to touch his wayward hair as it fell over his brow, but although they could be perfect physical companions, she could never be the innocent partner he wanted her to be.

When Holden pulled the car into the dorm's parking lot Mara jumped out without saying a word and slammed the car door. With some difficulty she kept at bay her desire to turn around as the car squealed out of the parking lot off into the black night.

CHAPTER 3

Since there is boundless interest in girls' dorms and since available information on said topic could not be more misleading, it is my duty as an agitating author and Mensa member (certified for four years now, although I've been a genius all my life) to give you an accurate depiction of what really *goes on behind the doors of a girls' dorm room.*

Case in point: there are rampant delusions (fueled by Web sites and videos ♥) that girls' dorms are so overheated that everyone must go topless.

Let it be known that Mara's dorm was neither too hot nor too cold and, aside from the rare nude sleeper, the majority of students stayed in their clothes. Mara, likewise, did not frolic naked in group showers; Norden provided separate bathrooms off every room.

Mara's dorm also suffered from a paucity of Asian-American twins who bounced around in lingerie. In addition, there wasn't what the World Wide Web might describe as the obligatory cute, but slutty, lesbian. There was one closeted lesbian on Mara's floor (who wasn't bad-looking if you're into the thick-in-the-waist, lipstick dyke thing), but she wasn't a slut. On the contrary, her rather butch girlfriend who schooled at Vassar was having a heck of a time getting under her skirt.

Furthermore, there were no secret cameras to catch Mara and her peers as they donned cheerleading outfits (which are not a standard in every co-ed's wardrobe) and released stress by masturbating with their high school cum-laude medals.

In conclusion, despite the fact that the young women would break out in frolicsome pillow fighting now and then, the pillow fights did not lead to group, cum-soaked orgies whose spirals of red-hot ecstasy could only be untangled by the gorgeous, but severe, whip-bearing R.A.

♥ For example, *Nude Co-ed Slumber Party,* or *Co-ed Girls Gone Wild.*

Instead of occupying her time with sudsy pussy-shaving parties with her three favorite girlfriends (a blonde, a redhead, and an intelligent, bespectacled brunette), Mara distracted herself from thoughts of Holden with…her homework. She decided to write her first paper on women serial killers: why there seemed to be so few; why they primarily killed their loved ones; and what brought them to action. She was well on her way through a four-hundred-page monograph on Hungarian serial killer Erzabet Batheroy when she heard a knock on her door.

"Mara, Mara open up!" came a buoyant female voice outside her door.

Mara rose and opened the door hesitantly.

It was Penny and Tippy in their uniform of oversized T-shirts, boxers, and fuzzy animal slippers. On this afternoon they had supplemented their costume with mud facial masks. Penny's fabricated nose was in green, and Tippy's orange skin was complemented with blue.

Mara thought there was something else different about them, but couldn't put her finger on it. And while she was still upset at them for their initial rude behavior, she was pleased to have any reason to break from her dry reading.

"Come in," Mara said with a wry smile.

The girls' hands were full of various colored liquids in little paper cups. As they filed into Mara's room they each dumped cups into Mara's hands. She was surprised that the contents didn't run through her hands until she realized they were actually filled with some gelatinous material and not fluids.

"What are these? Specimens?" Mara inquired.

Tippy laughed, keeping her face expressionless so as not to wrinkle her mask. "You're the specimen! They're Jell-O shooters. Have one!"

With a slurpy, snurfing noise Tippy threw one back past her glaringly white teeth.

"See? Mmm good."

She smiled at Mara like a mother trying to show her infant how tasty strained peas are.

Mara smelled a red one and then took a little bite of the top of it.

"It tastes weird," Mara replied dubiously.

Penny squinched up her button nose a quarter of an inch without cracking her mask.

"Mara, honey, don't be such a wad," she insisted. "Swallow it! Don't taste it. Let it wriggle down your throat."

Mara looked at the jiggly red portion and, with a shrug, downed the entire contents.

"Congratulations, you just did a Jell-O shot," Penny said.

Tippy added, "Eee, what a freak-job. What did you do in high school Mara? I mean besides milking the cows or carrying pigs across fields or whatever your people do."

Mara was not sure she understood the question. "I worked at my aunt's cheese shop one year…"

Penny plucked two shots from Mara's hands and they toasted. "No, Mara, she meant what did you do for fun? Didn't you play quarters or anything like that?"

Mara was uncertain as to why eating Jell-O qualified as sophisticated fun, but she swallowed another chunk of Jell-O, giggling at the sliminess of it. "No, I was pretty much a loner," and her brow creased as she recalled all the cow-tippings and mailbox baseball outings she had missed due to her outcast status.

"Well it doesn't look like you'll be a loner here. I heard that you're hanging out with the German program now. What do they call themselves, the Red Freako Army?" Tippy asked as she draped herself across Mara's unmade bed.

"The Red Army Friction. And I don't think that's what they call themselves. Actually I don't know what their group is called. They're so mysterious about everything." Mara said and took a seat on the floor.

"I thought you were a part of it." Penny said, toasting Mara from the only chair, this time with two lime Jell-Os.

"No," Mara exclaimed in a voice that was louder than she meant it to be. She modulated her voice and continued. "Holden invited me to a planning meeting for a Free Mumia Benefit. Apparently their other group is completely separate from that."

"Are you going to join?" Tippy asked, nursing an orange colored Jell-O between her bleached white teeth.

"Tiff-Puff, that's personal!" Penny quipped.

"It's all right," Mara insisted, pleased by the audience. "I don't know what I'm going to do. I might not even do the Mumia thing. I haven't decided."

Tippy lay back on Mara's bed and looked at the ceiling. "I'd do anything to be next to that hunk if I thought he was interested in me. I don't care what kind of secret club he belongs to. He could be worshipping the devil as far as I'm concerned. Know what I mean?"

Mara instantly felt as if she knew exactly what Tippy meant. In fact, she felt her complete understanding physically, in the pit of her stomach radiating out to her limbs and head in rippling waves. The waves made her feel nauseated and she began to appreciate her proximity to the floor; it helped her feel grounded. She would have lain down there if it weren't for her two guests.

"Ew! They're not into devil worship, are they?" Tippy tucked her fat ankles under her legs.

Mara was very relaxed and feeling close to the two girls in her bedroom.

"No! No! No!" She paused to slurp another shot. "They've got some other sort of deal going on. I'm not sure what it is. It's like activism but it's also got something to do with some cute dead Germans."

"Is there such a thing?" asked Tippy with rounded eyes.

"I guess so. It has something to do with the cars they drive, too. I don't know. Every time someone tells me something about it, someone else is telling that person to shut up. I think they halfway want to share it with me and then they kinda don't," Mara answered in a rambling fashion.

"Well, Holden's the sweetest guy at school; I think it's worth it. Even if the rest of those guys are freaks. I don't know why he hangs out with them," Tippy said. She started picking chunks of her dried blue mud mask off her face and putting them in an empty paper cup.

"Tippy! Leave your mask on!" Penny reprimanded. "I know what Tippin means, though. Holden could be hanging with the cool kids … there must be a reason he's with those guys. I hear some of them don't even go to school here."

Mara nodded. "That's true."

"I wonder why they're in the group?" Penny asked, looking at Mara.

"I think one of them does computer stuff or is undercover or something." Mara offered.

The two girls laughed when Mara said "undercover."

"I suppose he has some sort of goofy name like 'The Shadow' or something," Penny said giggling.

Mara laughed too. "No, his name is Ex-Pat."

Penny and Tippy gave each other a quick nod and launched into another fit of laughter. Mara suddenly became concerned. The people at the meeting were possibly her new friends and she was laughing at them. Her hands flew over her mouth in an effort to shut herself up.

Tippy, frowning, started to pick at her mask. Penny gave Tippy a curdling glare, causing Tippy to sit on her hands.

"Imagine what a babe Holden would be if he dressed a little better," Tippy gushed, "Like if you could get him in a nice suit, or even in some clean cargo pants. That and a decent haircut."

"You can't cut his hair," Penny disagreed, "that's half his appeal. It's the sort of I-look-like-the-greasy-car-mechanic-of-your-dreams-but-in-reality-I'm-a-model-with-20-dollar-an-ounce-hair-goop-and-wouldn't-be-caught-dead-with-you look. Except that his hair really is greasy."

"He is really greasy, but his greasiness is an act. It's not like job-related greasiness or like he can't afford a shower. His family has more money than both of ours put together." Tippy declared firmly.

At this point Mara was having a hard time distinguishing between Tippy and Penny. She tried to remember who had the manufactured nose and which one had the capped teeth, but she had forgotten who was wearing which color mask a couple of shots earlier.

"You're right. He's embarrassed to be rich. What's up with that?" asked Green.

"Maybe it's because all of his friends aren't," postulated Blue.

"Well, who asked him to make friends outside of society?"

charged Green.

"Regan is rich." Blue reminded.

"That's right, but Regan Thresh comes from *new* money," Green straddled the word "new" with audible contempt.

Blue confirmed with a nod, "Icky new money."

Green fluffed her hair as she explained to Mara, "Her parents were the first people to develop diapers for obese babies and toddlers. Which we need. I hear that some American children are so fat that five-year-old girls are actually menstruating. See, more fat creates more hormones that accelerate fertility. So there are obese little girls menstruating in kindergarten."

"It's sooooo gross," Blue squealed. "Maybe that should be the Thresh's next marketing deal: menstrual pads for preschoolers. They could get Barney to represent them. With a jingle, you know, 'I like you, you like me, use Barney's Menstrual pads for security.'"

"You are *so* gross, Tiff-Puff," Green replied and tried to wrinkle her nose but instead the whole thing just shifted up a half an inch.

"I'm an advertising major," Blue said to Mara, grinning.

"No. I'm in advertising. You're poli sci."

"Oh, yeah," said Blue with a grin.

"Anyway," Green continued, "the company was called Chubby Nappies. Regan, understandably, had a chip on her shoulder about coming from new money and didn't talk about what her parents did. But it all came out one day. Bismarck Vernal did an in-depth investigation on the local news about adult-baby fetishes. Have you heard of that?"

Mara shook her head.

"Mr. Vernal said the fetish was imported from Germany. According to his findings, although the fetish preexisted in some form long before, it was popularized after World War II when Germany was a traumatized and disgraced nation with a severe identity crisis."

"And suffering from major bad taste. I mean, *hello!* Dachau was so tacky!" Blue said.

"As the story went," Green expounded, "the people of Germany were humiliated and confused. In fact, they were so broken that the men were having trouble, well, with *bedroom matters.* All of the whorehouses started to go under. But then someone discovered that these broken men could 'get off' by crying for their stuffed dolly and soiling themselves. Almost overnight, the whorehouses were supplied with giant cribs, diapers, and strollers—the works. Instead of paying to have sex, men were paying to be spanked, burped, and changed. The nation that gave birth to the Nazis and the Third Reich was essentially giving birth to them again, as adult-babies. It was as if they knew that something went terribly wrong somewhere in their development and they were trying to start all over again, but his time they were getting off on it."

Green paused while she lightly tested the terrain of her mud mask with her manicured fingers. Until she continued with her story, the only sound was the creak-creak of Mara's bed as Blue restlessly rocked back and forth.

"Mr. Vernal said similar conditions to what gave rise to adult infantilism in Germany were now causing its popularity here. I can't remember exactly why, something to do with a stolen election, the widening gap between the rich and poor, hippies selling out, blah, blah, blah—whatever.

"So there's this booming group of underground adult-baby fetishists or 'Abies,' as they like to be called, in the U.S. And he's interviewing one, who's all pixeled out so we don't know who he is. Anyway, he says that the adult-baby movement is indebted to a company that was always supportive of their cause and that company was called…"

"Chubby Nappies," Mara said.

"The only cheap diaper that's large enough for adults," Green nodded. "And to make matters worse, 'Chubby Nappies' immediately took on a new meaning. I guess they weren't thinking of euphemisms for a semi-erect penis when they came up with the name. As if having a fat kid wasn't embarrassing enough, now those parents had to contend with the double stigma of possibly having an adult-baby fetish. Sales fell drastically because the grocery stores didn't want to be known for selling fetishware. So now the only sales they get are from the Web."

"Tell her about the vigil keepers," Blue solicited.

"Right, to further complicate matters, the Abies decided to show support for Regan's family, the Threshes, by standing outside their home in diapers with signs that said things like, 'Adult Babies Love the Threshes,' 'Chubby Nappies *Changed* My Life' and 'Infantalists for Freedom to Wet.'

"As insufferable as Regan was before the news broke, she was a hundred times worse afterward. And, to be honest, it probably wasn't very nice for half of Norden's student body to walk around with pacifiers in their mouths just to piss her off.

"Regan was ranting and raving to anyone who would listen about her new archenemy, Mr. Vernal. I guess Holden got sick of it because after their history-play-thingy, he left her, dropped out of school, and moved to the Funny Farm—which, by the way and contrary to the gossip, is not a mental institution. It's a communal organic farm run by Marxist hippies."

"Real hippies," said Blue. "Not the other kind. Oh, and some people think that Holden didn't leave Regan, it was the other way around. But look at him and look at her and see who you believe."

Green nodded her agreement, "Then Regan dropped out for the rest of that year. Some people say she got mental help because now she's back and seems to have a better attitude. Others say she spent time in the Middle East training with terrorists or some B.S. like that. In any event, she must have heard Holden returned to Norden because here she is again, trying to win him back."

Mara was flabbergasted, her head swimming with information. *Is Holden really still interested in Regan? Why would he hang out with her if they were* truly *over?*

Blue broke her train of thought, "So are you, like, an anarchist or a subversive element?"

Mara replied in slurred words, "No, I sss-study serial killers. The sadistic kind."

Green was examining her cuticles. "Is there any other kind of serial killer?" she asked dryly.

Mara wasn't prepared to answer that question, especially since the floor didn't seem as stable as when she had first sat down. She grabbed the bed for support.

Maybe Blue and Green are right, she was thinking. *Maybe it is worth putting my pride aside so that I can be with Holden.*

Mara decided to call him and apologize. She swallowed another shot to celebrate.

"Hey, what's in these thing-sh?" Mara asked, feeling noticeably strange.

"You know, the usual: sugar, color, horse hooves, Vodka, secret ingredient." Blue answered, feeling the terrain of her mask.

Green glared at Blue.

"How much Vod-ka?" Mara asked, dreading the answer.

"Like a shot."

"Each?"

"Yeah."

"Oops-sh," Mara said.

She had lost count of how many she had swallowed, but assumed it was too many.

"Oh, don't worry. They come up really easy if you need to throw up," said Blue.

"Tippy that is so tasteless!" said Green.

"Don't be such a prude! Besides, I'm not the one having to go into every derivation of the word 'chubby,'" said Blue.

The two continued their argument as Mara counted the paper cups on her floor, trying to determine how many of them were hers. She heard a knock on her door but it didn't occur to her to go answer it.

Green looked up, "It's probably Regan."

"That bitch! What does she want from you anyway? Doesn't she hate you 'cause of Holden?" hissed Blue.

Mara considered the question. "No," she said. "She's real nice-sh. She thinks I'm just his type and said she'd help me with Holden."

"Yeah, right!" Green said and did a snorting thing with her nose made it look as if it were levitating. "She says that so she can find out what's going on between you."

"No. She's nice," Mara said. She now had no question in her mind as to whether or not she was drunk. "Actually *she* said that I should look out for you two. That you guys-s are like, spies or something. Are you guys spies, or gomerment intelligence or what?"

The two girls exchanged a significant look and both fell on the floor laughing. Mara heard another knock on the door. But by then, even if it did occur to her to answer the door, it physically wasn't an option. Nothing short of a fire would move her.

"I mean government. No-no, you see, Regan is really nice and even if she has no eyebrows, that doesn't mean she's evil. I don't think you guys understand that s-she had a rough year. The eye palsy thing proves it. And no one knows why she has a mayonnaise jar with a spoon in it by her bed, but maybe it's like a facial thing, like with you guys-s. I think, maybe, all you guys have a lot in common. She's really nice."

Her drunken ramble was only half-listened to through the laughter it evoked. Mara didn't remember much else from that afternoon aside from one green face and one blue face lifting her off the floor and tucking her into her bed. Two smiles hovered over her like a couple of Cheshire cats. The sun went down and Mara slept.

The need to pee drove Mara from her bed and afterward a pounding headache sent her reeling back into it. She slept until the pounding interrupted her dream. After some time she realized the source of the pounding was outside her head. Mara spent a second disentangling her dream from reality.

The dream was Penny and Tippy, or Tippy and Penny, she wasn't sure which was which, in their green and blue masks holding syringes and shining a reading lamp in her face. They told her to get to know Holden better. The reality was Mara walking, head a-throb, to the door.

She opened it a crack and saw Regan. Her brows were drawn in dark-brown eyeliner with an angry tilt Mara wasn't ready for.

"Sleeping," Mara croaked and crawled back into bed.

Regan peeked in, "When is a door not a door?"

Mara looked at Regan's jagged silhouette in the doorway.

"What?" Mara croaked.

"When is a door not a door?"

Regan was still standing there, asking her stupid questions. Mara's bed had felt so good and Regan's voice was breaking into her peace.

"I don't know," Mara answered, as dismissively as possible.

"When it's ajar," Regan answered and walked in and sat on the edge of Mara's bed.

"Ha-ha. I'm drunk. Sleeping," Mara mumbled and turned away from her guest.

"That's no way to handle excessive drinking. Did you know that ninety percent of hangovers are due to dehydration?"

"Did you know that a hundred percent are due to stupidity?" answered Mara, now undeniably awake.

Regan turned on the light and brought Mara a tall glass of water along with two aspirins she found in Mara's bathroom.

"I told you those girls are trouble," Regan rebuked. "I hope you didn't give them any information when you were drunk. They're more than what they seem. I was passing by their room recently and I swear to God one of them was listening to Paul McCartney, *post*-Beatles. I mean, why?"

Mara took the aspirins and swallowed the water, scowling at the brightness of the light.

"Maybe they were listening to him in an ironic way. And I don't *have* any information, remember? I'm not *German* enough to be in your group. Besides, how did you know they were responsible for this?"

"Hmm...I see the telltale trailings of Jell-O shooters on the ground and I'm guessing that you didn't whip up a batch for yourself. Those girls are dangerous. They're like sorority girls without a sorority," Regan warned with a shudder.

Mara groaned. "They're nice. And since when is being normal a crime?"

"When is a man not a man?" Regan asked.

"What?" said Mara, now even more annoyed with Regan's games.

"When is a man not a man?"

"I don't know. I don't care."

"Fine, Mara. I can see that you are upset by something, but you don't have to chew my head off. When you want to talk with me, I'll be down the hall," she said and pretended to push herself off the bed.

"Wait, wait, I'm sorry, I just don't feel good," Mara latched onto her friend's arm.

Regan, settled back by her side. "Do you want to tell me what happened?"

For a moment Penny and Tippy's warning about Regan came to mind. Then she remembered Regan's warning about them.

They just have some problems with each other, she thought. *Regan's paranoid and the girls can't handle Regan because she's different.*

"Well, we were standing together, alone, and, I forgot that I was mad at him. It was like, uh, I don't know… I guess I'm just really attracted to Holden … physically. And when he was standing so near I just wanted to be with him. We started messing around and then I remembered that I was mad at him and confronted him."

Under heavy eye twitching Regan listened to Mara's tale of woe. When Mara was finished, Regan said, "It's just as I thought."

"What? What?" Mara exclaimed, eager to have some light shed on her conundrum.

"You have his interest. He's very interested in you."

"He is?" Mara asked as she tested her hair for the signs of bed-head.

"Yes, but here's the problem. Although he's interested in you, he's scared. He doesn't want someone who he'd have to commit to," Regan said blackly.

"No?"

"No, see, Holden is one of those special breeds of men who *think* they know what they want, but actually have zero idea what they *really* want. For example, when Holden decided that he's interested in you, what do you think he sees in you that makes him interested?"

"My inner beauty?" Mara suggested, taking Regan's question in all earnestness.

"Right, probably your inner beauty. But let's say that we *all* have an inner beauty. What particularly about you do you think he is interested in? Something different than all other women at Norden?"

"My acute interest in serial killers?" Mara offered.

"And?"

"And the fact that I am a loner?"

"Right! He sees a strong, young woman with unique inter-ests and tastes, an individual who doesn't follow the crowd. He sees someone who will call him on his shit and not let him be just mediocre, right? So then what does he try to do? He tries to get you to become some sort of stay-at-home wifey girl-friend. Does that sound like it makes any sense to you?"

Mara could now see what Regan was saying. Mara was a rugged individual, a lone mare roaming the ranges freely, a wild mare whom Holden was trying to break and brand.

He's trying to turn me into a hobbled horse, she thought.

"Why is he doing that?" Mara exclaimed, angered by the image of a beautiful Appaloosa with catlike eyes and fettered legs.

"Because he doesn't know that what he *really* wants is a strong woman who will stand by his side and join him in battle when need be. But now you know that's what he wants, so what are you going to do about it?"

Mara looked around for an idea. "I don't know."

"Sure you do," Regan said supportively. "You're going to show him that you're as capable as he is, maybe even more capable. It'll be hard going at first, but you have to show him you're a girl who knows what *she* wants and knows how to get it."

"Which is...?" Mara asked, not quite sure what she wanted other than Holden...and for her headache to go away.

"Which is to be a part of our Reading Group. He'll never respect you until you stand by his side. German program or no, you need to join the group."

Mara understood.

"How can I thank you, Regan?" she inquired.

"Just seeing the two of you happy together will be thanks enough," Regan said. She rose and headed for the door. "Oh, by the way, 'When he's abroad.'"

"What?"

"When is a man not a man?"

"Oh." Mara returned, suppressing the desire to call her a dork.

Regan shut off the light and closed the door, leaving Mara alone to ponder her new strategy and her aching head.

CHAPTER 4

Mara woke feeling like her brains were slooshing around loosely in her skull. After her psych lecture, "Post-Modern Postmortem: Autopsy in the New Millennium and Its Effects on the Modern Murderer," she was feeling slightly better in spite of all the talk of innards removal and brain weight. Due to the Jell-O incident she hadn't eaten since the morning before, so she made a beeline for the on-campus café for a real breakfast.

Sitting at a table in the back was Regan and a slight, blonde kid covered in a fine, white powder. They were poring over some sketches when Reagan saw Mara and motioned for her to join them.

Regan introduced Mara to the fair young man. "This is James. He's a sculptor. James, this is Mara. She's in Abnormal Psychology."

Mara waved at him, unwilling to dirty her hands before breakfast.

"Hey," he said softly and waved back. His movement stirred a faint and sour body odor that one only acquired through a mixture of hard work and heavy drink.

James turned to Regan. "Is she in the Games?" he asked, as he eyed Mara nonchalantly.

"I think she will be. I already have some ideas for her," Regan answered.

"Cool," he said stealing a quick glance at Mara's figure. Then he began shaking his leg to some internal rhythm, causing a small amount of dust to billow around him.

His face was slack with concentration as he started sketching on napkins some configurations Mara couldn't quite make out: odd hollow prosthetics and unfamiliar mechanized systems.

"Something like this?" he pushed a drawing toward Regan.

"Mmm-hmm. Yeah. Why don't you work on it and we'll talk more later, okay?"

James nodded and pulled the drawing back. He continued to add detail to a particular sketch of a woman with a metallic-looking hemisphere strapped to her stomach.

Mara spied the words "baby bomb" and "soft target."

"Like this?" he asked, pushing the drawing back to Regan.

Regan was annoyed, even though her eyebrows were drawn that day with a more contemplative bend. She reached for the drawing and in doing so knocked a full cup of coffee onto the napkins.

"Oh, I'm sorry, James," Regan said, "Let me take care of it." She used the rest of his drawings to wipe up the spill.

James watched her in horror. "Hey!" he cried. His leg stopped rocking and the slack flesh on his face tightened. "My sketches!"

"Yeah, remember not to let anyone else see them. That's part of the deal, right? We'll talk more later. Or you can show me some prototypes in a week." Regan handed him the dripping clump of napkins that were bleeding with blops of ink.

James stood up in a self-generated cloud of dust. He shrugged, grabbed the dribbling mess, and stuffed it in the back pocket of his old corduroys. His pocket immediately darkened from the leaking coffee and ink. Feeling the sides of his fuzzy blonde sideburns, James turned abruptly, leaving a billow of powder in his wake.

Like Pigpen, Mara thought. She sat down on his side of the table trying to avoid the white powder he left behind.

Regan rolled her eye and muttered, "Artists…"

"God, I know!" Mara said, not really knowing what she meant.

After she ordered scrambled eggs, bacon, hash browns, toast, coffee, and juice, she returned her attention to Regan.

"You hiring him?" Mara inquired.

"For the Games. We need someone to make the objects we can't buy in stores."

"Like what?"

"Different things," Regan answered as her eyes took a tour of the half-full café.

Mara couldn't think of anything else to say, so she just looked at Regan hopefully.

"Hmm," Regan hummed and she looked through her appointment book for something.

Then Mara remembered something.

"Regan?"

"Yes."

"What are 'the Games'?"

"Oh, good question." Regan put down her appointment book and drew herself up in lecture mode, "You know how I told you about the Baader-Meinhof Group and the RAF?"

Mara nodded.

"Okay, well, everyone you met on Saturday, except Ex-Pat and Rat, met in the German program here two or three years ago. Holden started a reading group and we all became Baader-Meinhof aficionados."

Mara gave Regan a confused look.

"That means that we are devotees," Regan explained. "We are interested in all things Baader and/or Meinhof and pursue them with fervor."

"So you guys are kinda like Trekkies?" Mara offered.

Regan's hand went to her eyebrow and was plainly surprised to find that it wasn't twitching.

"Yeah, I guess we are. But soon our gatherings pulled away from a purely aesthetic interest—you know, like getting the BMW 2002s or dressing like them. As we learned more about the RAF we came to realize that emulating their style wasn't enough. We tried to make their struggle our struggle."

"What was their struggle again?" Mara asked, knowing full well she would sound unsophisticated, but allowing her curiosity to win out.

"They were fighting the fascist German state, which was still being run by those who conceived of and gave birth to the Third Reich. Many old Nazis were still in charge, but the German Volk didn't know it or chose to ignore it. The RAF knew there was only one way to show their people the fascist underbelly of their government and that was to get the fascists to out themselves as such through violence.

"The idea was this: If they showed the people the claws of the beast, the masses would rise up in revolt against the state and a new, more socialist government would be created in its stead. So the RAF targeted the rich, their property, and those hired to protect them—the police, the army, etc. The government was scraping pieces of fascists off trees before they finally captured the RAF."

Although her voice remained calm, certain words like "claws," "revolt," and "fascist" caused Regan's knuckles to whiten in their intense clutching.

Mara grabbed the waitress and asked her if the milk for her coffee was two percent or whole. Regan waited patiently. When Mara was done insisting that, yes, she *could* tell the difference between two percent milk fat and six percent milk fat and to *please* refill her creamer with two percent milk, Regan asked Mara if she had any questions.

Mara thought for a while and then asked, "Does this have anything to do with why Holden always wears the same pants?"

"No," Regan snapped. "That's just because he lived with hippies for too long."

There was silence. Mara knew Regan expected something from her. Finally Mara asked with radiant eyes, "Do you think MK-Ultra doesn't like me?"

Regan made a sound that was remarkably similar to a tire leaking air. "I think MK likes you just fine. Some of the people in the group are a little standoffish at first. But as you work with them I'm sure they'll warm up to you."

Mara nodded. "But he seems really—"

Regan broke in, "Mara, do you still want to know what the Games are?"

Mara could tell by Regan's tone that she was expected to ask about them again. She nodded guiltily.

"We invented the Games two years ago. It was a collaborative school project at first, but then it grew into something bigger and even more important than school."

"More important than school," Mara echoed, trying hard to pay attention despite her rumbling stomach.

"What we do is we pick out certain events important to the Baader-Meinhof timeline and compress and reenact them in a ten-day and eleven-night open air festival."

"So it's like a passion play for terrorists," Mara offered.

Regan grabbed Mara's wrist, her eye ticking away like a metronome set at the fastest tempo. "Let me give you a word of advice. You *never* call the Baader-Meinhof Gang terrorists. They were heroes, activists, vanguard, or revolutionaries. But they were never terrorists. In fact, don't ever call them the Baader-Meinhof *Gang.* That was the moniker given to them by the fascist *Springer Press.* They are a *group, not* a gang. Do you understand?"

Mara nodded emphatically.

"Good. And you can also call them the RAF," said Regan and her eye stopped twitching. She continued as if nothing had happened. "The intention of the Baader-Meinhof Games is to educate Norden and neighboring towns about the RAF and their activities. We also publicize which people and organizations would become targets of a politicizing vanguard in the occasion that a group such as the RAF would again rise up out of the ruling elite to act as the vanguard for the proletariat. Which it will."

"So... you're announcing who you'd choose to be a terrorist—I mean *revolutionary* target—if you were the ARF. That's...different..."

Regan glared. "It's RAF—not ARF, okay?"

"Sorry," Mara murmured.

She couldn't help thinking that these "Games" might be misconstrued as thinly veiled threats.

The waitress arrived with the food. Mara wondered if it would be impolite to start eating or if she had to say something first. Her mouth was watering.

She looked at Regan.

She looked at her eggs.

Then she asked, "Why is this stuff being kept secret then? I mean, if it's a public event why are you and James acting like it's some covert operation?"

"No one would come to the Games if they weren't curious. We have to keep stuff secret. The only constant event is Death Night and the funeral procession."

Mara wanted to learn about Death Night, but she also wanted

to eat. Apologizing to Regan, she dug into her breakfast.

Regan shrugged. "You know where to find me," she said and left Mara alone.

Mara finished her breakfast and was heading to work with Professor Mahler in the psych lab when she noticed a couple of familiarly highlighted brown manes in neon banana clips sitting behind her.

"Is that Penny and Tippy?" she asked the backs of their heads, but they turned away. Mara thought it probably wasn't them. Every other girl at Norden had the same bland hairdo. Besides, she was having a hard time remembering what they looked like without their colored masks.

It was two more days before Mara saw Holden, lounging between the paws of the stone lion, just as on the day they had first met. As she crossed the grassy mall Mara once again felt immobilized by the magnificence of his long, sexy figure. She stood there, shaken and not unstirred.

Holden looked up and a genuine smile brightened his face.

"Well, if it isn't Mara," came his richly resonant voice.

She was too flustered to speak.

"Hey," he called, jumping off the steps of the Von Trapp Memorial Library. "How have you been? I haven't seen you around."

"You know where I live," Mara answered, more than a little peeved by his casual attitude.

"Yeah, I do." He stepped a little closer and dropped his voice to a softer, coaxing intonation. "Mara, I missed you. I didn't know how to tell you, but I'll tell you now." He searched for her eyes, which were everywhere but looking at him. When their eyes at last collided, he said in hushed tones, "I'm sorry. I was a fool. I didn't mean to hurt you."

The heavy lashes that shadowed her cheek flew up and she became instantly wide awake.

"You're apologizing to me?"

"Well...yes." He said simply.

"I was going to apologize to you, Holden."

They froze in a stunned tableau and the traffic on the mall receded from their vision until all they could see was a world of two. The tenderness of his expression amazed her. She tried to throttle the dizzying current racing through her. Caught up in each other's wonder, there was a deeper significance to their visual interchange.

Someone from somewhere yelled, "Get a room!"

The two laughed and they broke the gaze that was drawing them ever closer together. Holden ran back to the steps and grabbed his backpack.

"Listen, I have two fairly cold Frappuccinos in here. I was wondering, would you like to join me in a refreshing coffee beverage?" his gunflint eyes sparkling with warmth.

"Why, yes, I would, thank you very much," she said affably. Then she looked around. "Where, here?"

"No," he smiled, "there."

Holden was pointing to the forest where Mara had run following their first encounter. For a moment she thought Holden was making fun of her first-day jitters, but when she looked into his sable-hued pupils she realized he had no such intention.

They walked hand-in-hand toward the sun-dappled wood. Mara felt happy. Her fog of worries and cares lifted. Everything seemed clearer when she was with Holden.

Raising his heavy dark brows, he stepped in the woods and swung her into the circle of his arms. Mara laughed as she fell against him. Letting the momentum unbalance him, they toppled under a large oak. It was a tantalizing entanglement of long and short limbs. But it didn't take Holden long to order the confusion and soon he had Mara trapped beneath him. The two looked at each other earnestly. Holden's gold-ringed eyes asked Mara a silent question. Mara knew his question and had only one answer to give.

Holden smiled, understanding their silent exchange.

Reclaiming her lips, he crushed her to his chest. She felt an electric jolt as the hollows of her curvy body were pressed into his hard body. The embrace was at first surprisingly gentle but it rapidly became punishing and passionate.

Mara lost herself in the embrace momentarily and then

found herself yards away. They had been rolling over and over each other until they were in a darkened grove of trees.

Mara began to laugh; she had never been happier. Holden lifted his head to see her face, and then he, too, started laughing. She couldn't believe he was there with her again. And then she frowned.

Why am I frowning? she asked herself.

She looked at Holden, tall and dark, picking leaves out of his hair.

"Holden?"

"Yes, Mara."

"Why are you interested in me?"

Holden examined her, bemused. He looked above him to the latticework of the leaves against the sky. He gazed upward without expression and then turned back to Mara.

"Well, probably the same reason you're interested in me."

"But everyone likes you," she pulled away from him slightly.

"Yeah, but one has to be choosy. Don't you think?" he said while plucking a leaf from inside his shirt.

"You chose Regan, too," Mara said, immediately regretting it.

"That's a mistake I wouldn't make again," he reported, grinding the words out between his teeth.

Mara was letting the conversation get off track. She tried again, "But, what I mean is, you hardly even know me."

Holden threw his head into his hands and sighed. "I'm not very good at this. Do you just want to clue me in on what's eating you?"

Mara looked at Holden soberly, letting him feel the seriousness of her words.

"I want to know that you want me in your life, not just for fun, but in a significant way. I guess I need to know that you take me seriously."

"Of course I take you seriously. Actually I've been wanting to ask you something very serious, but I didn't know how you would respond," Holden said earnestly. "Do you want to help me with the Mumia Benefit? You know, send out letters and sift through court documents and stuff… let's say…" his tone became very intimate, "Saturday night?"

She couldn't dull the sparkle in her green eyes. "I'd love to, Holden."

"I'm so glad that you have concerns for humanity. That this is something we can share. This deserves a toast," he said. He gathered his backpack and pulled out the coffee drinks. "Here's to us!" he said, inclining his bottle to hers.

"To us!" Mara said. And they drank of the sweet, brown liquid in silence.

They spent the rest of the afternoon in the concealed grove, sharing stories and laughing at one another's bad puns. They sat with their legs tucked beneath them as they unraveled little bits of the thread that made up the intricate patterns of their lives. Now and then flat on their backs looking up at the trees, nestling a head in the other's lap, they talked like happy children, fascinating one another without trying to impress.

The conversation flowed. It was a rushing, crystal stream, much like the conversation of all young lovers. Breaking its banks, it became a flood, seeping and babbling through all their senses. It covered everything with its cool, refreshing clarity, its burblings of hopes and worries, its pondering of life's subtle mysteries.

It was a carefree time, so remote from every other moment in Mara's life. A golden-aired spell Mara was sure she would look back on again and again. Suddenly aware of the importance of the moment, she felt a foreign need to make it weighty and wanted to nail down the memory. Searching her repository of ponderous thoughts, she decided to confess.

"I have a desire to fight," she admitted.

"Wait, what?" Holden asked.

"The fight we had, it was probably my fault. Usually I avoid confrontation, but deep down, I want to ˈfight. I've always wanted to fight. Not a bloody fight, more like an argument. Well, maybe a bloody fight if no one got hurt. I don't know. I guess this stems from a friend I had in grade school. Her parents fought all the time and it tore at the core of their family. But they always made up."

Mara's eyes began to mist with the memory as she proceeded. "And when they did make up, the whole family went out to eat and each of the kids got presents. They could yell in the house, stay up as late as they wanted, and eat as many bowls of Count Chocula as they could stomach. The happiness in the house was so present, so indisputable." Mara sadly wiped a single, glistening tear from her eye. Then she tugged at a curl of shiny black hair on her large and lovely head and continued.

"I guess I was jealous of how the love in her family was right there for everyone to see, even if it did only appear after a fight. By comparison, my family's love seemed nonexistent, pounded so flat by monotony it was imperceptible." Mara paused, arrested momentarily by her recollection.

"My friend moved away, but my envy continued. I saw the same thing in acquaintances. They'd fight with their boyfriend or girlfriend, but when they'd make up, each would promise their love to the other and it was so obvious, so real. The fighting became their way to indulge in the best part of their relationship. Their fights actually defined their relationship. It's sort of sick, but it appealed to me.

"Eventually I figured out that those kind of people were addicted to fighting, and that it's probably unhealthy. But still, I craved it."

Holden looked at Mara empathetically as she continued.

"I always felt separate from people. I studied psychology not to be a scholar, but to understand people, to connect intimately with them, even if it was only through case studies. Serial killers interested me the most. I never understood why until I read about Jack the Ripper. I read somewhere that he'd vivisect his victims. He'd take out their reproductive organs and nail them to the wall. It was obvious that he had women issues, but I always wondered, why that particular act?" Mara's lovely emerald eyes lost their grip on Holden's as she dreamily fixated on a space three inches off the tip of his nose.

"One scholar speculated that the butcher was impotent. In other words, he couldn't touch or connect with women the way he wanted, so he did what any pathological psychotic would do: He touched them in a way he *knew* they'd feel, in a way he knew they'd understand for the rest of their lives. He touched them in the most significant way they'd ever be touched. He killed them. Since it was the reproductive organs that were the mystery behind his little problem, he tacked them on the wall, making them plain and ridding them of their hidden powers.

"I used to think each murder bred the guilt of the affair. Like a liaison where you get to know someone too well and the shameful residue stares up at you in the morning: a white splooge as a stand-in for a warm kiss on the cheek. A discarded condom reminding you of the absence of an 'I love you.' Except this time the stand-in for intimacy is dried blood under your fingernails and a faint memory of the flash of gleaming pink entrails."

Mara had been so swept up in her own story that she became confused as to what she was confessing and why it had anything to do with serial killers, or Holden, for that matter.

In normal people this would evoke self-consciousness. But Mara was not normal. She had a secret that, until now, she'd kept hidden: Mara knew she was a genius. Since she was a genius, these spewings and fulminations would be proved not only right, but righteously right in a sea of people and ideas that were so wrong it's amazing her extraordinary intellect survived in the midst of such mediocrity.

Yeah, she was one of them.

God save us all.

You may wonder why a romance provocateur such as myself would choose such an infuriating dunderhead for her heroine. While it's true that comrade Elizabeth Peyton Lovelace suggests in her book I Sing the Romance Novel *that a heroine should be likable and blah, blah, blah, it is also true that the heroine must be* believable *and, trust me, I know many of these bogus "genius" types.*

They are real, even if their version of reality is sadly fabricated.

You, for one, harbor such musings yourself, and if you don't, it's only because you're so vapid that the evidence against your "genius" (if that is what you insist on calling it) was insurmountable and you had to face facts. In that case, good for you!

As for the rest of us who possess above-average or superior intelligence—I, myself, being one of the latter (but, unlike you, I am in all certitude a genius)—we understand these musings and can

*choose to pay little or no heed to how annoying Mara is. That is, if
we are geniuses with empathy, as I am.*

Mara's face registered her confusion. Flustered, she found her
way from her improvisational solo back to the main theme.

"I don't know quite what it is, but I think there's some sort
of connection between the two. The desire to be closer to
someone, to be loved, and the desire to fight or even to kill."
She glanced sideways at Holden, partially flirting and partially
seeing if he had any inkling of the significance of her point.

Holden had sat enraptured through her whole monologue.
Now his eyes bathed her in admiration.

"Whoa," he exclaimed. "You are one deep little girl."

She looked up at him and her heart lurched madly.

He knows! He understands! she thought.

He bent down and kissed her slowly and thoughtfully. Then
he solemnly spoke, "I know exactly what you mean. Because
when I think of people who really love humanity and really
gave of themselves to the world, I think of the Baader-Meinhof
Group." He paused and drew up his head nobly. "I know that
I should hate them for killing innocent people. Hate them for
destroying millions and millions of dollars worth of innocent
property. But instead I can only admire them for their purity of
heart and action, for their love of the German people and their
love of the struggle.

"It reminds me of another activist: Jesus Christ. During the
massacre of the money traders in the temple, didn't he say, 'I kill
these people, not out of anger, but out of love. And those who
are blameless should cast the first stone'?"

"Yeah, something like that," Mara said, entranced by his
masculine charm.

Holden considered Mara with emotion. "We should go. The
air grows chill."

They gathered up their things and left the woods, the
promise of Saturday fresh on their lips as they parted. As the
sun set behind the stately oaks, each looked back more than
once as the ground between them widened.

CHAPTER 5

Mara's pretty head was whirling with excitement. Only two weeks ago she had worried that she wouldn't have a friend at Norden. Now she had three: the intensely driven Regan Thresh and the absurd but lovable duo of Tippy and Penny. And, dare she think it? It appeared as if she has a boyfriend, knock on wood!

Boyfriend. The word sounds absurd when applied to me, Mara thought.

But how else could she interpret his late call the night after their dalliance in the woods?

She was reading a book on serial killers and their working mothers, a conservative study calling for more stay-at-home moms, when the phone rang.

"Hello?"

"I didn't wake you, did I?" came the deep, familiar voice of Holden Rife.

Her heart skipped a beat. "No, I was reading. What's up, Holden?"

"I know we're going to see each other Saturday, but I was hoping you could help me out a little earlier this week…"

Mara noticed that Holden's silken voice sounded uncharacteristically strained. Her mind flashed briefly on the rumors about the Reading Group and she wondered if he was going to ask her to do something anarchistic or un-American. Then she heard a soft clicking sound on the line.

"What was that?" Holden asked, his warm masculine voice registering alarm.

"What?" asked Mara.

"That noise?"

"I don't know."

"I know this sounds crazy, but do me a favor after you hang up. Unscrew the mouth and ear piece on your phone and check for bugs." His voice was rough with anxiety.

"What do they look like?" asked Mara, her slender fingers tensed on the receiver.

"Uh, they look like they don't belong. If you find anything, take it out, but save it until you see me."

"Okay, but what is this…"

"Later. Listen, I have to ask you a big favor. I don't know if I should because we don't know each other that well, but something about you makes me feel like I can ask. But if I do, it might change everything…No! I shouldn't ask." Holden struggled with his thoughts in a passionate baritone.

"Of course you can," Mara gushed, "You can ask me anything. But, Holden, what is it?"

Holden took a deep breath and exhaled slowly before he answered. "It's Thursday night. Dinner. At—well, with my parents."

Mara laughed and ran a hand through her short, jet-black hair. All this buildup and he was only worried about her meeting his family.

"I'd love to come to dinner at your parents'."

"You have no idea what you're in for, but thanks. I normally wouldn't ask, but I need support. I haven't seen them in over a year and they're, well, different. Dinner is at eight, but mother likes to serve cocktails at seven. Shall I pick you up at 6:30?" His voice had regained the confident tone that Mara found so attractive.

"That would be fine," she whispered, her hand instinctively resting on her breast.

There was a knock at her door.

Holden added, "Okay, see you then. And remember to check your phone!"

They said their good-byes. Mara continued to stare at the phone, smiling as the humming dial tone switched to the abrasive message, "If you'd like to make a call, please hang up and dial again." To Mara it sounded like a Top 10 love ballad, her mood was so buoyant and gay.

Meeting the parents, she thought. Everything was racing so fast that she could barely keep track. *I'm beginning to resemble someone else. Someone with a life, a romantic life!* she thought with a laugh.

The rapping at the door disturbed her fanciful thoughts and she ran to answer it. There stood Tippy and Penny in their unvarying attire of sweatshirt, boxers, hair clips, and green and blue mud facial masks. Mara was annoyed that, even in a sober state, she still couldn't tell who was Tippy and who was Penny.

Is Penny the one with the silicone and the nose? Or is she the one with the orange skin and white-white teeth?

The whole idea of differentiating them was becoming a moot point anyway, since she really never had seen one without the other.

"Penny! Tippy! What's up?" Mara asked, carefully staring between the two when she said their names.

The blue and green masks pushed their way in and looked around.

"Hey," said Blue as she passed Mara and took a seat on her unmade bed. "Are we disturbing anything?"

"Yeah, can we come in?" Green asked as she sat in a chair.

"Sure," Mara answered and offered them a Triscuit.

"Nnn-nnn. I know we're sophomores, but it's never too late to gain that freshman fifteen," Green said.

Blue nodded emphatically, causing her curled bangs to stick to her fresh mud mask and stay there. "I know, did you see Regina Todd? Hello! Wake-up call! When you're looking that chunky you shouldn't be advertising it with an exposed midriff...I mean, kitsch-o-rama!"

"She's pregnant!" said Green in a tone that made the rolling of her eyes redundant.

"A completely avoidable deformity. No excuse!" said Blue.

Mara watched the two argue, wondering if Penny and Tippy were good enough friends to kick out of her room.

But Green had other ideas. "We thought we'd give you a facial."

"Yeah, you know, to exfoliate and revitalize your core skin cells. You'll look years younger," said Blue.

Mara wasn't sure she could afford to look years younger, but Blue already put on gloves and began to rub pink smelly stuff on her face.

"What is this?" Mara asked as the strange aromas hit her nose sharply.

"It's a mud mask, kind of like ours, but a little stronger 'cause you aren't doing daily treatments like we are," Blue said and seated Mara on her bed.

"Is it supposed to sting?" Mara asked.

"Herbal aromatherapy!" Blue said as she massaged the goo into Mara's temples.

Mara began to feel relaxed and tingly at the same time. "It's like a security blanket for your face," she murmured, enjoying its fuzzy, numbing sensation.

"So, what's up with you and your little boyfriend? Did you make up?" asked Green.

Mara struggled through wisps of sleepiness to answer. "We did! You guys were so right about that. He's so worth the effort."

Blue bobbed her head. Irked that her bangs were stuck in her mask, Blue started to pick them out, but Green's hand stopped her from touching them.

"No kidding, he is *such* a babe. Anyway, so what are you guys up to this week?" Green asked.

"Well, I'm having dinner with him on Thursday."

"And Saturday?" Blue asked and was immediately kicked by Green's fuzzy bunny slipper. "You know, Saturday being date night."

"Yeah, Saturday we're doing some Free Mumia stuff over dinner," Mara said.

Blue mumbled something that sounded like "cop killer."

"What?" Mara asked, not sure that she understood. She was so sensually sated that Blue and Green were starting to look like the same color.

"I said, 'top biller.' You know, all the celebrities come out in defense of him."

"Right," Mara nodded drowsily. "We're trying to get some. I heard Woody Harrelson is interested."

"Oh, that'll add some class to the benefit," said Green or Blue.

"Yeah, it will," said Blue or Green.

"I'm tired," said Mara involuntarily. She knew it was rude,

but trying to concentrate on the girls made her weary.

Green and Blue looked at each other. One of them smiled, nodded to the other, and went to the bathroom.

"We gotta go soon, but first we have to finish your facial. You're going to look so hot!"

"Holden is going to think you're so foxy!" said the one who came back from her bathroom with a warm washcloth and put it over Mara's face. Mara's achy eyes throbbed under its heat.

"So…what does Regan think of you dating Holden?"

With the washcloth still over her eyes, Mara heard a rummaging noise and sat up. But she was gently pushed back down. Then she heard a voice from across the room.

"Sorry, just looking for a tissue."

"It's by the phone," Mara said, and then continued, "Umm…" She had forgotten what the question was.

"Regan?"

"Oh, yeah," Mara said. "She's cool with it, the Holden thing. She thinks that I should join the Reading Group. She says that's the only way he'll ever really respect me."

The rustling noise stopped and the washcloth was lifted off Mara's face and someone began to wipe away the mask. Mara could just make out that it was Green looking in her eyes.

"She's right, you know. You need to join their club. It's the only way you'll be able to penetrate the enigma that is Holden Rife. He's an enigma. Enigma. Enigma."

Mara wondered if Green was repeating herself or if she had an echo in her head.

Through some unknown but not wholly unexpected alchemy, the word "enigma" appeared before her eyes in blue and green letters. Bit by bit the word bubbled, twisted and melted into the blue-green face of Holden who was smiling down on her saying, "Join my group, it's the only way I'll ever really respect you."

Mara nodded drowsily and said, "I will, but what should I wear to dinner on Thursday?"

Blue-green Holden asked, "Do you have any Chanel?"

"Of course she doesn't have any Chanel! Shut up!" the blue-green Holden answered himself. "Uh, wear the cleanest knee-length skirt you own and a loose-fitting blouse. Oh, and be sure to wash your hair with baking soda first to get rid of the waxy buildup."

"Yeah!" agreed the blue-green Holden.

"Okay, I'm gonna sleep now, blue-green Holden. Oh, what did you want me to remember again?"

"Sleep," urged blue-green Holden.

And Mara did.

The next morning after a less than stimulating lecture in her psych class, "Serial Killers' Cereal: Nutrition and its Effect on Modern Mass Murderers," Mara made her way slowly to the café to get a latté and a muffin. It was really too hot that day for coffee, but Mara had almost fallen asleep twice during class and needed something to pick her up.

Taking the food to a bar seat overlooking the campus, she tried to remember if it was "feed a schizophrenic, starve a psychopath" or the other way around.

Mara ate silently, her head nearly empty of all but exhaustion, while her eyes tracked the bustle of the campus. Amidst the tall, genetically superior specimens roaming about as if entitlement were their middle name, a precociously crotchety groundskeeper bent over a trash can. He appeared to be talking to it. Mara tried to place his mental ailment as she watched him pull out the sticky, overfilled garbage bag and put in a new liner, flashing half the campus each time he hunched over. Mara turned away from him. There, among the shifting but unchanging mass of blue jeans and cargo pants, she spied Regan's angular black-and-blue stooped figure loping in her direction. Even Regan's subtle foot-dragging gait suggested she was programmed differently than the others on campus. Mara wondered briefly if serial killers were as easy to spot in a crowd as Regan was.

Regan saw Mara and dropped heavily beside her. She gave Mara the requisite penetrating stare under navy blue, instead of her usual black, eyebrows.

Mara tried to think of an appropriate way to compliment

the subtle color change, but all she could think of was, "Nice eyebrows." So instead she took a big gulp of her latté.

"Mara," Regan barked, "I have some good news. But first, how are things with Holden?"

Mara quietly appreciated her new friend who cared so much for her happiness and well-being. "Great! Couldn't be better. We're having dinner two nights this week!" Mara said happily.

Regan nodded and preemptively brought a finger to her brow. Then she smiled so hard her cheeks must have hurt. "That's great! Why two dinners, though?"

Mara explained the last-minute dinner arrangements with his parents and Regan nodded supportively.

"Oh Mara, I'm so happy for you. But this means we have to act even faster. If Holden doesn't find out soon that you are the strong, independent woman he really wants, it could ruin everything. But I have a plan. See, not everyone in our group has to approve the new members. Holden's against consensus decision-making. In truth, *he* single-handedly decided that we should make decisions through majority vote."

Mara was confused as to how this applied to her relationship with Holden.

Regan continued, "What this means for you is that you can join our group without Holden's permission. We're a group of eight and I've talked to Apocalypse, Rosa, Rat, and Eric. They all want you…"

Mara didn't get it.

"I want you too, and that makes five, which means you're in the Reading Group, if you want," Regan said clearly and patiently.

"Oh! Cool."

Regan, in her attempt to hold her eyebrow twitch, smeared the penciled-in line. The result was a blue slash across her forehead uniting the two brows.

"Uh, you have a uni-brow," Mara whispered to her.

"What? What?" Regan snarled.

Mara pointed at her own forehead to demonstrate, "A uni-brow. You know, a single eyebrow, like Bert, the evil one in Ernie and Bert. Your pencil smeared."

Regan took out a compact mirror and began dabbing at her forehead with a Kleenex. She gave up trying to reshape them and wiped them off completely.

Mara thought as she gazed on the nude expanse of forehead, *She looks like an albino ape.*

Regan drew two arched lines on her naked brow. Now she appeared worried or hesitant.

"We gotta get you in the group soon. Thursday dinner we can't do anything about. So don't do *anything* with him afterward. We have a meeting on Friday; you can come then. That way, for Saturday's date he'll already have that appreciation for you as an individual."

Mara nodded. She wanted Holden to think of her that way.

"Have you read any Marx?" Regan asked pointedly.

"Brothers? Seen a few movies."

Mara knew her joke was feeble before she said it, but when she was nervous she always said stupid things. At that moment Mara was worried she didn't even want to belong to their group. *What if I don't agree with them? What if I discover Holden isn't right for me?* All she had to do, however, was think of Holden's tawny, smooth skin and his bright hazel eyes and she knew that she wouldn't care what their group did. She would follow.

"Ha-ha. Very funny," said Regan, voice heavy with sarcasm. "So, do you think you can read these before the meeting on Saturday?" Regan held some pamphlets out to Mara and two books, *Communism for Idiots* and *Beneath the Red Star: Kalashnikovs, Commandos, and the RAF.*

"I guess I can peruse them…" she answered, realizing that with her new reading material, class, and her internship, her paper on women serial killers would not get finished that week.

"Good. I'll also go over some stuff with you before the meeting. Come to my room at six." Regan's eyes tracked a dust-covered young man, presumably James, walking across the school grounds.

"I gotta go," She said, then squeezed Mara's delicate arm. "Remember, don't let things get too hot on Thursday night. You need to establish your new personality first or he'll never take you seriously."

"Right. Okay," Mara said, her mind occupied with trying to recall something Holden told her to remember yesterday, but all she could come up with was knee-length skirts and baking soda for her hair.

"See you Friday!" said Regan and she headed across the café to the dusty figure.

Then suddenly it came to Mara.

Bugs!

She remembered that she needed to check her phones. The memory coincided with a sharp pain in her left temple and she had to count to twenty before standing up and heading back to her room.

Between her internship, classes, and homework, Mara's week went by quickly. She didn't have time to be worried about her date with Holden, so she crammed all her nervousness into the few furious minutes before his arrival. Standing before her bathroom mirror, she took a deep breath and tried to relax while her stomach fluttered with anxiety. Twice in the last half-hour she kept herself from running to the phone and calling off the date. Now it was too late. Holden was due any minute.

What if his parents don't like me? Or if they think I'm not good enough for them?

She put her hand to her hair and touched one bouncy curl. Ever since she washed her hair with baking soda it was soft, light, and fluffy—just the way she hated it. It took two times the amount of hair gunk to get it somewhat back to normal, and now it was already time for a reapplication.

What was I thinking! Baking soda?

Mara heard a knock at the door and answered it.

Again she was shocked by the intense appeal that radiated from Holden Rife. Her eyes followed the line of his elegant suit that fell from his broad shoulders, down his rock-hard hips and long, sinewy legs to his gleaming black shoes. He was so unlike the fart-lighting, drunken yokels she knew growing up, or the constipated, vacuous rich boys who infested Norden.

While he could easily pass for a debutante's dream date,

there was a grave aspect about him and a strong sense of isolation, purpose, and sorrow emanated from his frame.

Maybe that's what makes him so irresistible, Mara pondered.

His expression was immobile as he took her arm and escorted her to his car. But Mara could see the tensing of his jaw betraying his deep frustrations.

"Holden? Is there something you want to tell me?"

"What? No. I'm sorry, you look beautiful," he said, distractedly.

"I don't mean that, I mean about this evening. Is there anything I should know before I meet your parents?" she asked as they drove off.

Holden pushed a stray hair off his brow. "You're so smart, I knew I couldn't hide anything from you. Not that you wouldn't find out soon enough. My parents are, well, they're rich. Filthy rich," he said in an agonized voice and then turned away.

"I know, Holden. You told me. And it's okay," Mara said comfortingly.

"Well, you don't know the whole story, but there is no way to prepare you for that. Let's just say they like to play games."

Mara nodded and tried to brace herself for the evening as they sped through the night.

After twenty minutes of winding curves through picturesque, autumn leaf-covered roads, Mara had forgotten her nervousness. Before she knew it they had reached a gatehouse where they were waved in by a twill-clad man. Mara couldn't shake the unreal feeling as they sped along the cobblestone drive flanked by perfectly mutilated hedges and pulled up to a mansion that seemed half the size of the Norden College campus.

She felt more dwarfed than usual when she looked up at the huge estate that Holden called home. After parking his car in the brick-lined semicircle in front of the mansion, Holden turned to Mara.

"I forgot to ask you, what happened with the bugs?"

"Bugs?" Mara asked innocently, biding her time.

"In the phone!"

"Oh, there were none."

"And you checked right away, right?"

Mara looked at his strained face. Could she tell him that she didn't remember to check until the next day? She balanced between the guilt of lying to him and the humiliation of explaining to him her failure to perform a simple task. Not wanting to give him any more reason to worry on the night of his reunion with his parents, she answered, "There was nothing."

Holden was temporarily relieved, but his face filled with a new apprehension when he turned to the house. "Here we go!" he said with a forced grin as he unfolded his tall, muscled body from the car.

Mara followed.

Under the shadow of the stately mansion, Mara tried to reassure herself, *They're just Holden's parents. How bad could they be?*

Holden rang the doorbell of the ivy-covered Tudor.

Mara gave him a questioning look, which he answered with, "It's my way of letting them know that I don't consider this exercise in excess to be my home. I'm a visitor and a visitor rings the doorbell."

In time a handsome, spare woman dressed in a simple herringbone skirt and an ivory-colored silk blouse answered the door.

"Oh! Hello! Oh my! You look awful, Holden! And who is your little friend?" She peered at Mara as if she might explode at any moment.

"My 'little friend' is Mara. Mara, this is my mother, Maxine."

Mara looked upon the face of a woman in her mid-fifties with a waxy, light complexion broken only by two harsh red lines emphasizing nearly nonexistent lips. What she lacked in a chin she made up for with her beak-like nose. Her eyes, small and closely set, stared out sharply from beneath her sparse eyebrows.

"I'm pleased to meet you," said Mara in what she thought was her sweetest and most cheerful voice.

"Of course you are my dear, not many of your kind get the pleasure, do they?" Maxine ushered them into the oddly cold entryway. "No. No they don't," the matriarch answered herself thoughtfully.

Mara turned to Holden who was wincing as if from a sharp pain. She reminded herself that this was more difficult for Holden than it was for her and turned back to his mother.

"What a beautiful home you have," she said, trying not to gawk at the finely lined puffiness surrounding Maxine's marble-sized eyes, her only tangible sign of age.

"This old thing? Nonsense! Nothing but trouble. You can spend a whole day looking for the telephone that's off the hook. But it's the General's and he's intractable, so there's nothing to be done about it."

She gazed at Mara as if scanning for a way to return a compliment. Apparently the job proved too taxing and she simply shook her head and said, "If it's past six, it must be happy hour!"

Her saffron hair remained unmoving as Maxine strode with remarkable aplomb through a series of halls and rooms. Just as Mara was convinced she could never find her way back to the door, they arrived in a large living room replete with a strange assortment of Indian rugs, Fabergé eggs, leaded-glass windows, a crystal chandelier, shrunken heads, and antique colonial-empire furniture. Under the circumstances, Mara thought it best to hide her admiration, so she clamped her mouth down before the oohs and ahhs started slipping out.

"Holden, would you call the General?" Maxine asked without taking her eyes off Mara.

Holden scowled, but obediently left the room. His mother watched as he left and then leveled a keen eye on Mara.

"So, Mara, if that is your real name, and I doubt it!"

"What?" asked Mara, taken aback.

"Nothing. So… mmm?" Maxine said as if she had just asked Mara a question.

"I'm sorry, I don't follow," Mara replied, feeling out of sorts.

"So you say, so you say… I'll never understand what compels him to show me his messes. It reminds me of his toilet training. He was always so proud of his ability to create filth," Maxine said to the ceiling and then brought her eyes back to Mara. "I once knew a Mara… a little flower of a girl. Or perhaps she was a flower? Mariposa Lily. That's right. Oh well, I wouldn't be the first to mistake a girl for a flower. So what are your intentions with my son?"

"I beg your pardon?" Mara said, unable to comprehend the very nature of the conversation.

"Begging my pardon is understandable, but it still doesn't answer my question," Maxine quipped.

"I don't have any 'intentions' for your son that he himself doesn't reciprocate, if that's what you mean," Mara answered, wishing for Holden's swift return.

"Then you are a fool, my dear."

Maxine walked over to a well-stocked bar, opened a mono-grammed silver ice server and plinked two sharp shards of ice into her glass.

"You're smart enough to catch him, but too stupid to know what to do with him."

She shook her nearly immobile honey-tinted hair as she mixed herself a drink.

"There is one thing I know about my boy: He needs to be ruled. Regan knew it. But she was made of insubstantial stuff." Maxine turned to Mara with a scurrilous look on her waxy, tight face, "You could be an improvement. Then again, you won't last long with your attitude."

Before Mara could respond the sallow woman grabbed her ample cheek. She gave it a sharp pinch and peered at it closely.

"You girls aren't like oranges, are you? One squeeze won't tell all…"

At that moment Mara heard the footsteps she'd been hoping for.

Maxine let go of Mara's cheek and turned to greet her family.

"Oh, there you are! We were just having the most lovely talk about the state of fresh produce, weren't we dear?" she said, aiming a saccharine smile in Mara's direction.

Holden's grim expression told Mara that he already surmised the content of his mother's banter. Mara gave him a reassuring smile as a tall, fantastically uniformed old gent strolled in behind Holden.

He's much older than Holden's mother, Mara thought.

"Mara, this is my father, the General. Father, this is Mara."

The elderly man walked up to Mara and didn't stop until his

face was practically resting on the top of her head. He smelled of Tiger Balm and Dippity-Doo and faintly of that ripe, old-man smell. Mara quickly scanned his antiquated powder-blue uniform with canary-yellow stripes down the side. The patriarch bent down so that his rheumy eyes were directly in front of hers.

"How do you do?" he said in a grave but dignified voice.

"Very well, thank you, Sir," Mara replied and she glanced with confusion at the antique sword that graced his left side.

What does he need that for? she wondered.

"Sir!" exclaimed the red-faced old man. "I am no Sir! You may call me 'General.'"

"Uh, yes S–, I mean, General. I'm not familiar with your uniform. What are you a general of?"

The room filled with silence.

The General stood upright, blinking vacantly in the air above Mara's head.

Maxine scowled at Mara.

Mara looked at Holden who was drawing a hand across his throat.

A little too late for that, she thought.

Mara felt as if she had just squatted down, defecated on their Indian rug, and demonstrated a particularly useful wiping technique to Holden's parents. She angrily wondered why Holden didn't tell her that his dad still hadn't found the right dosage.

Maxine broke the uncomfortable silence. "Yes, well, I suppose Holden and Mara would like a drink. Can you take care of that, dear?"

The General's demeanor brightened.

"Is Mara a Manhattan drinker?" the General asked his wife.

"She has a mouth, dear. What do *you* think?" Maxine droned.

"Right. Right. Two Manhattans and one for me makes three." The dapper old man busied himself with the drinks.

Maxine joined him to "freshen" hers.

Mara watched the unlikely couple with gape-mouthed wonder. After much clinking and muttering at the bar, the General came back with three reddish-brown, aromatically lethal drinks stuffed with bright green and red maraschino cherries.

Holden and Mara rushed to take the slipping glasses out of his hands.

"Well. Here's to us!" Maxine toasted and the four took a draw at what proved to be the worst cocktail Mara had ever tasted.

Holden nearly finished his in one ambitious swallow. Mara realized that she too might need a large amount of alcohol to get through the evening.

They settled in plushy chairs and Maxine asked Holden a series of questions about his last year and his plans for the future: "Are you distinguishing yourself in your chosen field? What classes are you taking? Can one make a career out of speaking German? What's the point of going to an expensive school if you aren't taking advantage of the powerful friends you can make there?"

Holden suffered the questions, giving as little information as possible in return.

Midway through Mara's second drink, a gong chimed from somewhere in the house. Maxine announced that dinner was served. By then Mara was feeling the numbing effects of the alcohol and had decided that the evening wasn't horrible and instead was almost seeming comic.

The four wandered through more halls lined with painted portraits spanning the ages. At one point the General stopped and pointed to a painting of a man with a similar uniform from a time long time past.

"You know what happened when the Anglos met the Saxons, don't you?" The General asked Mara in a wave of ripe breath.

Mara indulged what she took to be a joke by answering, "No."

The General backed up and gave her a scathing look. "You don't! Well!" Bristling with offense, he turned to his wife who only shrugged her thin shoulders as they continued down the hallowed halls.

Holden grasped Mara's hands and squeezed tightly as if to say, "Don't worry, this will all be over soon enough." Or maybe he was trying to say, "You think this is bad, just wait."

Mara's good humor began to sink.

They came to a long room with a large table made of a single cut of oak. It had four elegant settings with portions of dinner steaming on the plates. Whoever had laid the settings was nowhere to be seen. There was a carafe of wine and another of what she correctly assumed to be more Manhattan mix. The wood-paneled walls were covered with coats of arms and medieval tapestries. In her tipsy state, Mara half-expected Errol Flynn to swing by, rapier in hand. Or was she crossing centuries? What did she know? Even a self-proclaimed genius (however delusional this proclamation is in Mara's case) grants areas of ignorance.

Of course Mara's areas of ignorance seem to be expanding with each turning page. No, this is not (as my shrink has artlessly suggested) because of a mounting jealousy I have of the main character. The accusation is laughable. After all it is I who created Mara. She is a plaything in my hands. With a mere downswing of a finger I can obliterate her from our collective existence. But, as with all compassionate creators, I have imbued my creation with free will. As a non-genius, Mara falls prey to the same pitfalls of all of God's mediocre creatures: She disappoints.

So, why, (you ask) write the romance of an inferior species such as Mara or Holden? Why not write of true genius love?

It is a good question, even if you only thought of it through my prompting.

The love between geniuses is a heady tempest non-Mensan mortals cannot survive. Descriptions of the lovemaking would hurl the nation into a tailspin. Eyes would roll back in heads and stay there.

After reading about genius love (assuming you survive) you'll find yourself incessantly wondering, How does a man infuse his masculinity with such unflinching cryptic significance? or, How is it that a woman can calibrate her femininity to such a powerful scale of reticence? And wherefore has the act of genius love transformed the very scripting of mankind, making a profound difference in the world? You will search incessantly for answers to these questions, eventually giving up your shoes and clothes for a barrel and lantern.

Those lovers who have had the misfortune of reading about genius love will go into hiding for shame of their past offenses toward "love." Many will opt to live in all-male or all-female colonies. They will take to letter writing to express their mediocre affections for fear of effacing their memory of genius love. Whole populations will die out, leaving only the offspring of the illiterate and the geniuses. And quite frankly, we need literate non-geniuses to fill in the lower ranks of the revolution.

Oh? Now you are curious?

You don't want to know, nor could you ever discover on your own. The lingering eyesore of genius love would haunt you forever. This is too much responsibility for me to bear. 🐾

The little group sat together at one end of the table and picked at the delicious dinner. The main course was some sort of game animal Mara didn't recognize. She dreaded asking any questions and simply trusted it wasn't an animal she thought was cute. The quiet repast was sporadically interrupted by Maxine's questions; "Do you suppose that bad genetic stock accounts for the high rate of obesity and suicide in the Midwest?" and "If you put Liberace and Lawrence Welk in a sack together, who do you suppose would come out alive?" and "Not many sophisticated people come from Wisconsin, isn't that right, Mara?"

Mara let Holden volley the questions, although she attempted to look like part of the conversation through an increasingly dwindling smile. Even as Holden cringed his way through the meal, his presence was so commanding that everything else around him seemed diminished, almost inconsequential.

🐾 It is true that those who read romance novels often do so in order that they may simultaneously play out their fantasies and trauma vis-à-vis sex and relationships. For example, there is the trauma of a reader whose husband may or may not be having an affair. This woman has been wounded by romance's betrayal, yet needs to believe in the romantic ideal. She turns to the printed matter and finds her tonic in the genre of romance. In this case we romance novelists are similar to doctors ministering to invalids. We must follow the Hippocratic oath: First, do no harm. Genius love and sex unnecessarily inflicted on the masses is harmful. This aspect of the writer's bedside relationship to the reader, however, shouldn't be revealed. You wouldn't tell a five-year old his or her fear of the monster under the bed is about sublimated Oedipal desires. There are simply certain things you should keep from readers as they dip into your purply pages. Genius love is certainly one of them.

Mara looked at the older couple at the table. *Bless them, by comparison they seem so... so common.*

After dinner they relocated to an adjacent chamber where a roaring fire took the chill off the unseasonably cold, poorly lit den. They sat on high-back, ornately upholstered chairs facing the fire, clutching warmed brandies.

"Well, is there anything else you'd like to share with us about your purposefully rebellious lifestyle, Holden?" Maxine asked.

Holden screwed up his eyes as if he were weighing two equally bad options, which, in fact, was the case.

"Then I suggest we get started," she responded ominously to his silence.

"Can't we skip this? Mara has no idea how to play," Holden pleaded as he ran a firm hand over his chiseled jaw.

"Well, we *could* skip it," Maxine started in a tone only a mother could exact. "But that would mean you'd have to give up your vintage car, tuition, and off-campus housing, now wouldn't it?"

Holden studied his thumbs. Mara had never seen him so conflicted.

"Besides, it's only once a year, and you know how much the General looks forward to it."

Maxine's nearly invisible brows drew together over her small, glassy eyes in a pleading expression that was hard for Mara to believe. Mara knew instinctually that Holden's mother was a woman who always got her way.

The game seemed inevitable so Mara turned to Holden, saying, "Really, I don't mind. I like games!"

The General clapped his hands together and turned a deeper shade of red. "Goody-Good!" he said with a twinkle in his eye.

Maxine explained. "Since Holden has neglected to inform you, the game is called Pull-Yourself-Up-By-Your-Bootstraps. The General and I invented it with some legionnaires in South Africa. There are no rules. The object is to come up with the best get-rich scheme. The catch is that you must pretend to start from living on the street with nothing but the clothes on your back."

"*And* the clothing on your arse," the General added as he

rocked with excitement, of what kind Mara was uncertain.

Giving him a curt, dismissive nod Maxine continued, "You must detail how, as a pauper, you would sleep and eat and survive until you became rich, and what your get-rich scheme is. Do you understand, my dear?"

Mara nodded and flattened her palms against her skirt.

"I know you have an unfair advantage over us due to your…" she cleared her throat, "Ahem, *upbringing*. But since this is your first time playing I won't give you a handicap…"

The General abruptly burst in with, "Well, I suppose I should start so she can see how it's done. Now let's see, let's see…"

Holden seemed to grimace and his mother's taut skin tightened further at the General's offer. He didn't seem to notice as he stroked either side of his face and looked into the fire, eyes animated as jitterbugs. To Mara, it seemed he had too much face. Elastic rolls of it rippled under his hands and settled back, hanging loosely from his skull.

"Well," he said with all the jolly enthusiasm of someone auditioning for the role of Santa Claus. "There is no better return on an investment and nothing that people are willing to pay more money for than the polluted bloomers of girls in the blush of youth. Preferably blonde children, but the brunettes have a certain tang to them that is agreeable from time to time…Brunettes are less subtle, earthier, as if they were stored in the cellar. The underwear of course, not the girls," he explained to Mara with a laugh, excitement adding a shine to his eyes and a polish to his cheeks.

Mara was incredulous. She looked to Maxine who wore an expression of profound boredom and remarkably little distaste.

"General," Maxine said, "This is now your fourth plan for stealing little girls' underwear and selling them to Asian markets. Couldn't you come up with an altogether different scheme?"

The General's face detached itself slightly from his skull. "Well naturally they're going to be sold on the Asian market, how else does one become well-to-do peddling little girls' used unmentionables? The Oriental diet is a simple one. No meat or milk, an assortment of fish, soy, seaweed, and rice. Their little girls don't smell the same. They smell like daisies, jasmine, and morning dew.

"If you fancy an optimum price for U.S. panties, you have to sell it to a market that appreciates the choice, tangy odors created by an Occidental diet. The unaffected fragrances of mushroom, peat, brine, and cotton candy. You just can't acquire those in the Orient! Moreover, this is not the same old plan. This one involves two large Siberian Huskies.

"Now then, I would pilfer a pair of them, stout silver ones with great furry snouts. The olfactory cavities on those dogs are some of largest and most gifted in the canine species. They can detect a needle in an assemblage of hay. By daylight I would teach the hounds to sniff out the distinct perfume of a young girl's underclothing, rewarding them with dried meats comprising squirrels and partridges snared by my own two hands. On frosty winter nights I could curl up with them to stay warm. A toasty warm canine pile with me in the middle."

The General absently fingered the medals on his chest as he spoke into the fire. "When the Siberian huskies were properly trained I would take them from township to village to locate the highest concentration of little girls. It is probable the maximum density would be found at an abbey for incorrigible girls.

"Once I found my abbey, I'd filch decent wearing-apparel off a maiden's clothing line and wash my wretched, canine-sullied body in a river. Then I would tearfully set my faithful Siberian huskies free and, in utter solitude, set off for the abbey for wayward girls to secure an engagement. If there were no work for me I would sneak in at nightfall and drip the toxic juices of a hemlock root into the ear of whoever stood in my way."

The lips of the General were a cherry red, contrasting harshly with the white tongue that would intermittently dart over them, leaving behind a glistening layer of saliva.

"My position ultimately secured, I would purchase children's untalkaboutables in bulk with my first week's wages, so that each pair of soiled knickers could be labeled and put in an airtight cellophane bag and stored for future commerce. Then I would supplant the unsanitary indescribables with the freshly purchased ineffables that would begin their journey to slender hips of God's most precious flowers.

"All my earnings would go toward new bulk body-huggers and cellophane bags to keep the bouquet of the tainted accoutrements 'ripe' as they say. Now, if forty girls changed their underwear daily, which I could pretty much assure (as it is a house of God), then naught, naught, carry deuce, twenty-six, carry deuce, fourteen... I would have fourteen thousand, six hundred pairs of schoolgirl bloomers after a year.

"Bidding adieu to the chubby-limbed progenitors of my product, I would procure my passage on a steamship to the Orient. The merchandise on-hand would be used as collateral for the trip and I would make my way to the busiest port to find a man disposed to business. We would haggle, but once he had sampled my wares he would happily sell the product along the opium roads. Through my distributor I could exchange the pungent panties for goods to sell in the States at a handsome profit. Thus, by importing fine Asian wares and exporting Occidental underwears, I would be a very wealthy man within four years."

The General looked around the fire-lit faces as if to say, "So there!" He was clearly pleased with his yarn.

If fawning looks of approval and delight were what he expected, then he must have been disappointed by the look of consternation on Mara's well-modeled face and doom on Holden's classically handsome, but mostly hidden behind his hands, face. His wife's face accordingly maintained an I'm-keeping-up-appearances-now-but-don't-even-*think*-you're-sharing-a-bed-with-me-tonight cast.

Mara felt her dinner at the back of her lily-white throat and mildly wondered what it was doing there. She began to see why what from the outside might appear to be a desirable and well-appointed household could be such a burden for Mrs. Rife. When something is wrong, all the previously charming foibles recast themselves as repellent or ugly. Suddenly the endless expanse of halls and richly furnished rooms took on the aspect of a sinister maze to Mara, and what she formerly had thought of as an indulgent eccentricity—the General's uniform, for example—became a disquieting reminder of something deeply amiss.

But why do I care? Within an hour's time I'll be out of here and I can get on with my romance. This is just a digression. Holden and I are the real story here. Mara thought.

Maxine volunteered to go next in the hideous Pull-Yourself-Up-by-Your-Bootstraps game. She wiped a flat, waxy hand at the air as if to clear it of the General's story.

"It is always hard to go after you, General. While your stories *are* predictable, they are always a showstopper," she looked to Holden and Mara, calculating the inches separating them. "My idea is a much more *common* one,"

Holden flashed Mara an apologetic look she only understood in retrospect.

"As I have previously mentioned," Maxine intoned formally, "this game, much like life, has no rules, just an objective. I, therefore, choose to alter my 'character.' I will retain my gender, but I will shed my wisdom-accumulating-but-socially-undesirable-years and start this story at the ripe old age of, let's say, eighteen or nineteen.

"We must assume I've already suffered some mean schooling, as some form of education is free to all in this welfare state. That makes me eighteen with a high school degree, but, inexplicably homeless. As a young and, (did I fail to mention?) feasibly attractive woman, I am simultaneously the most vulnerable and most lethal creature on God's earth…"

Maxine paused and allowed her eyes to take a tour of the room. As she came under the older woman's caustic gaze, Mara noticed a remarkable expanse of white surrounding Maxine's irises. It reminded Mara of the wild, pain-filled eyes of a mare giving birth.

"…but not too terribly bright," Maxine remarked as her eyes stayed on Mara's. "Like all parasites I decide to hook my claws into a wealthy lost young man.

"How do I accomplish such a task? Very simple. Go where they are in abundance. Let's say at a facility of higher learning. Splendid! But how to get in?"

Again Maxine paused her monologue and looked directly at Mara.

"The reason these schools are rife with rich young men is

that they are *exclusive*. Their express purpose is to keep the riffraff, i.e., me, *out*. Perhaps I cheat on the entrance exam, or maybe I sleep with the admissions board. Anyway, does it really matter how I managed it? I'm in! Now I have to find a man who is, while of unquestionably noble breeding, a bit unconventional, a trait likely inherited from his father since defective genes travel along the Y chromosome."

While the crack was undoubtedly meant for the General, he failed to notice, and instead, hummed merrily into the fire, satisfaction pursing his scarlet lips.

"Once I find him it is a simple matter of utilizing my unremarkable beauty and instinctive skills of diabolical deception. But, what about the competition? Good question! I abolish it. Whatever it takes. A ball-peen hammer can shatter a skull and costs less than ten dollars. Ping! Competition's gone. But hold on, there's one more problem. The young man has yet to fall into his inheritance! Can I wait patiently for his virtuous parents to die a natural death? Absolutely not.

"Instead I have my betrothed arrange a gathering with his parents, perhaps over a meal. At the dinner, I note the layout of the house. Sneaking back in the mute of night, I kill the parents with a pillowcase filled with their collection of shrunken heads."

Maxine's voice grew more animated as she pressed on.

"I have a heathen's lust for blood and I smear it on my face. Blue blood, blue blood! I feel the premium-grade viscosity of blue blood dribble down my chin! As they invoke the name of their Lord and beg me for mercy I will spit in their faces and dance on their nearly lifeless bodies, screaming, 'You old boobies! The inheritance is mine now! All mine! And don't think your son will survive very long if he ever crosses me. He'll be joining you soon. Ah-ha! Ah-ha-ha-ha! Ah-ha!'"

Maxine's formerly composed face, lit by the glowing embers of the dying fire, had sprung to grotesque life. Looking at her, Mara was suddenly reminded of that unsettling thing dogs do when they suddenly swing their heads to the side and snap at a patch of unmistakably empty air. She felt a mix of sadness and horror that Maxine might actually have those type of murderous suspicions about *her, Mara*—a girl whose only real ambition was to quietly spend the rest of her life studying monographs of brutal murderers in an office with a window that opened and to come home to a white picket fence, a small garden, and someone she loved.

Holden looked longingly at Mara. As if her thoughts were contagious, he smiled warmly and touched the side of her cheek before he turned back to his biological genitors.

"Mother, Father," he began with remarkable calm. "I will go next."

He leaned back in his chair, eyes blazing with a deviant passion unfamiliar to Mara. She feared what was to come. Fortifying herself with a nip at the perfumy drink in her snifter, she flicked an imaginary speck of dust from her shirt, waiting for Holden to begin.

Holden cleared his throat and leveled grave eyes on his parents.

"There is more than one kind of wealth in this world," he said and slowly stood as he peered around the room from the bottom of his eyes. "There are the riches that shackle a man to a heritage of deceit and malice and there are the kind of riches that can only be achieved through actions of valor. Have you not heard, 'It is far easier for a needle to pass through a camel's eye than for a rich man to enter the vestibule of heaven'? I choose a character rich in the basest wealth, the wealth that is hidden from the taxman, but impoverished of the more essential wealth of dignity, due to his parents' complete inability to acknowledge anything deeper than breeding and maintaining their warped sense of honor.

"This young man is, however, gifted with the torturous insight that there is more to life than riches; there is a meaning beyond the cynical accumulation of money. Starved for this meaning, he reaches back in time to a group of upper-middle-class German revolutionaries. He finds they hold the same dissatisfaction of with the status quo. Ties that run deeper than any familial bond bind him to them. He has discovered the Baader-Meinhof Group.

"Their mothers and fathers, too, had robbed them of a meaningful inheritance. But with them it wasn't only their parents who stole their dignity and purpose, it was their

Fatherland and Mother country. Shamed and tormented by their heritage, they embraced Marxism and the philosophy of the lowly urban guerrilla and formed the RAF."

The General's wavering attention seemed to catch suddenly and he silently mouthed "RAF" with bewilderment.

Holden, unconcerned, continued, "The young man is inspired by their righteous fervor and through his diligent research he discovers, from a reliable e-mail source, that as an art student Baader also studied the work of a certain German clairvoyant whose name shall be kept secret, lest it fall into the wrong hands.

"This spiritual philosopher believed the body was made of three interpenetrating sheaths which, for you laymen, I will describe: the sheath of material accumulation, or the physical sheath; the sheath of life, or the ethereal sheath; and the sheath of the spirit, or the astral sheath. The young man's source explained that Baader, knowing RAF's ideas were too pure and futuristic for their corrupt time, pursued a quest for rebirth in hopes that their ideals might be astrally implanted in a body of the future."

Holden paused and his searching, multicolored eyes became inaccessible to Mara while his voice grew cold and removed, as if channeling words from a distant land.

"The young man is determined to become the conduit by which the roving soul of the dead, upper-middle-class German revolutionary could travel through time to the present. After many acts of contrition and tests of strength and virtue, he proves himself worthy of bearing the drifting soul of Baader. By a process I cannot reveal to you—I can only say that it involves extreme body purification, 'brain-free' thinking, and human sacrifice—the two come to share a single body with one radical aim."

Holden's usually serene voice rose with a dazzling passion, anger singeing the corners of its control.

"They're a perfect duo. The two men in one body become a single Über-Terrorist bent on overthrowing the corrupt establishment through all of the various means deemed essential to do it.

"Battling the Fatherland, as Andreas Baader would say, is the only way to vanquish the father's power and the sins of heritage. But this system isn't truly annihilated unless you take the Mother country down with it. For who is more to blame for the Fatherland's blindness to his folly than the well-dressed, well-fed, enabling Mother?

"Man and soul, the Über-Revolutionaries bring down the state through a series of activities that are too tiresome to detail. But as the blood of the state dries under the fingernails of the Über-Revolutionaries, our protagonist decides the *metaphor* of the Fatherland and Mother country is not satisfying his real drive to rip asunder that which truly haunts him: his own flesh-and-blood parents.

"It is a dark and stormy night when he finally succumbs to the urge to rid himself of his non-symbolic father and mother. Andreas and I creep into the home of my parents…"

"Oh really, Holden, you are just like your father," Maxine interrupted, with an unmistakable expression of ennui. "Can't you come up with something more interesting than you and the ghost of this 'Andre Baader' person winning the Indy 500, or finding Atlantis together, or forming a rock-and-roll band? Really, you'd think after all these years you'd have grown out of this obsession with your imaginary friend."

Holden darkened at his mother's remark.

"How many times do I have to tell you, Mother? Andreas Baader is *not* imaginary. He is a real man in history. People have written books about him."

"You'll never make history with an attitude like yours," Maxine launched in. "And you'll never even get into politics with that long hair. It's high time you show the signs of your upbringing."

The General stirred from his previous glazed state during which Mara assumed he'd been daydreaming about little girl's underwear.

"I don't see how you can play this game properly if you start out already wealthy," the General grumbled. "It defies the whole premise upon which we base the game. It's just not sporting, Holden. And how the Royal Air Force fits into your scheme, I'll never understand."

Holden drew himself erect and looked with full fury on his parent's flame-licked faces.

"Game over," he said and rose from his chair, holding out a hand to Mara.

"Oh, so soon?" Mara said as if she couldn't bear to part with these monsters posing as Holden's parents.

Holden replied, "Yes, we've served our time"

Glaring at his mother with contempt, he plucked Mara from her chair.

"Goodbye, Mother. Goodbye Father," he said curtly.

Without waiting for a response he dragged Mara out of the den, down a series of halls, and finally through the front door.

Looking back, the last image Mara saw of his parents was their crestfallen expression. Failure weighed down their crumpled faces, as if their life force was drained out of them by his departure. Mara gleaned from their expression that, although the couple was insufferable, they really did love their son and their very happiness hinged on his comings and goings.

Mara began to pity the twisted, old couple.

Back in the safety of his 2002, Holden turned to Mara. "Now you understand. I'm sorry I had to subject you to that, but if we were to become more… serious, then I'd feel like I was tricking you if you didn't know about them. I'd understand if you never want to see me again," he said and then grabbed the steering wheel as if to brace himself for bad news.

Mara brushed her hand through Holden's hair and loved him with her eyes.

"Holden, while your parents are…um…unconventional, it is clear they love you dearly. In that case, how could I dislike them or you, by extension? I feel closer to you now, knowing what drove you to search out such role models as the Baader-Meinhof Group."

She brushed at his hair as a smile played on the corners of his lips.

"That's better," she murmured. "I love your smile. It's heart-warming and contagious."

They looked into each other's eyes and the air between them crackled with electricity.

"Now, take me straight home. I have a big day tomorrow," Mara said.

Holden raised a brow but said nothing as he started the engine and left the sprawling estate that he had once called home. Mara smiled to herself. Little did Holden know that her big day involved joining his group, which she was convinced would bring them even closer together.

CHAPTER 6

The next morning Mara awoke with the first stirrings of the dorm. Like a bustling hen house, the halls were filled with a cacophony of activity as girls rose for their eight o'clock classes. The gentle resonance of running showers provided the rhythm to the syncopated slap of moisturizer application, subtle gutturals of Prozac swallowing, silky accents of eyelash curling, and the lush, low tones of heaving bosoms being nestled into silken bras and cashmere sweaters. It was the melody of youth, fertility, and readiness. If you listened closely you could almost hear the occasional genetically superior, financially favored egg dropping into a shiny, salmon-colored womb.

Mara's face was smashed against a book.

Still intent on joining the Baader-Meinhof Reading Group, Mara had tried reading Regan's material after the ludicrous dinner with Holden's parents. She had found, however, that the jingoism riddling the reading was tiresome and that the Manhattans coursing through her veins lubricated a dismissive perspective on the subject.

Why read about Marx? she had thought drunkenly. *A man whose ideas had been proved unsuitable by real life. And what was up with that beard? At least the Baader-Meinhof Group had a sense of style.*

These heavy thoughts had engulfed her body in a tide of weariness. Before long she was asleep, her pert, little nose getting up close and personal with Communism for Dummies.

I must have fallen asleep in the middle of it, she realized.

Mara pulled her face out of the book and wiped the scant drool from its pages.

Oh, today is Friday! No classes for me!

She thought of all the Baader-Meinhof reading left unfinished and realized that the day wouldn't be any picnic.

Mara slipped out of bed and, not bothering to dress, pulled

on a robe. She dropped three heaping spoonfuls of instant coffee into a cup of tap water and put it in her microwave. She needed the extra boost to get through the stretch of dull political propaganda that lay before her.

She was scanning the Baader-Meinhof Group's connection to Palestinian guerrilla training when her phone rang.

"Hello," she intoned as brightly as she could in spite of the early hour.

"Mara?" came a dignified baritone that wasn't Holden's.

"This is," she replied.

"Mara, this is Professor Mahler. Sorry to bother you on your day off but I'm going to need your assistance. You know the East Side Butt Slasher? I just became privy to a thrilling little fact: He created a Web site under an alias. My sources don't think that they can keep this news out of the public eye for long, so I need the site combed thoroughly and documented before it goes public and is shut down. This includes printouts of it and all of its links. Are you up to it?"

Mara sighed. She lived for this kind of work, but she was concerned about her lack of adequate preparation for the Reading Group meeting that evening. Half reluctantly, she told him she'd be right over.

When Mara finally came back from her long day of research, her guilt about the Baader-Meinhof reading returned. She wasn't looking forward to telling Regan that she hadn't studied for the meeting.

Mara quickly scanned a copy of Meinhof's *Armed Anti-Imperialist Struggle,* hoping to get the gist of the material before she had to leave. She read the following passage:

> In its first phase the guerrilla is shocking… It is shocking to
> see people acting on true experience, both their own and of
> others. The guerrilla acts upon facts which people experi-
> ence every day: exploitation, media terror, insecurities of liv-
> ing conditions despite the great wealth, and refined tech-
> nology in this country—the psychic illnesses, suicides, child

abuse, distress with the schools, the housing misery.

Mara looked up from the writing. Deep in thought, a salty tear hanging in the corner of her eyes reflected the passage she'd just read.

Oh, gosh! Mara thought with great urgency. *It hadn't occurred to me before… What am I going to wear tonight?*

There was so little time to get ready.

A cloud of anxiety settled on her fair features as she thought of the Baader-Meinhof Group, *Why couldn't I have fallen for a guy who's obsessed with something cool, like the rodeo or professional wrestling? At least then I might get some exercise when I shared his interests… But no, I have to fall for the Baader-Meinhof aficionado.*

From the limited material she did peruse while sitting on the toilet and from her talks with Regan, Mara came to understand that the Baader-Meinhof Group, or RAF, used bombs, murder, armed bank robbery, car thieving, and kidnapping to provoke a revolution that never happened. She also knew that Andreas Baader was the cute one.

As Mara worked though her daily routine of five hundred sit-ups, which made her taut stomach the envy of her peers, she wondered who was to blame for the no-show revolution—the people or the RAF?

Probably the Red Army Faction, themselves, she reasoned. *They could never inspire the masses to move against the insidious power of a Coca-Cola capitalist nation as long as the majority has heat and television and the minority is kept ghettoized and voiceless.*

Mara had learned in Professor Mahler's lecture "From Lullaby to Alibi: The Humanization of Murdering Miscreants" that feelings of cultural victimization are a common attribute of vicious killers. Through a process called *Leidensneid*, a German term meaning envy of suffering, serial killers see themselves as the downtrodden and, therefor, seize the victim role for themselves even as they create real victims.

Mara finished her sit-ups and began her stretches, which gave her muscles the lean, graceful suppleness that was her hallmark. *Maybe, the RAF traded their fascist German ancestry for victim status. That would explain why they trained with the Palestinians. Somewhere in their twisted minds it wasn't enough to assert them-selves as victims of World War II instead of the Jews; they also had to side with the self-proclaimed victims of Israel: the Palestinians.*

It's probably the same reason why Holden and the rest are so drawn to the B-M gang. They know their junk-bond and old-money, nepotistic class is the reason America is in such shambles. It's their parents' class feasting on the middle and lower class's desic-cated body, Mara thought, as she finished her stretches and lightly misted some hair spray on her short mane of glossy, black ringlets and then scrunched the ends to create a "wet look."

Although Holden and the others happily reap the benefits of their class, they envy its victims.

She examined the curling tendrils that resisted restraint and lightly caressed and framed her face. With a resigned nod, she gave up trying to control them and she applied her eye makeup, pink-hued lip gloss, and light face powder.

So they recast themselves as casualties of the state through identification with the Baader-Meinhof Group. Oh my. All this German/Jew stuff gives me a headache. And it's time for me to go. She snapped her compact shut and headed down the hall.

Considering that Mara's exposure to the subject was limited, she was drawing some brutal conclusions. Mara was always doing stuff like that. Her brain operated on automatic pilot, driven by inse-curities disguised as reason.

All the more vexing, no matter how banal her ideas (and no matter how many people had come to the same conclusion previ-ously), she considered them her own private accomplishment, which, as a self-proclaimed genius, could never be wrestled out of her clutching mind despite a preponderance of facts to the contrary. If, through some miraculous force, she did change her mind, it was a historic affair with all the romantic significance of an explorer breaching virgin intellectual real estate.

Earth-shattering stuff.

Mara was the Christopher Columbus of intellectual property.

You may ask how is it that people such as Mara get as far as they do in the world with this type of attitude lodged in their moderately sized brains.

Needless to say, someone encouraged this obnoxious perspective. Most likely it was her parents utilizing narcissistic identification, followed by a series of grade-school teachers who may have seen an element of themselves in her.

But please, you argue, narcissistic identification cannot account for nineteen years of being certain that one is a genius.

And you are right to point that out.

Let's just say that our heroine is intelligent and motivated enough to appear gifted to those disposed to believe it. And, despite all of her apparent insecurities, she is arrogant enough, when it comes to the matter of her own genius, to continue with her misguided delusions of grandeur in the face of contrary evidence.

So if you ever meet our heroine and you are not taken in by her genius posturing, don't be surprised if she writes you off. She rationalizes the Mara-as-genius theory by assuming that only first-rate thinkers can recognize superior brainpower.

Which, actually, is true.

But let's face it; Mara is no genius.

Not like you or I.

Well, primarily, me.

Let it go down in the records, however, that I agree with Mara's ✦ *conclusion that the RAF was infected with* Leidensneid, *or victim envy, with that I don't agree with her genius posturing.*

Mara knocked on the black door with the red star.

"Just a minute, Mara!" came Regan's shrill yell.

She heard some shufflings and rumblings within. A moment later the door opened and Regan stood before her, face flushed and blurry.

"Sorry, I had to clean up some things." Regan said as her eyes performed one last sweep of her room.

Mara looked around the cluttered mess and wondered what

✦ And by "Mara's theory" here I mean Horst Mahler's, the professor from whom Mara stole her hypothesis about the RAF.

Regan could possible have picked up. But Regan was her friend, so she overlooked the untidiness just as she hoped that Regan would overlook her lack of preparation.

Regan's brows were drawn at a rakish angle that evening, lending her a spunky, determined look that had just a tinge of threat.

Mara admired Regan's charming, unconventional ways.

"You're such a character, Regan!" she said easily.

"So, how did the reading go?" Regan asked, ignoring Mara's compliment.

"I'm sorry, I didn't finish it. Professor Mahler called me in at the last minute," Mara answered and lowered her head.

Regan gave her a penetrating stare. "Oh. What did you read? Anything about the Baader-Meinhof Group? Or the RAF? Anything about Brazilian urban guerrillas?"

"I scanned them all and read the intro to *Communism for Dummies*," Mara lied.

Regan cracked a smile that didn't have a chance of reaching her eyes, which were trying to maintain focus on Mara through her rapidly ticking eyelids.

"Okay. We have..." she looked at her watch, "one hour in which to make you fluent on all things Baader and/or Meinhof... That's great! Sit down and observe the poster on the wall."

Mara shoved aside three empty boxes of No-Doze and four empty wrappers from M&M's pounder bags and sat down on Regan's bed, her short legs swinging above the floor.

Regan pulled out her hip-pocket retractable pointer and directed Mara's attention to a young woman on the wanted poster with scattered eyes and well-defined cheekbones.

"This is Gudrun Ensslin. She and Baader were the heart of the RAF."

She looks like a revolutionary, thought Mara. *Or like Nico from the Velvet Underground. Wow, that's cool, I never connected "underground" from the Velvet Underground with the terrorist underground. It's so bizarre how everything seems to link together.*

Mara smiled at the enigma that was her life.

Regan began her "teach-in" by detailing Gudrun Ensslin's fateful run-in with the student activist organization, the Students for a Democratic Society, the night Benno Ohnesorg was shot.

"Benno Ohnesorg. Our first martyr. Killed by the *Kripo*—or German crime police—on June 2, 1967, at a student demonstration against the Shah of Iran. That's why one RAF splinter group is called 'The June 2 Movement.' Although a man was our first martyr, we must remember that it was Gudrun Ensslin who gave the battle cry that led the RAF to arms."

While Mara appeared to hang on Regan's every word, she was, in fact, not listening but instead wondering if any of the terrorists in the RAF were under five foot one, like herself. Not that Mara ever indulged in self-pity because of her height (or lack thereof). She had always kept her body strong and managed to accomplish everything she wanted despite her stature.

Mara thought wistfully as she again eyed Regan's Baader-Meinhof wanted poster, *It just seems that, to be truly successful at something as socially contingent as terrorism, you have to look the part. Like that Gudrun character and the roguishly handsome Baader. I bet Gudrun was at least 5'5".* Mara tried to imagine herself as a German underground terrorist.

Would I be taken seriously by the fascist German state? she wondered. *Doubtful. Maybe if I took up smoking.*

She tried to imagine herself with a cigarette.

Or better yet, what are these?

She saw a pack of beedies on Regan's bed, picked them up, and motioned a silent request, so as not to interrupt the lesson.

Regan nodded and continued her discourse.

"Baader and Ensslin planted two bombs in the furniture department of Kaufhaus, symbolically declaring war on decadent consumerism in the face of the imperialist domination of Vietnam."

"What does a furniture store have to do with the Vietnam War?" Mara asked.

"It was furniture for the bourgeois," Regan answered.

"So? I don't get it," Mara said.

"Look,' Regan snapped, "It's not a one-to-one relationship. It was symbolic. Besides, it's better to blow up a store than to own one in a fascist nation."

Mara frowned. "How would you feel if someone used that

same argument to blow up this school?"

Regan shook out her cherry-red hair. "Happy! I'd help them. Mara, there's a lot you don't understand and we don't have enough time for questions. Just listen and learn."

Mara sighed and lit the small, leaf-wrapped cigarette. She took a puff and exhaled it before a coughing reflex set in.

I bet these taste better after you blow something up, she thought. *Or declare symbolic war.*

She tried to listen, but Regan's instruction was as tiring as the reading material she had slept on.

What's the point? Cramming never worked for me. Maybe I'll just pick up everything subconsciously.

Regan's staccato was surprisingly soothing and easy to ignore, and it wasn't long before Mara's mind drifted around in its usual, ambling manner.

Mara studied Baader's picture on Regan's RAF wanted poster, again astonished by his strong resemblance to Holden. She wondered what it would be like to blow up something with him. Mara would be wearing a pair of those waxed jeans that look like a cross between vinyl and denim, and a rubber T-shirt like that girl in *The Matrix*. He'd wear a pair of vintage motor-cycle pants with the built-in padding, high leather boots, and one of those long-sleeved shirts with the stitching on the outside.

Their hair would shine like raven's wings and their cheek-bones would be so sharp you could cut yourself on them. They'd slouch in a dimly lit cafe with tar-stained walls, smoking Gauloises and sipping from *café crèmes*, no, espresso! No mother's milk for them!

"Darling," he'd say. "I love you, but how can I concentrate on love while the imperialist pigs are ruining our future?"

Mara imagined herself with a smoky-eyed look like that Gudrun chick and instead of the rubber T-shirt (which, on second thought, might make her look like a midget dominatrix), she would be wearing a thin, gray, oversized cashmere sweater with holes in it.

"Yes, my love, we must challenge the U.S. military action in (insert relevant country). We must fight violence with violence.

It's the only thing the fascists will understand."

Mara, who would be silently suffering from consumption, would then cough into a rough, white handkerchief. Seeing the blood spot left behind, she would quickly hide the evidence from Holden.

Holden would graze the top of his espresso with a sugar rectangle, watching it darken as it soaked up the warm, brown liquid. Then, popping the caffeinated cube in his mouth, he would jump to his feet with an upraised fist.

"But how can we seize the future from the fat, grubby hands of those capitalist pigs? We have no funds!" He would cry. "We've given all of our money to underprivileged schoolchildren in the inner city so that they may can buy guns to arm themselves against U.S. injustice."

Mara would come up with the brilliant answer, an answer that would be told to children in hushed voices for generations to come, "Capitalism must fund its own demise! Let's rob a bank!"

Was it my own idea, or did Regan just say that? Mara wondered, again vague on her sources.

Mara and Holden, emboldened by caffeine and ouzo, would grab their baguette and run to the nearest bank. Wearing Middle Eastern scarves…

Baklavas? Or is that the puff pastry with dates in it? Mara asked herself.

…over their faces, they'd walk right in. Everything would move in slow motion and some super-cool, trip-hop song would play in the background.

Holden would clutch his French bread under his long, snakeskin trench coat and scream, "Put your hands on your head and no one gets hurt!"

All the colors in the bank would be snapping and blurring as Mara gathered money from the tills. She'd secretly hand a stack of hundreds to a pregnant woman dressed in tatters with two scrawny, wide-eyed children straight out of Picasso's Blue Period. Mara would tell the gaunt woman big with child to get moving. With a grateful tear in her eye the woman would gather her children and slip off into the darkening night. Two of her children would grow up to be successful humanitarians and the third would discover a cure for cancer... and AIDS.

Holden and Mara would run away from the advancing cops, laughing, with the loot. But just as their escape was secured, a bullet from a desperate officer's gun would graze Holden's cheekbone. They'd run, blood flying, back to their secret hideout—a garret provided to them by an older woman whom Mara had charmed.

Mara would bend over Holden with a brown bottle of hydrogen peroxide.

"You'll live," she'd declare and then she would kiss the single trickle of blood dripping down his face. The red vital fluid would picturesquely gather in the hollow of his clavicle like the miraculous bleeding statue of Christ in Cochabamba, Bolivia.

After she cleaned his wound they would count their take and plan an attack on...on...

Mara tried to think of a place she wanted to blow up.

The Sallie Mae loan servicing agency?

"Mara!"

Mara would look into Holden's golden eyes as they laid the wire. He'd be wearing camouflage jet pants...

"Mara!"

"Yes, Holden, I'm here," Mara would answer her beloved.

"Mara!" repeated the insistent voice.

Mara's eyes, wide as big buttons, flew to Regan who was looking at her expectantly.

"Mara, where were you just now?" Regan demanded.

"Bank robbing," Mara answered guiltily.

"That's right!" beamed Regan. "Which is how they could afford to finance the revolution..."

Mara looked at Regan with wonder and relief.

Maybe I need Ritalin. I wonder if terrorists ever take Ritalin... Terrorists on Ritalin is a good band name. Better yet, Terrorists on Prozac—or Zoloft. Maybe I should take Prozac. Is that the stuff that helps your complexion, too? Or is that the pill? Mara chuckled at her ignorance of contemporary pharmaceuticals.

"I don't see what's so funny about the death by starvation of Holger Meins. Perhaps you could explain it to me," Regan said sharply.

Again Mara redirected her attention to Regan. She was pointing to a photo of a heavily bearded and thoroughly emaciated man.

"I'm sorry, I was thinking of someone else," Mara said as she examined the photo closely. "Hmm…he looks like a victim of a concentration camp," she said, remembering her professor's victim-envy theory.

"Fascist prison, fascist concentration camp—it's all the same in the end," Regan murmured and looked at her watch. "We gotta go. Damn it! We didn't even get to Death Night."

Mara watched as Regan flew around the room gathering papers and books. "Regan, you've done everything you can do. If I'm not wired the way Holden likes, then maybe Holden and I shouldn't be together," she said. Her face trembled with courage and conflict as the chilly realization set in. "Maybe we just aren't fated to be together. But I'm willing to take the chance that it's me he loves, despite my non-rebellious nature."

Regan eyed the short young woman with the slender body and tapered hips. She then pressed her face into Mara's so that the odor of stale makeup filled Mara's nose.

"Mara, who are you trying to kid? You need help to hold a man like Holden Rife and you know it. I suggest you heed my advice before you lose the one good thing you have going for you."

She crammed her face so close to Mara's that they were joined at the nose and forehead. Eye-to-eye with Mara, Regan said, "At the meeting tonight when you're asked questions about the RAF, you answer anything you don't know with, 'Enough talk! We've got to arm ourselves!' All right?"

Mara stared into Regan's anemic blue eyes.

"Yes." Secretly, she cherished her friend's apparent concern for her.

"Good." Regan pulled away from her and checked herself in the mirror before guiding Mara out the black door with the red star.

The ride to the meeting this time was not marked with Regan screaming "Fascist pig!" at whatever building they happened to pass. Regan, deep in thought, said only one, urgent thing to Mara the whole drive: "All you need to know about

Death Night is that Meinhof was already dead before it happened. And it was not, I repeat, *not*, suicide."

Mara was deep in her own thoughts. She wondered again what kind of upbringing caused a group of middle- to upper-middle-class activists to give up their comfortable lifestyle and become part of an underground terrorist organization. Before she could come up with any suitable theories, they were standing at Holden's door.

Regan rapped a strange series of knocks.

Holden answered. He did not look pleased.

"Regan, you're late. I need your notes."

He reached out to Regan's satchel. Then he saw Mara standing there, dewy-faced from the humid, autumn evening air.

"Mara, what are you doing here? Dinner isn't until tomorrow." He was amused by her mistake.

Regan answered before Mara could speak up, "Mara is here for the meeting. She's joining our group."

Holden laughed.

Mara almost agreed with his mirth. *Joining the group is a laughable concept. I mean, serial killers? Yes. German terrorist communists? No way.*

And yet here she was, trying to join. All for the love of this man who couldn't seem to keep his merriment at her expense to himself.

Can't he see that I'm doing this for him?

His laughter quieted. "But seriously, Mara, I'm busy tonight. I'll see you tomorrow. I'm making catfish. Do you eat cat?"

Mara wanted to react to his stupid joke but she knew that, for their sake, she had to stand up to him and ignore his winning ways.

"Holden, what Regan said is true," Mara said simply, craning her neck to look him in the eyes. "I want to join your Baader-Meinhof Reading Group. And I want to be in the Games. I'm a scholar of sadistic-serial-killers, but I'm also a budding Baader-Meinhof aficionado. You have to start somewhere. The German program doesn't have a monopoly on radicals." She bravely finished her thoughts, "I hope this doesn't ruin anything between us."

Holden glared at Mara and shot an even crueler look at Regan, who was smiling triumphantly.

"The girl has spoken," Regan said.

The ex-lovers exchanged a secret message without saying a word. Then Regan pushed Holden aside like a swinging door. She grabbed Mara's arm and pulled her inside.

From their high-voltage exchange, Mara experienced a visual flash of what Holden and Regan were like together. She felt a hurtful tinge of jealousy.

I could never command Holden's attention the way Regan does. But I'll show him I'm not a pushover, she thought as Regan dragged her through a series of rooms.

Holden's house was larger than she previously had thought. They passed through four rooms before arriving at a window-less, interior space that was painted red and filled with maps, charts, and books. Again, chairs were scarce, with people loung-ing on the floor on beanbags in their poverty gear. They were involved in an animated discussion.

"I'm serious, do you know how many rat hairs and feces per ounce the FDA allows in chocolate and cereal? It's more than you think!" Eric said to Rosa and Apocalypse.

Rosa didn't look up from picking at her split ends. "If it's more than zero, then it's more that I thought."

When he saw Mara, MK-Ultra quickly turned a dry-erase board around and flung some newspapers on top of what looked like a series of sophisticated diagrams.

"Security alert!" said Ex-Pat.

"What's *that* doing here?" asked MK-Ultra as if he were referring to dog feces.

"Shut up, MK! She's a comrade. Some of us want her in the group," said fuzzy-headed Apocalypse, leaving no uncertainty as to *her* reasons for wanting Mara there as she gazed at her curvy hips and narrow waist hungrily.

"Yeah," agreed Rat, who also sized her up as he wiped a tan, foamy mustache off his tattooed upper lip.

Rosa walked over to Mara and said quietly, "God, Mara, I really love your hair. It's so curly."

"Really? Because I always wanted straight hair. I can't do

anything with mine," Mara said.

"Shut up! I hate my hair," Rosa said to Mara's feet.

MK-Ultra motioned at the two to Ex-Pat. "See what I mean? This is why the RAF failed. Too many girls."

"Seriously, you shut up!" Rosa stormed over to MK-Ultra.

"Ooo! *Seriously!*" MK-Ultra mocked.

With the group thus occupied, Rat approached Mara.

"Hey, uh Mara. You look really nice today."

Rat was wearing tight black jeans, eighteen-hole military boots, and red suspenders. His ensemble was tattered to a stereotypical degree, right down to the rip in the knee of his jeans where red long underwear peaked out.

"Uh, thanks. You do too," Mara said hesitantly.

He leaned his illustrated head toward hers and Mara caught a hint of motor oil and stout ale.

"Um, I was wondering if you were going with anyone to the benefit. Regan said if I get a date that I won't have to serve the dinner so…what do you say?"

But Mara's attention was bound to MK-Ultra and Ex-Pat, who eyed her coolly. It didn't occur to her that anyone other than Holden didn't want her in the group. Under the young men's hostile gaze she wanted to crawl beneath the diagram-covered table and disappear. She looked around for Holden.

"Uh, Mara, what do you say?" Rat's voice interrupted her worries.

Holden entered the room with a glowering look on his face.

Silently Mara mourned the gentle closeness they had established the night before. Now he had abandoned her for reasons she couldn't understand. Mara turned to Rat who seemed to want something from her. What it was she could not couldn't imagine.

"Yes, Rat?" she asked.

Rat's camouflaged face broke into a puzzle of delight. He ran over to Eric and whispered something in his ear.

Eric turned to Mara, shock outlining his freckles.

"She said 'yes'?" Eric asked with surprise and dismay.

Rat nodded. "Yeah, man."

Mara, meanwhile, was distracted by Holden's stern brow. She turned to Regan who nodded at her reassuringly.

"Hello? I ask again. What is *that* doing here?" green haired MK-Ultra asked.

"We are a communist-style collective," Regan said, "and consideration for membership is not determined by whether you wear boxers, MK."

MK-Ultra shot back, "I don't care if you bring another red rag in here. But she's not even from the program."

"True. Mara isn't in the German program, but neither are Rat and Ex-Pat," Regan countered.

"Ex-Pat and Rat serve a specific purpose in our group," Holden argued. "They bring field experience. What can Mara possibly bring?"

"I don't think we should add criteria for potential members just because you don't want your new sweetheart tainted with our activities," Regan shot back at Holden and then addressed the whole group. "We don't know yet what kind of help Mara could be. Maybe during the Baader-Meinhof Games someone gets sick, or worse. With Mara, we'll have an understudy to take their place."

"We've never needed an understudy before," countered Ex-Pat, who didn't like being compared with Mara.

"Well, we may this year," said Regan as she wove in a serpentine fashion toward Rosa. "Maybe some of us have secret plans. For example, maybe some unnamed person is surreptitiously going to job interviews for the German fashion magazine *Der Style*. Were something like that true, we may need to replace that person next year." Regan rested her hand on Rosa's long head.

Rosa turned a deep crimson. "It's not true!" she said, fiddling with her long, brown braid.

"Like hell it's not true," spat Regan.

Everyone was staring at Rosa with surprise and disdain except Eric, who had long ago stopped paying attention to the non-food-related talk and was working a dreadlock, nervously rolling it between two flat palms. To his surprise, he inadvertently twisted off a chunk of hair.

"Great!" he exclaimed garnering everyone's attention. He spoke quickly to cover up his untimely preoccupation with his dreads, "I suppose next I'm going to hear that one of us is a spy, too."

Apocalypse colored, then yelled uncomfortably, "Enough talk. All we do is talk. Let's take some action! Either she's in or out. I think we should keep her. But we need to settle this!"

Holden leaned back on the table in the center of the room. "No. That's my final word."

Mara's heart sunk. Winning Holden's respect would be more difficult than she thought.

"Fine. Holden votes no," Regan said. "Anyone else?"

"Who said there'd be a vote?" Holden demanded.

"You're the one who didn't want the meetings run by consensus, so you're going to have to deal with a vote. Unless you want to use this as an opportunity to declare yourself dictator of the group?" offered Regan, her voice heavy with sarcasm.

Holden slunk back, momentarily defeated. "I don't know what you're up to, Regan, but this ploy won't do you any good. I'll find you out."

Regan rolled her eyes. "Uh, O-Kay, Holden. I'll keep that in mind while we're taking the vote. All right. We have one 'no.' Anyone else?"

Apocalypse said, "Yes."

"Rat?"

Rat eyed the bottom of his beer and tilted it back to get the last yeasty dregs. "Gee, do I want Mara in our group? Hell, yeah!" he said lustily.

Eric slugged Rat's fit biceps, "I'm with you, comrade!"

"Three 'yes' votes. Ex-Pat?"

Ex-Pat looked at MK-Ultra, who was shaking his head.

"Uh... No." Then he turned away from Mara.

"That's three 'no's," said MK-Ultra.

Rosa, who was still mad at Regan for revealing her less-than-radical career pursuit, said, "Anything that Regan wants has to be a bad idea. I say 'no.'" She turned to Mara, "No offense, you're probably better off this way."

"That's four 'no's and four 'yes's. Shit!" Regan shot a thunderously hot look at Rosa, who cowered under its intensity. "You told me you'd vote yes."

Rosa just examined the end of her braid, methodically tearing off split ends.

Holden turned slowly to meet Regan's face. "You've been campaigning for her? Behind my back? *Et tu, Judas?*"

"That's *'Brute,'*" Regan said mockingly and then murmured, "God, you're Über-lame, Holden."

Holden's anger became scalding fury. He drew himself up perfectly straight so that his height rivaled the door frame and reached out to Mara, pulling her off the floor. He then fixed his hands on her shoulders and walked her backward out of the room, slamming the door behind them with his foot.

After Holden pushed her down the hall, he composed his expression. He spoke to her slowly, as if considering the weight of each word.

"Mara, I don't know why you're doing this. And, if you subtract whatever Regan's been telling you, I'm sure *you* don't even know why you're here. I'm telling you now: these people are not the idealists they appear to be. They're here for their own reasons. Not one of them is altruistic.

"Apocalypse is here because she's a freak and people on the left put up with that. Rat's here because we feed him and give him our business. He restores our BMWs. It's almost full-time work. The dude's a complete wack-job. Think about it, if you want to blend in you go to the Gap, you don't cover yourself in camouflage tattoos. Eric is only here because the Eco-Feminist group kicked him out and he didn't have an audience for his radical vegetarian proselytizing. Rosa's in it because she has a crush on me. MK-Ultra? Same thing. And he isn't even a communist. And Ex-Pat's here because of MK-Ultra. That and because pretending to be undercover at a software company is more romantic than actually being a suit in a software company. I mean, he snags us all free software, big deal! And as for Regan, she just wants to *be* the Baader-Meinhof Gang."

Mara turned away from Holden.

"I'm not kidding. She's got an ax to grind."

Mara looked at Holden. He sounded earnest, but all she was hearing was that he was pushing her away.

"Oh, Holden, this isn't about any of them," Mara insisted. "It's about you and me. You say you're interested in me, but you don't trust me. What kind of relationship can we have if you don't love me yet?" Mara asked and then immediately regretted it.

Didn't I mean to say he doesn't "trust me" yet? Too late, it can't be unsaid. Mara mourned.

The effect of her words registered on Holden's fine features. It was as if he had tasted rancid milk.

Mara wondered what he was thinking as she stared up at the sculpted underside of his chin. For a moment she knew with resounding clarity that she had made a grave mistake.

What if I lose him? she thought. *What if Regan is wrong and all I gain from this is membership in a club I don't even want to be in.*

But something told her that Holden would never respect her unless she stood up to him.

"Mara, there's a reason that I don't want you involved in this group," Holden confided, turning away from her so as not to be influenced by her troubled beauty. "There's something you should know about it. I shouldn't even talk about it because I'm not one hundred percent sure… It's a bad feeling I get, but I take my feelings very seriously."

He touched her cheek lightly.

"Like my feelings for you."

He continued in a serious tone. "Things are changing. We're becoming so much more than just a reading group."

His expression stilled and grew serious and he took a step forward and gently grasped her hand.

"It's like if you put anything in a pickle barrel for long enough, it doesn't matter if it's a cucumber or a rat. It's gonna wind up pickled. Well, that's what's happening with our group. If we immerse ourselves in the life of violent revolutionaries, what do you think will happen to us? The group is pushing itself in a dangerous direction. Each time someone raises the stakes to see if the others will follow, they bring the group closer to the brink of disaster. Can't you see? It isn't that I don't have feelings for you. It's that if my feeling is ever to deepen, it can't be within that group. You're far too pretty to become a pickle. It's like Jesus said, 'Hang ye not with villains lest by that hanging a villain ye become.'"

Holden looked in her eyes and suddenly Mara felt like the only person in the universe.

"Mara, I'm begging you. Back down."

At that moment Regan burst out of the room and called down the hall, "Rosa changed her vote, it's three against five. Mara's in. Now let's get this meeting started."

Mara looked at Regan.

Regan knows all about Holden. She knows more about Holden than he probably knows about himself.

Then she looked at Holden and instinctively knew everything he told her was true. Mara didn't know what to do, which course of action would cause her to lose Holden. Before she could make up her mind she felt the iron strong grip of Holden's hand jerking her down the hall to the front door.

As he pulled her, he yelled to Regan, "You guys start the meeting without me. Mara's changed her mind. She wants to be driven home."

Mara's mood veered sharply from confusion to anger as he dragged her out the door and, with a force she couldn't begin to counter, pushed her into his gleaming black 2002.

"Holden!" she exclaimed.

He entered the driver's side and, with a grim look nestled in his furrowed brow, started the engine and peeled away.

As they sped through town his expression clouded with anger.

"It's Regan. She takes everything and stamps the life out of it until all that's left is a flattened hull of what was previously there. She's leaving her mark on you, too."

Mara spoke without turning her face to Holden's. "I don't know what's between you two, but Regan is my friend. And she treats me with dignity and respect, which is more than I can say for you."

Holden slowed down and pulled over on the outskirts of town. "What's between me and Regan? What's between us and Regan? She's pulling you away from me."

"The only thing pulling me away from you is your own behavior," Mara spat out the words contemptuously. "Don't try to run my life! Don't try to protect me! It says that you can't take me seriously."

"Take you seriously?" Holden's sculpted face registered his anguish. "I'll show you how seriously I take you." And he grabbed her waist and pulled her to him. His hot kisses fell on her face, her lips, her neck.

Even as his kisses seeped into her willing pores, nothing could melt the coldness creeping into her body. The knowledge that he would never want her in a significant way, as long as he thought he could push her around, froze her desire for him. She turned abruptly and looked out her window.

His passions thwarted at every turn, Holden stopped his advances on her conflicted body and rested his head on the steering wheel.

"What do you want me to do, Mara? How can I prove that what I feel for you is real?" he pleaded beneath his tormented countenance.

Mara's usually warm voice was cool and clipped. "Either take me back to the meeting, or take me home."

Curses fell from his mouth. Holden started the engine and continued on until they reached campus. As he pulled into the car park Mara glared at him with reproachful eyes.

"I'm not a child!" she said and slammed the car door.

Back in her room, Mara hadn't been crying into her pillow for more than a minute before she heard Tippy and Penny knocking.

"It's us! Open up!" their voices bubbled through the door.

Mara was not in the mood to entertain her new friends, but she didn't have the presence of mind to shoo them away.

"I'm coming!"

Checking her face for any telltale signs of crying (puffy eyes, soggy makeup), she noticed that Holden was right about one thing. Regan was leaving a mark on her.

She must have smeared her makeup on me when she pressed her head to mine earlier, Mara thought as she spotted two dark lines of makeup angrily accentuating her natural brows.

She wiped them off and went to the door.

Tippy and Penny, in their usual uniform of boxers, T-shirts, and fuzzy slippers, and (Mara was disappointed to notice) their blue and green mud masks, pushed their way in.

"Do you guys ever *not* wear mud masks?" she asked with as much of a jovial lilt as she could muster in her foul mood.

"Oh, Mara! You are the living end," said Blue who then sat on Mara's bed, putting her hand on her pillow. "Hey, have you been crying in your pillow?"

One look at Mara's downcast expression answered her question.

Green grabbed Mara by the hand and sat her down on the bed so that she was in a blue/green mud-mask sandwich.

"There, there, Mara. What's the problem? Is Holden being a big old meanie?" Blue asked.

"Please don't speak to me like I'm a baby," Mara sniffled, overwrought from the stressful evening into which she had poured all her hopes.

"Yeah, shut up." Green said to Blue. She turned to Mara. "Mara, tell me what happened. Didn't the meeting go well? Or was it something else?"

"He, he doesn't want me in the group. He says it's becoming too strange," Mara said between sobs. "I don't even want to be in the stupid group. But something deep inside tells me you guys and Regan are right; he'll never appreciate me until I stand up to him and show him that I'm my own person. But there's this other part of me that says, 'Mara, your own person doesn't even want to be in the group, so what are you doing?' And I'll tell you what I'm doing. I'm making my life miserable!" Mara tossed her anguished head into her clenched hands and succumbed to racking sobs.

Blue and Green looked from Mara to each other and back to Mara again.

Finally Green spoke, "I think you are very brave, Mara, to ignore your lazy 'I'll do anything to win my man' voice. You are a role model to all us girls."

Mara lifted her head slightly. She'd never thought of herself as a role model. Green smiled as Mara looked into her eyes hopefully.

"That's right," Green assured her, "a role model."

Blue chimed in. "Yeah, like, you're super-inspiring."

"So I don't get what happened," Green said softly, "You were joining the group and now you're here crying. What's the story?"

Mara explained the sad story through halting sobs. When she finished, Green nodded her head.

"What is it about men?" Green asked the space above her enormous bosom. "Well, it's obvious he's just trying to get your attention."

"He is?" Mara asked, hurtling back to Earth with the weight of Green's words.

"Oh yeah," agreed Blue. "Why do you think he's giving you the caveman act? Dragging you everywhere and stuff? He knows you're not going to stand for that. He's doing it because he wants to be put in his place."

Mara looked from Blue to Green.

Green made a whipping motion with her arm. "Kee-rack!" she said. "Discipline is a special kind of love!"

Mara shook her head. Did this sound right to her? She felt that something was off, but she couldn't deny the voice in her head that said Holden would never respect her unless she was in the group.

"What should I do?" she asked her multicolored friends. "I can't go back to the meeting."

"Actually, going back to the meeting is exactly what you should do," said Green.

"But how?" Mara pleaded. "He lives on the other side of town and I don't have a car."

"We'll drive you," Blue said and they pulled her to her feet. "Let's go!"

Mara was swept away with their sense of urgency. They were halfway out the door when she realized her friends were still in their masks and slippers.

"Don't you guys want to change or wash your masks off?"

Green and Blue said in unison, "No, no time."

They brought her to a black, shiny Lexus and the three of them slid in the front.

"Whose car is this?"

"Mine," they both answered.

"Well it's hers, but I always drive it." Blue said.

Mara nodded. She had other things on her mind.

The Lexus arrived at Holden's house sooner than she expected, and she found herself standing at the front door as the blue and green masks held "thumbs up" signs.

Blue yelled, "Remember, tell him to act like a hero, not a zero!" and she spun off, leaving behind a trail of dust.

Mara tried the front door.

It opened.

She walked back down the hall and found the door leading to the inner meeting room. Heart pounding, she pushed the door open just a crack and peeked inside. Through the crack Mara saw the group was engaged in an animated discussion from reclining positions on the floor. Regan and Holden were out of view.

Apocalypse shifted in oversized overalls to peek at Rosa's notebook. Rosa quickly pulled it from her view, but Mara caught a flash of what looked like a drawing of a pair of jeans with padded riot-gear protection built into the front.

"Oh! Oh! I got one!" Apocalypse said with excitement. "What about Carlos the Jackal?"

"Hot," said MK-Ultra.

"Hot," voiced Ex-Pat, who was leaning on MK-Ultra.

"Hot," concurred Eric.

"Not," said Rosa petulantly as she sketched in her notebook.

"Hot," said Rat from his spot in the corner. His eyes were closed and tattoos completely covered his face in camouflage that stood out brightly against the red walls of the study. "He was a total player. He also stayed underground for three decades."

"He killed innocent people!" Rosa exclaimed. "And he's not even in the Baader-Meinhof Group."

"He was associated with them in Jordan. And what is this innocence you speak of? If you're benefiting from a fascist state and do nothing to stop it then you're not innocent," MK-Ultra drawled from a hammer-and-sickle-patterned beanbag.

"That gives anyone the right to kill us," Rosa asserted.

"Not me, I'm doing something for the cause. Besides, you

probably just disagree with Carlos's fashion sense," Ex-Pat said.

"What fashion sense?" Rosa and MK-Ultra said in unison.

Eric, who was neither enjoying nor had anything to add to the conversational digression, said, "Agent Scully!"

"Hot," said Rat.

"Hot," affirmed Apocalypse.

"Hot," said Rosa.

"Not," countered Ex-Pat. "How is she hot? She spent the first five years holding Mulder back. And then she became a breeder!"

"Hey, she saved Mulder's ass tons of times. Besides, her nose is so hot!" maintained Eric.

Apocalypse agreed, "Yeah she's hot."

"She doesn't even exist, you guys. That's called 'TV.' Heard of it?" Ex-Pat said flatly.

MK-Ultra backed away slightly from Ex-Pat. "Don't bad-mouth *The X-Files*. That show did a lot for our cause by outing government conspiracy and uncovering alien involvement in fascist states."

"All right, so what about Meinhof?" asked Rosa timorously.

"Not," said Rat.

"Not," Ex-Pat agreed.

"Not," said MK-Ultra heavily as if the question didn't really merit his reply.

"Not," said Eric.

"Why not?" Rosa demanded.

"No guts," MK-Ultra said.

"No ass," said Rat.

"She's kinda hot. I like smart chicks," said Apocalypse warmly as she draped a nurturing arm around Rosa's sad shoulders.

"This game blows," said MK-Ultra.

"Oh yeah? You got a better one?" said Apocalypse.

"*Yes*. I do. It's called 'Who-would-you-kill-if-you-had-to-kill-someone'?" MK-Ultra said with a lilt in his voice.

"Gross. I don't believe in killing," said Eric.

"This is too easy," said Rat. "I mean the only question is, who wouldn't I kill?"

"Yeah. I got mine," said Ex-Pat.

"Well before you put your dibs on Microsoft, listen to the parameters," MK-Ultra said and stroked his sharp nose with index finger and thumb. "You can't just kill one person, it has to be a whole family."

"Nuclear?" asked Ex-Pat.

"Yes. Spouse or significant other, siblings, kids, and parents," said MK-Ultra.

"You're just a sicko, MK," Rosa said and turned away from the group.

"Ooo! I know!" said Ex-Pat.

"Me too!" said Apocalypse and then shot a guilty look in Rosa's direction. "You'll like this one, Rosa."

"Who do you got?" asked MK-Ultra.

"Grubman," said Apocalypse.

"What's that?" asked Rat.

Then the group quieted; Holden and Regan had returned.

"What family would you kill, Regan," queried MK-Ultra.

"Who says I'd kill someone?" Regan glared at the group.

"It's just a game, Regan," whispered Ex-Pat.

"Killing is *not* a game and should be left to the professionals," Regan said brusquely.

Still peeking through the door, Mara saw Holden. He stood there, his beauty radiating. His sinfully sexy lips were set in a hard line above his chiseled chin.

"Okay then. We sent off the faxes for the permits, so all we have left tonight is to choose who's playing who." Holden said. "To keep it simple, why don't we play the same roles as last year? Does anyone have a problem with that?"

Rosa sheepishly raised her hand.

"Rosa, someone has to be Meinhof this year," Holden charged. "Regan's Gudrun and Apocalypse is the narrator, which leaves you."

"I'm sick of being Meinhof. I'll be anybody else, but I won't be Ulrike Meinhof," Rosa protested adamantly as she picked at the ends of her hair.

"Well we can't have the Baader-Meinhof Games without Meinhof," Regan ground out her words.

Before she knew what she was doing, Mara opened the door.

"I'll be Meinhof," she said.

Shocked eyes locked onto hers. But Mara only felt one particular pair scowling at her angrily.

CHAPTER 7

"Knock! Knock! Knock!"

From under her covers Mara wondered ruefully if she would ever get a decent night's sleep at Norden College. She thrust a pillow over her lustrous, jet-black curls and snuggled back into her comforter.

"I said, 'Knock! Knock! Knock!'" yelled an unbecoming voice from the hallway.

Mara recognized her interchangeable hall mates' nasal tones. "Go away!" she shouted.

"Mara, open up! We have something for you!" called the companion voices from the hall.

"Fine!" grumbled Mara. She threw a terry-cloth robe over her sheer pajamas and let the girls come in. After carefully pushing aside the remains of a late-night study session, they sat on either side of Mara.

Penny and Tippy, or Tippy and Penny, again sported blue and green mud masks. It had been so long since Mara had seen their faces she'd forgotten to even care what they actually looked like beneath the drying layers of scented mud. The duo sat expectantly in their boxer shorts, Norden College T-shirts, and fuzzy animal slippers, picking at the banana clips in their fluffy, highlighted hair.

Mara ran a delicate hand through her short, bed-tousled locks and yawned under half-closed eyes. "What time is it?"

The one in the blue facial mask squealed, "Time for brownies!" and from behind her back pulled a brown paper bag spotted with oil.

"Brownies? I thought you guys were worried about gaining the freshman fifteen," said Mara as she sleepily noticed that her alarm clock read 8:10 A.M. "Besides, isn't it a little early for brownies?"

Blue grabbed a square of brownie and took a large bite.

"Mmm. Mara, the time for Brownies is when they're hot!"

Mara had a paper to write. She knew it was no use contradicting them once they had their minds set on something, however. She mentally reassigned part of her morning to brownie-eating, if only to get the girls out of her room faster.

She took a brownie from Green and bit into its moist warmth. It tasted strange and fibrous.

Blue bit into a hunk of steaming brownie. "Aren't they great? They're my dead grandmother's recipe, God rest her soul."

"Um. Yeah. They're really... super," Mara remarked, not wanting to hurt her well-meaning friends.

"So what's all this stuff?" Green motioned to the papers spread around the room. It looked like a tornado had swept through and deposited half the library in its wake.

"Research," Mara mumbled while pulling a small round seed out of her mouth. "I'm writing a paper on Gilles de Rais."

"What's that?" queried Blue.

Mara drew herself up, happy to be asked about one of her favorite subjects. "Well, it's hard to say. Once you delve into it, you realize that history may have gotten it wrong."

Green stifled a yawn and stretched her arms out in front of her, emphasizing her silicon-enhanced spheres.

Mara ignored Green's boredom and pulled her slender, shapely legs up under her and tucked a corner of her thick terry-cloth robe over her dainty toes.

"No one really knows who or what he was. History records him as a murderer of anywhere from 150 to 800 children in France during the Fifteenth Century," Mara exclaimed.

"Eight hundred? That puts Donner to shame!" exclaimed Blue, whose robin's-egg blue mask perfectly complimented her orange-hued skin.

"The reindeer or the party?" probed Mara.

"The party?" queried Blue.

"Yeah, are you talking about the Donner party?" Mara wondered.

"No, she means Dahmer," Green explained flatly.

"Yeah, I'm not talking about the Donner Bash," Blue admitted.

"Party," corrected Mara. "Whatever. Anyway, that's one kid

a day for almost two and a half years, which is only one of the reasons people doubt the claim. People now believe he was a victim of the fallout of the political wrangling between his brother and the king of England."

"Oh, right. He was set up like that cop killer you guys like so much…Mummy? Munchie?" Blue attempted.

"Mumia," corrected Mara. "Check it out: Gilles de Rais was a really wealthy guy for back then. But eventually he pissed off the king and wound up accused of being a witch. He was tried and put to death in the same way as Jeanne d'Arc was nine years before him.

"Unlike Jeanne d'Arc, who was a total freak by the way, Gilles confessed his accused perversions and murders and so was spared the torture of being burned alive. They still burned him, they just killed him first."

As Mara spoke, Green pulled down the neck of her T-shirt and with her index fingers moved her breast implants from one side of her chest to the other, making corresponding slooshing sound effects with her throat.

"What a cheery world we live in," Green said lightly. "Speaking of which, how was it last night? Are you in the group now?"

Mara closed her eyes and tried to recall the meeting of the night before. It was a difficult task. She was feeling sluggish and fuzzy, simultaneously wanting to take a nap, get a drink, and eat another brownie. Mara opted for the brownie because it was the one option that didn't require moving. Pointing at the bag she tried to answer Green's question.

"Oh, yeah. Thanks for taking me there, you guys. I'm in the group. I'm going to be Ulrike Meinhof in the Games. Holden's pissed. He wouldn't even look at me, at least not in a nice way. But Regan assures me that that'll pass."

Blue looked at Mara sympathetically and tossed her a brownie. "Did you know that the average human swallows a pound of spiders before they die. And not on purpose!"

Mara immediately forgot about Holden as she struggled to grapple with the disturbing factoid.

"What?" asked Mara.

"A pound of spiders. Just like humans, spiders live in a state of constant need. But unlike humans, they don't have big enough brains to complicate their needs, so their needs are boiled down to warmth, food, and water. When we fall asleep with our mouths open the spiders crawl right in to the wet and warmth. They think they've killed two birds with one stone. Eventually we close our mouths and swallow them. And, get this, ninety-nine point nine per cent of the time we don't even know we swallowed one. Normally we just keep right on sleeping. It happens all the time."

Green looked ready to throttle Blue. "A pound of spiders? That's so asinine! Do you know how many spiders that would be? That's slews!" she fumed.

"That's what I mean!" Blue earnestly looked at Mara. "Humans are involved in death all the time. What's a couple hundred kids in comparison to a pound of spiders?"

"You can't compare children with spiders," Green spat.

"I just thought since Mara's into gross stuff she'd be interested in the spider thing." Blue cringed from Green's rebuff, causing her mask to crumble slightly.

Green ignored Blue's explanation completely. "So anyway, about that Baader-Meinhof meeting—"

"No! No!" Mara cut her off. "See, you guys are missing the whole point, there's another side to the story. For having killed up to eight hundred kids, the Church that conducted the trial found very few 'actual' parents whose children had been taken. Those witnesses they did procure had a habit of disappearing. Fishy, huh? Plus, the trial could hardly be called impartial because, after his death, Gilles's vast wealth went to the Church.

"Then there was the whole thing about the trial being conducted in Latin, a language only the upper class knew. The people of France were really annoyed about that. It was also written that at one point a judge covered a painting of Jesus hanging in the court because Gilles de Rais's confession was so detailed and horrific. But whose details were they to begin with? They were probably force-fed to him by the Church as was the case in all the other witch trials of the time."

Blue nodded her head, "There's no pervs like self-righteous pervs."

Flushed with excitement, Mara spoke on, "You can imagine what was in his confession: blood sport, fondling intestines, playing with the heart like a rubber ball. The confession was the pornography of the times, which is why the Church's reaction to it was so interesting."

Mara stared straight ahead for a spell and hiccuped before she continued. "He also confessed to using the children's blood for ink, reading blasphemous books, and meeting with witches. But that was just fifteenth-century code for reading non-biblical books and hanging with learned people."

Typical Mara.
The minute she comprehends something, it becomes her personal property.
Fortunately for us, she understands very little.

Mara's voice grew ever louder as she closed in on the crux of the story. "Some believed the trial was held in Latin to keep the titillating information from the public," Mara blathered on. "Others thought it an exercise in power. When pressed to respond to the protests over the language barrier, the Bishop of Nantes replied something like, 'There are things so horrible they can only be spoken about in Latin.' Except he said it in French."

Blue's eyes were as wide as pancakes she began to pick at her crumbling mud mask.

"Hey, stop that!" Green said to Blue.

Blue looked at her hand as if surprised by its behavior.

"So, so what you're saying is that Latin is, like, evil?" Blue asked.

"No. Because for the Church any written document in the wrong hands was evil, as if it were a book written in children's blood. The Church had the means to share knowledge in the Dark Ages. It just didn't want to. But this was the end of the

Dark Ages. So it could be that the Church sensed the coming of the Renaissance and was using its power to forestall a return to secular humanism by eliminating perceived threats. Knowing it was on shaky ground, that no real crimes were being committed, the Church trumped up the worst charges they could think of: child corruption and murder."

"Mara, you are ridiculous," Green declared. "The Church was the only institution in Europe that kept education alive in the Middle Ages. Who are your sources for this baloney?"

"Bataille and Aleister Crowley," said Mara.

"Well. I don't know who this Batty dude is, but everyone knows that Crowley's a devil worshiper or warlock or whatever—not exactly a reliable source on the Church," Green said, and went back to playing with the silicon sacks in her breasts. She cupped them in her hands, lifting them up slightly.

"You know, I hate it when people call these fake," Green said, squishing her breasts together for emphasis. "I mean, they're not fake. They're real. See? You can touch them. They even have their own smell." She pulled down the neck of her T-shirt and pushed up the implant to create a taut softball-sized lump over her right clavicle. The "breast" now lay a full four inches above her nipple. "If these are fake, then everything is fake. And then what do we have to live for?" Green asked.

Blue looked at her friend with dismay. "You know what? You really are *really* tedious sometimes, 'My fake breasts are real,' " Blue mimicked. "Real deep. Earth shattering! Hello? Nobody cares. Besides, it's tacky and Hooters-esque. The spider thing was way cooler than your infantile breast fixation!"

"Why do all breast fixations have to be infantile with you? Can't a girl just like her breasts?"

"Um, gee, I wonder why someone might think a breast fixation is infantile. It couldn't have anything to do with nursing, could it?" said Blue.

"Not everything is about nursing, you know. Some things are about power," Green insisted.

A fight was certainly brewing between the two roommates, but Mara could not be dissuaded from the point that was revealing itself to her in brilliant clarity.

"Here's what it is!" Mara's voice overpowered the girl's bickering. "The Church was trying to control its image. Killing Gilles de Rais shows up as a blot on their already heavily blotted history. So they made up a bunch of junk to make it look like they were doing us all a favor by offing him and stealing his money. But, through their act of control, they revealed their hypocrisies."

Mara swallowed and wondered for a moment about her fuzzy, dry mouth before she pressed on.

"'There are those things so horrible that can only be spoken about in Latin.' They're speaking about themselves. Just as Gilles de Rais's confession was more about the Church's desire than anything else, their fears of an intellectual's wealth and power caused them to reveal themselves as the very thing they were trying to repress. In trying to preserve their image, they killed it. I mean, covering a painting of Jesus from their own perverse words? How messed up is that? It's so Jesse Helms. And besides, why are there leaves in your brownies?"

Mara had taken her thought process as far as she could. It unraveled before her as the brownies' special ingredient secured its hold on her already addled perception.

Green passed a puzzled look to Blue and fell on the floor in a fit of laughter. She wiped at her red eyes, causing little bits of green to sprinkle on the carpet.

"Wow, you are something else," said Green. "Haven't you ever heard of space brownies?"

Mara regarded her friends with puzzlement. "What are you saying? You made them for astronauts?"

The two girls broke into spasms of laughter at Mara's remark.

Blue swallowed her titters to say, "Mara, Mara, Mara. You know so much, and yet you know so little. Just remember, the secret is the butter."

Green, woozily, stood up and turned to Mara offering her hand.

"You might need to take a little rest now."

"What do you mean?" Blue asked. "I thought we were supposed to fi—"

"Just look at her, she's in her own world—useless. Besides,

I'm not interested in hearing another paper outline. Let's get
while we can," Green said.

The two helped Mara under her covers.

Mara didn't know how long she watched her ceiling swirl
with blue and green shapes. But eventually her thoughts drifted
back to the night before.

After she had volunteered to be Ulrike Meinhof, Mara had
felt Holden's eyes like a steel wool rubdown on her cheeks.

Was Regan wrong? Mara wondered. *Will I lose Holden instead
of gain his respect?*

In spite of the fact that Mara's attention wove in and out of
the affairs of the meeting, she managed to learn that Regan was
in charge of props and target selection.

Rat, catching Mara's confused look, explained target selection. "We choose people or organizations who we'd want to hit
if we were the Baader-Meinhof Group. It draws negative attention to their business or politics and 'outs' them to the town as
fascist."

"Oh, I remember now," Mara said.

"Don't you think that's a lot of work for one person to do?"
Rosa argued, still miffed at Regan for making her material
career aspirations public knowledge. "I mean, maybe I should
do targets. I'm only doing costumes right now. If you—"

"Absolutely not," Regan snapped. "I've been planning this
for too long for an amateur like you to mess things up."

"Don't *wet* yourself, Regan," Rosa mocked, knowing the
expression would remind Regan of her family's embarrassing
diaper wealth. "I just want to contribute here. Let's be *adults*
not *adult babies.*"

Her cruel aim found its mark; Regan's already severe face
clenched against the humiliating jibes.

Holden drew his body up to its full, swaggering
magnificence. "I agree with Rosa. She should do targets.
Remember your mess-up last year? It was a real buzz-kill.
Maybe you should do fewer jobs and do them right."

Anger lit up Regan's eyes.

Rat whispered to Mara, "Last year some of the pyrotechnic
bombs didn't charge and, since Regan didn't get the fake gun

permits in time, we had to use Super Soakers.

Mara held in a giggle.

"I should do *my* job right?" Regan roared. "Excuse me? You wouldn't have anything if it weren't for me. You waste all your time and our money on your Internet 'research.' Thanks to your bogus e-mail informant for the 'secret Baader/anthropos-ophy' connection, we're operating on a shoestring budget."

"He wasn't bogus," Holden yelled, losing his composure. "There's tons of proof that Baader was waging secret spiritual battles against the Knights Templar. If you didn't threaten my source—"

"You're right, Holden," Regan drawled sarcastically. "And this stuff around you? It's not air; we're inhaling fairies and exhaling pixies. You are so gullible. The people in the RAF were anarchists and Marxists. You can't believe in religion *and* be a Marxist. That guy was taking advantage of you. Besides, there's no one better suited to choose targets than me. This whole operation is still suckling at my breast."

To Mara's horror Holden examined said body part. Mara, too, looked at it. It was firm and well defined, about the size of a tightly clenched fist.

Holden strode to the center of the room and said, "Since you're so vote-happy today, Regan, let's vote on it. Hands up for those who wants Rosa in charge of targets."

Rosa, Apocalypse, Eric, and Holden all raised their hands. At the sight of Holden's upraised hand, MK-Ultra and Ex-Pat also added their votes. Rat was about to raise his hand, but Regan shot him a scowl that made him think twice. Mara was thankful she didn't need to vote as the majority was already in Rosa's favor.

Holden counted the hands smugly. "That's six. Well, I guess it's settled then. Rosa's in charge of picking targets. Rosa, I expect a list by next week. Meeting adjourned!"

Holden shot one last seething look in the direction of Regan and then cast a strangely vacant stare at Mara. He stormed out of the room without saying goodbye to his fellow RAFians.

Regan watched Holden's retreat with great interest, lingering on the space left vacant by his absence. The air was charged with hostility and thick with silence. The group began to trickle out of the room.

"Stay here!" Regan said to Mara. Then, catching Rosa's long braid, Regan dragged her through the hallway behind her, whispering hotly into her ear.

Mara remained seated on a metal folding chair, waiting for Regan's return.

Apocalypse walked over to Mara and said softly, "Hey, I know. Guys can be real jerks."

Mara nodded but said nothing.

Apocalypse fingered Mara's shirt as she spoke, "If you're in the mood for company, some friends and I are having a small 'Howl' party. We drink, gossip, and try to memorize *Howl* by Allen Ginsberg. Sometimes we write our own poetry. Here's mine—" She pulled out a worn sheet of notebook paper from her front pocket.

> *Upstate New York, I sing your song and now I am hoarse.*
> *Upstate New York, Norden Town hipsters hide amidst the upwardly bile.*
> *Upstate New York, your hands always clutch for that Big Apple; the bitter fruit, the juicy temptation…*
> *Answer me this, are the well-to-do ne'er-do-wells?*
> *Upstate New York, really we must get together sometime.*
> *Upstate New York, can you cry? Or has Botox stolen your expression?*
> *Upstate New York, your trust funds run red with the blood of oppression.*

"Well, that's as far as I got." Apocalypse admitted, but with pride.

"That's really nice, Apocalypse," Mara said halfheartedly.

"Okay, well, just let me know if you're interested," she said and ambled down the hall.

Finally alone, Mara let one silent saline drop fall into her lap and another trace its wet path down her cheek.

What am I getting myself into? she asked herself. *These people are just like Eric's meals: all appearance and no meat. Just another tofu mountain lion in a sea of carnivores…*

A chill stole down her spine and settled into the dimpled part of her lower back. Mara knew, as sure as her cat eyes were a lovely emerald green, that Holden was standing behind her, watching her with a potency only he could muster. Quickly, she brushed her eyes to hide the drippy evidence of her sorrow. Then she slowly turned, keeping her head down to deflect the full force of his withering gaze.

Pain was etched deeply into his handsome face.

"Why did you do it, Mara?" He fixed his eyes on her with a steely cold glare. "Why did you have to join the group?"

"I– I…"

Mara didn't know how to answer, how to say the very thing that could bring them together or push them apart.

Turning his broad shoulders on her, he snatched up some paperwork, threw it down, and spun back around.

"Everything I say to you just flies right over your head, doesn't it?"

Mara cringed at the insult to her below-average height.

"Do you think the Baader-Meinhof Games is a game?" Holden yelled, too furious to notice Mara's despair. "It's not a game! It's real. More real than you'd care to guess. I can tell you right now, the outcome of this year's Games is not going to be pretty! Why do you think I'm putting so much energy into the Mumia thing? It's because I want to be remembered for having done some good. Something other than associating with this nest of vipers."

Holden screwed up his eyes like some kind of beatific martyr. Mara fought the urge to throw herself at his feet and, then and there, beg for his forgiveness.

"And now you've gone and complicated everything. You ignored everything I've said and put yourself directly in the path of danger."

He threw his anguished head into his hands.

Mara was startled by his extreme reaction. She reached up, gently pulling his hands away from his face. She wondered if maybe the tofu mountain lion still had a bite to it.

"Holden, what do you mean? Where's the danger? How can I help you?" she implored.

Holden looked over her head to the door and his expression stiffened. "It's too late. Forget it."

Mara followed his eyes to where Regan was standing at the door, arms akimbo, eyes calculating and steady.

Keeping her gaze fastened on Holden, Regan said, "Okay, Mara, let's get you home."

Holden frowned as Regan tore Mara from his side. Mara found herself again wondering if the exaggerated anger between the two ex-sweethearts didn't really hide a feverish passion. After all, she knew that only a shadow lies between love and hate.

What is the difference between the Baader-Meinhof Reading Group and the actual RAF, aside from notoriety and six feet of earth?

Mara tried to put the meeting out of her mind. In spite of her anxieties about the night before, she finally drifted off into a troubled sleep. Her last vexatious thought was wondering which disturbed her more, that Holden might be involved in a real terrorist organization, one that she is now a member of, or that she couldn't tell if Holden still held a torch for Regan.

Of course there are worse troubles than thinking one's boyfriend may hold a torch for his ex. I dated a man once (only once) that had tackle the size of a baby's pinky.

Really.

Perhaps you think I'm unkind, or that we women should be the generous ones. ★ *Such presumptions are unfair, for we, too, yearn and dream and desire. In this revolution we may tower like Titans, but we are, after all, human, formed in flesh and blood. We are entitled to a modicum of judgment, a bare minimum requirement to meet our standards.*

★ See, it's this kind of overly obsequious attitude toward men that causes them to "step out" for "a little strange." You've got to define what it is you expect from them and what the consequences will be if they don't meet your expectations. Maybe if you showed a little more backbone you would be out with your adoring husband instead of wondering where he is at this hour of the night. Also, I suggest you consider changing your perfume. What is that chemical slush that permeates everything you touch? Its stench lingers even after a shower. Do you mark your territory that way? By the empty driveway you can see how well it works.

Oh, I know it's hard enough for you boys to even be reading this book. (Heaven forbid, you may be caught with a romance novel in your hand! No matter that this may be the very book that frees your soul.) And now I'm threatening your masculinity by reducing your pecker to the stingiest representation: Size.

All I can say is, "Yes, I'm guilty." But it could be worse.

To wit: I could go into an endless diatribe about the reams of inferior man-roots I've had to bear witness to, not to mention poorly named dicks, dicks that swing with the tedious regularity of a metronome, and old gym sock dicks. I could spend hours on the subject of downright uninspiring peni I've come across, but the tirade wouldn't serve the romantic aims of this novel. 🎵•

Back to Mr. Small, he took me to his domicile and we proceeded to perform all the customary activities that lead to "lovemaking" (body shots were taken, obscure French movies mentioned, arrests were recounted, beloved childhood pets discussed. She: "I'm too drunk to drive home." He: "There's plenty of room in my bed." She: "Oh, I'm so hot. I might have to remove my clothing." He: "I just want to lie here holding you all night like this," etc.). Without sharing too many details, when it came to the moment of unveiling, there was nothing there.

At first I had thought maybe he wasn't excited. I kept fishing around and coming up with nothing. Finally I realized that a soft, thin nub of a thing I kept passing over was his excuse for a pecker.

It was the size of a one-inch julienned carrot.

Yes, really.

To make matters worse, just a week before I asked a different young man out and his response was, "No."

I realize many men are intimidated by genius in women. But my overlying beauty should help them overcome the obstacle of superior intelligence. For example, I've been told my ass is incomparable and it is a plain fact that my legs are shapely and my ankles particularly well turned. Many are also of the opinion that my

🎵• By the way, you girls needn't worry; Holden's member is large, proud, and classically proportioned. If you were to shake hands with it you would enjoy its hygienic warmth and unassuming yet manly qualities. You would not be afraid or disgusted by it. You would find it quite handsome while not being so overwhelmingly good-looking as to detract from your natural beauty.

length of limb and preponderance of soft, golden-hued skin are con-
siderable assets to my overall above-average looks—definitely secur-
ing my status in the phylum of comeliness. ♬

And what was this naysayer? This whelp of a man?

He had something to do with the Internet. ✊

He wasn't even dressed well. I mean, earth to Internet guy: If
you have to wear hideous clothes at least get a good haircut. And if
you don't have either, you'd better be gorgeous, or at the very least
grateful when someone asks you out. Need I explain how this is
doubly so when the person who asks you out has a most singular
intellect? And he said no to me?

Be that as it may, the point is that Herr Tic-Tac…to be honest,
I can't remember what the point is, but my therapist suggested it
could greatly improve the thickness of my stomach lining if I didn't
censor my thoughts.

The point is: There are worse things than Mara's man troubles.🖐
Obviously, as I stated previously, most of them don't prove to be
good romance novel material, and knowing what to leave out of a
revolutionary romance manual is exactly what makes a good
romance novelist.

♬ In my lifetime I have also received compliments on the following features and body parts: hair, eye color, hairline, shoulders, feet, fingernails, and neck.

✊ I mean, really.

🖐 And furthermore, Mara is obviously inflicting these problems on herself. If you don't believe me, perhaps you could ask yourself why is it that Mara is so quick to give credence to Regan's suggestions (in the upcoming pages) that her beloved is possibly a serial killer? Answer: because that is how she wants it. Like so many young women, she is infected with a lack of self-worth. All narcissists are shockingly insecure, if only because they've never had their megalomaniacal fantasies fulfilled by the world. Mara, extremist in everything, punishes herself with a man who not only may still be smitten with his ex-girlfriend (a completely pedestrian affliction) but who could also be responsible for numerous women being turned into organic fertilizer. Of course Mara has been nourishing this particular romantic peccadillo with years of evenings locked away from peers and popular culture, gazing on the faces of the worst of the bad men our society offers: sadistic serial killers. The poor girl's always admired those who don't pause to take action, even if that action is perverse. No wonder one of her favorite erotic fantasies takes place behind the bars of a prison and is composed of her in the arms of a serial killer (well, these days the serial killer has been supplanted by a terrorist). I don't blame Mara, actually. I blame society and its own ubiquitous romance with the criminal element. I also blame those law-abiding citizens who are so tedious that the sheer poverty of stimuli drives the genius into the arms of the evildoer.

The sun beat through her window.

What time is it? Mara wondered.

Her clock said 1:00 P.M.

It can't be that late. I never sleep that late.

She lay in the drowsy warmth of her bed thinking, remembering.

Oh yeah, Tippy and Penny came by. And I still have my paper to write.

Fortifying herself with plenty of coffee, Mara put her nose to the grindstone and worked on her paper diligently for the remainder of the day. At six-thirty she heard a knock at her door. Mara answered with a sigh.

Regan stood there, raking her browless eyes over Mara's disheveled appearance.

"My, don't we look nice today?" Regan oozed with sarcasm.

"Yeah, I had a run-in with the girls this morning," Mara offered as she admired Regan's black, suede-trimmed jodhpurs, black woolen military sweater, and leather, knee-high boots. Regan's brows were drawn low and mean, giving her words a dark manner.

"The girls? Do you mean Tippy and Penny? I thought I told you to avoid them!" Regan brushed past Mara angrily, scanning the room.

"Regan, I appreciate your concern, but I can handle them," Mara countered.

When Regan determined the room was secure, she closed the door and motioned for Mara to sit down.

"Just be careful. Seriously. Watch yourself around them. They're damaged goods. Daddy issues, I think. It sets electrical storms off in their heads. I saw one of them reading *Chicken Soup for the College Soul*. I swear. How pathetic is that?"

"Very," Mara had to admit.

"I think their mud masks are seeping into their brains. Anyway, I don't want to talk about them. There's something else on my mind. Did you see how furious Holden was last night?"

Regan's question brought back a flood of painful memories.

"Regan," Mara said in a small voice, "do you think you were

wrong about me joining the group?"

"Oh, God no. You were perfect last night! That was just Holden not coping. He'll get over it. I'm talking about how mad he was at Rosa."

"He was mad at Rosa? But he wanted her to be in charge of choosing the targets."

Regan crossed her arms and gave Mara a cross look. "Oh yeah, he was angry at her. I've never seen him so angry. Angry for voting you in. He knew she couldn't handle the targets. He was just giving her an opportunity to fail so he'd have a legitimate excuse to kick her out. Organizations do that kind of stuff all the time. It's called 'exiting.' Also, Rosa told me that he threatened her during the break. She better watch it. I heard he didn't leave the Funny Farm on good terms. There are rumors..." and then her voice dropped off.

Mara was puzzled by Regan's insinuation. "What kind of rumors?"

Regan turned to face the wall. "Oh, you know, the usual. The disappearance of people, *certain* women from the Funny Farm who crossed Holden, coupled with the discovery of a surplus of organic fertilizer..." She turned to Mara and, leaning closely, whispered, "And I haven't seen Rosa all day..."

Regan grandly walked to Mara's bed and draped herself over its rumpled surface. The shine on Regan's boots caught the light, momentarily blinding Mara.

"So, you're saying that Holden might be..." Mara couldn't bring herself to say it.

"I think it's clear what I'm saying. Holden is a case, at best. You study these kinds of people... I mean, what do you think of the 'Holden' thing?"

Mara frowned. "What 'Holden' thing?"

Regan opened her eyes alarmingly wide. "His *name*, Mara. I thought you knew, serial killers and deranged people always have a copy of *The Catcher in the Rye* on them or in their bookcase at home..."

Something about this conversation was toying with Mara's confidence in Holden.

"Regan, what are you talking about?" she prodded urgently.

Regan watched Mara carefully. "Don't you remember the name of the main character in *The Catcher in the Rye*? It's 'Holden.' Have you ever seen Holden's driver's license? Unless he got a new one, you'll see that Holden is not his real name. He chose that name. Why that name? And why do you think high schools are always trying to ban *The Catcher in the Rye*? Mmm-hmm. The book clearly breeds insanity. Plus there's the fact that Mark Chapman asked John Lennon to autograph a copy of *The Catcher in the Rye* before assassinating him."

Mara's mind refused to absorb Regan's point. "So, you're saying that…"

"I'm not saying anything. I'm just wondering where Rosa is, that's all. And I'm worried about Holden. He's been acting strange lately." Regan shifted her tone to casual as she stood up, leaving a serpentine body print on the bed.

"Wait, so now Rosa is *missing*?" Mara asked, alarmed.

"Unless you know where she is…" Regan answered and then brightly, as if they had just shared their favorite quiche recipes, she held her hand out to Mara. "Now, shall we begin our Baader-Meinhof lesson?"

Something tugged at Mara. There were times when her friend seemed less together than her confidence would lead one to believe. In addition, Mara knew she was forgetting something, but couldn't remember what it was. Dazed, she followed Regan to the room with a red star on the black door.

An hour into the session, Regan tapped her pointing stick on the grainy image of an unremarkable woman. "Ulrike Meinhof was a prominent voice of the chic left in Germany and a mother of two before she gave up her safe and lazy ways to join forces with the others in the RAF. Gudrun Ensslin used Meinhof's authority as a well-known journalist to free her boyfriend, Andreas Baader, from jail."

"So when do Baader and Meinhof get together?" Mara asked.

Regan sighed loudly. "When she breaks him out of jail."

"No, I mean when do they…" Mara searched for the right words. "You know, fall in love?"

"They don't," Regan announced as she slapped her stainless steel pointing stick against her jodhpurs. "Mara, this isn't Romeo and Juliet or Bonnie and Clyde. Baader and Meinhof were united by one thing: an insatiable lust for justice. But Meinhof was never Baader's lover. In fact, Andreas called her a 'red rag' and a 'cunt.' Holden, I mean Andreas, may have been the very reason Meinhof committed suicide."

A cold knot formed in Mara's stomach as she listened to Regan.

If Holden is playing Baader and Regan is Gudrun, it'll be like Regan and Holden will be dating during the Baader-Meinhof Games. Oh, where do the Games end and reality begin? wondered Mara.

"Is— is that what Death Night is?" Mara asked somberly. "The night that Ulrike Meinhof died?"

"No, I already told you," Regan chuckled and the knot in Mara's stomach loosened. "Meinhof commits suicide a half year earlier. Death Night is when Baader, Raspe, and Ensslin are found dead in their cells, murdered by the fascists."

Once again Mara felt ill. "Why did Baader turn on Meinhof when she was the one who got him out of prison and sacrificed a good life for him?"

Regan looked at Mara as if she were daft, but took the time to answer her question, punctuating each word to Mara's annoyance.

"She may have *helped* to get him out of prison, but it was Gudrun Ensslin's idea and she could have used anyone. Meinhof was just a convenient pawn."

Suddenly Mara wasn't sure she wanted to know any more about the Red Army Faction. She was horrified that Holden could admire a group so rife with ingratitude.

"That's hateful!" Mara exclaimed.

"Hateful?" Regan spat out her response. "Yes, I suppose so. But no more hateful than Baader and Meinhof stealing all the glory for a revolution they didn't plan. And no more hateful than the *Springer* so-called 'Press' giving the group a name that belies the real genius behind the group: Gudrun Ensslin. She could have gone far if she weren't tied down by her love for the handsome-but-horribly-pedestrian Andreas Baader. But Gudrun always gets the last laugh," Regan chuckled lightly to herself.

"Why? What happened with Gudrun?" Mara queried.

Regan returned her eyes back to Mara and said hurriedly, "Oh, nothing. She dies on Death Night with the rest of them."

Mara sat forward on Regan's bed, her pointed toes just grazing the floor. "Then how does she get the last laugh?"

Regan's absent eyes narrowed. "What? What are you talking about?"

Mara pressed on. "You said Gudrun got the last laugh."

"No I didn't. I mean they all had the last laugh, sort of, because even though the fascists made it look like they committed suicide, no one believed it really was."

Mara rubbed her temples. "But Meinhof did commit suicide?"

Regan's voice hardened ruthlessly. "Meinhof was just a pampered journalist who couldn't handle her upper-class guilt. If she hadn't have offed herself there were other ways the group could have freed themselves of her incompetence. They did 'in-house cleansing' as much as any other organization, as Ingeborg Barz found out."

Regan paused to light a beedie then proceeded to give a lengthy diatribe on Meinhof and Barz's lack of dedication to the cause.

"So what happened to Inge-whoever Barz?" Mara finally asked.

Regan sucked from the beedie as if it were an asthma inhaler. "She disappeared after she tried to leave the group. Later a decomposed body of a young woman was found in the woods with a bullet in the back of her skull. Many thought it was the body of Frau Barz."

Mara immediately thought of Rosa and pictured her body stretched out under a stately oak in Norden's surrounding forest. She tried to banish the thought.

"Um, I gotta go. I'm really tired and I think I've learned enough tonight," Mara said. "Maybe too much," she added under her breath.

"Suit yourself," Regan said and stopped her eyes in mid-roll, leaving her expression unfinished.

Mara wandered down the hall with downcast eyes and heart. When she bumped into a warm, solid mass, she let out a cry of surprise. She immediately knew who it was, instinctively sensing his rugged, masculine presence.

"Holden? What are you doing here?" Mara said.

His form loomed above her.

"What am *I* doing here?" his handsome face contorted in a grimace. "Where were you? We were supposed to have dinner at seven."

Mara felt the import of her mistake cause her heart to beat faster.

Or is it Holden who is causing my heart to beat so quick and strong?

She quietly opened her dorm door and slipped inside with Holden fast on her heels.

"I— I forgot."

She never had Holden in her room before. He filled the tight space as no one else had. Mara was surprised that his enormous, rock hard body fit in the little room at all.

"You forgot? That's rich! First you nearly kill our relationship by becoming best buddies with my ex-girlfriend and joining the Reading Group, which I specifically asked you *not* to join, and then you 'forget' we're having dinner? Well I give up! If you're not in this for me—and I don't think you're in this for activism—then what are you doing this for?"

Mara sank into her chair. She felt her strength diminish in the face of Holden's anger.

"It isn't like that, Holden. You were the one who told me to catch a ride with Regan. I probably wouldn't be her friend if it weren't for you. And, as for dinner, I really forgot. I'm sorry."

Anger gleamed in his warm, brown eyes and coated his words. "Then why didn't you answer the phone when I called?"

Mara's own rage almost rivaled his. "Do you think I sit by the phone all day waiting for you to call? I have a life too, you know."

Holden sat down on her carpet, his powerful stacks of muscles at rest.

"Oh. I thought you weren't speaking to me anymore," he said simply and let his head fall.

Mara's spleen melted before his bent figure. "I'm speaking to you now, aren't I? Holden, look, you have to drop this idea that you can control me."

Holden raised his dark head, swinging it meaningfully to the side. "I know. I just don't want you to become like the others."

For a moment Mara wondered which others he was talking about: the people missing from the Funny Farm who Regan spoke of or the others in the Baader-Meinhof Reading Group.

Holden interrupted her thoughts. "I'm not happy that you're in the group, but I can live with it." He looked at her intently, relishing her with his eyes. "I just don't want it to get in the way of us." Holden gently reached out to Mara and let his index finger explore the contours of her strained face. "Okay?"

Mara gulped and tried to respond. As she gazed into his light-blue eyes, the ground of her anger broke beneath her and she fell back in love with Holden Rife.

Holden dragged her chair to him until her knees hit his chest. With one large hand he spread them apart while his other hand reached behind her waist and pressed her into the hard plane of his torso until their noses were touching. His hot breath punished her lips as she herself gasped for air.

Mara was overcome by their closeness. Suddenly all doubts fled from her mind and all she was left with was a carefree desire for this marvelous human specimen.

It was pointless to deny her attraction to him.

Holden pulled her closer yet until her feminine cleft pressed warmly against his throbbing, muscular chest.

Mara exhaled with a gasp.

Holden whispered hoarsely into Mara's ear. "Mara, will you join me at the Mumia Benefit next weekend?" He gazed deliberately into her deep green eyes.

Mara looked at the man she loved. She could never resist his devastating charm. "Holden, I would do anything for you."

Holden suddenly grew serious and his baritone voice dropped yet another octave. "Anything? Do you really mean that?"

Mara reflected his solemn look and spoke with her heart, "Yes, I do."

Holding her at arm's length, Holden examined the woman before him closely. "Even Saint Peter betrayed Jesus for some lousy rooster, but I believe you, Mara. Some day, some day soon, I'm going to ask you to remember that promise. I'll want you to remember how you feel now, in my arms, and remember you pledged to do anything for me."

Mara was stilled by his earnestness. She knew something important was transpiring and she should be wary. Despite understanding the dangers of speaking with her heart and not her head, she uttered in a low, voice, "It's just as I said. I would do anything for you, Holden."

"Good girl." Holden smiled a devilish grin and crushed her silky curves into his youth-carved muscles.

His hands explored the gentle slopes of her back, her waist, her hips. Her rosy peaks grew to a pebbly hardness and her breath came in gasps. Then Holden murmured breathlessly into her ear, "Ulrike, my Ulrike," causing icy fear to seize Mara's heart.

CHAPTER 8

To say Holden Rife was an attractive man would be a grave understatement. Shoulders in splendid proportion to his above-average height, he was an easy-muscled, golden-skinned type, a virile giant of a man, a Colossus striding over his peers. Holden radiated a swarthy youthfulness and a swashbuckling flare for recklessness that caused heads of women—and—men to turn.

There was something about him—something polished and something harsh; something that spoke of wealth and breeding, and something that denied that breeding but in such an eloquent manner that it reified the very upbringing it denied. It was complex. His abundance of dark, wavy hair was stylish without a hint of the desperate stench of a fop. Soulful, silvery-gray eyes with high-winged brows exuded controlled strength. And his finely carved, arrogant face was softened by a sensuous mouth, a mouth that twisted with the realization of the blunder it had just made.

"*Ulrike?* What do you mean, *Ulrike?*" demanded Mara.

She was trying to ignore the inner voice telling her that his slipup shouldn't matter and she should resume kissing this fabulous man instead of tracking down the source of this minor infraction.

But he called me Ulrike! You can't let a man off the hook if he calls you by another girl's name, especially in a moment of passion.

Holden tried to explain his tongue slip. "Ulrike. You know, Ulrike Meinhof. I guess I thought it would be a cute pet name for you, now that you're playing her in the Games."

Mara was only slightly relieved that her "competition" was a dead German terrorist. "A bomb-planting, gun-toting terrorist who committed suicide? That's a cute pet name? You are twisted, Holden, really twisted," she snapped angrily.

His complexities were proving to be too much for her to bear.

"Mara, what—? why—? Look, don't make this into a big

deal. This doesn't mean what you think. I was just playing." He reached over to punch her shoulder, but her grave expression caused him to stop.

Mara was furious and she didn't know why. She only knew one thing: that she was unsure about Holden.

And if I'm unsure about him, he sure as heck shouldn't be in my room with the door closed after the late night news.

"Holden, you have to leave. It's been a hard week and I have tons of stuff to think about. I'll call you later."

Then Mara did what few women have even had a chance to do and no woman had ever done. She kicked Holden Rife out of her bedroom.

He left silently. Mara looked at the spot of slightly crushed carpet where Holden only moments ago had been kneeling; the mark left behind was the exact shape of a heart.

What wonderful kisses! she reflected. *What's my problem? Why can't I give him my trust? Why should I let a little thing like him calling me Ulrike Meinhof get in the way of our happiness?*

Mara thought back to the photo of Ulrike Meinhof. Bookish and unremarkable, a pawn, a poser.

Maybe that's how Holden sees me, as a poser. Meinhof died alone and by her own hand after a tongue-thrashing from Baader and being snubbed by Gudrun. Gudrun Ensslin was the real thing and she was dating Baader. Their simultaneous deaths on Death Night forever united them under a romantic shroud of conspiracy theory. Gudrun the bitch!

Mara surprised herself with her negative feelings toward Gudrun Ensslin, a woman who had been dead for three decades.

Am I jealous of Gudrun? Or am I just mad that Regan's playing her, Holden's girlfriend, in the Games? What if Holden really isn't over Regan and that's why he didn't want me in the group—or for Regan and me to be friends. The energy between the two of them is unmistakable.

Mara got up, entered her small bathroom, and peed, all the while thinking, *I don't want to be a Meinhof to Holden's Baader. Until I figure out who Holden Rife is, I better cool this relationship down.*

She flushed the toilet and the problem away and returned to her room. Mara jotted down the nagging questions about the Reading Group and the Baader-Meinhof Gang before she went to bed.

Who are they really? Why do they choose to fall out of society's norm in favor of the life of an outsider? Where is that fine line between admiration and idolatry? What is the tipping point between anger and action? When does the incalculable price of human life become something worth shedding in favor of an idea or desire? And, afterward, how can they dream when they rest their tired, murdering, terrorist heads?

With Mara thus occupied, I should inform you that her suspicions of Holden's romance with the Baader-Meinhof Group are well founded.

Every revolution must have a heart. Although at the outset the RAF may have had idealistic aims, I don't think it was appropriate for them to use sixty-pound bombs to kill and maim U.S. and German citizens without warning or provocation. And the RAF could have been more thoughtful when it came to their historical relationship with Jews. For example, Meinhof calling the victims of the Holocaust "Money Jews" in her trial was possibly a lousy attempt to recast the Nazis and their collaborators as good communists. ❷ *But instead it made her sound like a Nazi apologist. Not to mention the embarrassing fact that the initial brain power of the Red Army Faction, Horst Mahler (not to be confused with Mara's professor, Horst Mahler, whose identical name is purely coincidental), joined a Neo-Nazi group. Both circumstances heighten the likelihood that at least some in the RAF were motivated by racism, be it conscious or sublimated. And so it is that the heart is corrupted by human failings despite its initial idealistic intentions.*

So how is it that the RAF, SLA, NPR, and other violent three-lettered, political groups charm so many people? I believe that just as we project our desires on our loved ones (so that we don't notice

---

❷ Meinhof morally recasts anti-Semitism here as fighting against the class system. It is, perhaps, this romanticized revision of plain old racism with which most Germans in World War II were afflicted.

their faults and foibles) for as long as we possibly can, so do we blindly embrace those groups that seem to adhere to our ideals. To complicate matters, people who are already wary of the information provided by their governments (i.e., rational people) search out alternative media as sources for information, making them more susceptible to the lies, propaganda, and conspiracy theories that cover up and rationalize the atrocities the terrorist groups carry out. This is why the only well-placed faith is the faith in a loved one or a loving insurrectionist. ⚓

Having said that, just as it's easy to direct a football game from an armchair, isn't it a little too easy for those academic types like Mara to sit back, read books, and judge? It's time we ask ourselves what it takes to come to action, to move away from the realm between one's own ears and into the world. What sort of vim enables one to add one's footfalls to the great march of history? The same vim, I posit, that Mara is lacking and that the Baader-Meinhof Reading Group (albeit often terribly misguided) has.

"Cowards die many times before their deaths," wrote Shakespeare. Cowards and academicians. Marx said, "Philosophers have only interpreted the world; the thing, however, is to change it." Sometimes we armchair historians have to put down the book, turn off the TV we've been yelling at, and do something to make a change! Although Marx also said, "Outside of a dog, a book is a man's best friend. Inside a dog, it's too dark to read." (Different Marx—the one with brothers.)

I doubt either Marx would endorse the perpetual stay-at-home-ism or complain-at-your-local-coffee-shop/bar-ism or your incessant attend/partake-in-another-panel-discussionology to which you subscribe.

What I'm saying—and I'm sorry to be so brief, but this is, after all, a romance manifesto—is: Isn't it just like students to behave as if they have all the answers only to never act on them? This is the very reason why, in certain circles I respect, "academic" has become

---

⚓ Of course, I'm not speaking here of that misguided faith wives have in men who are just too wild and majestic to be caged within a petty, loveless marriage. Who said the marriage bed should be sacred while the Sleepy Eye Motel bed, where every passion gets stirred up to frothy peaks only to be doused in the most mind-numbingly provocative zeniths known to mankind, is profane? Certainly not the romance insurrectionist, who abhors the capitalistically motivated social contract of marriage.

a dirty word and not the good kind of dirty, either.

The RAF and Holden's Baader-Meinhof Reading Group were people of action. Romantic? Yes. Stupid? Yes. Murderous and therefore hateful? Yes! (Well, in the Reading Group's case that remains to be seen.) In every "action," however, there is an "act." In "academic" what do you have? "Ac"? "Demic"? Nothing, that's what.

As for the Maras of the world? Aside from being whiners, sputterers of denunciations to those who don't reflect their narcissism, and sellers of cheese to tourists in Baraboo, Wisconsin, I don't see them contributing much to humanity.

Maras, what do you fear? Jump into the fray! Revolt against your preprogrammed personality deficits.

And live!

Live!

A few days before the Mumia Benefit, while trekking from the library, Mara noticed wanted posters covering a stately old oak tree in which so many young sweethearts had carved their oaths of love. She moved in for a closer look and was met with a black-and-white photo of none other than Rosa from the Baader-Meinhof Reading Group.

She's a criminal. A real criminal, Mara concluded and a giddy thrill raced through her. *But wait! What's this?*

Mara noticed the poster didn't say "wanted," but instead, "missing."

Rosa's missing! It's just as Regan feared.

Mara tried to calm down.

Regan doesn't know anything about this. I'm getting caught up in her assumptions.

Still the image of Rosa's body rotting in the Norden woods swirled in Mara's head with that of Holden picking leaves out of his hair. A chill wriggled down her spine and pooled in her underwear.

The poster looked real to Mara. There was the telephone number of the local police and the promise of a reward for information. It also said that the last time Rosa had been seen on campus was right after the Reading Group's last meeting.

Mara chewed on her lower lip.

Maybe Regan was right. Maybe Holden did get rid of Rosa, she let herself admit, disheartened. Testing the thought against her feelings for Holden, Mara discovered it didn't seem to make a bit of difference. Her love for Holden appeared indelible.

Mara returned to her room and changed into sixties-style corduroys of a faded, wheat shade with a rainbow turtleneck sweater that hugged her curves like the wheels of a good race car. She just finished slipping on clogs when her door opened.

Tippy and Penny, or Blue and Green, as Mara now called them, scurried into her room dressed in their usual dorm attire. Green held one of the missing posters of Rosa in Mara's face.

"Hey, don't you know this girl? Isn't she in the Reading Group?"

Mara couldn't deny it. "I know her slightly—barely at all. You guys, I really have tons of work to do. Can we talk about this later?"

"Mara, you are such a pooper! Now try this!" Blue sprayed a mist of perfume directly into Mara's face.

"Hey!" yelled Mara, "Watch the eyes!"

Blue showed her perfect white teeth as she smiled. "Like it? It's a soporific. It's relaxing."

Mara could immediately see what Blue meant. Forgetting about kicking the girls out of her room she inquired, "What's a 'soaprific'?"

Before Blue could answer the question, Green said. "Aromatherapy. The scent is called Soporific. Soporifa is a Greek goddess of feminine odor."

Blue agreed. "Yeah, she was the cousin of Sappho."

Green kicked Blue, but continued smiling at Mara.

"You guys, I don't know what it is about you, but every time you come around I get really relaxed," Mara murmured happily as she sunk down in her bed.

Her clogs hit the floor in two deadened clunks.

"It's a karmic thing. We're totally into karma." Blue said as she cuddled next to Mara. "How's that hunky boyfriend of yours?"

An image of Holden appeared before Mara's eyes. "Dreamy. But I'm worried about him. And Rosa," Mara intoned airily.

Blue put her head on Mara's shoulder. "Why are you worried about Holden? Is he in danger?"

Mara thought for a moment and then answered, "No. But I keep hearing things about him…"

Green put her head in Mara's lap. "Really? What kind of things?"

Mara scratched her head, forgetting for a moment what she heard. "Well, there's the things about people disappearing from the Funny Farm when he was there…"

Green sat up and looked openly at Blue. "Yes, we've heard something about that…"

Blue smiled vacuously.

"Well, it's just a rumor I heard." Mara continued, "I guess Holden got mad at Rosa at the meeting the last evening."

Blue stroked Mara's curls. "What do you mean, 'I guess'?"

"Well I didn't think he was so mad at her."

"Who did you think was mad at Rosa, Mara?" Green asked softly as she lay her head on Mara's lap and began tracing the curve of her leg with her fingers.

Mara thought about the meeting. For some reason it seemed to help her thinking to tilt her head to the right side at a forty-five-degree angle. When she found the perfect position she suddenly remembered Regan glaring at Rosa for the adult-baby remarks, and for getting voted to choose the targets this year.

"Maybe Regan! Regan wanted to choose the targets. No, Regan said Rosa was afraid of Holden, that he threatened her…"

Blue stroked her head evenly and slowly. "So, by 'targets' do you mean the targets for the Baader-Meinhof Games?"

Mara knew she shouldn't be talking about such things, but didn't really see how it would matter since Tippy and Penny were such good friends of hers. "Yeah," she answered.

Then, from her lap, Green asked, "And Regan *was* going to choose them?"

"Yes," Mara responded. Her mind, however, wanted to drift back to Holden. "Blue, what should I do about Holden?"

Blue smiled at Mara. "I like that nickname, Blue. Umm…Well, Holden's a fox. I'd say only cut him loose if you have to."

"But what if… if he makes people disappear?" Mara asked in a timid voice.

Blue calmed Mara with her soothing voice. "Mara, you know, all guys are annoying to some degree or another. Some have back hair, others make you split the check, some ask you to sleep with their friends to prove that you love them, and some have a fetishistic fascination with German terrorists…If I were you, I'd hold on to Holden until you know there's a problem you can't live with."

Green's voice from Mara's lap agreed. "Yeah, it's like my mother used to say, 'You've got to know when to hold 'em, know when to fold 'em, know when to walk away, and know when to run.'"

"Your mom said that?" Blue asked.

"Daily." Green replied, lifting her head out from Mara's lap. "We need to go, Mara. Sleep well."

Mara wondered why Green thought she was going to fall asleep, then realized her eyes had been closed for quite some time. She let her body sink into the pleasant horizontality of her bed as the aromatic mist on her face slowly evaporated.

Friday came all too quickly for Mara. She tried all week to think of something to wear to the Mumia Benefit that was both elegant and rebellious. She finally chose tight, black dress pants with a black, beaded handkerchief top that exposed her delicate clavicles and interrupted the graceful line of her back with nothing more than a single spaghetti tie. To give the outfit a tough look, she borrowed from Green a glittering black choker that reminded Mara of a dog collar.

I look more like a lapdog than a secret agent, she thought as she examined herself in the mirror.

Mara sat at her desk and gave a final review of the paper she had to turn in on Monday. When she finished proofreading it, she checked her watch. It was six-thirty, easily a half-hour past the time Holden said he would pick her up.

Oh, so this is how it starts, Mara fretted.

Mara swallowed her thoughts as she heard a hesitant knock

on the door. Smiling and happy to be proved wrong, she swung it open.

"Holden, I'm so happy to see you!"

But the space where Holden's head should have been held only emptiness. Mara looked down and saw the considerably shorter MK-Ultra preening his green hair in utter disregard of her presence. He didn't bother to look at her when he said with obvious boredom, "Okay, let's go."

Mara felt a chilly draft at her shoulders. "Go? Where's Holden?"

MK-Ultra pulled at a spike of hair and started pulling it methodically between his fingers. "Busy. He said I should pick you up. Come on, let's go."

He grabbed Mara's hand without meeting her eye and gave it a tug.

"Hey, hold on," Mara tore her hand from his grasp. "Why can't Holden pick up his date?"

MK-Ultra made a sound that was something between a snort and a laugh. "Did Holden specifically say this was a date?"

Suddenly Mara was embarrassed. *Was I wrong? Was this just a political outing he had planned for us?*

MK-Ultra examined his upper eyelids. "I don't know who has a more pathetic love life, you or Rat. Whatever. Okay, no time for drama. Let's go, *date-girl*."

His crass attitude annoyed Mara. "Don't call me date-girl."

"Okay Su-ey."

"And don't call me a pig!"

MK-Ultra grabbed another chunk of his hair and began to work it. "Su-ey is short for suicide," he said wearily. "You are Meinhof and Meinhof commits suicide. Thus, Su-ey."

It was clear that MK-Ultra had no intention of being civil with her.

Mara cursed Holden under her breath and grabbed a jacket from her room angrily.

They drove off in his purple BMW 2002, leaving behind them a cloud of sooty exhaust. Mara was glad MK-Ultra's deafening muffler problem meant that she wouldn't have to sustain a conversation with him. Still, she couldn't resist yelling over the clatter, "So what have you heard about Rosa?"

MK-Ultra spit into his hand and used his spittle to style his eyebrows.

"That horse should never have been in the group. The only girl who pulls her weight is Regan, and you can hardly call her a girl," MK-Ultra yelled, still not looking her in the eye, but getting closer as he spoke to his watch.

"What do you mean by that?" Mara yelled, taking his bait.

"Regan is exceptional. The rest of you are tokens."

Mara sat silently by his side until they pulled into a community center that sat alone on the outskirts of Norden Town. The parking lot was nearly full.

"Well attended, thanks to Maxine, I'm sure. Hooray," MK-Ultra said without enthusiasm. He pulled his car in between two SUVs, leaving Mara almost no room to get out.

Without complaint, she squeezed between the cars as MK-Ultra watched her, amused.

"What is your problem?" Mara snapped at him as she tried to brush the car grime off her slacks. "Why do you have to be like that?"

MK-Ultra chuckled at her coarse display of emotion. "I just like things done right. Face it, Mara, you don't belong. That Holden likes you is his misfortune, but I don't see why he has to inflict you on the rest of us."

Mara smiled at MK-Ultra's unintentional compliment. *Even moss-head thinks Holden likes me.*

MK-Ultra took up the unmistakable male stance for urination. As he expelled hot fluid onto an SUV, Mara turned away, offended that he didn't deem her presence something worthy of even a modicum of modesty.

"Holden knows who and what is running things around here," MK-Ultra continued. "Which is why I agree one hundred percent with his plan to rid the group of the dead weight. This isn't just dress up, Su-ey, this is life."

"What, 'plan to rid the group of the dead weight'?" Mara asked.

He ignored her inquiry and finished sprinkling the shiny new car. Shaking off the last few drops, MK-Ultra then extended an unwashed hand, the hand that was conducting business only moments earlier, to Mara. She twisted her face in disgust. MK-Ultra shrugged, turned his skinny back to her, and headed to the benefit.

Mara followed, but slowly, so as not to catch up with him. She wondered apprehensively if MK-Ultra meant Holden thought Rosa was dead weight.

I shouldn't have agreed to go with MK-Ultra. If Holden didn't think I was worth being picked up, then why should I bother coming here? she thought as she entered the lobby scattered with glittering socialites.

She considered calling a cab. Then she heard a familiar voice coming from the main hall. Mara turned toward the ballroom and gasped at the spectacle that greeted her eyes.

Fancy dinner settings, much like those she had seen at the Captain's table on *The Love Boat*, were laid out before a sizable crowd of surgically augmented women and deeply smug men in elegant formal wear. From the pale necks of the women hung jewels whose value rivaled that of Mara's generous scholarship. These comparatively younger women were draped around their men in a manner not dissimilar to the jewels draping the women.

Members of the Baader-Meinhof Reading Group were discreetly on hand, pouring wine along with a team of hired caterers. Even Rat looked presentable; with the help of a thick layer of base makeup his tattoos had virtually disappeared.

Rat spotted Mara and gave her a withering look. Mara registered it and for a moment it caused her to wonder, but she soon went back to taking in the opulence of the evening.

Her eyes grazed slowly over the leather-trimmed tables and chairs to the fabric- and mahogany-lined walls. The stage was bedecked with glittering upraised fists that spelled out "Free Mumia." In the center of the stage a giant, illuminated backdrop displayed a touching silkscreen of Mumia himself. The face was familiar to Mara, although she had always thought he was a Reggae musician.

So that's Mumia.

She stared at the picture with awe and felt her confidence slipping. She had no idea this event would be so posh. After all, it was the first large dinner she'd been to where there weren't manners tips or pictures of dinner specials hanging within plain view.

The chandeliers were dimmed to a silhouetting low and Holden walked onto the stage facing the large hall.

That's no rental, Mara thought as she spied the fabulous, tailored tuxedo that draped perfectly over Holden's stalwart shoulders.

Holden nonchalantly accepted the rapt attention as the crowd around him grew hushed in anticipation of his words. Allowing the silence to linger a moment longer, he cleared his throat and put a hand to his brow, shading his eyes. He was looking right at her with his cerulean eyes.

Mara moved back against the wall, trying to make herself invisible. In her darkened nook, she watched Holden address the vast, bejeweled crowd. She was struck with wonder at his casual, yet eloquent manner.

Holden thanked the contributors to the Free Mumia cause and he read the names of the major donors and celebrities who were present. Mara noted with chagrin that Holden also thanked a certain ex-girlfriend.

"...And, I'd like to thank all the members of the Reading Group, particularly Regan Thresh, without whose hard work the organization would not be what it is poised to become today," Holden uttered with what seemed to Mara to be a special emphasis. "Your contributions are noted."

Mara caught sight of Regan. She was striking in a lounge-singer style dress with a plunging neckline that amplified her missile-shaped breasts. Her emerald gown complimented her burgundy hair that was swept up to reveal a proud, high hairline.

Mara thought, *I've never seen Regan look so stunning.*

She turned back to Holden who seemed, to Mara, entranced by Regan. She watched as he sent his ex-girlfriend a secret, flaming message with his eyes.

What does it mean? wondered Mara. *Too many secrets. Too many complications.*

Standing next to Regan was a significantly altered James, the sculptor, without the usual layer of white dust.

He cleans up well, Mara noted. *I wonder why I can't fall for men like him? Dedicated, hardworking, simple…and,* she thought for the first time, *not bad-looking.*

James slouched in his slightly rumpled suit, swaying a bit as if the orchestra had already started. His right leg was on autopilot, tapping away. He turned to Mara and smiled.

Mara smiled back, but turned away. Her eyes were drawn magnetically to Holden, who dwarfed any thoughts of James with his commanding presence.

There's no hope for me. As long as Holden is around I will love no other.

Holden, however, observed Mara's lingering examination of James and glowered in her direction.

He began his speech. "We lie on thin, sweat-laden mattresses, you and I. Sleepless, our worried heads almost touch the cold, steel toilet. Our room is ten by ten by five. No window lets sunshine in, only a barred chasm gapes into the blackening cells, reflecting our blackening thoughts."

As he spoke, beauty breathed from his lips and his eyes kindled with a fire that burned without fuel. His easy eloquence excited the guests; none were immune to his polished but unaffected brilliance.

"Why are we here?

"Because society cannot accept a smart, strong black man who does not abide by its racist rules. Because, the racist society we live in needs a scapegoat to sacrifice to its blasphemous god. Because 'uppity' African Americans such as ourselves will always be punished for the crimes of our skin. Because, if a cop dies it's the black man who must pay."

Mara tried to remember if there were any African-Americans in the crowd. She couldn't think of one. *Maybe they're all passing,* Mara thought as she squinted at the dimly lit, lily-white patrons.

"How do we know this?"

Holden paused and silence filled the room. A fifty-something man in an Armani suit and a full head of gleaming black hair discreetly looked at his watch. His platinum-blonde escort, in a designer evening gown, which revealed a bed of freckles spotting the cavern between her *aging,* but not yet aged, breasts, nibbled on her pearls as she tracked Holden's every move with lusty trepidation.

Holden swept an open-faced hand across the pale crowd of hobby activists. "Because we are Mumia!"

He stopped to wait for the tumultuous applause that rocked the hall to die down.

"What does it take for a group of privileged white people to identify with an imprisoned black activist?" Holden paused and dramatically cast his dark eyes over the silent crowd.

"Do you need to be a prisoner? I say no!

"Do you need to be black? Again, I say no!

"Do you need to be poor? No, I say!

"You only need a little compassion for human suffering! And until Mumia is free, we shall suffer right along with him. We will waste away in his small, gray cell until he is free. Our compassion imprisons us. As long as Mumia sits behind bars, our spirit will be in chains.

"And even tonight, as we dance, socialize, and dine, we will, in spirit, be rotting away in jail, because we are Mumia!"

Again applause filled the hall.

"We are Mumia eating only prison food.

"We are Mumia reading only prison books.

"We are Mumia wearing only prison clothes.

"We are Mumia dreaming only prison dreams!"

Mara became unsettled and her mind scampered around restlessly. She realized Holden had finished his speech only because of the sudden eruption of thunderous applause.

Then Holden left the stage. A band set up while Reading Group members and other hired staff served dinners.

Mara exited the great hall and walked to a pay phone in the lobby. She thought she should try to leave before Holden found her. An iron grip fell on her shoulder as she rifled through her purse for change. She looked up and saw Holden, eyes furious like lakes of fire.

"Who are you calling?" he demanded.

Mara was tongue-tied, paralyzed by his rage.

"Who—are— you—calling?" he asked again.

"I'm calling a cab," Mara responded, fighting an instinct to cower as she spoke.

"A cab? Why?" Holden looked truly perplexed.

"Well…you couldn't bother picking me up so I assumed I had to find my own way home."

He was now less angry than annoyed. "Mara, there was an emergency I had to attend to. That's why I couldn't pick you up. Didn't MK-Ultra tell you?" Holden's expression crossed from anger to confusion.

Mara looked down. "MK-Ultra didn't tell me anything except that this is not a date."

"He said that?" Holden's eyes softened.

"Yes," Mara held back a sniffle as she answered. "Why did you have him pick me up? You know he hates me."

Holden bent down to catch Mara's catlike eyes. "Hates you? I doubt that. He's maybe jealous of you." He cupped her chin in his large hand. "And who can blame him? Come on," he said as he offered her his hand. She took it reluctantly.

They were about to return to the hall when Holden stopped abruptly. He crouched so they were face-to-face and spoke with a quiet unease, "What was that look you were giving James in there? Is there something between you two?"

He was dead serious as he gazed deeply into her pale, lovely face.

Mara answered immediately and with solid conviction. "James? No. There's nothing between us. Well, one thing. One big thing. You."

She twinkled her first smile of the evening and Holden swept her into the hall just as the band started.

The band, a white-haired four-piece dressed in tuxedos with tie-dyed cummerbunds, played what sounded like a Glenn Miller arrangement of "Redemption Song." Without missing a beat, Holden twirled Mara into the center of the dance floor and soon they were circling around to the hypnotic sway of the music. Mara felt weightless in Holden's masterful lead, which had been honed by countless country club cotillions. Like the queen and king of the prom, they were the first and only couple to dance and all eyes were on them. The moment was magical.

Holden looked down into Mara's pretty, upturned face,

pleased by the glow in her cheeks and the sparkle in her eyes.

"There's the girl I know," he smiled and plunged her into a graceful dip.

In her upswing Mara saw Regan approaching. Mara could tell by the rapid clip of her step that Regan meant business.

Regan came to Holden's side and put a firm hand on his chest, stopping him mid-step. The gesture was too familiar for Mara's taste. To make matters worse, Holden didn't seem to notice the hand moving from his chest and over his stomach as she whispered in his ear.

Okay, now, don't be jealous, Mara told herself. *Regan is your friend and would never do anything to hurt you. If anything, it's Holden you are uncertain about.*

Unwilling to witness any more of their exchange, Mara looked away. She kept her eyes down even as she heard Regan depart.

Holden bent low to whisper in Mara's ear, "I'm terribly sorry."

Thinking he was referring only to Regan's interruption, Mara nodded, prepared to forgive everything.

"I have to leave now," he finished. "Unexpected—uh—things have come up."

Mara watched as he quickly walked away, following Regan out of the hall.

Mara was alone in the middle of the hall. Despondent as she was, she neglected to leave the dance floor. She just stood there, unmoving, her mind still crunching the awful events of the evening.

What's so important that he can't even finish a dance with me? Holden, our dance is always too short.

Mara looked left and right. Sympathetic faces of the other guests gazed back at her. *They pity me!* she thought with horror.

She tried to think of the least humiliating way to leave the dance floor. Then, from the watching crowd, a lone young man stepped forward and took her hand.

"James!" Mara exclaimed.

James in his rumpled suit and his soft brown eyes led her in a stilted box step. James wasn't nearly as graceful as Holden, but Mara was grateful to be saved from further embarrassment. The music transitioned to a big-band style "One Love" and the floor filled with dancers. With the room's attention diverted, James led Mara off the dance floor.

Mara's eyes brimmed with gratitude as she looked again into the kind face that she could never love now that she had tasted Holden's deeply complex passion.

"Thank you, James," Mara said meaningfully. "You know just what to do."

James looked at the floor and chewed on something nonexistent. He looked back down into her eyes and Mara could see he had a schoolboy's crush on her. She felt touched, if not a little guilty.

"James, do you like this?" She motioned around the room.

James picked at a roughened cuticle. "Nah, this blows."

"I think so too. Let's go home."

James gave Mara a wide grin. "Right on!"

As they drove back to Norden College in his van, James felt his fuzzy sideburns and pulled a marijuana cigarette from his breast pocket, "Pot?"

"I don't do drugs." Mara said.

He lit it and took a draw, held it for a beat, and blew the smoke out explosively. "Tweakers," he said.

"What?" asked Mara, uncertain if that was a drug term or art lingo.

"It's always an emergency with them, huh? Tweak! Tweak! Tweak!"

Mara turned to him, astonished that he echoed her own thoughts so completely.

"You mean the Reading Group?"

He nodded, licked his lips and pulled at the tip of his nose. "Where's the sirens? Where's the bomb squad? They've got no worries. And this Baader-Meinhof thing? Pffff! Devotion is always a parody of its object," James said sedately, his pleasing face slack with disinterest.

Mara raised her brows. "That's pretty deep, James."

James bowed his head with embarrassment. "Yeah, it's not really me, it's Apocalypse Now."

Mara thought he may have been referring to Apocalypse

from the Reading Group. Then she thought he was talking about the movie. Either way she knew exactly what he meant.

The deadlines, the secrecy, the drama, she thought. *Why is everything so damned important in their lives? It's because they don't know what a real emergency is. They've spent so much time in rarefied-air-land that they think every time they draw a normal breath, it's an event.*

Mara turned to James who was tapping out some sort of code of unused energy as he drove. "You're right, James. The deadlines, the secrecy, the drama. Why is everything so damned important in their lives? It's because they don't know what a real emergency is. They've spent so much time in rarefied-air-land that they think every time they draw a normal breath, it's an event."

James nodded. "They couldn't pass Introduction to Candy Ass 101."

Mara chuckled and looked at James in a new light.

He may be an artist, but he understands Regan and Holden better than I do.

"You may be an artist, but you understand Regan and Holden better than I do," Mara said and then realized she had just thought that.

"Hey, James. How are Regan's plans coming along?"

James gave Mara a quick sidelong glance. "What plans?"

Mara was hurt by his secretiveness. "Oh, I'm sorry. I didn't know that you were keeping them under wraps."

Dipping his head slightly he said, "Sheesh…It's all good. But they aren't Regan's; they're Holden's."

Mara felt the blood drain out of her face. "Are you saying that—"

"Holden's designing the props. Regan just delivers them because Holden's not on campus."

"I see. Well, what is he having you make?" Mara queried. She was confused that Holden should be designing the props when the group thought Regan was.

"Oh, the usual, fake bombs, fake guns…you wouldn't be interested." James shot an apologetic smile at Mara.

She found herself wondering again, *If this is all on the up-*

and-up, what is there to be secretive about? What is Holden up to?

Then it occurred to her.

Perhaps Holden is less of a Baader-Meinhof aficionado than a real revolutionary…Perhaps Holden intends to hit the town with real guns and real bombs…And maybe the "props" James is designing are going to be turned into actual arms without James knowing it…That would explain why Holden is pretending that Regan is designing the props and why he doesn't want me in the group. I can only hope that my suspicions are wrong.

"James?"

"Yes?"

"If you think those guys are tweakers, then why make the props?" Mara asked.

James stopped shaking his leg and his face glowed with passion. "Umm…" he took another drag from his marijuana cigarette. "Well, it's like, those guys are terrorist wannabes, right? But most *terrorists* are *artist* wannabes. They wanna change the way people think, but they're too lazy to do something cool about it like, say, make a sculpture, paint a picture, or whatever, so they resort to violence. I mean, violence does change thinking, but never for the better. If you think of the most radical stuff in Germany in the seventies, you don't think of the Baader-Meinhof Gang. You think of Fassbinder or early Kiefer. The Baader-Meinhof Gang wasn't so great because of their activism—they were total losers on that front. Like peanut butter without the jelly. They're only popular because stupid people love senseless violence. Sure they had a lot of sway when they were alive, but now that they're gone, *nada…*"

"Art is, like, a way more rad form of struggle. I mean, name a politician or revolutionary who was a contemporary of Goya… See? I can't think of anyone. And both Baader and Hitler were failed artists before they came to their 'political calling.' Politics and terrorism are like teaching; people only hide in those professions when all else fails. I'm contributing something to history far greater than anything those tweakers ever could. History remembers symbols, not acts."

His face reverted to its slackened mask and his leg began pumping again.

Mara had never seen that confident, almost arrogant side of James before and she was instantly sorry she had asked.

Regretfully, I suppose I must weigh in with my understanding of art and terrorism, lest you assume I harbor the same preposterous pretensions as James. My first significant and telling experience with artists was in a middle school "art class" where the teacher (a ridiculous man who wore his paint-splattered clothing with all the pride of a beauty queen sporting her tiara) had us copy the cover of our favorite record album. The person who copied it the most slavishly was praised as the best artist. It was then I discovered that art had nothing to do with so-called artists and vice versa. Sadly, this is even more true outside the classroom. "Artists" are mere laborers with delusions of grandeur.

What do most artists do anyway? They imitate nominally better artists or (worse yet) copy what other professions do, but poorly. Can't make a movie? Become a video artist. Can't articulate a coherent idea? Toss paint around. Can't act, dance, or write? Become a performance artist. And so on.

It's true that there was a time when art had significance, but those days went out with the fox-trot. Now it is writing that is the higher form of art. Case in point: To become a great artist one need only dupe a handful of rich people into buying your work—Bang! The museums and galleries blindly follow and you're an artist. To be considered a great writer your book must appeal to thousands or millions. Writing is a far more democratic ★ art than its visual counterpart, whose sole purpose is to flatter the rich into self-satisfaction.

Need more proof? Think of what people talk about when they look at art. Either they're blathering about silly, unimportant things like color, taste, and size (attributes only important if you are sticking something in your mouth or other parts of your body), or they invoke the names of (you guessed it) writers. Visual artists need theorists from my encampment 🎵● to "fortify" their pitiful bar-

★ In the idealistic sense of the word.

🎵● The cadre of writers.

racks. The more impotent the work, the more books they need to justify it. It won't be long before art shows come with their own set of footnotes.⅍ Conversely, what do people talk about with writing? Only the three most important things: love, power, and death. Which, by the way, are the three mediums terrorists work in, so if there is any convergence between art and terrorism it takes place in the art of writing.

James's claim that terrorists are artist wannabes is absurd. If anything artists are terrorist wannabes. They just wish anything they did had as much impact as a rag, lighter fluid, and an empty Coke bottle—or as a romance manifesto.

When James and Mara arrived on campus, the parking lot was blocked off by an assortment of fire engines, cop cars, and unmarked police vehicles. There were uniformed men walking about and men in leather jackets milling around with their pads and pens.

"What's all this?" Mara asked.

James shrugged. "Maybe one of the elite had an acute fingernail chip."

Mara tried to laugh but fear cut her off. They parked on the street and, unable to avoid the commotion, they headed toward the flashing lights and the sirens.

"Hey, what's the deal?" James asked a scruffy young man in designer combat gear.

"They found something of Rosa's in the woods. I heard they'll make an arrest," the young man answered, munching on a bag of popcorn as if he were watching a movie.

Mara pushed to the front of the crowd where an officer was talking with Tippy and Penny, who looked very cold standing around in their boxers, sweatshirts, and mud masks. To their left stood the red-faced groundskeeper who was always talking to himself. His lips moved as he tied the loose ends of a plastic garbage bag together. It was only when he bent to pick some-

---

⅍ I cringe to imagine that there are places where they already have. Can you think of any other medium operating on this level? "Here is my book, and here are the five Winnebagos filled with infantry to back it up."

thing up that Mara spied Regan standing behind him.

Giving her thanks to James, Mara ran to Regan's side.

"Regan, what's going on here? And where's Holden?" she asked over the racket of the crowd.

Regan glowered over the chaos. "It's Rosa. They found her scarf and think they found their man. As soon as I heard about it I grabbed Holden and we raced back here to see if we could help."

"How did you hear about it?" Mara inquired.

The groundskeeper guffawed and a strange look came over Regan's face. She was about to answer Mara when the clamor of the crowd suddenly grew louder. Mara turned to see Holden amidst a clutch of uniformed officers who were pushing him along. An officer laid a thick-wristed hand on his head and guided Holden into the back of a police car. Mara watched in frozen horror as the door closed on her beloved.

Then, in an emerald-green blur, Regan sprinted to the police car bearing Holden. She exchanged a few words with the arresting officer and jumped into the passenger seat beside Holden before the police car drove off into the night.

CHAPTER 9

Often I try to imagine you reading or rereading ❧ this book. I see you snug-a-bed in your winter cabin, heavy comforter pulled up to your armpits, three fingers of port bathing my words from time to time in a sea of red. You haven't left the house all day, taken, as you are, by the import of this tome. It's adorable the way your lips trace the words I write. Sometimes you set the book down to indulge in a daydream that involves Holden shoveling the walk so that you may step with ease to the limousine that waits to drive you two to the airport en route to your Paris vacation. His muscles strain under the cardigan you knit for him (as if you could ever finish a sweater) and a sheen of sweat sparkles on his noble brow in the crisp winter air, etc., etc. (And why shouldn't you enjoy a private daydream? After all, your husband is on another "business trip." Or is he?)❦

Other times you try to imagine me: my face, my underground home, the rebel notes I scratch on stray sheets of paper and then chew up and swallow for fear of being discovered.

Look at us. Caught in our musings. Tangled up together in our web of love. Writer, book, and reader—what a lusty pyramid, an unbeatable triumvirate we make.

Today I imagine that you wonder why a genius would choose to write a manifesto on romance instead of, say, a treatise on Universal Theory. Comrades, my interest in romance spins around the location of my genius. My genius lies not in anything so mundane as "math," "science," or "problem solving," but instead can be found in the richly intricate and succulently diversified realm of perception. I am a keen observer of the sociological and am capable of making exacting decisions derived from my insight.❧ This doesn't

❧ Here I blush.

❦ Don't get all uppity with me. You're the one checking all his e-mails, spying on him at the office, and giving him the twenty questions over his "long commutes." You know, sometimes it doesn't make the news when police shut down freeways. Still, it makes you wonder, doesn't it?

*mean I rely on a special ability to read minds or that I boast a fem-
inine—or other kind of—intuition.*🕮*Let's just say having observed
humans over tedious spans of time, I'm now able to surmise a thing
or two about them.*

*I know. You, too, consider yourself a keen observer of
humankind. But I beg to differ.* Watching *humans is not the same
as* observing *them in the spirit I propose. For example—true
story—a child of six quietly watches his father play chess with a
visiting friend. In the child's first contact with the game, his father
loses, not once, but an Oedipally devastating twice. The emotion-
ally traumatized child asks if he can play the visitor. The father,
thinking his son doesn't even know how to move the pieces, much
less be competition for the man whose enormous brain has repeat-
edly whipped him soundly, laughingly allows his son to play.*

*As the small child, whose eyes are scarcely higher than the plane
of the chess board itself, cautiously moves the pieces with his
dimpled little hand, it is revealed that not only did the child learn
the rules for the game (although he had never seen chess before that
very day), but also he is a superior player. He annihilates his
father's conqueror, the visitor, thrice.*

*This is the kind of observation I am talking about. Genius
observation.*★

*I do not mean to say chess proficiency is in any way comparable
where, once the rules are learned, you're just beginning.*🌑 *Even
the precocious six-year-old had a long way to go before he would
become the famous international chess champion whose name
escapes me now.*🜪

🐢 Such as: She's an ass. Or: Insofar as stringing someone up is concerned, I think that person is a particularly good candidate.

🕮 God forbid! We have enough charlatans running around with their "divining rods,"
their "theory," their "God saves," and their "healing butter," or what-have-you. I, for one,
will not be added to their minions.

★ It is a faux pas in Mensa circles to mention the exact numerical assessment behind one's
I.Q., but I will have you know mine is considered very high (in the triple digits!).

🌑 It is also a game counter to the aims of our loving revolution. Perhaps if the queen and
king were capable of expressing their deepest passions in the royal bedchamber (or wher-
ever) they wouldn't ruthlessly spend their loyal subjects' lives in pointless wars.

🜪 My genius does not reside in details, but instead in the big picture. I see the forest, not
the trees. It's been said, and I concur, that this particular type of genius is especially suited
to leadership positions. Leaders need to see forests; let the peons sort out the trees.

Humans, on the other hand, are easy. Once you know the rules, game over. The rules are as follows: First, humans are as bad as they think they can get away with being. Second, there are no exceptions to the first rule. "What of saints and the like?" you protest. Saints exist because they don't think they can get away with anything. You know, faith in God's all-knowing omnipotence and all that. As for the rest of the good-doers, they're just scared. &

One of the wonderful things about being a genius is that (with proper self-training) you can read humans like a book. The downside of human transparency is you discover humans are indeed all out to get you. ♟

Mara is an easy read. She appears innocent, but beneath her bulging lips and pearly whites lies a second row of shark's teeth. And, of course, she gets insanely defensive if you contradict her preposterous claims of genius-hood. It's sad really. I won't give you all the details because she has to be a sympathetic character for this book to work. Actually, just forget about the shark teeth thing.

"He didn't do it!" Mara exclaimed.

"Duh!" replied her blue mud-masked friend.

"We know that!" Green said in comforting tones.

"Why did they take him away?" Mara sniffled.

Blue squeezed Mara's hand, "What do you expect from a bunch of amateurs?"

"What she means is, even, like, the police fuck up," Green added, glaring at Blue.

Mara perked up. "I should go there and tell them they have it wrong."

Green pulled Mara's duvet over her legs. "They'll find out soon enough. Give it time. He only got arrested an hour ago. Kick back!"

"Besides, Regan's there if he needs anything." Blue added.

& That is correct. In other words, the thing we call conscience is merely a subcategory of fear, and being nice is just another way to say, "Please, don't hurt me."

♟ This, needless to say, is doubly true if you are good-looking—a fact that (if this is the case for you as it is for me) you should never bring up with your shrink because in her jealousy she'll diagnose you as "paranoid." As if!

Mara groaned.

It should have been me *in the police car with him, not Regan. Maybe that's why Holden and Regan are so passionate about each other, because Regan can handle these calamities and I can't.*

She thought of Holden in jail. Although the thought troubled her, there was also something disturbingly erotic about imagining Holden's lean form in horizontal black and white stripes, captive to the erotic whims of the severe female warden.

Blue looked into Mara's troubled, yet still pretty face. "How did you know this was going on? Weren't you all at the benefit?"

"I didn't know. Regan knew. Holden and I were dancing and she interrupted us. The next thing I knew, they ran off together."

Blue scratched her head. "There've been people searching the woods all week. How could she know they'd find Rosa's scarf tonight?"

Mara shrugged, no longer interested in anything other than Holden's well-being.

Green was squishing her arms together in front of her, joyfully changing the topography of her artificially enhanced chest. "So what's up with you and that art kid?"

"James? Nothing," Mara answered disinterestedly. "Um… Do you guys mind leaving? I need some time to myself."

Blue and Green left her alone with her sorrow.

As the door closed, Mara's thoughts flew to Holden once more.

If I were the real Ulrike Meinhof, I wouldn't let him sit in jail. Let's face it, I could never be an underground revolutionary. Regan could. With no mind for anyone but Holden, she jumped into the police car with him.

The thought of Regan and Holden at the police station together disturbed her more than she'd care to admit. Mara threw her head into her flannel pillow and moped.

It wasn't the first time Mara shed a tear because of her association with Holden. And with a grimness of heart, she knew it wouldn't be her last.

Holden is too secretive, too complex for me. I don't know if he's a terrorist or just a terrorist wannabe. Lies, secrets, and strange disappearances are not the signs of good boyfriend material. No matter what happens next, I have to stay away from Holden Rife.

Mara fell into a deep and troubled slumber.

The phone woke her sometime in the middle of the night.

"Hello? Holden?" she gushed into the receiver.

"Wrong!" said a thickly sarcastic voice. "It's Regan. Listen, Holden wanted me to let you know that, quote, 'he didn't do it' unquote, that he'd be out by tomorrow and he wants to stop by your dorm to explain everything. And don't worry, he's in good hands."

Forgetting she was on the phone, Mara nodded and hung up, falling back asleep.

Wanting to avoid Holden's imminent visit, Mara spent the next day alternately in the library and at her job and took her meals at the campus café. Arriving at the dorm late that evening, she found a note on her door from Holden and her answering machine was filled with messages.

She threw the unread note in the trash and erased the phone messages without listening to them.

Mara was deeply disheartened by her separation from Holden Rife. She knew that it would not be easy to push him out of her mind. Nor could she stop herself from imagining what her life might be like as the girlfriend of a terrorist.

I wonder if terrorists get married…

Mara guiltily slipped into a daydream. She was Ulrike Meinhof, but much prettier. Holden, as Andreas Baader, would run into the secret French garret where she'd been filling shells with gunpowder and shrapnel.

Out of breath, but dashingly so, Baader/Holden would set down a wheel of cheese and a baguette he had stolen from a nearby grocery, grab Ulrike/Mara's gun-callused hand, and blurt out, "Darling, I can't stand it anymore. I must have you!"

"What about Regan?" Meinhof asked, gazing deeply into Baader's yellow-specked eyes and noticing that the wound above his left cheek was healing well.

"Who's Regan?" Baader asked.

"Er, I mean Gudrun. I thought the two of you were an item."

Andreas spit on the ground. "That wench? She is a serpent. The only thing she understands is guns, power, and vengeance. She isn't deep and introspective like you are, Ulrike Meinhof. She doesn't understand that a revolution needs compassion and warmth."

Baader stepped closer to Meinhof and gently pulled her grenade-filled hands to his heart.

"You've set off something in me that I cannot ignore. It's as if you dropped this very bomb in my heart. You've robbed me of all my defenses, pillaged my mind of everything but desire for you. You are the arsonist of my flaming need. This consuming fire cannot be squelched, except by you. Meinhof, you have freed my body from jail, but in doing so, you have set my heart in shackles. Please, we've been denying destiny too long. It is time I claim you. Claim you like a man claims a woman."

Meinhof had always known that grenades were approximately the same size as a human heart. But, for the first time, she realized that a heart could cause as much destruction.

Baader pulled Meinhof to him until her feet left the floor and, carrying her to a pile of blankets in the corner, set her down gently. He knelt by her side, brushed a stray hair from her face, and looked tenderly into her startled eyes.

Electricity arced through her as he lightly brushed his fingers over her skin. For the slightest of touches, it shook her to her core and ignited a radiating passion. Gusts of desire shook her as she fingered Baader's bullet wound. His eyes widened with the desire and pain brought on by her gentle probing. Then, she pulled him roughly to her so that his weight fell warmly on her body.

Meinhof exulted in his strength, cleanliness, and beauty as their bodies pressed together. The air around them was ripe with the smells of gunpowder, warm cheese, and passion. Soon they were half-naked, kissing and touching each other, melting into one animal, one loving, caring human pile.

Meinhof was breathless, but still able to utter, "Baader, from the first moment I saw you, you had taken my heart hostage. Now it is time for you to take all of me!"

Baader, answering Meinhof's plea, eased his throbbing

missile into her sleek, moist feminine silo. Meinhof gasped as his murderously slow, even strokes became vicious, meaty jabs. Again and again he pierced her core. Even as she flinched she couldn't hold back her appreciation.

"Baader, you kill me!" Meinhof gasped.

Baader smiled devilishly, "Killing is what I do best!"

The two made ruthless, beautiful love and as Meinhof's body shattered with delight, so that at that moment she was more open than at any other moment in her life, Baader shuddered as well, filling Meinhof with his terrible essence. It was terrorist sex, taking no prisoners, save their mounting love. Rebelliously they combined forces to one violent objective: two "little deaths."

Afterward they rested in each other's arms. Baader traced the lines of Meinhof's body as he stared dreamily into space.

"You know, the press had it right. 'Baader-Meinhof' has a nice ring, don't you think? We belong together, like Adam and Eve, Romeo and Juliet, Bonnie and Clyde. Baader-Meinhof…We should hyphenate our names permanently." His eyes beamed as he toyed with the phrase.

"Andreas, are you saying—?" Meinhof couldn't finish her sentence.

"You're darn right I am! I've already stolen a wedding band for it. We should get married and have a whole gang of Baader-Meinhof children. Let's do it, Ulrike. Let's get married now!"

Meinhof brushed aside her rich, black hair. "But, Baader, how can we? All the churches are closed. And we're wanted by the authorities."

A devilish light gleamed behind Baader's eyes. "Then we'll have to get married the only way we can. We'll have a terrorist wedding."

Dressed in Prada and Helmut Lang bulletproof vests, the two terrorist lovers stealthily stormed a church in the dead of night. They scaled the exterior with the help of ropes and grappling hooks and stole in through an unfastened stained glass window. Baader found a priest and ushered him at gunpoint to the altar. Meinhof, meanwhile, found a nun for a witness and met them there, under the eyes of God.

With a rifle aimed at the startled priest's head, Baader asked through his Gucci ski mask, "Are you certified to wed couples?"

The priest nodded.

"Good, because a church wedding is no good unless it's recognized by the state as well," he said to Meinhof. Then to the priest, "Let's get on with it, Father. We want to be united under the eyes of God and the state, albeit a fascist pig state."

The priest tried to look through Meinhof's veil. "Are you entering into this willingly?"

"Very," she said with ebullience.

The clergyman shrugged his shoulders and paged through the great Bible on the lectern.

The ceremony started without a hitch and, aside from the nun having to be twice revived from fainting spells, it was the most beautiful and perfect wedding that Meinhof could imagine.

Dimly lit by a pale-yellow moon that streamed through the ornate stained glass windows, and bathed in the flickering shadows of multiple votive candles gathered by Baader, the altar was mystically romantic. Wind rushed from the window above and blew through the pipes of the organ so that the ceremony had musical accompaniment, compliments of nature's chaotic hand.

At a critical part of the ceremony the priest paused.

Baader shoved his rifle into his ribs.

"What are you waiting for, old man? Can't you see that we are two revolutionaries in love and we cannot bear to have our love go unrecognized and unofficiated for a moment longer?"

The priest turned white, but held his ground. "I need your names. I can't say 'Do you, so-and-so, take this man...' Unless I know your names the wedding will never be official."

Baader frowned and whispered to Meinhof, "If we tell him our names, we'll have to kill him."

Meinhof gasped under her DKNY veil. "But darling, if we kill him, how could we live with ourselves? Although we would be married in deed, we would not be married in essence. Blood shed would assassinate any legitimacy our wedding once had."

Baader slammed an open hand to his head, stymied by the

irony of his plight. He turned back to Meinhof. "Then we'll have to take our chances. We may be signing a death warrant by giving up our identities, but if that's what it takes to marry you, Ulrike Meinhof, then so be it."

Andreas turned to the priest and, pulling the ski mask off his face, said proudly, "Our names are Andreas Baader and Ulrike Meinhof."

Once again their impromptu witness fainted as the echo of his statement rang through the all but empty church.

The priest eyed the two terrorists and, looking at Baader, asked, "And which one are you?"

Baader rolled his eyes and spat out, "Baader. I'm Baader. She's Meinhof."

Nodding, the priest turned his head back to the Bible. "Right, right. Well, you never know with you kids and your crazy names…"

Again Baader shoved his gun into the priest's ribs and whispered harshly, "Get on with it, old man! My love cannot wait."

The priest blanched, but continued, "Do you, Meinhof, take Baader to be your lawfully, or perhaps in your case, unlawfully wedded husband."

Tears rimmed Meinhof's eyes as she examined the trim and darkly handsome man beside her with a gun in one hand and a freshly stolen gold band in the other.

"I do," she uttered.

"And do you, Baader, take Meinhof to be your wedded wife, until death do you part?"

Baader gazed down on Meinhof with deep feeling roaring in his eyes. "I do."

"You know the drill. Exchange rings and kiss," the priest intoned nonchalantly.

Baader looked as if he might give the Father another poking, but instead broke into a smile. He gently slipped the simple gold ring on Ulrike's finger and engulfed his wife in a warm embrace and a passionate kiss that sang through her veins.

Meinhof knew now nothing could separate the undying and everlasting love shared by them. She was united with Baader at last. United in an anti-imperialist struggle. Urban guerrillas united against the bourgeoisie. Man and woman comrades made one against the ruling class. Righteous rebels fighting for the masses. A brave new world swirled around them as Ulrike Meinhof surrendered to the ardent kisses of Andreas Baader.

Then a voice over a megaphone broke through her bliss.

"Put your hands up, Baader and Meinhof. We have you surrounded!"

The two terrorists tore themselves from one another's lips and looked around.

The priest had run away and had apparently dragged off the unconscious nun too. The church was now filled with police, each pew lined with the rounded tops of riot-gear helmets.

Baader looked at Meinhof and she at him. She gave him a smile and a nod, telling him with her eyes that it was all worth it.

Baader tapped his bulletproof vest and said, "Thank you, Helmut Lang."

He pulled a gun from his utility belt and shot a grappling hook to the stained glass windows above. The hook shattered the glassine eye of the baby of Nazareth and caught on a roof railing.

With one arm around Meinhof's waist, and amidst a rain of bullets, Baader pushed a button on the device and the two went flying toward the rooftop. On her ascent Meinhof drew out her Prada-designed AK-47 and took out a few storm troopers kneeling in the pews.

Amidst a barrage of bullets they pulled themselves to the roof and searched for means of escape.

Spying the adjacent rectory, Baader casually asked, "So, how does it feel to be Mrs. Baader?"

Ulrike regarded him superciliously. "I thought we were going to hyphenate our name to Baader-Meinhof. You said it had a ring to it."

The two jumped in tandem from the church roof to the rectory, and from the rectory to a quiet alley where Baader hotwired a HUM-V parked conveniently in the rectory lot. He then carried Meinhof over the threshold of the car door, setting her gently in the passenger seat.

"Did I say that?" he asked, eyes shining like blue jewels.

"You most certainly did, Andreas Baader-Meinhof!"

They sped through the night while Meinhof picked flattened bullets from their lead-lined vests. And…and…?

As quickly as Mara fell into the daydream, she fell out of it.

It's a silly daydream, especially now that I'm trying to rid myself of Holden, Mara chastised herself.

She knew very well that being an outlaw probably wasn't as much fun as she imagined.

Things don't always turn out fine in the end. In fact, they have a nasty habit of doing just the opposite. For example, maybe designer bulletproof vests wouldn't hold up under police gunfire… And maybe Holden would just shoot the priest.

She thought of Regan's suspicions of Holden. Mara wondered if this is what it felt like to be underground: always suspicious and always vulnerable; waiting for the next bang to be the bullet that pierces your heart; to die an agonizing death…

The next day as she exited the dormitory, Mara heard a familiar masculine step at her heel. She knew at once who it was.

"Holden!"

Framed by the doorway, he looked wild and savage, yet deeply refined.

"Mara! Where have you been? I've been trying to get a hold of you." Holden pleaded with his eyes.

Mara averted her gaze as she spoke. "Holden, I— we can't do this anymore. I can't live under this reign of secrecy. I want out."

Holden shriveled a little at her words. "What do you mean, out? What secrecy? Mara, what's going on?"

Mara wanted to explain, but suddenly became tired of the games and knew Holden would always have an explanation for everything. She also knew that she could never resist Holden's devastating charm.

"Let me see your driver's license, Holden," she asked, trying a new tactic.

"Why?"

"Just let me see it!" Mara demanded.

Holden shrugged, pulled a worn, calfskin wallet out of his back pocket and took his I.D. out.

"Here, but what's this all about?"

Mara didn't answer, but instead examined the card. Even under the horrible lighting conditions Holden's I.D. photo looked fabulous. Mara pried her reluctant eyes off the picture and looked at the name.

"Holden Chancy Rife."

The date was from September of that year.

Just as Regan said, it's a new license. She was right. Holden must have chosen a new name for psychotic or criminal reasons.

Mara peered up at him, wondering who he really was. "So, Holden is your real name then?"

Holden was perplexed. "Of course it's my real name. What do you mean?"

Now Mara was desperate, hoping against all hope that Holden would come clean. "I mean, is it the name your parents gave you?"

"Yes, it's my name!" Holden responded, exasperated now.

Mara set the trap and, to her despair, he fell right in. "Why did you get a new license then?"

"My wallet was stolen. Mara, what is this about?" Holden was doing a good job of conveying confused innocence.

But it's an old wallet!

Mara looked at the ground, dejected and heartbroken by his disingenuous demeanor.

Lies! Lies! It's nothing but thin, wavering tissues of lies and intrigue!

"It's about you and me being over, Holden. I can't take it. I can't take the secrecy and the emergencies and stories and— Holden, we're through."

Holden looked as if he saw his own death. "Through? Mara, we can't be through. 'Consider the lilies, do they not bend with the weight of the wind? So, too, shall we bend, and by toiling not and bending, become stronger within the storm.' Mara, the storm is about to pass. Can't you just wait until the Games are over? Then I'll pull out of the group and we can have a life of our own."

Mara laughed weakly. "Wait until the 'games' are over? And when would that be, 'Holden'? You just don't get it do you? The damage has already been done. We're through."

"Mara, What do you want of me?" He shook his head regretfully.

Mara's face became hard and cold. What could she say that could make any difference? Could she live with herself if she joined forces with a man who had possibly murdered Rosa and perhaps countless other girls for unknown reasons? A man who was possibly planning something nefarious for the community of Norden during the Baader-Meinhof Games?

He was standing so close that Mara was instantly reminded how virile he was. There was strength in the tanned column of his neck and in his shoulders, a force evident even when defeated, as he looked now. She dropped her gaze to his bare forearms with their covering of fine, dark hairs, to his hands, fearless but sensitive, and finally to his denim-encased thighs, lithely muscled and powerful. Even his tender lips conveyed an abundance of power and masculinity as his tongue glided over their terrain unconsciously.

"Holden, I'll be Ulrike Meinhof for the Games, but after that we're through. I—I don't love you any more." Mara lied, but she thought only a lie would get Holden out of her life.

Holden gripped the door frame as she uttered those words, crumpling slightly. "So be it, Mara," he winced. "I just thought—No. It doesn't matter. You're right to leave me. Just leave now, before I'm unable to help myself, before I try to win you back."

She looked at his face, beautiful and creased with pain. Mara took his warning and ran away. By the time she reached the old oak tree with the initials of lovers carved inside hearts, tears streaked her lovely face. She felt hollow, as if her very life force had been squeezed out of her and all that was left were raw sores on an aching heart.

When Mara returned from the library late that evening she ran into Regan in the dorm hallway.

"Oh, hey, Regan." Mara tried to sound less despondent than she felt.

Regan walked toward her excitedly. "Mara, just the person who I was looking for. I've got some great news. Do you have a second?"

Mara gave her a cheerless smile. "Not really, I'm sort of bummed out. I just want to go to bed."

Regan followed her down the hall. "Well then, this will cheer you up."

Mara stopped at the door, not wanting to let Regan in her room. Regan was her friend, but she couldn't help but feel jealousy over her special relationship with Holden.

"Did Rosa show up?" Mara asked.

Regan's eyes widened. "Show up? What do you mean, show up?" she demanded and then softened her tone as she opened the door and let herself in. "Mara, you got to face the facts, Rosa is probably in a dumpster somewhere, or fertilizer for another organic garden. She's gone. No, Holden got out because he has the best lawyer money can buy, and, without a body, there isn't much they can do, even if his DNA is on the scarf."

"It is?" Mara exclaimed as she followed Regan into her room and set her heavy backpack on her desk.

"I don't know, but it wouldn't surprise me. Holden is a man of many secrets. He doesn't tell me every time he offs a girl."

Now Mara was becoming very upset. "He told you he killed someone?"

"No, but he did tell me that Rosa got on his nerves."

"That's not the same thing, Regan!" Mara said with rising impatience.

"It is if you're a psychopath who murders anyone who gets in your way," Regan responded.

Mara couldn't deny Regan's logic, and yet her mind was rioting against drawing the same conclusion. "I guess you're right. That's why I called things off with him."

"Off! You can't! Not after all the trouble I went through!" Regan spewed and stood upright.

"Don't worry, Regan, I'm still in the Games. I gave you guys my word and I always follow through. After the Games, though, I'm out."

Regan slipped back to her delinquent-slouch. "After the Games? Oh, right. Good, that's what I wanted to tell you about. You know, since Rosa's gone and Holden might go to jail any time, I'm back to choosing the targets. Which means I won't have time to take Rosa's part in the Games. Do you think you could?"

Mara sank into her chair. "But I'm Meinhof."

"Yeah, well Meinhof's a minor character. She dies early on, afterward you can be Susanne Albrecht."

The name sounded familiar to Mara. "She's the one who…"

Regan waited to see if Mara could finish the sentence on her own before she completed it. "Who brings the flowers to the capitalist-pig-businessman's door. Then the flower bomb goes off and they die a horrible death."

Mara remembering reading that only the banker died. "Weren't guns hidden in the flowers? And didn't Susanne survive?"

"Right, guns. It's hard to keep it all straight, you know."

Mara nodded, she could barely keep up with her own life, much less the lives of a bunch of dead and/or jailed Germans. "So who's the banker? Have you chosen the target?"

"You probably haven't heard of him. He's a fascist journalist. Bismarck Vernal. A real enemy of the people. I mean, talk about manufacturing media consent? That guy is in everyone's back pocket."

The name was familiar to Mara, but she couldn't quite place it. "So does he know yet?"

"No, no one knows. It's like Publisher's Clearinghouse—they find out when we go to their door. I only told you, so don't tell anyone, not even people in the group. And, Mara, don't tell Holden and especially not the galloping gossips, Tippy and Penny."

Mara was growing tired. "Yeah, all right. I'll do it. Can I get some sleep now?"

Regan gave Mara a sympathetic smile. "Mara, I understand. I broke up with him too. But you know, there is life after Holden, trust me. I've been there. And don't worry if he starts bad-mouthing you like he did me." Regan guffawed, "He's even saying I'm the reason he was arrested, that I made up the threat

he gave Rosa. Can you believe it? It's all part of how he recon-
structs his sick ego."

Regan kissed Mara's cheek and left. Mara shut off her light
and stared into the darkness.

The days before the Baader-Meinhof Games dwindled
uneventfully. Mara kept her distance from Holden and ignored
as best she could his pained expressions during the preparation
meetings for the Games.

Despite Rosa's disappearance the group decided to continue
with the Games, but morale was low.

Apocalypse was on pins and needles, worried sick about
Rosa. Her complexion suffered the most. Harassed by crops of
pimples, whiteheads, and red rough areas, it looked as if the end
of the world had made its resting-place her face.

Eric, hearing that Mara and Holden were no longer an item,
made his version of shameless passes at Mara: "Hey, Mara, did
you know that eating meat and oppressing women are intimately connected?" and "Studies have shown that meat eaters
are three times more likely to suffer from premature ejaculation
than vegetarians." His efforts were to no avail; Mara's interest in
him was as nonexistent as his underwear.

Rat wouldn't even say hello to her, but, had Mara been
observant, she would have noticed him constantly staring at her
out of the corner of his eye. Mara hardly noticed anyone in the
group as all was obscured by her continued preoccupation with
Holden. The work for the Games kept everyone so busy that no
one bothered to acknowledge that Holden was still the only
suspect in the disappearance of Rosa, or that Mara was sinking
into the dullness of depression.

Highest on the list of the Reading Group's tasks was the creation of a fake newspaper to chronicle the Baader-Meinhof
Games. Entitled *Baader-Meinhof Daily*, but abbreviated to the
affectionate *B-M Daily*, it chronicled the reenacted crimes of
the day before, providing both historical meaning and contemporary rationalizations. The group also circulated a program
that listed the time and location of Baader's jailbreak, court pro-

ceedings, Death Night, and funeral services. Since only Regan knew the names and locations of all the targets, she was responsible for writing the *B-M Daily*.

"*The Daily* is the most important part," she told Mara as they drove to Holden's house for a meeting. "It's called pedagogy. It's what we're about. Without the explanation we're just a bunch of whiners in the eyes of the masses."

Mara nodded. She didn't care anymore.

Mara completed her chores for the Games like a drone. She role-played bank robberies, police shoot-outs, and car-jackings on automatic pilot. She didn't want to feel anything because that would require being aware of the searing pain of giving up Holden. Holden had anchored her life at Norden. Without him she was like a small sailboat in the big blue ocean. A sailboat without a rudder or GPS, lost at sea and tossed back and forth by the force of the tide, subject to every rush of a storm. Mara wasn't sure there was life after Holden.

Don't think I can't hear you, oozing with superiority.

"Please!" you're thinking, "why is Mara is such a drip?"

So now you are better than Mara.

Interesting.

Has it ever occurred to you why no one has ever written your love story? Why you don't grace the pages of a romance manifesto?

The difference between you and Mara is "romance."

You don't have it.

She does.

You fall under one of three categories.

One, you are still waiting for the proper love object. On weekends you perform a pathetic ritual of aping the latest fashion, dragging your sorry ass to the party/café/Laundromat/bar/7-11. You stand around in ill-fitting clothes and form-hugging faults, trying not to appear as stupid as you are when talking to the opposite/same sex. It's embarrassing to witness your desperation as you pitch yourself at your chosen object of desire.

Two, you are moping because you a) met/slept with/dated/married the "perfect" love object for you, but b) they hate you/you dumped them, and now c) they won't have you back/not only are they not interested in you but d) they asked for your best friend's number/they put a restraining order on you/they don't know that you are obsessed with them and still wouldn't give you the time of day if they did.

Three, you are currently with someone and a) you desperately convince yourself that they are the proper love object for you, b) you know you've settled for a mediocre object and tell yourself that "settling" is part of becoming a mature adult, c) you know that your partner is a huge mistake and you'd dump him/her if you weren't so afraid of dying alone, or d) you know that your partner is a huge mistake and you'd dump him/her if you didn't know with an overwhelming certainty that you're not such a great catch yourself.

I shouldn't discount the fourth option, that you are a romantic, a rebel warrior for whom love is as necessary as air and as widespread as gays in the military. Perhaps you, like Mara, wage the bloody battle for the brass ring of love on the carousel of life.

If so, I applaud you. If not, scoff at Mara all you want for having a love she could die for. At least she hasn't settled. At least she has a worthy object choice and is fighting the valiant fight. This resentment of Mara's romance has more to do with the pitiful state of your affairs⬛ *than with her. You're just jealous.*

Yes, you!

One the eve of the Games, Mara returned to her dorm room to see Penny and Tippy sitting on her bed.

"No way, you guys, I can't hang out," Mara insisted flatly. "I'm way too tired. The Games are tomorrow, you know. How did you get in here anyway?"

Green shot her a vicious look. She stood up and put her mud-laden face against Mara's, her fraudulent breasts grazing Mara's shoulders. "Listen, Wad! You've been avoiding us, and I, for one, don't like to be avoided. You know, we've been pretty

---

⬛ The word "affair" is too accurate a word here, isn't it? So now you know. What are you going to do with him? My suggestion? Set him free. We romance guerrillas have a credo: "If you love someone, set him free. If he comes back to you, then keep him. If not, then pay for therapy and get over it."

good to you. Watched out for you and stuff. It's so not cool to blow us off. Isn't that right?"

Blue was looking a little worried. "I guess, but hey, take it easy. Mara's our friend, remember."

Mara tried to back away but found herself up against her door looking up Green's surgically altered nose.

"I'm sorry. It's not personal. I've been really busy and I just haven't felt like company."

Green didn't budge an inch. "Guess what? It doesn't matter. You have responsibilities to us and you've been neglecting them. I know when I'm being dissed."

Mara was sure she was inhaling the very air Green was exhaling.

Gosh, Green is really mad, what should I do?

Then Blue came to Mara's rescue. "Aren't you overreacting?" she asked Green and went over to Mara, putting her arm around her slender waist. "Don't listen to her Mara, she just misses you. I miss you too."

She led Mara to her bed and whispered conspiratorially, "You may not believe it, but we don't have many friends, so we have to hold on to the ones we have."

Blue gave Mara a little squeeze on the shoulder and Mara felt a sharp prick, followed by a stinging sensation.

"Ouch!" Mara exclaimed, pulling away from Blue and rubbing her shoulder.

Green rushed over. "What's wrong now? Can't handle affection?"

Mara's head was whirling around. "No, I felt something."

"It's called 'emotion,' Mara," Green snapped. "Open your heart to your friends. Don't be so damn cold."

Mara massaged her shoulder. The pain was subsiding and a serene warmth was taking over. She sat down, forgetting what she wanted to say. She looked at her two friends and suddenly felt her heart pulse and fill with happiness until she thought it would burst. It suddenly amused her that two of her best friends were colors. Mara knew there was deeper meaning in there somewhere but couldn't quite tease it out.

"You guys are the best!" she tilted her head. "But what's with those boxers you always wear?"

Blue and Green looked down at their boxer shorts and back to Mara in silence.

Green finally asked, "Don't you know?"

Mara laughed.

I'm so stupid, she thought and then answered, "No."

Blue, quietly stunned at Mara's ignorance, held out the bottom of her men's underwear. "They're victory shorts."

"Oh, I see," Mara said, not seeing at all.

"Mara, what it means is that the next morning, you know, after you sleep with a guy, you say to them, 'I couldn't possible wear the same,' and then you fill in what you need: hat, socks, T-shirt, coat, whatever. 'I couldn't possibly wear the same shirt that I wore last night. Then people will know we slept together.' Right? So the guy provides you with said article of clothing and there you go. He's not gonna say no after you just slept with him. It would look ungrateful. Later, he's too embarrassed to ask for it back because he's guilty he hasn't called you or for having a one-night stand, or maybe he just doesn't want to see you again. Doesn't matter why, the outcome is a victory shirt! Or victory hat or victory boxers, whatever. It's a proud addition to any girl's wardrobe. A keepsake with a practical applica-tions." Blue pointed to her boxers, "These, my dear, are victory shorts."

Mara giggled as she thought how funny it would be to sleep with someone for just an article of clothing. She tried to remember if there was anything of Holden's worth borrowing.

Maybe that Helmut Lang bulletproof vest. Oh wait, that was in my fantasy. Plus, I never even slept with Holden.

Mara frowned with the knowledge that she would never know what it would be like to be truly united with Holden Rife.

"Mara, what is it? What's wrong?" Blue asked.

Mara hung her head. "I broke up with Holden."

Blue knelt at Mara's feet looking up at her tear-streaked face. "What? When?"

"After the night he got arrested. I just couldn't take the secrets, the lies, and the unhealthy adoration of tried and con-victed terrorists."

Mara threw her head in her hands.

Green stood over Mara, stoking her hair. "You take your time, Mara. And when you're ready, you'll tell us all about Holden and everything you know about the Baader-Meinhof Games."

Mara sat silently for a good five minutes, and then she began to talk.

CHAPTER 10

It was a fine autumn day. The air smelled of wood stoves, fallen leaves, and apple crisps with plenty of cinnamon and nutmeg. Although the sun possessed the strength to burn frost off the lush green lawns of Norden College and warm the midday air, its rule was weaker and it fell from the heavens ever earlier each night. Stringy, food-stressed squirrels dragged nothing smaller than half-eaten bagels out of trashcans in preparation for their winter hibernation. Certain species of birds made Vs in sky while Norden students made beelines to Barney's Summer Clearance Sale.

Others at Norden College were also preparing for the threat of winter. The grounds and maintenance staff took to wearing caps with earflaps and red scarves. They looked to the sky with a scowl every so often, as if challenging it to snow. Female students, in defiance of the weather, still walked around in next to nothing, flaunting their dewy, supple limbs. This pleased the North Campus groundskeeper, Dave, just fine.

He liked the ever-changing supply of *freshies*. That's what he called young girls: "freshies." Dave knew how they extended their wardrobe during their three-season school year by wearing summer clothes in the early fall and fall clothes at the onset of winter, winter clothes only when the wind-chill was below zero, and spring clothes once the thermometer went above thirty-two degrees again. Dave knew how their need to model four seasons of clothes left long stretches of time with large expanses of skin exposed to his flesh-hungry eyes. He knew and approved.

Dave talked to himself about *freshies* and other things.

"Too bad about that Rosa girl being gone," he said. "Not exactly a looker, but I wouldn't kick her out of my bed," he mumbled as he picked up programs for the Baader-Meinhof Games tossed to the ground by an apathetic student body.

If anyone had asked Dave where Rosa was, he'd tell 'em

straight off. Sure he might talk about the weather, the pros and cons of the new stitching on Dickies, and maybe spend a moment or two commenting on the evils of chewing gum. But after that—boy, howdy!—he'd have an earful to tell them.

Dave thought Norden College underutilized him.

Who cares for a school more than the groundskeeper? Nobody. Not them dime-store janitors. A bunch a loafers, the whole lot of them. Unionized so they could take long lunch breaks while hallways fill with dirt and the bathrooms teem with AIDS and Ebola. But old Dave always comes to the rescue, always ties up the loose ends, he thought as he did just that to the garbage bag outside the administration building and threw it in the dumpster in the rear.

Dave was no slouch. He got the job done and without complaint. What's more, Dave listened and watched. He knew the names of most of the students and he discovered more about them than anyone could suspect.

"Trash talks," he said out loud. Three students walking by gave him wide berth.

Dave worked his way to a table where a young man with drawings on his face was sitting at a table covered with the very programs and pamphlets he'd spent the last half-hour picking up.

He looks like the Sunday comics.

The illustrated young man was picking at his hair.

"Thinks he doesn't have to show manners in front of old Dave."

Dave scratched his head.

Sure, I could tell him he made a grave mistake and he should get that junk off of his face before he gets skin decay. What's more, no one cares about whatever it is he's trying to peddle. I should know. I've picked up a half a bushel full. And he won't care either two years after he graduates, by gum! If he graduates. I doubt he's a student. Looks more like a grease monkey.

Dave never put his nose in anywhere it wasn't wanted. "If the circus freak is too stupid to ask for Dave's help, Dave sure as shit isn't going to offer it."

Dave trudged past Rat and found a pile of crumpled pamphlets stuffed in a bush not three feet away from an empty trash receptacle.

"Kids. Don't know what's important. Don't know their bellybuttons from a screwdriver in the ground and think everything that comes out of their body is a tasty frozen treat. I still have a thing or two to show them."

Dave knew his butt crack showed when he bent over to pick up programs, but he didn't care.

"Let 'em look," he muttered. "Maybe they'll learn something."

He silently swept up at least a quarter of a bag's worth of pamphlets from the Reading Group.

"Don't know shit from Shinola. Smart-ass kids with their ninety-eleven pamphlets."

He spat a phlegm-ball into a trashcan and proceeded to the café deck.

As he passed the blond kid who was always covered in white dust, Dave thought, *Always liked the squirt. Smells real.*

James was sitting with Regan, who was looking through a bag filled with guns and bombs.

Always with that eyebrowless good-for-nothing, Regan. Don't know when he's being used... Dave shook his head and spoke under his breath, "Girl can buy anything and everyone but can she buy herself a pair of eyebrows?"

Regan looked up from the duffel bag that was as covered in fine white dust as its owner and issued Dave a scathing look.

Dave nodded at her threat, acknowledging it without engaging it. "You can't buy me so easy, Missy."

He continued to mumble his way along the tables at the café. Dave paused as he passed two girls with matching highlighted manes drawn up in banana clips sitting behind Regan. They were scrunched down low in their booth, whispering softly to one another.

"Pretty fishy, if you ask me," he said at the girls who, in addition to always skulking around, were trying a speck too hard to fit in by his estimation.

The one with the huge assets winked at him and put a long nailed finger to her mouth and pointed behind her.

That's all right by me if they want to play spy games with the kids who are playing terrorists. Dave swept under their feet at a phantom piece of dirt in order to get a better view of the winker's bosom.

"Shouldn't you be graduated by now?" was his parting commentary as he swept his way to the commons.

Pushing through the crowds of kids came one of his favorite freshies: Mara.

Self-absorbed pumpkin-head, he thought, as she shot past him and the two crouching girls without a half a glance. *I like 'em like that. That way they don't know what you're up to until you're halfway done.*

Mara rushed past the groundskeeper who was always talking to himself and took a seat at the table of James and Regan.

"Sorry I'm late! It's—" Mara cut herself off before she explained that Tippy and Penny had stopped by.

James brightened visibly when Mara sat down. While finishing the last-minute specifications on the props he had been thinking of all the different ways he could ask her to pose nude for a sculpture of a nymph. But now, in her rosy-cheeked, parted-lips presence he was tongue-tied.

Mara smiled at him openly. "Good morning, James. Did you get the props done?"

James' foot started tapping, causing white dust to fly up from his plaster-encrusted coveralls. He looked to the ground and smiled sheepishly.

"It's all good." Then he cursed himself silently, *What does that even mean?*

Mara nodded and looked to Regan.

She's so cool, thought Mara.

Regan was wearing her red hair straight down and her bangs were freshly cut straight across her barren brow. She was outfitted in a tight, unbecoming black sweater and pre-sullied jeans. Her deep-set eyes were blackly lined, contrasting with her sharp, white face. There was an inch-long line of wax, posing as a scar above her right penciled-in brow. Mara gasped at the similarity.

"Regan, you look just like her."

James, finding his more articulate voice, asked, "Who?"

Mara answered, thankful to appear knowledgeable at least to someone. "Gudrun Ensslin, one of the leaders of the B-M group. You look super great, Regan."

Regan smiled tolerantly. "I'm supposed to look post-partumly depressed."

James looked from one girl to the other, then proclaimed, "I thought you and Holden were the leaders, Mara. Aren't you guys Baader and Meinhof?"

Regan's eye seized. "That will be all, James," she said through its convulsions. "I'm sure Holden will be pleased with the workmanship of the props."

James shot a wistful glance at Mara who was too preoccupied to notice he was being dismissed. Then he shrugged and left. Doing a double take at the young women crouched in the booth behind Mara and Regan, he made dusty, white footprints across the North Campus.

"So, what's on tap today?" Mara was trying to sound nonchalant even if everything about the Baader-Meinhof Games was making her stomach churn.

Regan gauged the question for a moment before she answered. "It's 'We Must Arm Ourselves! Day' with the demonstration against the Shah of Iran. Eric's playing Benno Ohnesorg. He gets shot and I run into a SDS meeting," Regan registered Mara's confusion, "—that's Social Democratic Students—and say, and I quote, 'They'll kill us all. You know what we're up against. That's the generation that built Auschwitz we've got against us! You can't argue with the people who made Auschwitz! They have weapons and we don't.' (Or is it 'we haven't?')"

Regan fumbled around with her notes. "Ah-ha!—'kill us all... blah, blah, blah—the people who made Auschwitz...' Euh! Okay, 'They have weapons and we haven't! We must arm ourselves.' Thus starts the revolution. I also meet a certain failed artist, Andreas Baader." Regan kept a close eye on Mara when she said that name.

Mara winced. "That reminds me, Regan, I have a favor to ask."

Regan raised her pencil-lined brow.

"Can I be excused from the Games until you need me? Day…"

Regan rolled her eyes but filled in the information. "Day five, 'RAF Day.' I don't see why not, if you're heart isn't in it. We don't really need the people. We have a group from Hampton College busing in to help with the demonstration reenactment."

Mara stiffened and thought, *If Regan only knew. I don't want to be there because my heart is too much in it. I don't think I can handle watching Regan and Holden together in terrorist bliss, even if it's just pretend. The decision to go without him is hard enough when he's not around. When he's near me, it's unbearable. I don't know what I'd think if I saw him in the arms of another woman.*

Mara exhaled with relief. "Thanks for understanding. I'll use the time to practice the prison break scene. I'm—I'm not looking forward to it."

"Right, the Holden thing. Don't worry, it'll go fast. Day six is 'Capitalism Must Fund Its Own Demise! Day,' so you won't have to see him at all that day. Then it's the trial and prison and after that you kill yourself. That's the last you'll have to see of Holden, because after 'Violence is the Highest Form of Class Struggle! Day' you're playing Susanne Albrecht and she's in the second generation of the RAF. The two generations do not hang."

A little voice in Mara's head reassured her, *The ten days will go by fast.* A deeper voice, nestled even farther in the recesses of her mind warned, *That's what you're afraid of.*

Mara left, passing the set of strangely scrunched-down students without a second glance. She breezed by the Baader-Meinhof Games information tables without saying hello to Rat, or even noticing his adoring look in her direction turn into a gloomy glower. Immersed in maudlin musings, she didn't become aware of the groundskeeper in her path until she walked right into him.

"Excuse me!" Mara said in her voice of silken oak.

"The vision talks, it seems," Dave responded, not disliking that she bumped into him.

On the contrary, he purposely put himself in her path

hoping to discover her scent before he had to empty the trash at quad four.

Mara scrutinized the grizzled, not-so-old man whom she had seen uttering soliloquies to the wind. Simultaneously hearty and dilapidated, he looked like one of those people who could lose a tooth as easily as one might misplace their keys and with less complaint. She was surprised that he could address something other than the air around him and wondered what other secrets he hid from the world.

"You weren't the one who found Rosa's scarf the other day, were you?" Mara queried.

Dave had a twinkle in his eye. "A man don't look for things that ain't lost, now, does he?"

Her tone became chilly. "What do you mean by that?"

Dave leaned forward and lowered his voice. "What I mean is if I were looking for something that was lost, I'd sooner look for you than I'd look for Rosa."

She peered into his loose, red, inscrutable face. "But I'm not lost."

"Sure, and grits ain't groceries."

Mara scratched her head. "Are you trying to tell me something?"

"Depends." His voice, although quiet, had an ominous quality.

In spite of her reserve, a tinge of exasperation came through her reply, "Well then I don't get you."

Dave took some time to look her over, close up, "Of course *you* don't get *me*, Mara. That is a dictum of language. 'I' don't get 'you' either. The only thing 'I' gets is 'me' or 'I.' And for 'you' it's the same. Personally, you'll never occupy or retain 'you.' Unless you jump out of your skin. Which, believe me, is not pretty."

Mara was beginning to wonder if the man was a few currants short of a fruitcake. "What are you talking about?"

There was a hushed stillness virtually unknown to college campuses and Dave's voice dropped in volume. "Let's just say that 'we' are one, but if you're going to 'you' and 'me' everything 'I' get confused. See 'me' and 'you' are empty signifiers. 'We' have to anchor them down with additional meaning. I have to give up my 'I' before 'you' can speak it, then 'I' take your 'you' while 'you' use my 'I' or maybe even my 'me.' It's all about taking turns or the whole thing gets thrown out of whack, 'you' see? Or do 'I' see? You see? Much too confusing. But say we're a 'we,' then 'we're' talking? Aren't we?"

Dave inched his way closer to Mara as he spoke, causing her degree of discomfort to rise.

"I got to go," she said and walked away from the bizarre man.

He yelled after her, "No, 'I' got to empty trash. But if 'I' were 'you,' and you are, I'd beware the flowers. They've got more than thorns these days."

Mara waited until she rounded a shrub and then started running.

Freak! she thought, gladly widening the distance between them.

Dave watched her go, chuckling softly. "Hee, hee, hee. I can fancy-talk with the best of them."

He bent at the waist to pick up another program, giving Rat a privileged view of his derrière.

It was no surprise to Mara that she couldn't stay away from the Games. When she returned to the café for lunch James asked whether she planned to watch the Baader-Meinhof protest and the SDS meeting. Mara wanted to decline, but realized her curiosity would win out in the end and so agreed to go with him after dinner.

Together they drove to Norden Town's park to catch the student protest of "We Must Arm Ourselves! Day." With the police investigation of Rosa's disappearance and a rich and handsome Norden student as the only suspect, the whole town came out to see if they could rub shoulders with scandal. In addition to the thrill seekers was a group of masked, bonnet-wearing men and women in diapers or footed pajamas holding signs that read, "The Abies are behind you, Regan!" with an image of a "behind" falling out of a diaper, and "Adult Babies won't snubby Nappies made by Chubby."

Mara and James had to sit on a city mailbox to see over the throng of spectators. From atop her perch Mara watched the staged student protest against the Shah of Iran.

"I think that's Rat! Oh, it's hard to tell when he wears makeup," Mara exclaimed excitedly.

She was impressed with the degree of realism the Baader-Meinhof Reading Group employed. Even the seventies activist costumes looked authentic. Mara felt a pang of sadness when she remembered that Rosa had designed them.

Over the din, Mara heard two ladies of retirement age discussing the Games. One was wearing a red and green Christmas sweater with felt candy canes and presents sewn on. The other sported lavender earmuffs, a lilac turtleneck, and a large, purple sweatshirt with a giant teddy bear juggling striped balls on the front.

The Christmas-sweater lady peered through opera glasses and whispered, not very quietly, into the other's earmuff, "See the tall one with a gypsy's good looks? That's Holden."

Mara forced herself not to look in the direction the woman was pointing.

The Christmas lady handed her friend the glasses. The purple, teddy-bear lady adjusted the mini-binoculars and dropped her jaw.

"Oh, is that Baader? He is so good-looking! He has that velvet look Elvis had. I bet he's a killer with the ladies."

The Christmas lady nodded, creating an abundance of chins with every downward dip. "I think you don't pronounce the 'r.' It's more like 'Baddee,' with a hard 'd,' rhyming with 'paddy.' You don't know how apropos your lady-killer remark is! My neighbor's son is a police officer and he told her the whole precinct has had to take a crash course in Baddee-Meinhof history. They think they might find clues to that girl's disappearance and maybe those other girls on that organic farm cult. Apparently a girl in the Baddee-Meinhof gang was killed by her fellow gang members and buried in the woods just because she wanted to leave."

The purple lady pulled down her glasses and considered this piece of information.

"Oh that's awful. They're just like the mob! And look at these kids. With such a future ahead of them? So privileged! So ungrateful! Always yelling about the patriarchy. We should be so lucky to have a patriarch in office. All I see are little boys in the White House."

Christmas concurred, "Too much inbreeding, I suspect. Instead of bleeders the rich are producing terrorists these days. It's a pity." She reached out expectantly for the binoculars.

"You know what they say, 'Be careful of what you pretend to be!'" her friend responded as she reluctantly handed back the binoculars.

Mara silently wondered if those women's suspicions about Holden were correct. *Oh well, it doesn't matter any more. That's why I broke up with him in the first place…*

You must by now be thinking that the heroine of our story is an unbelievably shortsighted nitwit to believe it doesn't matter if Holden is a killer so long as she isn't dating him. You have to remember that our friend Mara is a narcissist, and, (as I stated previously) like all narcissists, she suffers from a mutilated ego.

Have pity on her then.

Why shouldn't a mutilated ego experience love?

Why can't monsters love other monsters? ⚑

Maybe you should ask yourself what exactly is your problem with her? (Don't think I haven't noticed you rejecting her.) Maybe you think love should be reserved for the pure of heart. Maybe you think love can only come to the gods and a few select movie stars. But where would humanity be with an attitude like yours?

Where would love be?

We humans are flawed beings. And yet, we are the only known conduits of love. Perhaps humans need narcissism to be in love. Perhaps it is this narcissistic blindness that allows us to believe we can succeed where others have failed, allows us to broach the boundaries, to take the risk. If love was a sure deal, would it be love, or would it be an arrangement?

⚑ After our revolution even those who collect dandruff on their bushy eyebrows will have access to love.

I know that "accepting criticism" is Chapter 10 of The Completely Oblivious Guide to Writing Romance, but don't forget that Chapter 2 says conflict is the fuse that turns your incendiary romance material into a bomb… ★

It's Mara's implausible stupidity that keeps the conflict in the book flowing. As Zen Master Shunryu Suzuki has said, ♪ *"If your mind is empty, it is always ready for anything: It is open to everything. In the beginner's mind there are many possibilities; in the expert's mind there are very few."*

So don't be so quick to judge her. Who else but this dazzlingly self-absorbed ingénue would be so easily molded by the many manipulative characters of this story and bring us to the brink of insanity without calling the police with all her suspicions? Moreover, who else could capture the heart of Holden Rife? ♪ *Certainly not you!* ♧ *Holden doesn't think much of your cynicism or your choice of reading. And while I'm certain that Holden would be interested in me, he's frankly not my type.*

Back to Mara, whose attention was dislodged by the sight of pseudo-German police officers shooting Eric, who was playing the part of Benno Ohnesorg. A crowd of students crouched around him as he mimicked the throes of death. One student with long red hair stood tall in silent outrage amidst the clearing smoke.

It was Regan.

James nudged Mara, "Nice smoke bombs, huh? They're mine."

Mara was too entranced to respond.

A pool of fake blood formed around Eric. A floodlight shone through the smoke and lit Regan's stark face. She looked imperially to the heavens and raised a fist.

"Benno!" Regan shouted, so that even the edges of the

★ My paraphrase.

♪ According to my Silk Vanilla Soy Drink carton.

♪ For reasons that still baffle me.

♧ Just go ask your husband. Oh. He's not home again? Hmm…

sizable crowd could make out her words. Her yell had the same marrow-chilling resonance as Brando's "Stella!"

The smoke cleared and Regan stood there like a Lenin statue, all chiseled and noble as she pledged for all humanity, "Benno! You will be avenged!"

The street cleared and Regan/Ensslin ran to an open-air stage on the other side of the park where members from the Baader-Meinhof Reading Group enacted an SDS meeting. Apocalypse used a bullhorn to direct the crowd's attention to the new venue.

Mara gasped when she saw Holden as Baader. She had not prepared herself for his stunning, masculine looks.

He was suave and swarthy in a scruffy two-day beard. A rumpled old Swiss military sweater hugged his upper body and dirty jeans conformed to the magnificent lines of his legs, the denim folds dancing around his waist and thighs, revealing and deliriously concealing the outline of his manhood.

Holden had a natural talent for acting and he seemed custom-fit to play the charismatic Andreas Baader. He moved around the outdoor theater like a boxer or a caged wildcat. The rest of the Reading Group was there as well, but Mara only had eyes for her former love.

James, sensing Mara's conflicted feelings, gave her hand a squeeze while Holden yelled at the group.

"Why should we care about the state?" Holden/Baader asked the group. "It's a shithouse that has already been shat in!"

Just then Regan/Ensslin came running in and shouted, "We must arm ourselves!"

Her words commanded attention and Holden/Baader turned his striking head slowly.

Having seen some of the script, Mara recalled that his face was to emanate a wondering desire. She knew Holden well enough, however, to see the look he gave Regan was something far more heated and powerful than that. Mara shuddered as Baader/Holden embraced Ensslin/Regan under the setting sun.

The two held their amorous pose and Apocalypse bellowed that there was to be Baader-Meinhof parade to City Hall.

Mara had already seen enough.

"Take me home, James. I can't bear any more of this."

James promptly slid off the mailbox and held his art-roughened hand out to Mara.

Again she found herself wondering why she couldn't fall for a simple man like James, but Mara knew that she would only ruin him with her persistent desire for Baader/Holden.

Leaving the carnivalesque atmosphere behind, the two went back to the dorms, each silently caught in a painful snare of unrequited love.

According to the Baader-Meinhof Games pamphlet, the next day was called "Talking Without Action Equals Silence Day." It commemorated the bombing of the Kaufhaus and Schneider Department stores by Baader and Ensslin, along with their symbolic marriage.

In the company of James, Mara tortured herself again with the sight of Regan and Holden running gleefully hand-in-hand down the streets of Norden Town until they came to a GAP mega-store, replete with GAP Women, GAP Men, GAP Kids, GAP Maternity, GAP Body, and Baby GAP. There they planted two of James's fake bombs on the outside of the evil bourgeois establishment.

As they watched the theatrics, James told Mara a story he heard about the Baader-Meinhof Reading Group. "So, I guess a couple years ago they devoted a whole meeting to whether they should pretend-bomb the GAP or Banana Republic. Can you believe it? Some of them were in favor of bombing Banana Republic—just for the audacity of their name. I mean, it is true that they could only be more offensive if they called themselves 'Exploited Darkies' or something. Others were in favor of bombing the GAP due to its oppressive and tedious universality. A fight broke out during the meeting and the Banana Republic-ites won the vote of fists. That was when the B-M Reading Group decided only one person should choose the targets for the Games."

"Wow," Mara replied. "They really need to take a soporific."

"What's that?"

"It's like a chill pill, but smells better," Mara said.

James tossed his head around as a sign of affirmation, "Anyway, I guess all of their wrangling could have been avoided if just one of them knew that the same company, GAP Inc., owned both stores."

"Gosh," said Mara.

"Yeah, I know," said James.

James and Mara watched as Regan and Holden finished planting the bombs. Then Apocalypse and Rat brought large, cardboard cutout graphics of bombs exploding and pasted them over the window display, covering the current campaign's phrase, "For Every Generation." Next they took fake German police tape and blocked off the entire GAP storefront.

In the crowd of onlookers a girl Mara recognized as a regular sunbather on campus skimmed through a Baader-Meinhof Games pamphlet with growing annoyance. She flipped her long brown hair as she turned to her friends and said, "It says here that GAP stands for 'Generic Automaton Puppets,'" she read from the pamphlet and then looked up. "I don't get it. If we don't go to the GAP, where are we supposed to get cheap, reliable clothes?"

A short, equally bronzed young man with an FBI baseball cap said, "Maybe they're saying that off the rack is tacky and we should have all of our clothes custom made."

"No," her blonde friend disagreed as she adjusted a clear plastic bra strap, "I think that they want us to get all our clothes from the second-hand store like they do."

"Then they are seriously shortsighted," responded the young woman. "I mean where do they think their dirty old clothes come from? The old clothes tree? You have to have new clothes first."

The young man threw an arm around the brunette. "Don't worry, sugar, they probably just want us to wear all hemp clothes."

She snuggled into his arm. "I guess I can live without the GAP. As long as I don't have to dress like *them*…"

James guffawed.

Holden and Regan ran down the street. Mara, James, and

the rest of the spectators ran to catch up. The performers stopped in front of a new Ikea and Regan/Ensslin turned to Holden/Baader and shouted, "This is just the sort of junk that capitalist pigs want you to believe you need, but you do not!"

Holden/Baader nodded. "It is for these reasons that we are doing Germany a favor. After all, it is far better to burn a store than it is to own one!" Rat and Apocalypse slapped more cardboard cutouts of explosions and fire on Ikea's storefront as Holden grabbed Regan's hand and said, "Gudrun Ensslin, let us be symbolically married under the glowing ruins of these burning imperialist institutions."

This scripted display of affection caused grief and despair to tear at Mara's heart.

Holden/Baader bent to kiss Regan/Ensslin, but instead of making contact with her lips or cheek, he caught air.

What is that about? Mara wondered.

Mara and James skipped Ensslin and Baader's trial that evening because the thought of Regan and Holden in jail together came too close to some of Mara's personal jail fantasies involving Holden. She couldn't bear to see them played out with another woman.

Mara also skipped day three: "Praxis Youth: Revolution Outreach Day," when Holden/Baader and Regan/Ensslin were let out of prison pending the outcome of their appeal. The day celebrated the fledgling RAFians who had teach-ins for kids in welfare homes.

The entire Baader-Meinhof Reading Group, save Mara, used the day as an opportunity to politicize Norden's youth by holding teach-ins at local high schools. The day culminated in a flurry of craft-making and face-painting at local grade schools. Apocalypse became quite adept at painting upraised fists and red stars on the chubby faces of Norden's youth.

Mara didn't feel bad about missing day four, "Five Fingers Are Not a Fist! Day." It covered the denial of Baader and Ensslin's appeals and their subsequent resolve to go underground. While in hiding, they fled Germany for Paris, then to Switzerland, Germany, Naples, and Germany again where Baader got caught en route to retrieve firearms that the RAF heard were buried in a graveyard. Day four was to draw attention to the importance of patronage by rich leftists, the *Schili,* who underwrote the RAF's travels.

Flattering rich leftists didn't bother Mara so much as the thought of watching Holden getting put under arrest again. Even if it was make-believe and for a cause, it made Mara edgy. It was too close to the thoughts that haunted her every day, thoughts that Holden might be a real criminal and responsible for the disappearance of Rosa.

Day five, "RAF Day," was, as it said in the pamphlet, "Red Army Faction or Righteous Alternative to Fat-Cats Day." It started with Holden/Baader in prison without possibility of appeal or parole. It was time for Ulrike Meinhof to save the day. Or that's how Mara liked to see it. It was the day Meinhof broke Baader out of jail, and Mara's first day participating in the Games.

For Mara, it came all too soon.

Mara was thankful that Rosa had at least made the Ulrike Meinhof costume before she vanished. Meinhof began as part of the establishment, so her outfit was dressier than Baader's and Ensslin's: a loose black sweater and black polyester pants. With a major hem job, it suited Mara's seductive young body and only needed a minor adjustment of trading the pants for jeans when she went underground.

Rosa also had provided two wigs: one a dark, short bouffant-style for when Meinhof was a member of the establishment; and then the "underground" wig, which was long and straight.

Mara was trying on the bouffant the morning of day five, when she heard a knock at her door.

It was, of course, Penny and Tippy.

"We have something for you, Mara!" Blue gushed.

Mara smiled nervously at her two friends and let them in.

They stood in the middle of her floor admiring Mara in her Meinhof outfit. Green examined her closely from behind her mud-mask.

"Wow, Mara, what a transformation! I didn't think you could ever be, like, a terrorist. But looking at you now, I can see it!"

Blue added, "Yeah, you're, like, dangerous! WATCH OUT!"

Mara chuckled apprehensively. "I got to go soon, you guys. Are you going to watch the Games?"

Blue looked at Green who shook her fluffy-haired head. "Naw, we've got a full beauty regimen scheduled this week... sorry. But maybe this will make up for it."

Green pulled out a little gold pin.

Mara brought it close to her attractive face and brushed a stray wig hair from her vivid, green eyes.

The pin was small—about the size of a dime—with a symbol on it Mara couldn't decipher: a capital "P" followed by a capital "A" and what looked like a circle with a vertical line through the middle: РАФ

Mara put a hand on Green's shoulder. "It's so beautiful, but what is it?"

Blue grinned a mask-cracking grin. "It's Rho Alpha Phi! Your own personal sorority!"

Mara maintained her confused expression.

Green explained, "Rho Alpha Phi is Greek for RAF! Those are Greek letters there. We figured that even if you aren't in a real sorority, you're in a three-lettered organization and that's close enough! Anyway, we thought you'd want something for luck. You know, with the suicide and flower delivery scenes."

"Gosh, I know, I'm so nervous about that day. I've never committed suicide before!" Mara looked at the gift that was charmingly inappropriate to the terrorist aesthetic.

To conflate a sorority with a revolutionary student activist group is just ding-y, she thought. *Or is it?* Mara reconsidered and immediately pinned it on her sweater.

Blue squeezed her knees together. "It looks so super-cool on you!"

"Thanks you guys! It's so thoughtful! I'm sure it will bring me good luck."

Mara had nervous butterflies in her stomach as she rode with Regan to Norden Town's park where the jailbreak would be staged. The crowd had doubled since the first day. Although their numbers were diluted by the Woodstock '99-like atmosphere, the diapered men and women could be spied among the spectators.

"Wow, there's so many people here," Mara said, her mind a blurry mixture of hope and fear.

"Yeah, and those damned Abies are still here," Regan said with quiet vehemence. Then she looked sideways at Mara. "Don't worry, everyone's here to see the real revolutionary masterminds, Gudrun Ensslin and Andreas Baader, reunited. People are coming from three towns over now to see our Games. It's great press for us. There's even a reporter from New York City. Just think if this was a real revolution! We'd be superstars!"

Mara nodded, but wondered if Regan wasn't wrong about the reason for the crowds.

Aren't they really here to see the man suspected of Rosa's probable murder?

Her suspicions were confirmed as she wove through the crowd. Again and again, she was identified by whispers saying, "That's her! That's the ex-girlfriend! Maybe she's next."

Her debut as Meinhof was coming up. Mara already practiced her lines. She wasn't a trained actor, but she knew about human psychology and how to sound realistic—quite a task considering the nature of her lines. When her time came, Mara spoke them with as much authenticity as she could loudly muster so that the crowd could hear her.

MEINHOF: So wait a minute, Gudrun Ensslin. I understand the struggle is important, but don't you think breaking the law for it is going too far?

ENSSLIN: What kind of revolutionary are you if you are not willing to stand up for the causes you believe are right? No kind of revolutionary that I know of. It is only the pampered activist—

—*The Abies went wild when Regan said "pampered"*—

—It is only the…coddled activists who have internalized the jingoism of the anti-revolutionary laws to the point of childish mimicry. They pay the oppressive state the taxes of the so-called "order" and "morality."

MEINHOF: [Ulrike chews on lips and wrings her hands.] Yes, but there is fear deep in my gut, Gudrun Ensslin.

ENSSLIN: Then you must learn, as I have, that fear gives courage wings!

MEINHOF: [Now on knees, grabs Ensslin's feet] I want to do it, but I am made of poorer stuff than you, Gudrun Ensslin.

ENSSLIN: [Looking upward in three-quarter profile] Either you come along or you stay forever an empty chatterbox!

MEINHOF: You have inspired me to do it. Although I am too weak to manage the task on my own, your courage will fortify my cowardly heart. Following your plans to the letter, I will help you, Gudrun Ensslin, help you to free your beloved.

ENSSLIN: Although you are merely *Schili* journalist scum and a revolutionary wannabe, I will show you the path to becoming part of the cadre so that your life can resound with meaning and your name may go down in history.

MEINHOF: For that, I thank you, Gudrun Ensslin. Although I fear I have tumbled into something that is bigger than me, too big for my inferior, bourgeois core to withstand.

[Actors pause for applause and quietly exit, stage right.]

Mara thought the scene went well, but she puzzled over the writing. While waiting for the next scene, she asked Regan about it.

"Why does Meinhof address Ensslin with her first and last name every time she speaks?"

Regan did not look up from her daily organizer. "I'm righting a wrong. If people take anything from 'RAF' day, I want them to remember who was the real revolutionary in the Red Army Faction: Gudrun Ensslin!"

Mara silently reminded herself to see if history painted Ulrike Meinhof as cravenly as Regan's script did.

After a quick lunch break, the prison breakout scene began.

Mara both anticipated and feared seeing Holden again as she climbed the steps to the stage while Apocalypse set up the scene for the audience, professionally barking through her megaphone.

"Gudrun Ensslin convinced Ulrike Meinhof to use her journalistic celebrity to get permission to work on a book with the imprisoned Andreas Baader," Apocalypse bellowed. "But it was all a ruse to get Baader out of prison and back in Gudrun's arms. Baader was granted permission to leave jail, under guard, to do research with Meinhof at the German Institute for Social Questions in Dahlem. It was there the RAF ambush took place."

Mara was led onto the stage by guards played by MK-Ultra and Rat. She awaited Holden/Baader, who arrived shortly after in handcuffs. Dressed in prison garb, Holden's sexy presence was overwhelming and Mara's heart lurched madly.

"Hello H-Andreas. Are you ready to do some research?" Mara said in her stage voice.

Holden/Baader looked at Mara with a deep, pained expression.

"Yes, I am ready, but how am I to look through books with my hands impeded by these chains?"

Mara/Meinhof wondered what was the nature of the sadness that hung around his hollowed eyes as she flatly delivered her line. "Guard, remove his chains. How is a man to study in chains?"

MK-Ultra roughly removed the handcuffs from Holden. Attention was then diverted to the antechamber, where two wig-wearing students, Ex-Pat and Regan, enacted their attempt to gain access to the private library.

Holden whispered to Mara, "Mara, Mara!"

Mara, looking down as if studying a book, responded quietly, "What, Holden?"

"Mara, do you remember when you said you would do anything for me?"

Mara almost sobbed out loud; the thought brought a rush of painful memories to her. "Y-yes, but things have changed…"

Holden looked up slightly and Mara stole a glance at his impossibly handsome face, more noble than ever with its soulful, tortured look.

"Mara, some things have changed, but not this. I know, if you look deep in your heart to the place that is untouched by all this chaos and gossip, if you look, you will find the part of you that still knows I would never ask you to do anything that would hurt you. It's like Jesus said, 'Blessed are those with faith in the stone casters, for it is they who shall see the rocks and stones themselves sing.'"

Mara didn't need to look so far as deep in her heart. All she needed to do was gaze on Holden's boldly strong features in their perfect glory to know that she could never resist him, at least to his face.

"Yes, Holden, I know that."

Holden bowed his head with relief and then spoke quickly and distinctly, "After Meinhof commits suicide, who are you playing?"

Mara noted the insistence in his voice and answered with haste, "Susanne Albrecht."

Holden hung his head. "It's just as I feared. Listen! I don't care what you do, but don't deliver those flowers! Do you hear me? There's something fishy going on. I don't know what it is, but I think I know who's behind it."

Before Mara could agree, Regan and Ex-Pat shot MK-Ultra and Rat. They broke into the library, tossing their wigs to the ground.

The prison break was nearly over. Mara knew that it would be the last time she'd allow herself to be so close to Holden. Her eyes feasted on his features and loved him.

Regan and Ex-Pat motioned for Mara and Holden to jump out the window.

Holden passionately grabbed Mara's arm and her skin thrilled beneath his iron grip. Holden wielded the might of his persuasive charm at Mara when he urged her in a ferocious whisper once more, "Promise me!"

Mara looked into his warm eyes with their long, dark lashes and melted.

"I promise, Baader."

As they jumped through a candy windowpane, Mara felt Regan's eyes like talons on her back.

CHAPTER 11

"No, really, you did a great job!" Regan patted Mara enthusiastically on the head as they pulled out of the park and away from the din of the third annual RAF Day Jailbreak Dance Party.

Mara ripped the bouffant wig off her head.

"Really?"

"Absolutely!" Regan affirmed.

Mara basked under Regan's encouragement. "Thanks, Regan!"

Regan turned onto the curving, tree-lined road that would lead them through the woods and eventually drop them at the foot of the Norden College campus.

"I wasn't so sure about the DJ this year," Regan sighed. "Do you think MK was right about old funk being the way to go? I thought that KMFDM and Atari Teenage Riot were more appropriate…"

Mara sank her itchy, lovely head into the passenger headrest, glad to be done with the long and grueling day.🖤

"The Atari group sings that song 'Fuck All,' right?"

"Yeah."

Mara thought for a moment. "What's KMFDM?"

"Well some people thinks it stands for 'Kill Mother Fucking Dépêche Mode.' But I happen to know that it's an acronym for 'No pity for the masses' in German."

Mara scratched at her head and pulled absently at her full bottom lip. "Well, maybe you're both right. Maybe KMFDM is more *appropriate,* but Rick James is more…um…festive." Mara's words started drifting off as the excitement of the day melted into tired relief.

Mara wondered if the Games were actually raising political

🖤 The chorus is as follows: "Fuck all! Fuck all! Fuck all! Fuck all! Fuck all! Fuck all! Fuck all! Cut all policemen into pieces! Fuck all! Fuck all! Fuck all! Fuck all! Fuck all! Fuck all!"

consciousness. She considered a conversation she overheard in the park's bathroom. Two girls were checking their makeup and generally occupying the sinks while Mara waited to wash her hands. A waify girl in braids and heavy eyeliner was talking loudly so that it was clear that her target audience was everyone within hearing range and not her friend.

"I look like every girl on MTV," she said as she mugged for the mirror. "Every girl on MTV looks just like me! Me and my boyfriend were watching MTV and he was like, 'God! Mallory, every girl on MTV looks just like you!' And I go, 'God, Collin! Like, you don't have to use that as an excuse to look at the girls on TV.' And he goes, 'No, check it out!' And I was like, 'Oh my god! I look like everyone on MTV!' And I really did!" Mallory tugged a tight braid to achieve her optimum mirror look.

Her quieter, less MTV-looking friend stared at her with the smidgen of interest that was needed to keep her talking. In other words, with no interest, but she also wasn't plugging her ears.

At the time Mara wanted desperately to say something mean to the loudmouth girl or at least berate her for not respecting the political significance of the Games. But now Mara was beginning to wonder if the Games were any better than MTV. They both had good outfits. Both fetishized stupid youthful exuberance and hotheaded passion. She was too tired, however, to sort the two out. The hum of the car lulled her to sleep.

"Mara, what was Holden making you promise?" Regan asked casually.

Mara was pulled slowly out of her slumber. "Mmm?"

Regan asked again, enunciating more clearly this time. "What was Holden making you promise, during the jailbreak?"

"Mmm…something about the Games," came Mara's distracted response. She got lost in the memory of Holden's tantalizing grip on her arm.

Regan's insistent voice, however, dragged her from her honeyed reveries. "What about the Games?"

Mara frowned. "I can't remember, Regan… He said I shouldn't deliver the flowers."

Then she snuggled back in the seat, feeling heavy and warm. Her serenity was cut short, as a jolting swerve of the car woke her. Mara opened her eyes. They pulled over to the side of the road and stopped in the woods halfway between town and campus. Regan's eye was spasming and she smeared her penciled brow all over her forehead trying to manage the convulsions.

"What happened?" asked a startled Mara.

Regan paused for a moment. "Oh…There was a…deer. Mara, I need you to explain this to me. What exactly did Holden ask you to do?"

Mara could tell her friend was very serious so she answered with equal gravity. "He asked me not to deliver the flowers… for the Susanne Albrecht thing, I guess."

Regan turned her head to Mara, looking quite pale and grim. "How did he know you were going to be Susanne Albrecht in the Games?"

Shamed by her loose lips, Mara looked down and said in a wee voice, "I guess I told him."

Regan was fuming. Her seismic eye tics consumed her entire face in a clutch of tremors.

"Did you tell him who your target is?" asked Regan from within her vibrating expression.

Mara turned red remembering that, although she didn't tell Holden who her target was, she would have if he asked. "No."

Regan expelled some air loudly. "Mara, now this is very important, did he tell you why he didn't want you to deliver those flowers?"

Mara racked her brain, *What did he say? Something about? No… Oh yeah.*

"He said something about something fishy going on. He didn't know what, but he knew who was behind it."

"Who?" demanded Regan impatiently.

Again Mara thought long and hard. "I don't know. He didn't say."

Regan looked intently at the forest for a drawn-out moment, then she turned a reptile eye on Mara. "I don't know why, Mara, but for some reason what he said to you scares me."

"Why, Regan?" Mara asked as her head danced with questions.

Regan peered into the still of the night. "I wish I knew.

Something about that threat he gave Rosa before she disappeared. He gave me a similar threat today," Regan whispered.

"No!" Mara whispered back.

"Yes. He said that I'd pay for getting you in the group... That he has his ways..."

Mara rubbed her eyes in disbelief. "His ways? Well, what does that have to do with me not delivering the flowers?"

Regan brought her hand up to her pointed chin. "I wish I knew, Mara. But if you don't deliver the flowers, who does that leave? There must be some reason why Holden wants me to take your place as Susanne Albrecht... maybe something related to his designing the props clandestinely. If only I could figure out what it all means." Regan drummed the steering wheel with her crimson crescents.

Something clicked in Mara's head.

What if Holden is going to try to get rid of Regan just like he got rid of Rosa? Maybe the flower vase is lethal. That would explain why he would want Regan to go instead of me and why he wants people to think Regan designed the props. He may be trying to frame Regan for her own death...

Mara was unsettled by the eerie conclusion, but she tucked the thoughts away for further contemplation while she tried to unravel another part of the mystery.

"So, why are you guys pretending that you are designing the props if only he is?"

Regan pursed her tight red lips and shook her head causing her blood-red mane to collide with Mara's milky, soft skin. "It was his idea. Now, for the life of me, I can't remember why I agreed to it. I guess it was his irresistible charm. Why did you promise to not deliver the flowers?"

Mara blew some air out of the side of her mouth while she remembered his dark, unfathomable eyes burbling with volcanic eruptions of meaning. "Same reason I guess. He's just so dreamy!"

Regan grabbed Mara's hand and squeezed it tight. "Mara, we have to remember that our attraction to him will not save us. Rosa was his number-one fan when she vanished. Those girls from the Funny Farm also had a thing for him. Our attraction to Holden may be our undoing!"

Mara felt like a character on a WB drama. Her exterior life was finally beginning to reflect the sense of importance and weightiness of her interior life. An excited shiver ran the length of her spine and she gasped and threw her arms around Regan's neck. "I know! I've always felt powerless in the face of his devastating charm. What if it's this very charm that devastates us?" She pulled away from Regan's neck and looked off into space. "The funny thing is, when I'm with him, I can't believe him capable of anything even remotely nefarious. Oh, Regan! It's all so confusing!"

Regan tried to smile through her marked look of fear. "I know, Mara. We'll just have to look out for each other. We'll take care of each other, that's what we'll do!"

In the silence of the woodland, the two girls made a pact of solidarity.

The next day Mara traded her bouffant for the straight-haired wig. She was now officially a pretend underground revolutionary. Donning her black sweater, replete with newly ripped holes to make it look more rebellious, Mara again examined the pin given to her by Tippy and Penny.

РАФ. *Rho Alpha Phi? The Terrorist Sorority. Those goofs!* she thought, and started to take off the pin. She paused to look at it again, this time in the mirror. She gave a chuckle and left it pinned to her sweater.

It's a symbol of the one time I actually belonged to something. Even if Holden is in the midst of a politically motivated murder spree, I'll still have this pin to remember these golden days… and him.

Day six, "Capitalism Must Fund Its Own Demise! Day," commemorated the RAF's training in Jordan with the Palestinians and the subsequent bank robberies upon their return to Germany.

In honor of the PLO's and RAF's political alliance, the Baader-Meinhof Reading Group invited local activists to give demonstrations. The Cyber Rebel Underground Directive

(CRUD) displayed the best way to steal long-distance service and how to filch clothes that have plastic anti-theft tags (cover them with tin foil.)

The Revolutionary Anarchist Bowling League (RABL) demonstrated how to make an effective bomb out of powdered nondairy creamer. They also revealed secret methods to gain access to files the government keeps on its citizens. Putting the rabble in "adorable" (as their motto said), they concluded the morning with a panel discussion of the pros and cons of paint bombs versus an old-fashioned egging.

The Urban Guerrilla Hit Squad (UGHS) led an afternoon seminar on the best stretches for outrunning the police and provided an obstacle course to simulate police evasion tactics. Following that, the Baader-Meinhof Reading Group demonstrated how to hot-wire cars and which kind of essential oils are the most enduring for tossing into the back seat of a police car. Although most concurred that patchouli was both sensually the most obnoxious smelling and longest lasting, some dissented, claiming amber to be more olfactorily revolting.

It was a tight schedule, already disrupted by the infighting of RABL members—the Baader-Meinhof Reading Group had to call the police to break it up—and by a rash of car thefts following the hot-wiring demo. Mara spent most of the day doing hospitality: gathering lattés, snacks, and sandwiches for people in the various organizations.

Day seven, "Violence is the Highest Form of Class Struggle! Day," was similar to the evening of day six. The pamphlet recounted how the RAF, now confirmed outlaws, had to resort to violence to illustrate their philosophical differences from the fascist German state. Day seven memorialized the untimely deaths of RAFians Petra Schelm and Thomas Weisbecker at the hands of the police. The two were honored through a dramatic reconstruction of their heroic demise. In fact, the entire day was one staged gun battle after another between the Baader-Meinhof Group and the German police.

The group also commemorated the vengeful bombings by the RAF of U.S. Army Headquarters in Frankfurt, army barracks in Heidelberg, police headquarters in Augsburg, and the

Springer Press in Berlin. There were also the car bombings of Federal Judge Wolfgang of Buddenberg and the State Criminal Investigative Office in Munich. To give Norden a taste of its heroes' activities, the Baader-Meinhof Reading Group planted more fake bomb props around the town of Norden.

James had crafted the bombs from of old army water bottles. Aiming for historical authenticity, he had welded a handle onto each bottle and styled a detonator out of hexagonal nuts, a circuit, a 50-volt dry-cell battery, and an egg timer. Because of their similarity to real, homemade bombs, the Baader-Meinhof Reading Group had to get permission from the Norden Fire Department to use them. Inexplicably, every year permission was granted, although some people said it was only because of the influence Holden's mother held over the Norden community.

Mara's job was planting the bombs and supplying two-dimensional artistic renditions of explosions at each target, which they called a "hit."

Each "hit" was followed by the distribution of conscious-ness-raising pamphlets, so that the townspeople could under-stand why the targets were chosen and what steps they should take in the future in order to throw off their chains. Mara felt a little silly taping designs of explosions and handing out pam-phlets at the Sunny Honeycomb Organic Food Co-op where, if political activism was measured by the number of unshaved armpits, chins, and other body parts, this place had it coming out of its ears.

A bookish girl in a flowered skirt and straight hair held back with a red bandanna gave Mara quizzical look when she was handed a pamphlet entitled, "Why Your Fascist Organization Was Chosen by the Baader-Meinhof Reading Group To Be Bombed in the Event of a Real Communist Uprising."

The girl pushed back her glasses and stammered, "W-w— b-but we're an organic f-f-food c-c-co-operative! All our pr-profits go to the w-workers and the f-farmers. And I'm a t-triple leg."

Mara's face screwed into a look of puzzlement. *I've got to find out what "triple leg" means,* she reminded herself.

The co-op worker, noting Mara's confusion explained, "M-my c-communist *legacy* g-g-goes b-back three generations."

Mara looked at the ground, pretending she didn't hear the fuzzy-limbed girl.

The girl placed herself directly in front of Mara, crouching only slightly to meet her eye, "W-w-w-ell?"

Mara looked up into her pale communist face.

She looks like an ugly mouse, Mara thought. *But she does have a point.*

"I'm just following orders," Mara explained feebly.

The mouse girl stayed in Mara's face. "J-just f-following orders? Wh-Wh-Who's the fascist n-now?"

Mara shrugged, all the while thinking, *No fashion sense. I mean, I'm from Wisconsin and even I know better than to mistake a bandanna for a hairstyle. And not shaving? Can you say "affected?" And not even in a cool way...*

The mouse girl with the speech impediment stared at Mara a moment longer. "I don't know why you ch-chose to pick on us. I ride my b-bike to work, even in the w-winter. I make my own c-clothes and I use Doctor B-Bronner's ecology-friendly soap for all of its one hundred and one uses. And *you're* w-wearing..." she crinkled up her pinched white face and said, as if it were the coarsest of swear words, "leather." The mouse girl turned away briefly as if to hide her eyes from the horrific sight of Mara's leather shoes.

Mara had nothing against the co-op but was developing a strong dislike for this more-politically-correct-than-thou creature who mistook cutting her own hair and composting for political conscience and character.

"Everyone knows that co-ops are salve for upper-class guilt," Mara said. "The only way to get any change is through violence. I quote the Unabomber Manifesto, 'In order to get our message before the public with some chance of making a lasting impression, we've had to kill people.' You guys are too comfy with your wheat grass juice and your all-natural oat bran dish detergent. It's even in the name: 'co-op'. You've been *co-opted.* You're on a false path and that's why you must be eliminated."

Mara smiled, proud of her diatribe in which she was able to quote her favorite serial killer/terrorist crossover, Theodore Kaczynski.

"That m-made no s-s-sense," the mouse girl said, not even remotely willing to take on the words of someone who strayed so far from the proper lineage of Marx as the Unabomber did.

"Oh, and I suppose socks with sandals does?" Mara threw back.

"Y-you're d-d-daft. T-t-tell R-r-Regan that w-w-we're on t-t-to her."

She gave Mara one final look of disgust and walked off in a waft of patchouli.

I wonder what she means? Surely Regan chose this organization because she truly believes they're fascist pigs and not merely to grind her own ax. Oh, life is too confusing! At least I commit suicide tomorrow.

Caught up in her thoughts, Mara forgot she was scheduled to be faux-arrested until Rat and MK-Ultra had her in a head-lock. They tied her arms and carried her to a rented, unmarked van. Inside were Regan/Gudrun and Holden/Baader blind-folded, hog-tied, and lying nearly on top of each other. The image of their bodies lying so close again stirred her fears that Holden and Regan weren't quite over one another. This thought was quickly supplanted by another: surprise at the sadistic exuberance with which Rat tossed her onto the carpeted floor of the vehicle.

The rest of day six was devoted to reenacting the trials of the RAF on the outdoor stage. Ex-Pat played the lawyer with a stylish panache as he talked the watching crowd through the crimes committed by the fledgling militant group.

Mara thought Regan/Gudrun had the best line in the trial: "If those pigs over there open their snouts once more, we will go!" Mara/Meinhof had a few good lines, too, like, "You threaten me with your Eichmann box, you fascist? You pig?" And "Oh, of course, blood. That is what you want!" The defiance of Meinhof's words, however juicy, felt empty to Mara, as they were her swan song.

Holden/Baader shouted obscenities and whispered to his lawyer, Eric, for most of the trial. But despite the activist's elegant defense, the RAF members were sentenced to jail. The trial ended with a flourish of activity, as the whole cast marched from the stage to a nearby jail set with the throngs of onlookers following.

Since "Death Night" was arguably the most important event in the Baader-Meinhof timeline, the set where it took place was built with extra care. MK-Ultra had designed the jail cell with real bars on the windows and regulation German prison cots, circa early seventies.

Even though Regan had radically pared down Meinhof's suicide scene, the crowd waited in a somber, expectant hush.

Mara entered her blue-lit cell to complete the life cycle of Meinhof.

From an adjacent cell Holden/Baader called to her, "You're worse than useless."

Identifying with Meinhof, the loser, Mara felt a sting upon hearing his words.

I may as well be Meinhof. Holden thinks I'm useless. That's why he doesn't want me in the group. That's probably why he doesn't want me to deliver the flowers! she thought mournfully. *Just like Meinhof, I'm an outcast even among misfits.*

Mara/Meinhof dutifully put on a specially devised safety jacket with a built-in harness. She then cursed the fascist pigs and pretended to fashion a noose out of the prison bed linens. Suddenly Mara didn't want to go through with the scene. A feeling of loss as a result of her imminent death had unexpectedly overtaken her.

I thought this is what I wanted, to be Meinhof, the martyr. Oh, who can know the twisted labyrinth that is my heart?

Sullenly Mara fastened her harness to the bed-sheet noose prop and threw the other end so that it looped around the beam. Then, stepping off a metal chair, she "hanged" herself. While her weight was actually supported by a harness, the gasps that issued from the silent crowd gathered around affirmed how authentic the hanging appeared. Mara concluded her brief stint as Ulrike Meinhof swinging unhappily above the floor like an effigy to misguided passion, a piñata filled with misbegotten meanings.

Mara didn't sleep well that evening. Thoughts of doom sur-

rounding her impending flower delivery to the fascist journalist Bismarck Vernal kept her mind churning.

When she did finally sleep, the ghost of Ulrike Meinhof
entered her dreams.

Dressed in a black cloak with long, stringy hair, Ulrike
fingered a collar of bruises around her neck. She looked up as if
she had just noticed that she had stumbled into Mara's dream
and pointed to her black-and-blue rope marks.

"Maaaara, don't beeee like meeee! Heed Baaaaader. Death is
not the aaanswer!" she moaned eerily.

With a dramatic flourish, Meinhof pulled from her cloak a
beautiful canary that was throwing itself against the slender bars
of its cage. The canary then fell to the floor of the birdcage and
lay there, quiet and flat. Mara knew, as one simply knows in
dreams, that, like a canary in a coal mine, the refined, sensitive
ones such as she and Meinhof were doomed to be the first to
die in a hazardous environment.

Mara woke with a start. It was six-thirty in the morning.
Her heart fluttered wildly inside her chest, throwing itself
against her ribs again and again. She knew she couldn't fall back
asleep.

At that moment the phone rang. She answered it timorously,
secretly hoping it would somehow save her from having to
choose between keeping her promise to Regan or to Holden.

"Mara?" came a warm voice that could belong to none other
than Holden Rife.

Mara melted at his magnetic tones, "Yes, Holden?"

"Mara, I know these things are supposed to be a secret, but
tell me who's your target today."

She hesitated, torn by conflicting loyalties and emotions.
"But, Holden, you know I can't tell you."

There was muffled cursing at the other end of the line, and
then his voice came back again, with a quiet emphasis. "Mara,
this is very important, lives may hang on this. Please. Please.
You know I'm on your side."

Mara fought through the cobwebs of her nightmare-filled
sleep.

Is this true? What do I know about Holden? Why should I

*agonize over someone if I don't even know his real name? Then
again, I don't know that any of Regan's suspicions are true. After
all, Regan believes Tippy and Penny are spies…*

Just then she heard a knock at her door.

Saved!

"I've got to run, Holden, there's someone at my door."

His voice hardened and became demanding. "Damn it,
Mara! I must know! You must tell me, please!"

Mara looked at her door fretfully as the pounding became
ever more insistent. "Holden, I got to go. I'll see you later, I
guess," she whispered, not knowing if she actually would ever
see him again.

Mara heard him yell as she hung up, "Remember your
promise, Mara!"

Regan was at the door, fully dressed with a coffee in her
hand and a thick, four-inch scar over her right brow. Mara
admired the scar, which was now even bigger than Ensslin's was.

"Come on, Mara, we've got to go!"

Mara was still in her pajamas.

"Where? Why now?"

She looked at her watch. It was still six hours before she had
to deliver those flowers, if she delivered them at all.

"We have to check out your target. Then you need to study
your plan of action. Get dressed!" Regan ordered.

Mara didn't like being rushed. "What do I wear? I don't have
a Susanne Albrecht costume," she whined, disappointed that
she had missed the opportunity to get one fitted before Rosa
vanished.

Regan grabbed the Ulrike Meinhof clothes that were draped
over a chair. "Here, put these on! It doesn't matter what you
wear. No one will see you but Bismarck and believe me, he's not
gonna care. Come on. Put these on. We need to go! Now!"

Although she thought it gauche to wear the same clothes
three days in a row, Mara followed Regan's orders.

Within minutes they were in Regan's car, racing away from
campus to the home of Mr. Vernal. Regan stationed her car at
a small park in an unassuming neighborhood and, pulling out
a pair of binoculars, spied on a yellow house across the street.

Regan pointed it out to Mara. It was modest home, a modified box, two stories with hedges that needed trimming and toys scattered across the lawn. Mara thought she caught the scent of bacon or sausage wafting from an open window along with the harmonies of a mop-topped pop band from a time long forgotten: the Beatles.

Mara started humming along with the tune. Soon she found herself singing.

"You say you want a revolution, well, you know…You ought to feed mm-mm-mm mm-mm mm-mm-mm mm-mm… Cause you know it's gonna be…doot-doo…all right…"

"Mara? Do you mind?" Regan snapped.

Mara crossed her arms across her chest. "Why are you so edgy this morning, Regan? This will go fine. I know what I'm supposed to do."

Regan turned to Mara, "Yeah, and you're about as stable as a meth lab."

Mara gasped at the cruelty of Regan's remark.

Then she thought, *she's right. Even now I'm contemplating betraying Regan to keep my promise to Holden.*

Mara silently made an oath to not betray her friend.

Regan, as if she knew Mara's thoughts, softened her tone. "I'm sorry, it's just that I have so much responsibility right now and I really want everything to come off well. Then, you know, there's the Holden threat thing…Well, it makes me edgy." She smiled at her friend and asked in a sunnier voice, "Mara? Do me a favor and walk to the neighbor's front door, will you?"

Mara walked to the neighbor's house, nearly the same as the Vernal residence but in blue. She touched the front door and walked back to the car.

Regan beamed. "Thirty seconds, add stalling time, and—perfect!"

She looked past Mara to the Vernal residence, eyes filled with brimstone.

Regan dropped Mara at a café near the Vernal house, but nowhere near Norden Park where the rest of the Games were taking place.

"Okay, Mara, you have breakfast and I'll have Rat pick you

up in a couple of hours. Here's your mission." She handed Mara a manila envelope. "You can look over your lines while you're waiting for Rat."

"Why aren't you picking me up?" Mara asked.

"I'm supposed to be in prison, remember? Death Night is tomorrow."

Mara looked at the drab greasy spoon. "Well, why can't I hang out at the Games until I have to drop off the flowers?"

Regan answered quickly, "Because, if you run into Holden he'll change your mind and I'll have to play Susanne."

Mara waved goodbye to Regan and took a seat at a table in the café.

She was surprised at the quality of food the little café kicked out. She ate biscuits and gravy with a four-cheese and bacon omelet.

I've got to remember where this place is, she thought, as she sopped up her gravy with the remainder of her biscuit. After she finished eating Mara paged through her mission notes whose title, emblazoned with block letters, read, "Day 8: Destroy What Destroys You!" She perused Regan's remarks on Susanne Albrecht:

> *As a young woman, Susanne fought against the tyranny of slum lords by squatting in empty houses. Soon she became involved with the second generation of the RAF called Red Morning. Red Morning fought for the release of Baader, Ensslin, and other RAF political prisoners through bank robberies, multiple assassinations, and taking hostages from the exploiter class.*
>
> *Your mission is to go to fascist journalist Bismarck Vernal's door as Susanne Albrecht. Carry a bouquet of flowers as if you are delivering them. Ring the doorbell. When he arrives at the door, hand him the flowers and say, "This is a symbolic gesture on behalf of the Baader-Meinhof Reading Group. In the event of an uprising these roses would self-destruct, leaving you splattered all over the lawn." Then you are to hand him literature on his exploitative ways and depart.*

Mara was sure the experience would be humiliating for her, but afterward she could wash her hands of the Baader-Meinhof Reading Group and go on with her life.

Of course, I won't see Holden again, and I'll be breaking my promise to him...

She brushed aside the idea and tried to think about her mission.

I wonder what horrible and fascistic thing Bismarck Vernal did that Regan would deem him dead meat in the occasion of a real revolution. Not that you can really tell from just looking at a person's home, but he seems like a nice guy.

To keep her troubled thoughts at bay Mara read her lines over and over. Memorizing her lines killed time and it wasn't long before Rat arrived.

Eyeing Mara from behind his camouflaged face for a prolonged moment, he smiled the briefest of smiles. "Come on, Princess, let's go!"

Mara saw his hostile expression and suddenly didn't want to get into a car with him.

"Oh. Is it time?" she asked, stalling.

Methodically selecting sugar packages one by one, Rat ripped them open and dumped the contents on the table while saying in his dullest sounding voice, "What do you think?"

Mara was frustrated that she had to spend her last moments as a member of the Baader-Meinhof Reading Group with Rat, who was acting very strangely.

Rat emptied all the sugar packages and started unscrewing the salt and pepper shakers, dumping them onto the table.

"Come on. Regan said that we need to be on time. Now, without resorting to arm twisting, do you think we could just finish your tour and get you home?"

In order to keep Rat from doing any more damage to the table, Mara put down a ten and walked to his army-green BMW 2002.

Rat smiled as she stepped past him, plucked her ten-dollar bill from off the table, and followed her out the door. Mara fumed as she imagined her poor waitress seeing the mess he left and no money to cover the bill.

"Hey, why'd you do that?" Mara fumed. "Now I can't go back there!"

Rat smiled and mysteriously intoned, "You could if you were with me…"

They sped off to the Vernal residence.

Mara's mind was a blur. There was a pensive shimmer in the shadow of her eyes as Mara was about to break her promise to Holden. She tried to convince herself that it didn't matter.

How can I promise anything to a man so shrouded in mystery? And those rumors, those horrible rumors!

Rat arrived at the park and stopped the car. "Let's go!"

They got out of the car and he opened the trunk to pull out a strange-looking metal vase and a white uniform jacket.

"Put this on." He tossed the jacket at her.

"What's with you today, Rat? You used to be so nice," Mara wondered aloud.

"Oh, now the princess notices me. It used to be you couldn't even give me the time of day!" Rat grumbled, his pain battling the tattoos for his expression.

"I don't know what you're talking about," Mara replied and threw the jacket over her sweater.

Rat did something to the bottom of the vase and stuck a bouquet of pastel colored flowers in it. He handed it to her. It was heavier than she imagined it would be. A plaque on the bottom read, "A hundred flowers have bloomed. They are one hundred armed revolutionary groups!"

"Here. Go! Go! Go!" urged Rat.

Perhaps it was only nerves, but Mara thought there was something amiss in the way he was rushing her along.

She eyed him suspiciously. "What's the hurry?"

Rat became peeved at her stalling. "I got a deadline. I have to get back for a kidnapping. Now go!"

He pushed her in the direction of the Vernal house.

Mara stopped in the middle of the street. "But I don't have the pamphlets!"

Rat rolled his eyes. "Doesn't matter, go!"

Mara was shaken up and Rat's prodding only added to her

flustered state. She started up the walk and heard Rat yell, "No! The yellow house! Not the blue one!"

"Oops!" Mara said and then hurried to the house next door.

She grew more uncomfortable by the second and, as her dismay mounted, her heart was racing, beating madly, almost as if it were ticking.

It is ticking! Mara realized with alarm. *No, wait, that's not my heart. It's the vase that's ticking. How odd.*

She reached the door and rang the bell.

As the doorbell sounded, an equally loud alarm rang in her head, *There's a bomb in this vase. That explains the ticking.*

As soon as she thought it, she knew it must be true.

So Holden was trying to kill Regan! That brute!

Mara realized in dismay that her assignment was a suicide mission. She turned around to see Rat drive off.

I'm doomed anyway. Without Holden, my life means nothing!

She couldn't deny the evidence any longer. Mara finally admitted that her love for Holden was stronger than her will to live.

If it's a murderer I love, then I may as well die.

She choked back a heaving sob as footsteps approached the door.

Mara became painfully aware of her surroundings. She felt the late morning sun on her cheek and heard nearby birds singing in a tree. Off in the distance a school bell rang, followed by the silvery laughter of children at recess, a sound punctuated by a screeching of car wheels rounding a nearby corner. Each detail down to the glint of sunlight coming off the Rho Alpha Phi pin that showed above her jacket became etched in her brain. Everything was at once beautiful and tragic and held a new gravity with the knowledge that, in a few moments, she'd be dead. Tears rolled down her lovely cheeks.

Oh, why, Holden? Why?

The door opened and a non-fascist looking man with soft, ruffled hair and patches sewn on the elbows of his worn, flannel robe answered the door. His jaw dropped slack as he saw the flowers and Mara's tear-streaked face.

She looked into the doomed man's face. "I'm sorry," she said.

A car screeched to a halt somewhere behind her.

Mara turned around.

A door opened and she saw a tan girl with short hair and stylish clothes get out of a new black Lexus.

Rosa?!

The woman yelled, "No, Mara. It's a bomb!"

Mara was paralyzed. She had suspected it, but she didn't know for sure until then. Like a deer in the headlights, Mara thought that it didn't matter which way she jumped, that it was too late and each direction would be equally lethal.

Behind the Rosa look-alike came Holden.

Holden! Too late for us! Too late! Oh why did you plant this bomb? At least I'll die looking at you, Mara thought as two strangely familiar women jumped out of the car followed by Apocalypse.

Mara looked down at her imminent destruction, the vase.

What does this mean?

Then, before she could answer herself, Holden was at her side, tearing the vase out of her hands. Holden flew through the air at breakneck speed, vase held in front of him, running away from Mara and the very ashen Bismarck Vernal. With long, purposeful strides, he rushed the vase out into the street.

Mara saw a radiant white flash come from the vase just as Holden threw it toward the empty park. Then an explosion blinded Mara, ripping Holden from her vision.

"No! Holden!" Mara screamed.

Fire still seared the air as Mara, roused from her immobilized state, ran to the place where she last saw him. The air was thick with sulfurous smoke and flowers flying around in chunks. Mara ducked as she ran, ignoring the danger of the flaming flower projectiles as Holden's fate seized her thoughts.

He saved me! He saved my life! And Rosa's back! She's not dead! Holden didn't kill her!

For the first time in weeks Mara's heart felt untroubled— only to fill again with a new poisonous thought.

But what if Holden *is dead? Then what?*

She found his body covered in soot and riddled with flower shrapnel. Mara leaned over his ailing, broken body. She pulled flowers out of his hair and mouth and wiped the soot off his face.

"Holden! Holden! Speak to me! I'm sorry I didn't keep my promise. Holden!"

His face was handsomely placid. Sensuous red lips were frozen in a slight curl. He did not move.

He died smiling! Mara thought and wept over his exquisite corpse.

Then, a miracle happened!

Mara saw Holden's chest convulse and he began to cough violently. It was the most beautiful sound Mara had ever heard.

Holden opened his wonderful rainbow eyes. "Mara, thank goodness I arrived in time!"

Mara pulled his limp body to hers and the two lovers lavished each other in kisses and loving touches.

Their passionate embrace was broken by a loud, "A-hem."

Standing above them were Apocalypse, Rosa, and two strangers. One of the strangers, the taller, large-breasted one, said in a familiar voice that was years younger than her face, "Hey, like, this isn't exactly the most private place to get it on with someone."

Mara realized with shock that the older woman was Green, either Tippy or Penny.

"Yeah, totally, like, get a room!" said the voice of Blue in a very tan mid-thirties woman's body.

"Penny? Tippy?" Mara looked back and forth between the two women who she almost didn't recognize outside their mud masks and boxer shorts. "I don't get it. How did you guys get so old?"

Blue and Green looked at each other and broke into laughter.

Green gathered her composure and smiled benevolently at Mara. "The truth is, Mara, we aren't Penny and Tippy."

Mara sat on the ground with a confounded look on her face. "Wha–?"

"I'm Special Agent Sheila Skylar and this is my partner, Special Agent Stacy Kelly," the woman formally know as Blue said. "We were investigating the disappearances of young women at the Funny Farm Organic Vegetable Cooperative."

Mara recalled that the Funny Farm was where Holden spent

his last year after he broke up with Regan.

"So those rumors of missing women there are true!" Mara said.

Agent Kelly continued. "Oh yes! We followed one of our only two leads, Holden, to Norden College. When we discovered you were becoming close to him, we asked two girls in your dorm, Tippy and Penny, if they wouldn't enjoy an all-expenses-paid semester in Paris. Then, with a little help from plastic surgeons, we took over their identities and befriended you. Of course, in such a short period of time we couldn't get our faces perfect and then there would still be bruises, so we wore the mud masks and no one seemed to notice a difference. I got a free breast job out of it!"

Agent Skylar nodded. "Yeah, and now we cracked our first big case, thanks to you. You were the perfect unwitting spy. But we're really sorry about the drug thing."

Mara looked up at the women. "What drug thing?"

Agent Kelly responded quickly, "Nothing, she doesn't mean anything. Anyway, it's because of you and Holden that no one died today and we were able to apprehend the real terrorist."

Mara was dumbfounded. Then she remembered that Rat had set something on the vase before he sent her off to the Vernal household. "Oh, you mean Rat."

The agents looked at each other.

Special Agent Skylar said, "No, we mean Regan Thresh."

Again shock flew through Mara.

"Regan? How? Why?"

Agent Kelly knelt down by Mara's side. "I'm sorry, Mara. I know this must come as a surprise to you. Regan was using you to get Holden back the only way she knew how: by cutting him off from the rest of humanity. She would accomplish this by framing him with your murder."

"Yeah, that's why she wanted you in the Baader-Meinhof Reading Group to begin with," Agent Skylar added. "She knew Holden was interested in you. She got you in the group so that you would be the one to deliver the bomb. James would say Holden designed it. And since Regan already spread rumors about Holden killing Rosa and threatening you, Holden would be suspect number one. Once the police were after him, her plan was to help him go underground. Cut off from society, she would then be his savior and forever have him all to herself. By sending you to Bismarck Vernal's home, she was killing two birds with one stone."

Mara brushed the obliterated flower parts off herself as she stood up. "How's that?" she asked and quietly wondered if she should be offended that she was being called a bird.

Agent Skylar explained, "Regan had a vendetta against Bismarck Vernal. He was the journalist who broke the story about her family's Chubby Nappies Diapers for Pleasantly Plump Babies company being the foremost supplier of Adult Infantilism fetish-wear. So killing him was an act of revenge."

Mara nodded. "Oh, I thought his name was familiar…But what about you, Rosa? What happened to you?"

Rosa looked at the ground, shamefaced. "I didn't know that Regan was using my disappearance for her nefarious plans. After the meeting when you were voted into our group Regan took me aside and offered to send me to a beauty makeover retreat in the Bahamas. She said that I'd be a shoe-in for the magazine job at *Der Style* if I just changed my image, but I'd have to leave that night and not tell anyone where I was. It sounded like a good deal at the time, but eventually I got home-sick and came back a week early."

"Wow!" said Mara. "Not only do you have a better haircut, but you got a trip to the Bahamas out of this."

Rosa smiled. "You inspired me, Mara. I had always thought I couldn't do the short hair thing, but it was your courage that led me to believe that I could. And look at me now! I have you to thank for it!"

Agent Kelly threw an arm around Rosa. "We knew something was up when Regan seemed to know ahead of time that Rosa's scarf was going to be found in the woods the evening of the Mumia Benefit. How could she know unless she planted it?"

Mara looked around at her friends and loved ones. "Oh, but how did you all find me? Did Rat tell you were I was?"

Agent Kelly curled her lips at Mara's innocence. "No, Mara, you told us who your target was. You probably don't remember, you were half asleep. The only thing we didn't know was when the strike would take place. We had to catch Regan in the act of killing you, otherwise we couldn't put her away. She's probably being picked up by Norden's finest right now. We have some officers working undercover as Abies. Since last year we've had our eye on her as our only other lead in the Funny Farm disappearances, but have been unable to prove anything. That's why we gave you the pin, by the way. It had a homing signal in it so we could trace you."

Agent Skylar agreed, "Yeah, It was my idea to put the Rho Alpha Phi symbols on it though."

Mara shook her head in admiration. "Wow! And I almost didn't wear it today."

Holden pulled himself up from the ground and brushed himself off.

Mara turned to him. "But, Holden, how did you know that Regan would make a flower bomb?"

Holden began to pace as he talked. "I didn't know for sure, but one day Regan dropped a list of ingredients: red phosphorus, sulfur, potassium chlorate, charcoal and batteries. The *Anarchist Cookbook* identifies them as ingredients for a bomb. Written above the list were the words, 'Flowers to be delivered by Rosa.' But Rosa's name had been crossed off and above it read, 'Mara.' Also, all of those same chemicals were charged to one of my credit cards that was stolen the same time my driver's license disappeared. I guess I just put two and two together."

Mara remembered Regan's ploy to get her to think that Holden changed his name. "Oh, so she stole your wallet to frame you for building the bomb and make me suspicious of you by getting me to think that you changed your name."

Holden's eyes brightened. "Right! I thought it was strange when Regan gave me one of those new 'distressed' wallets as a gift. Now I know it was all a setup. I noticed when I checked my credit card receipts at the stores where the fraudulent purchases were made that the signature looked like Regan's handwriting. But I took it to an expert just to be sure. The test came back this morning: one hundred percent likelihood that it was signed by Regan."

Agent Kelly nodded in admiration at Holden's amateur

detective work. "We found out almost the same way," she said. "Regan had thrown a similar draft of her plans into a trash can on campus. It was a Mr. Dave something-or-other, a Norden groundskeeper, who found it and brought it to the police's attention. We ignored it at first, but when we read the title across the top of the page, 'How I plan to get rid of Rosa and Mara by Regan Thresh,' we thought we'd give it a second look."

Agent Skylar brushed her hands together. "Who knew that you can learn something from a groundskeeper? He was also the one who discovered that Regan designed the props for the Games, and not Holden, as James thought. He saw her creating the specs."

"As Jesus said, 'Now I know, and knowing is half the battle,'" Holden uttered, and shook his head gravely.

Mara kissed him squarely on the lips.

"You're so smart, Holden, but how did you wind up in the car with Blue and Green?"

Holden glowed at her compliment. "I was driving around trying to find you when the police saw me and picked me up. I guess they have orders to stop all BMW 2002s. They passed me on to the FBI agents, thinking I could help. When I saw you delivering the bomb, my life flashed before my eyes and I realized that I didn't want to live in a world without my favorite burgeoning expert on serial killers, so I dove after it. I guess being a former high school quarterback comes in handy because I was able to throw the vase into the park garden just before it blew up. Fortunately, I wasn't too late!"

"I know that!" Mara said. "I was there, remember?"

"Oh yeah," Holden smiled sheepishly.

Mara sunk into the warm embrace of Holden's arms. "Oh Holden, I had the same reaction when I heard the vase ticking. I figured there was no point in living in a world where my one and only love is a heartless murderer. That's why I just froze."

Bismarck Vernal joined the group standing on the street not far from a giant, burning crater where a flowerbed used to be. He gestured to the flaming chasm and said, "Thanks a lot! That could have been me."

Everyone laughed.

A news van pulled up and Apocalypse flagged the crew over. "I have a confession to make, you guys," she said. "Like agents Skylar and Kelly, I'm not really a student either."

Mara gasped.

"I'm actually a broadcast journalist undercover on assignment for 'Hard Wired: Under the Edge Extreme Goes on Campus.' I had no idea how big my scoop would be. This is really going to make my career. And I have you guys to thank for it!" Apocalypse stepped forward and gave Mara a big hug, whispering in her ear, "If you ever decide to switch teams, give me a call."

"Thanks," Mara said, "but as they say, once a cheddarhead, always a cheddarhead. Green Bay will always be my team."

Apocalypse shrugged and instructed the cameraman where to set up.

Agent Skylar laughed. "Actually, our careers will take off from this, too. Not only did we save people from terrorist bombs, but also we found the source of the supplier of Neo-Nazi literature right on Norden campus. Would you believe your Professor Mahler is the culprit, Mara?"

"No, I never would have guessed he was a racist," Mara said.

"We didn't either. It was Dave the groundskeeper who cracked that case for us," admitted Agent Kelly.

Mara sighed and looked deeply into Holden's warm, blue eyes flecked with yellow.

Holden said in a low, husky voice, "Mara, let's get out of here!"

She knew exactly what he was thinking and responded regretfully, "I'd love to Holden, but the police must be coming with questions and then there's the news team, and besides, we don't have a car."

Holden smiled a devilishly handsome smile. "I'm a Baader-Meinhof aficionado, remember? I know how to hot-wire."

Amid the confusion, the two slipped away to Agent Skylar and Kelly's car and peeled off, leaving the two agents laughing at their final prank.

Holden drove to his house where he extracted the Rho Alpha Phi pin from Mara's sweater and threw it as far as he could into his yard.

"Let's stay undercover," he said and drove away from the tracking device.

"I don't understand, Holden, where are we going?"

Holden gave her a sly smile and said nothing.

Mara enjoyed a good secret and so dropped her line of questioning. A simple pleasure stole over her as she watched Holden drive in silence.

He's alive and we're together at long last! Mara thought happily. Her pleasure, however, was squelched by a nagging thought that could not be repressed. *But Holden shall never be truly mine. He will always hold a greater passion for Regan.*

"Holden?" Mara asked hoping to distract herself from her gloomy thoughts. "What *did* happen to the other girls who disappeared from the Funny Farm? Did Regan send them to the Bahamas too?"

Holden chuckled good-naturedly. "Actually, that's kind of funny. Agents Skylar and Kelly told me Regan learned that trick from my mother. They found out from Dave that my mom had hired someone to spy on me while I was at the Funny Farm. Mother didn't think any of the girls there were right for me, so if it appeared that one was becoming too friendly with me, she would give the girl seventy-five thousand dollars to disappear without a trace for two years. Not only are all of those girls alive, but they are financially better off for having known me."

"Dave is truly an amazing man!" Mara said and then let out a giggle despite her darkening mood. "And your mom! What a nutburger!"

Holden nodded. "You're telling me! It was getting a little confusing, though, to have all these women vanishing out from under me. That's why I went back to school."

Mara leaned heavily into his hard musculature. "And thank goodness you did!" she exclaimed.

Holden gave Mara a lusty gaze. "You're not whistling Dixie!"

Mara reflected on the strange events that shaped her life so distinctly. "What about James and Rat? Are they going to jail too?"

Holden creased his brow when she mentioned James, but

when he saw Mara was adoring him with her eyes, he relaxed. "James didn't know he was making real bombs, so he's off the hook. Once the publicity hits, I bet he sells a lot of his sculptures."

"Lucky him!" Mara exclaimed.

"No kidding! According to Regan's notes, Rat didn't know the vase was a bomb either, at least not a lethal one. Regan had told him it was a stink bomb, and he was plenty happy to pull a trick like that. I guess he felt snubbed by you when you went to the Mumia Benefit dance with me after you already said you'd go with him. I suspect he'll think twice the next time he's asked to set up a fake bomb attack."

"Gosh, I don't remember saying I'd go with him. I guess I'll be more careful too," giggled Mara.

Holden took the back roads to Norden Park, the site of the Baader-Meinhof Games. He parked the car. From across the park Mara saw a very angry looking Regan being led into a police car by a couple of diapered men.

"I wonder where they kept their handcuffs and guns," Mara said.

"You probably don't want to know," Holden responded with humor.

They exited the Lexus. Holden pulled Mara to him and together they watched Regan throw her hand to her brow.

The police car containing Regan drove slowly past them. Her prosthetic forehead scar had mixed calamitously with her eyebrow make up. What little beauty she had a claim to was now deformed.

Horrible from without and horrible from within, thought Mara as she watched Regan glaring back at them beneath her seizing eyelids.

From behind the bulletproof glass Regan screamed silently at the two lovers and then she was gone.

But not from Holden's heart, Mara thought ruefully.

Holden shook his head.

Mara sighed. "I'm sorry Holden, I know you still have a thing for Regan. I understand."

Holden grasped Mara's face, forcing her to look at him.

"What on earth are you talking about?"

"Well, you must love her, otherwise why would you two fight all the time? And why would you spend so much time with her?"

"I spent time with Regan for two reasons: First, because she wrote all my speeches. Then, later on, I was trying to find out what she was up to. I knew you wouldn't believe me without proof, so the only way to move forward with our relationship was to find out what Regan's real plans were for the Games." He smiled a crimson smile. "The only thing I had for Regan was hatred. Now that she's in the hands of the law the hatred has turned to pity…but mild pity," he added quickly.

Mara's heart soared as she heard those words.

Then the passion I saw between them was not the passion of love, instead it was the passion of hatred!

Instinctively she threw her arms around him. "Oh, Holden!"

He lifted her in his arms and carried her across the empty park toward the prison set. Mara was secretly thrilled by his display of savage masculinity.

"Where is everyone?" asked Mara who noted pleasantly that the park was back to its peaceful tranquility with the exception of the jail cells still standing across from the stage.

"There's no one here because of a bomb threat. The FBI thought Regan might have planted real bombs all around town, so they closed down the town center. But I talked to James this morning and he said that all of his bombs, except the vase, were accounted for. I didn't mention this to anyone because I wanted the Games to be closed down. I've had enough games now to last me a lifetime."

Holden carried Mara to the jail cell and threw her on the cot. "Well, most games, that is," he said with a devious grin.

Mara felt blood coursing through her veins like an awakening river. "Here, Holden?" she inquired, not daring to believe he had the same jailhouse fantasy as she did.

Holden looked at her shyly. "Call me Baader… Meinhof."

A brief shiver rippled through her as she tentatively voiced, "Okay then, Baader."

Holden was already tugging the sweater over her head. After

taking a long lingering look at Mara's supple, white body he professed, "I'm tired of violence, Mara, even pretend violence. The Bible says, 'Thou can chop off thine hand only twice. And the second time thou needst help.'"

He pulled off her pants and started freeing himself of his clothing.

Mara saw his stately manhood standing upright like a brave soldier and her insides jangled with excitement.

Holden lowered his body onto hers and she luxuriated in the warmth of his closeness.

"I was a kid when I got into the Baader-Meinhof Group. First I liked their fashion and I definitely thought the girls were hot, but later I came to appreciate their spirit and rebellious, can-do idealism."

Tantalized by her pucker factor, Holden took a moment to cover Mara's mouth with his own, then, reluctantly, he pulled away from her, but only a few inches. "But as an adult I see that they had some things all wrong. Maybe thinking of the personal as political is enough. You know, that and sending money to NPR and PBS. The American spirit of volunteerism will surely take care of the rest."

From the RAF to NPR, maybe that's what it means to grow up… Mara mused.

He kissed her taut nipple, rousing a melting sweetness that begged for occupation.

"Besides, Baader himself says, 'The anti-imperialist struggle and sexual emancipation go hand in hand. Fucking and shooting are the same thing!' So, if it's all right with you Mara, I think I want to get into politics instead. I'm sick of this activism and idealism stuff. And this publicity is just the thing to jump-start my career. Maybe I'll run for president someday. That way I can let other people do the thinking for me while I focus on things that really matter, like sexually emancipating you!"

She writhed against him and their legs intertwined.

At that moment his hands began a lust-arousing exploration of her base camp. Passion pounded the blood through her heart, chest, and head.

"I'm sick of fighting, Mara. From now on I want my battles

to be fought here, between sheets."

They were flesh upon flesh, man against woman, skin to skin, pressing, pushing melding, locking, and loading. A carpet bombing of love flowed between them and Mara cried out for more, now needing her desires to be sated. Her defenses weakened.

"Now, Holden. I surrender. Take me now!" Mara gasped

His grease gun entered her wet target, causing her to explode in waves of sensuous pleasure. As he electrified her foxhole, Mara couldn't control her outcry of delight.

"Oh, Baader, I never knew it could be so good!"

The passion was raw and devastating.

Holden took social action against her slippery slope and beheld eager response. "Ulrike… Mara…while my body is free, my heart will forever be in chains until I know that you will be mine. Will you go steady?"

Mara looked at the marvelous man looming over her. "Yes," she said with all of her heart and soul. "I'll go steady with you, Holden, I mean, Baader. There is nothing else I could do with this love I have for you."

Beneath the very beams from which Mara/Meinhof had hanged herself, they slowly, stupendously delivered one another into the infantry of ecstasy. The sky grew inky and moonbeams danced over their jail cell cum love nest. Mara/Meinhof knew that Holden/Baader loved her with the same undying love she felt for him. Her daydreams of Baader and Meinhof were no longer a fantasy. They had come gratifyingly true!

And so it is that Holden and Mara pulled off the greatest crime, the most supreme insurrection known to mankind.

But what, you may ask, could be more banal than a happy ending, especially in a story beset by revolutionary terrorist aficionados?"

Have you learned nothing, Comrade?

The answer to this question is as plain and simple as the questioner and as overlooked as the organ ticking in your chest. There is nothing *more fugitive and agitating than matters of the heart.*

And the struggle that must take place for a heart to override the fears and boundaries set in place by one's ego and society is nothing short of a revolution.

While you recline in the embittered ivory tower of repression, it is idealists like Mara and Holden who dig the trenches for your fantasies. So go ahead, enemy of romance, scoff at true love when you see it. Throw the suffocating mustard gas in order to scare love out of its secure furrow, making it run for cover in secluded restaurants where the wife (in name only) can't find us.

It's your firebrand kind of cynicism that is love's number-one enemy. Haven't you accused the most untainted of lovers with such rotten declarations as, "She's a money digger," or, "He's only interested in her body." (Ridiculous. I am the one in Mensa, not you.) Or, "He's married to me!" (Yes, but I didn't sleep with him until he assured me that it was a loveless marriage) or the inevitable, "Those two deserve each other"?

So you see, it's Mara and Holden who are the real rebels of the story and you, Dear Reader, are the Fascist State. While you try to pull real love out of the heroes' clutching hands in the name of "decency," "authenticity," or "good writing," we fight for the romantic love that knows no bounds, that follows no societally proscribed mandate, that doesn't fall (just yet) under the conservative convention of marriage. We loving transgressors now have something to believe in: a romantic love, a love we could die for.

SAVAGE LOVE!

Who knows love better than Erin Cosgrove, the self-proclaimed rabble rouser of romance? If you enjoyed what you just read, then we've got

False Puppy Love

He wore a faded T-shirt that revealed much of the muscular chest beneath it and American jeans that hung around his legs like a desperate lover waiting for a goodbye kiss. As her eyes roamed his body, Lark knew it would be no small feat to resist his savage charms. But Lark Breeze proves to be difficult game for this persistent hound.

The Hand-me-down Boyfriend

Corlis is interested in the fabulously gorgeous Russell Pierce, but, like a favorite old shirt, she hands him down to her younger sister, Kitty. To Corlis' surprise, Russell and Kitty appear to hit it off! Did she hand down the man who could be her one true love?

Kate's M.R.S. Degree

Kate Trace's window of opportunity is closing. She needs to get a man to save her career. And fast! She's not getting any younger. Now she's going back to college, this time to get her "M.R.S."

TORRID PASSION!

an offer you can't resist! Secret Romance has six new Erin Cosgrove titles that are bound to get your blood racing and your heart a thumpin'.

The Two-Timing Two Stepper

Beautiful and effervescent Bubbles DeSilva takes two-step lessons from the dashing, barrel-chested Angus Dastur. The chemistry between the two Is undeniable, but Bubbles is convinced that he will betray her like all the other men.

Love's Other Shoe

"Who are you?" Missy whispered.

"Let's not be trite. Between us names have no meaning." He peered into her wide, green eyes and murmered, "But you can call me Brandon-Brandon."

"Brandon-Brandon? Is that your real name?"

He rose slowly and effortlessly like a great snow tiger. "No."

Sycophant Love

Ferren is vying with Mott, for the big school scholarship. Will Ferren achieve her heart's desire? Or will Ferren and Motts's competition lead them into each other's arms?

This romance novel is written in Esperanto, the international language of love.

We are pleased to introduce Erin Cosgrove as the first Secret Romance featured writer. She's the author of seven red-hot romance novels, including *False Puppy Love, The Hand-Me-Down Boyfriend, Kate's M.R.S. Degree, Love's Other Shoe, Sycophant Love,* and *The Two-Timing Two-Stepper*, but admits limited personal experiences with actual romance. Blessed or cursed with a mammoth intellect, (she graduated summa cum laude and is a member of Phi Beta Kappa and Mensa), she has selflessly dedicated her sizable brain and sleepless hours to the romance genre. When she isn't writing the love column for the Mensa newsletter, Erin loves to reign over her Romance Revolutionary Web Ring, take long walks on the beach, and sketch her two housemates: Carlos and Trotsky, her adorable coolie loaches.

THE LOEB CLASSICAL LIBRARY

FOUNDED BY JAMES LOEB

EDITED BY

G. P. GOOLD

JOSEPHUS

LCL 456

JOSEPHUS

JEWISH ANTIQUITIES, BOOK XX
GENERAL INDEX

WITH AN ENGLISH TRANSLATION BY

LOUIS H. FELDMAN

HARVARD UNIVERSITY PRESS

CAMBRIDGE, MASSACHUSETTS
LONDON, ENGLAND

First published 1965
Reprinted 1969, 1981, 1993

ISBN 0-674-99502-3

Printed in Great Britain by St Edmundsbury Press Ltd,
Bury St Edmunds, Suffolk, on acid-free paper.
Bound by Hunter & Foulis Ltd, Edinburgh, Scotland.

CONTENTS

PREFATORY NOTE

THE text of this volume, as of the previous volumes of this version of Josephus, is substantially that of Niese in his *editio maior*, but with a number of changes suggested by other scholars. The manuscript tradition for the last ten books of the *Antiquities* is discussed at length by Niese in the third volume of his edition, pp. iii-lvii, and summarized briefly by Ralph Marcus in the prefatory note to the sixth volume of this series. In translating these books I have, in a number of places, adopted felicitous renderings found in the rough draft left by Dr. Thackeray. Whiston's version may contain many inaccuracies, but it often is hard to improve upon for sheer verve of style, and I have not hesitated in several places to adopt his phraseology. In composing the commentary, I have learned much, especially as to bibliography, from the notes of the late Prof. Ralph Marcus in his personal copy of Josephus, which Mrs. Marcus has been kind enough to place at my disposal.

The text, translation, and commentary of this edition were submitted to the printer in September, 1960. Scholarship after this date has elucidated several points in the commentary ; for references see my critical bibliography, *Scholarship on Philo and Josephus* (*1937–1962*), published this year under the auspices of Yeshiva University.

PREFATORY NOTE

In a number of textual matters I have received assistance from Prof. Hans Petersen and from the editors of the Loeb Library. In the translation I owe much to the suggestions of my mentor, Prof. James A. Notopoulos, and the editors. Rabbi Isaiah Molotin has elucidated several passages for me from his fund of Talmudic knowledge. Finally, in the preparation of the index,* I have been aided greatly by Nathan H. Epstein, Julian Plante, Fred Schreiber, Emanuel White, and, above all, my wife Rivkah. To all of them I am sincerely grateful.

LOUIS H. FELDMAN

13 *August* 1963

* The index, covering all the works of Josephus, has been compiled independently of those at the end of volumes I and III of this series, as well as of that of Niese in his *editio maior*, but it has been checked against all of these.

JEWISH ANTIQUITIES

ΙΟΥΔΑΪΚΗΣ ΑΡΧΑΙΟΛΟΓΙΑΣ

ΒΙΒΛΙΟΝ Κ

(i. 1) Τελευτήσαντος δὲ τοῦ βασιλέως Ἀγρίππα, καθὼς ἐν τῇ πρὸ ταύτης ἀπηγγέλκαμεν βίβλῳ, πέμπει Μάρσῳ διάδοχον Κλαύδιος Καῖσαρ Κάσσιον Λογγῖνον, μνήμῃ τῇ τοῦ βασιλέως τοῦτο χαριζόμενος, πολλὰ διὰ γραμμάτων ὑπ᾽ αὐτοῦ περιόντος ἀξιωθεὶς μηκέτι Μάρσον τῶν κατὰ τὴν Συρίαν 2 πραγμάτων προΐστασθαι. Φᾶδος δὲ ὡς εἰς τὴν Ἰουδαίαν ἐπίτροπος ἀφίκετο, καταλαμβάνει στασιάσαντας τοὺς τὴν Περαίαν κατοικοῦντας[1] Ἰουδαίους πρὸς Φιλαδελφηνοὺς περὶ ὅρων κώμης Ζιᾶς[2] λεγομένης πολεμικῶν[3] ἀνδρῶν ἀνάπλεω· καὶ δὴ οἱ τῆς Περαίας χωρὶς γνώμης τῆς τῶν πρώτων παρ᾽ αὐτοῖς ἀναλαβόντες τὰ ὅπλα πολλοὺς τῶν Φιλαδελ- 3 φηνῶν διαφθείρουσιν. ταῦτα πυθόμενον τὸν Φᾶδον σφόδρα παρώξυνεν, ὅτι μὴ τὴν κρίσιν αὐτῷ παρα-

---

[1] τοὺς τὴν Περαίαν κατοικοῦντας] Iudaeos habitantes trans fluvium Lat.
[2] Reland : μιᾶς codd. : meas Lat.
[3] MWE : πολεμίων A : armatorum Lat.

---

[a] Ant. xix. 350.
[b] Consul in A.D. 30, proconsul of Asia in 40, governor of Syria from 45 to 50. His pre-eminence as a jurist is noted by Tacitus, Ann. xii. 12 ; for an example of his legal mind see Ann. xiv. 43-44.
[c] Procurator A.D. 44–45. Cf. Ant. xix. 363-366.
[d] For a description of Peraea see B.J. iii. 44-47, according

2

JEWISH ANTIQUITIES

BOOK XX

(i. 1) On the death of King Agrippa, as I reported in the previous book,[a] Claudius Caesar sent Cassius Longinus [b] as successor to Marsus. He did this in deference to the memory of the king, who in his lifetime had often sent him letters asking that Marsus might no longer have charge of the administration of Syria. Fadus,[c] on his arrival in Judaea as procurator, found that the Jewish inhabitants of Peraea [d] had fallen out with the people of Philadelphia [e] over the boundaries of a village called Zia,[f] which was infested with warlike men.[g] Moreover, the Peraeans, who had taken up arms without the sanction of their leaders, inflicted much loss of life on the Philadelphians. Fadus, on being informed of this, was greatly incensed that the Peraeans, granted that they thought

Cassius Longinus is appointed governor of Syria. Fadus arrives as procurator of Judaea.

Dispute about boundaries between the Peraean Jews and the people of Philadelphia.

to which it was a trans-Jordanian region extending in length from Machaerus to Pella and in breadth from Philadelphia to the Jordan.

[e] Biblical Rabbah of Ammon, modern *Amman*, capital of the kingdom of Jordan. It was called Philadelphia after Ptolemy II Philadelphus.

[f] MSS. " Mia," *i.e.* " one," the name of the village having dropped out, according to Niese. Reland, followed by Havercamp, Tuch, and Schürer (ii. 146 and n. 348), reads Zia, the name of a village fifteen Roman miles west of Philadelphia. On Zia see Eusebius, *Onom. Sac.*, ed. Larsow and Parthey, pp. 200-201.

[g] Variant " their enemies."

λίποιεν, εἴπερ ὑπὸ τῶν Φιλαδελφηνῶν ἐνόμιζον
4 ἀδικεῖσθαι, ἀλλ᾽[1] ἐφ᾽ ὅπλα χωρήσειαν. λαβὼν οὖν
τρεῖς τοὺς πρώτους αὐτῶν τοὺς καὶ τῆς στάσεως
αἰτίους δῆσαι προσέταξεν, εἶτα τὸν μὲν αὐτῶν
ἀνεῖλεν, ᾽Αννίβας[2] δ᾽ ἦν ὄνομα τούτῳ, ᾽Αμαράμῳ[3]
δὲ καὶ ᾽Ελεαζάρῳ τοῖς δυσὶ φυγὴν ἐπέβαλεν.
5 ἀναιρεῖται δὲ καὶ Θολομαῖος[4] ὁ ἀρχιλῃστὴς μετ᾽ οὐ
πολὺν χρόνον ἀχθεὶς ἐπ᾽ αὐτὸν δέσμιος[5] διατεθεικὼς
μέγιστα κακὰ τὴν ᾽Ιδουμαίαν καὶ τοὺς ῎Αραβας,
ἐκαθάρθη τε λῃστηρίων ἅπασα τοὐντεῦθεν ᾽Ιουδαία[6]
6 προνοίᾳ καὶ φροντίδι τῇ Φάδου· ὃς δὴ καὶ τότε
μεταπεμψάμενος τοὺς ἀρχιερεῖς καὶ τοὺς πρώτους
τῶν ᾽Ιεροσολυμιτῶν[7] παρῄνεσεν αὐτοῖς τὸν ποδήρη
χιτῶνα καὶ τὴν ἱερὰν στολήν, ἣν φορεῖν μόνος ὁ
ἀρχιερεὺς ἔθος ἔχει, εἰς τὴν ᾽Αντωνίαν, ἥπερ ἐστὶ
φρούριον, καταθέσθαι κεισομένην ὑπὸ τῇ ῾Ρωμαίων
7 ἐξουσίᾳ, καθὰ δὴ καὶ πρότερον ἦν. οἱ δὲ ἀντιλέγειν
μὲν οὐκ ἐτόλμων, παρεκάλουν δ᾽ ὅμως τόν τε

---

[1] ἀλλ᾽] ἀλλ᾽ ἀδεῶς E.

[2] AW : ᾽Αννίβα M : antibam Lat.

[3] ᾽Αμεράνω Busb. teste Hudsono.

[4] Θοδομαῖος E teste Hudsono et i. marg. A : Θολεμαῖος codd.
i. argumento : Ptolemaeus Lat.

[5] ἀχθεὶς ἐπ᾽ αὐτὸν δέσμιος] A (ἐπ᾽ αὐτὸν . . . μέγιστ i. ras.
m. 2 angustius scriptae) : ἀχθεὶς ἐπ᾽ αὐτὸν MW : ἀχθεὶς δέσμιος ὑπ᾽ αὐτὸν E : captus et ad eum deductus Lat.

[6] ᾽Ιουδαία A : ἡ ᾽Ιουδαία MW : ἥ τε ᾽Ιουδαία καὶ ᾽Αραβία E
teste Hudsono.

[7] κατὰ τὴν κέλευσιν τοῦ αὐτοκράτορος ante παρῄνεσεν add. E.

---

[a] " In chains " is found in the Ambrosian ms. and in the
Epitome only.

4

themselves wronged by the Philadelphians, had not waited for him to give judgement but had instead resorted to arms. He therefore seized three of their leaders, who were in fact responsible for the revolt and ordered them to be held prisoner. Next he put one of them, named Annibas, to death, and imposed exile on the other two, Amaramus and Eleazar. Not long afterwards Tholomaeus the arch-brigand, who had inflicted very severe mischief upon Idumaea and upon the Arabs, was brought before him in chains *a* and put to death. From then on the whole of Judaea was purged of robber-bands, thanks to the prudent concern displayed by Fadus. *b* He also at that time sent for the chief priests and the leaders of the people of Jerusalem and advised them to deposit the full-length tunic and the sacred robe, which it was the custom for the high priest alone to wear, in Antonia, *c* which is a fortress. There they were to be entrusted to the authority of the Romans, as in fact they had been in times past. *d* They did not dare to gainsay him, but nevertheless they petitioned Fadus and

Fadus orders the high priest's vestments returned to Roman custody.

b Cf. another account in Josephus of the following incident, *Ant.* xv. 406-407.

c Restored by Herod the Great and called Antonia in honour of Mark Antony (*B.J.* i. 401 and *Ant.* xviii. 92), described at length in *B.J.* v, 238-247.

d *Ant.* xv. 406. Cf. *Ant.* xviii. 93, which notes that after the reign of Archelaus, the successor of Herod the Great, when the Romans took over the government of Judaea, they assumed control of the high priest's vestments. According to *Ant.* xviii. 90, Vitellius, the Roman governor of Syria, had agreed, in A.D. 36–37, to allow the Jews to resume custody of these vestments. The passage parallel with ours, *B.J.* ii. 220, praises Cuspius Fadus for abstaining from any interference with the Jewish customs and for thus keeping the nation at peace ; but the advice to deposit the high priest's sacred garments in Antonia did constitute such an interference.

5

Φᾶδον καὶ τὸν Λογγῖνον,[1] ἀφίκετο γὰρ καὶ αὐτὸς
εἰς τὰ Ἱεροσόλυμα πολλὴν ἐπαγόμενος δύναμιν
φόβῳ τοῦ μὴ τὰ προστάγματα Φάδου τὸ πλῆθος
τῶν Ἰουδαίων νεωτερίζειν ἀναγκάσῃ, πρῶτον μὲν
αὐτοῖς ἐπιτρέψαι πρέσβεις ὡς Καίσαρα πέμψαι τοὺς
αἰτησομένους παρ' αὐτοῦ τὴν ἱερὰν στολὴν ὑπὸ τὴν
αὐτῶν ἐξουσίαν ἔχειν, εἶτα δὲ περιμεῖναι μέχρις ἂν
8 γνῶσιν, τί πρὸς ταῦτα Κλαύδιος ἀποκρίναιτο. οἱ
δὲ ἐπιτρέψειν αὐτοῖς ἔφασαν ἀποστεῖλαι τοὺς πρέσβεις, εἰ λάβοιεν τοὺς παῖδας ὁμηρεύσοντας. ὑπα-
κουσάντων δ' ἑτοίμως ἐκείνων καὶ δόντων ἐξεπέμ-
9 φθησαν οἱ πρέσβεις. παραγενομένων δὲ εἰς τὴν
Ῥώμην αὐτῶν γνοὺς ὁ νεώτερος Ἀγρίππας ὁ τοῦ
τετελευτηκότος παῖς, καθ' ἣν ἥκουσιν αἰτίαν,
ἐτύγχανεν δὲ ὢν παρὰ Κλαυδίῳ Καίσαρι, καθὼς
καὶ πρότερον εἴπομεν, παρακαλεῖ τὸν Καίσαρα συγ-
χωρῆσαι τοῖς Ἰουδαίοις ἅπερ ἠξίουν περὶ τῆς ἱερᾶς
στολῆς καὶ Φάδῳ περὶ τούτων ἐπιστεῖλαι.
10 (2) Καλέσας δὲ Κλαύδιος τοὺς πρέσβεις ἔφη
ταῦτα συγχωρεῖν καὶ ἐκέλευεν αὐτοὺς Ἀγρίππᾳ
χάριν εἰδέναι, ταῦτα γὰρ ἐκείνου ποιεῖν ἀξιώσαντος,
ἐπί τε ταῖς ἀποκρίσεσιν τοιαύτην ἐπιστολὴν ἔδωκεν·
11 " Κλαύδιος Καῖσαρ Γερμανικὸς δημαρχικῆς ἐξουσίας τὸ πέμπτον ὕπατος ἀποδεδειγμένος τὸ τέταρτον αὐτοκράτωρ τὸ δέκατον πατὴρ πατρίδος Ἱεροσολυμιτῶν ἄρχουσι βουλῇ δήμῳ Ἰουδαίων παντὶ
12 ἔθνει χαίρειν. Ἀγρίππα τοῦ ἐμοῦ, ὃν ἐγὼ ἔθρεψα
καὶ ἔχω σὺν ἐμαυτῷ εὐσεβέστατον ὄντα, προσαγα-
γόντος μοι τοὺς ὑμετέρους πρέσβεις εὐχαριστοῦντας

---

[1] τὸν τῆς Ἀραβίας ἐπίτροπον post Λογγῖνον add. E.

Longinus—for the latter, out of fear that Fadus'
commands would force the Jewish people into rebellion, had himself come to Jerusalem with a large
force—first to allow them to send a delegation to
Caesar to ask him for permission to keep the sacred
robe in their own hands, and secondly to wait until
they knew what answer Claudius made to this petition. Fadus and Longinus replied that they would
permit them to send a delegation if their children
were delivered as hostages to them. To this they
promptly agreed and delivered the hostages, whereupon the envoys were dispatched. On their arrival
in Rome the younger Agrippa, son of the deceased
king, who, as I said before,[a] was, as a matter of fact,
at the court of Claudius Caesar, took note of the purpose of their coming and entreated Caesar to grant
the Jews their petition regarding the sacred robe and
to send a letter to Fadus to that effect.

(2) Claudius, when he had summoned the envoys, *Claudius*
informed them that he was granting their petition, *allows the*
adding that they must thank Agrippa for it, since *Jews to*
he was acting at Agrippa's request. To confirm his *keep the high priest's*
answer, he gave them a letter, which I quote : " Clau- *vestments.*
dius Caesar Germanicus, in the fifth year of tribuni-
cian power, designated consul for the fourth time,
Imperator for the tenth time, Father of his country,
to the rulers, council, and people of Jerusalem [b] and
to the whole nation of the Jews, greeting. My
friend Agrippa, whom I have brought up and now
have with me, a man of the greatest piety, brought
your envoys before me. They gave thanks for the

---

[a] *Ant.* xix. 360.
[b] On Jerusalem as the civil centre of the Jewish state *cf.*
Ant. xiv. 74.

7

JOSEPHUS

ἐφ᾽ ᾗ πεποίημαι τοῦ ἔθνους ὑμῶν κηδεμονίᾳ, καὶ
αἰτησαμένων¹ σπουδαίως καὶ φιλοτίμως τὴν ἱερὰν
ἐσθῆτα καὶ τὸν στέφανον ὑπὸ τὴν ἐξουσίαν ὑμῶν
εἶναι, συγχωρῶ καθὼς ὁ κράτιστος καί μοι τιμιώ-
13 τατος Οὐιτέλλιος ἐποίησεν. συγκατεθέμην δὲ τῇ
γνώμῃ ταύτῃ πρῶτον διὰ τὸ ἐμαυτοῦ εὐσεβὲς καὶ
τὸ βούλεσθαι ἑκάστους κατὰ τὰ πάτρια θρησκεύειν,
ἔπειτα δὲ εἰδώς, ὅτι καὶ αὐτῷ βασιλεῖ Ἡρώδῃ καὶ
Ἀριστοβούλῳ τῷ νεωτέρῳ, ὧν τὴν πρὸς ἐμαυτὸν
εὐσέβειαν καὶ τὴν περὶ ὑμᾶς² γινώσκω σπουδὴν
πάνυ χαριοῦμαι³ ταῦτα ποιήσας, πρὸς οὓς ἔστι μοι
πλεῖστα δίκαια φιλίας κρατίστους ὄντας κἀμοὶ
14 τιμίους.⁴ ἔγραψα δὲ περὶ τούτων καὶ Κουσπίῳ
Φάδῳ τῷ ᾽μῷ ἐπιτρόπῳ. οἱ τὰ γράμματα κομίζοντες Κορνήλιος Κέρωνος⁵ Τρύφων Θευδίωνος
Δωρόθεος Ναθαναήλου Ἰωάννης Ἰωάννου. ἐγράφη
πρὸ τεσσάρων καλανδῶν Ἰουλίου⁶ ἐπὶ ὑπάτων Ῥού-
φου καὶ Πομπηίου Σιλουανοῦ.''
15 (3) Ἠιτήσατο δὲ καὶ Ἡρώδης, ὁ ἀδελφὸς μὲν
Ἀγρίππα τοῦ τετελευτηκότος, Χαλκίδος δὲ τὴν

¹ αἰτησαμένων] αἰτησαμένους coni.: αἰτησαμένων ⟨αὐτῶν⟩
Richards et Shutt.   ² Α: ἡμᾶς MW.
³ πάνυ χαριοῦμαι] ed. pr.: amplissimas amicitias collocabo
Lat.: om. codd.: lacunam post σπουδὴν indicat Niese.
⁴ καὶ ἐκέλευεν (§ 10) . . . τιμίους] δι᾽ Ἀγρίππαν Ε; πρὸς
οὓς . . . τιμίους] potentium personarum Lat.
⁵ Κέρωνος] MW: καὶ Λέων Α: Leo Lat.
⁶ Ἰουλίου] Hudson ex codd. Lat. dett.: om. codd.: lacunam indicat Niese.

ᵃ Ant. xviii. 90. Tacitus, Ann. vi. 32, mentions his intimacy with Claudius. Suetonius, Vit. 2 and Dio lx. 21. 2,
note that he shared two regular consulships with Claudius and
was in charge of the empire while Claudius was away on his
British expedition. His extreme flattery of Claudius, as well
8

tender care that I have shown your nation and
earnestly and zealously requested that the holy vestments and the crown might be placed in your hands.
I grant this request, in accordance with the precedent
set by Vitellius,[a] that excellent man for whom I have
the greatest esteem. I have given my consent to
this measure, first because I cherish religion myself
and wish to see every nation maintain the religious
practices that are traditional with it, and secondly
because I know that in doing so I shall give great
pleasure[b] to King Herod[c] himself and to Aristobulus
the Younger[d]—excellent men for whom I have high
regard, men of whose devotion to me and zeal for
your interest I am aware and with whom I have very
many ties of friendship. I am also writing on these
matters to my procurator Cuspius Fadus.[e] The
bearers of this letter are Cornelius son of Ceron, Tryphon son of Theudion, Dorotheus son of Nathanael,
and John son of John. Written on the fourth day
before the Kalends of July,[f] in the consulship of
Rufus and Pompeius Silvanus."[g]

(3) Herod, brother of the deceased Agrippa, who
was at this time charged with the administration

*Herod of
Chalcis ob-
tains fur-
ther con-
cessions.*

as of the latter's wives and freedmen, is also stressed by
Suetonius.

[b] " I shall give great pleasure " is from the *editio princeps*.
The MSS. apparently have a lacuna.

[c] King of Chalcis, brother of Agrippa I.

[d] Son of Herod king of Chalcis ; *cf. Ant.* xviii. 134, 137 ;
xx. 104.

[e] In *Ant.* xv. 407, where the embassy to Claudius is also
mentioned, the emperor is reported to have ordered Vitellius,
who was then commander in Syria, to grant the Jews control
of the vestments.

[f] The Greek MSS. lack " July," which is supplied by some
of the inferior MSS. of the Latin version. [g] 28 June A.D. 45.

JOSEPHUS

ἀρχὴν κατὰ τὸν χρόνον ἐκεῖνον πεπιστευμένος,
Κλαύδιον Καίσαρα τὴν ἐξουσίαν τοῦ νεὼ καὶ τῶν
ἱερῶν χρημάτων καὶ τὴν τῶν ἀρχιερέων χειροτονίαν,
16 πάντων τε ἐπέτυχεν. ἐξ ἐκείνου τε πᾶσι τοῖς ἀπο-
γόνοις αὐτοῦ παρέμεινεν ἡ ἐξουσία μέχρι τῆς τοῦ
πολέμου τελευτῆς. καὶ δὴ ὁ Ἡρώδης μεθίστησιν
τῆς ἀρχιερωσύνης τὸν ἐπικαλούμενον Κανθήραν[1]
Ἰωσήπῳ τῷ Καμεὶ[2] ἀντ᾽ ἐκείνου τὴν διαδοχὴν τῆς
τιμῆς παρασχόμενος.

17 (ii. 1) Κατὰ τοῦτον δὲ τὸν καιρὸν τῶν Ἀδιαβηνῶν βασιλὶς Ἑλένη[3] καὶ ὁ παῖς αὐτῆς Ἰζάτης[4] εἰς
τὰ Ἰουδαίων ἔθη τὸν βίον μετέβαλον διὰ τοιαύτην
18 αἰτίαν· Μονόβαζος[5] ὁ τῶν Ἀδιαβηνῶν βασιλεύς,
ᾧ καὶ Βαζαῖος[6] ἐπίκλησις ἦν, τῆς ἀδελφῆς Ἑλένης
ἁλοὺς ἔρωτι τῇ πρὸς γάμου κοινωνίᾳ ἄγεται καὶ
κατέστησεν ἐγκύμονα. συγκαθεύδων δέ ποτε τῇ
γαστρὶ τῆς γυναικὸς τὴν χεῖρα προσαναπαύσας
ἡνίκα καθύπνωσεν, φωνῆς τινος ἔδοξεν ὑπακούειν[7]

[1] Κανθηρᾶν E et ex corr. A.
[2] Καμεὶ] Niese : Καμεῖ i. marg. γρ A : Καμνὶ A : τοῦ Κανεὶ
MW : τοῦ Καμεὶ E : Cami Lat. : cf. § 103, ubi Καμοιδὶ vel
simile extat.
[3] Ἐλένη hic et infra M et plerumque W.
[4] Iazates Lat.
[5] Μηνόβαζος E.
[6] A : Βαζέως MW : Bazeus Lat.
[7] A : ἀκούειν MWE : ut . . . subito . . . audiret Lat.

[a] Or " from that time."
[b] The last high priest mentioned by Josephus before the
appointment of Joseph the son of Camei is not Cantheras but
Elionaeus the son of Cantheras (or Cithaerus : *Ant.* xix. 342) ;
and Schürer, ii. 271-272 n. 14, says that our Cantheras must
be Elionaeus. Kirsopp Lake, " The Chronology of Acts,"
in Foakes Jackson and Kirsopp Lake, *The Beginnings of
Christianity*, v, 1933, p. 455, presents two conjectures : (1)

of Chalcis, also asked Claudius Caesar to give him
authority over the temple and the holy vessels and
the selection of the high priests—all of which requests
he obtained. This authority, derived from him,[a]
passed to his descendants alone until the end of the
war. Herod accordingly removed the high priest surnamed Cantheras [b] from his position and conferred
the succession to this office upon Joseph the son of
Camei.[c]

(ii. 1) [d] At the same time Helena, queen of Adiabene,[e] and her son Izates became converts to Judaism
under the following circumstances. Monobazus, surnamed Bazaeus, king of Adiabene, seized with a
passion for his sister Helena, took her as his partner
in marriage and got her pregnant. On one occasion
as he was sleeping beside her, he rested his hand on
his wife's belly after she had gone to sleep, whereupon
he thought he heard a voice bidding him remove his

Monobazus,
king of
Adiabene,
his wife
Helena, and
their son
Izates.

Cantheras was a surname of Elionaeus; or (2) Josephus may
have omitted the appointment of a high priest named Cantheras. He suggests, on the basis of *Ant.* iii. 320-321, which
mentions that a famine occurred during the reign of Claudius
while Ishmael was high priest, that Josephus has neglected
to mention the high priesthood of this Ishmael, and that it
was he who was surnamed Cantheras. The Talmud, *Pesaḥim*
57 a, probably refers to the family of Cantheras when one of
the rabbis laments the evil decrees promulgated by the house
of Kathros.

[c] *Cf. Ant.* xx. 103. Niese conjectures that this is perhaps
the same name as Camith (*Ant.* xviii. 34); so, more posi-
tively, Schürer, ii. 272 n. 16.

[d] Thackeray, in his copy of Josephus, appropriately remarks that the story of Izates is written in an easy flowing
style very different from that of *Ant.* xvii-xix. He also notes
that there are certain obvious parallels with the story of
Joseph in Genesis.

[e] A district in northern Mesopotamia, its chief city being
Arbela.

JOSEPHUS

κελευούσης αἴρειν ἀπὸ τῆς νηδύος τὴν χεῖρα καὶ μὴ
θλίβειν τὸ ἐν αὐτῇ βρέφος θεοῦ προνοίᾳ καὶ ἀρχῆς
19 τυχὸν καὶ τέλους εὐτυχοῦς τευξόμενον. ταραχθεὶς
οὖν ὑπὸ τῆς φωνῆς εὐθὺς διεγερθεὶς ἔφραζε τῇ
γυναικὶ ταῦτα, καί γε[1] τὸν υἱὸν Ἰζάτην ἐπεκάλεσεν.
20 ἦν δὲ αὐτῷ Μονόβαζος τούτου πρεσβύτερος ἐκ τῆς
Ἑλένης γενόμενος ἄλλοι τε παῖδες ἐξ ἑτέρων γυναικῶν. τὴν μέντοι πᾶσαν εὔνοιαν ὡς εἰς μονογενῆ
21 τὸν Ἰζάτην ἔχων φανερὸς ἦν. φθόνος δὲ τοὐντεῦθεν
τῷ παιδὶ παρὰ τῶν ὁμοπατρίων ἀδελφῶν ἐφύετο
κἀκ τούτου μῖσος ηὔξετο λυπουμένων ἁπάντων, ὅτι
22 τὸν Ἰζάτην αὐτῶν ὁ πατὴρ προτιμῴη. ταῦτα δὲ
καίπερ σαφῶς αἰσθανόμενος ὁ πατὴρ ἐκείνοις μὲν
συνεγίνωσκεν ὡς μὴ διὰ κακίαν αὐτὸ πάσχουσιν
ἀλλ' ἤτοι[2] παρὰ τοῦ πατρὸς αὐτῶν ἕκαστον ἀξι-
οῦντα[3] εὐνοίας τυγχάνειν,[4] τὸν δὲ νεανίαν,[5] σφόδρα
γὰρ ἐδεδοίκει περὶ αὐτοῦ, μὴ μισούμενος ὑπὸ τῶν
ἀδελφῶν πάθοι τι, πολλὰ δωρησάμενος πρὸς Ἀβεν-
νήριγον[6] ἐκπέμπει τὸν Σπασίνου χάρακος βασιλέα,
παρακατατιθέμενος ἐκείνῳ τὴν τοῦ παιδὸς σωτη-
23 ρίαν. ὁ δὲ Ἀβεννήριγος ἄσμενός τε δέχεται τὸν

[1] καί γε] γρ καὶ γεννώμενον i. marg. A: καὶ E: καὶ γενόμενον ed. pr. : et natum Lat.   [2] ἴσης Ernesti.
[3] coni. : ἀξιῶν MW: ἀξιών, ὡ ex ὁ corr. A : ἀξιοῦν Cocceji :
ἀξιοῦσιν Ernesti.
[4] ἀλλ' ἤτοι . . . τυγχάνειν] sed quoniam singuli favorem
patris habere desiderabant Lat. : ἀλλ' ἢ τῷ παρὰ τοῦ πατρὸς
αὐτὸν ἕκαστον ἀξιοῦν εὐνοίας τυγχάνειν Bekker : ἀλλ' ὅτι τῆς
παρὰ τοῦ πατρὸς αὐτοῦ ἕκαστος ἀξιοίη εὐνοίας τυγχάνειν coni.
Niese.
[5] A : Ἰζάτην MWE Lat.   [6] MW : Σαβιννήριγον A.

---

[a] Zoitos (*Midrash Rabbah on Genesis* xlvi. 10). According
to F. Justi, *Iranisches Namenbuch*, 1895, *s.v.* " Yazata," pp.
145-146, the name Izates in Iranian means " genius," " godly
12

hand from her womb so as not to cramp the babe within it, which by the providence of God had had a happy start and would also attain a fortunate end. Disturbed by the voice, he at once awoke and told these things to his wife ; and he called the son who was born to him Izates.[a] He had an elder son by Helena named Monobazus and other children by his other wives ; but it was clear that all his favour was concentrated on Izates as if he were an only child.[b] In consequence of this, Izates' half-brothers by their common father grew envious of the child. Their envy grew into an ever-increasing hatred, for they were all vexed that their father preferred Izates to themselves. Although their father clearly perceived this, he pardoned them, for he attributed their feeling not to any bad motive but rather to the desire that each of them had to win his father's favour for himself. Yet, as he was greatly alarmed for the young Izates, lest the hatred of his brothers should bring him to some harm, he gave him an abundance of presents and sent him off to Abennerigus [c] the king of Charax Spasini,[d] to whom he entrusted the safety of the boy. Abennerigus welcomed the lad and

being " (especially used of Mithra), and later (in the plural) " God."

[b] For the use of the term " only-begotten " (μονογενής) in the sense of " favourite," " best-beloved," or " one who has no equal," see P. Winter, " ΜΟΝΟΓΕΝΗΣ ΠΑΡΑ ΠΑΤΡΟΣ," *Zeit. f. Religions- und Geistesgesch.* v, 1953, pp. 335-365.

[c] Abinerglos according to one of his coins. He reigned from A.D. 5 to 21.

[d] Lit. Spasinus' Camp. *Cf. Ant.* i. 145. It is Palmyrene *Karak Aspasinā* or *Karkā*, the capital city of the tiny kingdom of Charakene. *Cf.* Ptolemy vi. 3. 2 (Χάραξ Πασινοῦ) and Dio lxviii. 28. 4 (ὁ Χάραξ ὁ τοῦ Σπασίνου καλούμενος). It lies between the mouths of the Tigris and the Euphrates.

νεανίαν καὶ διὰ πολλῆς εὐνοίας ἄγων γυναῖκα μὲν
αὐτῷ τὴν θυγατέρα, Σαμαχὼ¹ δ' ἦν ὄνομα ταύτῃ,
δίδωσι· δωρεῖται δὲ χώραν, ἐξ ἧς μεγάλας λήψοιτο
προσόδους.

24 (2) Μονόβαζος δὲ ἤδη γηραιὸς ὢν καὶ τοῦ ζῆν
ὀλίγον αὐτῷ τὸν λοιπὸν ὁρῶν χρόνον ἠθέλησεν εἰς
ὄψιν ἀφικέσθαι τῷ παιδὶ πρὸ τοῦ τελευτῆσαι. μεταπεμψάμενος οὖν αὐτὸν ἀσπάζεται φιλοφρονέστατα,
25 καὶ χώραν δίδωσιν Καρρῶν² λεγομένην. φέρειν δ'
ἡ γῆ πλεῖστον τὸ ἄμωμον ἀγαθή· ἔστι δ' ἐν αὐτῇ
καὶ τὰ λείψανα τῆς λάρνακος, ᾗ³ Νῶχον⁴ ἐκ τῆς
ἐπομβρίας διασεσῶσθαι λόγος ἔχει, καὶ μέχρι νῦν
26 ταῦτα τοῖς ἰδεῖν βουλομένοις ἐπιδείκνυται. διέτριβεν οὖν ὁ Ἰζάτης ἐν τῇ χώρᾳ ταύτῃ μέχρι τῆς τελευτῆς τοῦ πατρός. ᾗ δ' ἐξέλιπεν ἡμέρᾳ τὸν βίον ὁ
Μονόβαζος ἡ βασιλὶς Ἑλένη μεταπέμπεται πάντας
τοὺς μεγιστᾶνας καὶ τῆς βασιλείας σατράπας καὶ
27 τοὺς τὰς δυνάμεις πεπιστευμένους. οἷς ἀφικο-
μένοις, "ὅτι μὲν ὁ ἐμὸς ἀνήρ," εἶπε,⁵ "τῆς βασιλείας

¹ E : Σαμαχὼς Niese : Σαμαχὼ· A : Σάμαχος MW : Amachos Lat. : Συμαχὼ Dindorf.
² A : Καιρῶν MW : Καρεῶν (κ ex ν corr.) E : Carrorum
Lat.   ³ E : ἦν codd.
⁴ Νῶχος E : Νώεον Dindorf.
⁵ τῆς βασιλείας (§ 26) . . . εἶπε] A (in ras.): om. MW Lat.

ᵃ Various spellings : Samachōs, Samachōs, Amachos,
Symacho. The name in Syriac means " recreation."
ᵇ The location of Carron presents considerable difficulties.
It is not Carrhae, which is in northern Mesopotamia. The
emendation to Gordyene (cf. Ant. i. 93), on the Armenian
border east of the sources of the Tigris, is more acceptable
geographically, since it is closer to Ararat, the Biblical site
where Noah's ark rested. Hence, the reading proposed by
J. Macquart, Osteuropäische und ostasiatische Streifzüge,
1903, p. 289 n. 4, is Καρδοῦ.

viewed him with such goodwill that he gave him his daughter, named Symmacho,[a] as a wife and conferred on him a territory that would insure him a large income.

(2) Monobazus, being now old and seeing that he had not long to live, desired to lay eyes on his son before he died. He therefore sent for him, gave him the warmest of welcomes and presented him with a district called Carron.[b] The land there has excellent soil for the production of amomum [c] in the greatest abundance; it also possesses the remains of the ark [d] in which report has it that Noah was saved from the flood—remains which to this day are shown to those who are curious to see them. Izates, accordingly, resided in this district until his father's death. On the day when Monobazus departed this life, Queen Helena sent for all the high nobles and satraps of the realm and those who were charged with military commands. On their arrival she said to them : " I think that you are not unaware that my husband

Izates receives the district of Carron, containing remnants of Noah's ark.

---

[c] An aromatic plant of the ginger family, though its exact identity is unknown. See Wagler, " Amomum," Pauly-Wissowa, i, 1894, pp. 1873-1874.

[d] In *Ant.* i. 90 the ark is said to have landed on a mountain-top in Armenia. In *Ant.* i. 92 Josephus notes that the remains were shown by the Armenians even in his own day. Berosus the Chaldaean (third century B.C.), as quoted by Josephus, *Ant.* i. 93, also notes that a portion of the ark was still said to be extant in Armenia on the mountain of the Cordyaeans (modern Kurdistan) and that people carried off pieces of the bitumen which they used as apotropaic charms. As Nicolas of Damascus tells the story (quoted by Josephus, *Ant.* i. 95), during the time of the flood, a man, who, he thinks, might well have been Noah, landed with his ark upon a great mountain called Baris in the country of Minyas in Armenia close to the Ararat mentioned in the Biblical account.

αὐτῷ διάδοχον Ἰζάτην ηὔξατο γενέσθαι καὶ τοῦτον
ἄξιον ἔκρινεν, οὐδ᾽ ὑμᾶς λεληθέναι δοκῶ, περιμένω
δὲ ὅμως καὶ τὴν ὑμετέραν κρίσιν· μακάριος γὰρ
οὐχ ὁ παρ᾽ ἑνός, ἀλλὰ πλειόνων καὶ θελόντων τὴν
28 ἀρχὴν λαμβάνων.᾽᾽ ἡ μὲν ταῦτ᾽ εἶπεν ἐπὶ πείρᾳ
τοῦ τί φρονοῖεν οἱ συγκληθέντες¹· οἱ δὲ ἀκούσαντες
πρῶτον μὲν προσεκύνησαν τὴν βασιλίδα, καθὼς
ἔθος ἐστὶν αὐτοῖς, εἶτ᾽ ἔφασαν τὴν τοῦ βασιλέως
γνώμην βεβαιοῦν καὶ ὑπακούσεσθαι χαίροντες
Ἰζάτῃ δικαίως ὑπὸ τοῦ πατρὸς προκριθέντι τῶν
29 ἀδελφῶν κατὰ τὰς εὐχὰς τὰς ἁπάντων. βούλεσθαί
τ᾽ ἔφασαν προαποκτεῖναι² πρῶτον αὐτοῦ τοὺς
ἀδελφοὺς καὶ συγγενεῖς ὑπὲρ τοῦ τὴν ἀρχὴν Ἰζάτην
μετ᾽ ἀσφαλείας κατασχεῖν· φθαρέντων γὰρ ἐκείνων
καθαιρεθήσεσθαι πάντα τὸν φόβον τὸν ὑπὸ μίσους
30 τοῦ παρ᾽ αὐτῶν καὶ φθόνου γινόμενον. πρὸς ταῦτα
ἡ Ἑλένη χάριν μὲν αὐτοῖς ὡμολόγει τῆς πρὸς
αὐτὴν καὶ τὸν Ἰζάτην εὐνοίας ἔχειν, παρεκάλει δ᾽
ὅμως ἐπισχεῖν τὴν περὶ τῆς ἀναιρέσεως τῶν ἀδελφῶν γνώμην μέχρι ἂν Ἰζάτης παραγενόμενος συν-
31 δοκιμάσῃ. οἱ δ᾽ ἐπεὶ ἀνελεῖν συμβουλεύσαντες οὐκ
ἔπεισαν,³ ἀλλὰ φυλάσσειν αὐτοὺς δεσμίους παρῄνουν
μέχρι τῆς ἐκείνου παρουσίας ὑπὲρ ἀσφαλείας τῆς
ἑαυτῶν. συνεβούλευον δ᾽ αὐτῇ μεταξὺ προστήσα-
σθαί τινα τῆς ἀρχῆς ἐπίτροπον, ᾧ μάλιστα πιστεύει.
32 πείθεται τούτοις ἡ Ἑλένη, καὶ καθίστησι τὸν πρεσβύτατον παῖδα Μονόβαζον⁴ βασιλέα περιθεῖσα τὸ
διάδημα καὶ δοῦσα τὸν σημαντῆρα τοῦ πατρὸς

¹ ἐπὶ πείρᾳ . . . συγκληθέντες] om. E; μαθησομένη post συγ-
κληθέντες add. A.

had set his heart on Izates succeeding to his kingdom and had deemed him worthy of this honour ; nevertheless, I await your decision. For he is blessed who receives his realm from the hands not of one but of many who willingly give their consent." She said this to test the disposition of those whom she had called together. They, on hearing her words, first of all, according to their custom, made obeisance to the queen, and thereupon replied that they gave their support to the king's decision, and would gladly obey Izates, who, as one and all had prayed in their hearts, had been justly preferred by his father to his brothers. They added that they first wished to put his brothers and kinsmen to death in order that Izates might be seated on the throne with full security ; for if they were destroyed, all fear arising from the hatred and envy that they bore towards Izates would be removed. In reply Helena expressed her gratitude for their goodwill to herself and to Izates ; but she nevertheless entreated them to defer their decision about putting the brothers to death until after Izates had arrived and given his approval. Failing to persuade her to put the brothers to death as they advised, they, for their own safety, admonished her at least to keep them in custody until his arrival. They also advised her meanwhile to appoint as trustee of the realm someone in whom she had most confidence. Helena agreed to this and set up Monobazus, her eldest son, as king. Putting the diadem upon his head and giving him his father's signet ring and what they call

Izates is named to succeed Monobazus.

---

2 κατὰ . . . προαποκτεῖναι] et omnium pariter esse votum ut . . . occiderent Lat.

3 ἐπεὶ . . . ἔπεισαν] om. E.

4 om. E.

17

δακτύλιον τήν τε σαμψηρὰν[1] ὀνομαζομένην παρ’
αὐτοῖς, διοικεῖν τε τὴν βασιλείαν παρῄνεσεν μέχρι
33 τῆς τοῦ ἀδελφοῦ παρουσίας. ἧκε δ’ οὗτος ταχέως
ἀκούσας τὴν τοῦ πατρὸς τελευτὴν καὶ διαδέχεται
τὸν ἀδελφὸν Μονόβαζον ὑπεκστάντα[2] τῆς ἀρχῆς
αὐτῷ.[3]
34 (3) Καθ’ ὃν δὲ χρόνον[4] ὁ Ἰζάτης ἐν τῷ Σπασίνου
χάρακι[5] διέτριβεν Ἰουδαῖός τις ἔμπορος Ἀνανίας
ὄνομα πρὸς τὰς γυναῖκας εἰσιὼν τοῦ βασιλέως
ἐδίδασκεν αὐτὰς τὸν θεὸν σέβειν, ὡς Ἰουδαίοις
35 πάτριον ἦν, καὶ δὴ δι’ αὐτῶν εἰς γνῶσιν ἀφικόμενος
τῷ Ἰζάτῃ κἀκεῖνον ὁμοίως συνανέπεισεν μετακλη-
θέντι τε ὑπὸ τοῦ πατρὸς εἰς τὴν Ἀδιαβηνὴν συνεξ-
ῆλθεν κατὰ πολλὴν ὑπακούσας δέησιν· συνεβεβήκει
δὲ καὶ τὴν Ἑλένην ὁμοίως ὑφ’ ἑτέρου τινὸς Ἰουδαίου διδαχθεῖσαν[6] εἰς τοὺς ἐκείνων μετακεκομίσθαι
36 νόμους. ὁ δ’ Ἰζάτης ὡς παρέλαβεν τὴν βασιλείαν,
ἀφικόμενος εἰς τὴν Ἀδιαβηνὴν καὶ θεασάμενος τούς
τε ἀδελφοὺς καὶ τοὺς ἄλλους συγγενεῖς δεδεμένους
37 ἐδυσχέρανεν τῷ γεγονότι. καὶ τὸ μὲν ἀνελεῖν ἢ

---

[1] MW : συμψειρὰν, ει i. ras. A : sampseram Lat.
[2] E : ὑπερεκστάντος codd. : ὑπεκστάντος Niese.
[3] καὶ διαδέχεται . . . αὐτῷ] et fratri denuo successit in reg-
no, quod ille absenti perceperat conservandum Lat.
[4] A : καιρὸν MWE.
[5] ὁ Ἰζάτης . . . χάρακι] Gaius in vallo Spasini Lat.
[6] A : διαλεχθεῖσαν MW : eruditam Lat.

---

[a] Clementz, in a note in his translation of the *Antiquities*
into German, explains that *sampsa* means the sun among the
Arabs and that the *sampsera* was a golden shield in the form
of the sun which was carried as a symbol of sovereignty.

X   [b] G. Klein, *Der älteste christliche Katechismus*, 1909, pp.
137-138, holds that Jewish traders often acted as mission-
aries. They pretended, he says, to sell the balm of life, *sam*

the *sampsera*,[a] she exhorted him to administer the kingdom until his brother's arrival. The latter, on hearing of his father's death, quickly arrived and succeeded his brother Monobazus, who made way for him.

(3) Now during the time when Izates resided at Charax Spasini, a certain Jewish merchant [b] named Ananias visited the king's wives and taught them to worship God after the manner of the Jewish tradition. It was through their agency that he was brought to the notice of Izates, whom he similarly won over with the co-operation of the women. When Izates was summoned by his father to Adiabene, Ananias accompanied him in obedience to his urgent request. It so happened, moreover, that Helena had likewise been instructed by another Jew and had been brought over to their laws. When Izates came to Adiabene to take over the kingdom and saw his brothers and his other kinsmen in chains, he was distressed at what had been done. Regarding it as impious either

ḥayyim (*Tanḥuma Meẓora* 5), but instead offered the prescription of the good life as described in Psalm xxxiv. 14, *sam* representing, according to Klein, the first letters of the words *sur mera'* (Ps. xxxiv. 14), " depart from evil." But this is simply a parable, of which the Midrashic works have many, that happens to use the merchant (a common symbol) as the instrument of conveying its moral; it does not necessarily indicate that such an incident was a frequent occurrence. It is interesting to note that the same point made in the *Tan-ḥuma* is also made in the Talmud, *Abodah Zarah* 19 b, by a rabbi named Alexander without using a merchant as the medium of a story. W. D. Davies, *Paul and Rabbinic Judaism*, 1948, p. 133 n. 1, citing Klein, adds : " It is tempting to suggest that the use of καπηλεύοντες, from the verb meaning ' to be a retail-dealer,' by Paul in 2 Cor. ii. 17 may have, as its background, this trading missionary activity of which Klein speaks."

φυλάττειν δεδεμένους ἀσεβὲς ἡγούμενος, τὸ δὲ
μνησικακοῦντας ἔχειν σὺν αὐτῷ μὴ¹ δεδεμένους²
σφαλερὸν εἶναι νομίζων, τοὺς μὲν ὁμηρεύσοντας
μετὰ τέκνων εἰς τὴν Ῥώμην ἐξέπεμψε Κλαυδίῳ
Καίσαρι, τοὺς δὲ πρὸς Ἀρταβάνην³ τὸν Πάρθον ἐφ᾿
ὁμοίαις προφάσεσιν ἀπέστειλεν.

38   (4) Πυθόμενος⁴ δὲ πάνυ τοῖς Ἰουδαίων ἔθεσιν
χαίρειν τὴν μητέρα τὴν ἑαυτοῦ⁵ ἔσπευσε καὶ αὐτὸς
εἰς ἐκεῖνα μεταθέσθαι, νομίζων τε μὴ ἂν εἶναι
βεβαίως Ἰουδαῖος, εἰ μὴ περιτέμοιτο,⁶ πράττειν
39 ἦν ἔτοιμος. μαθοῦσα δ᾿ ἡ μήτηρ κωλύειν ἐπειρᾶτο
ἐπιφέρειν αὐτῷ κίνδυνον λέγουσα· βασιλέα γὰρ
εἶναι, καὶ καταστήσειν εἰς πολλὴν δυσμένειαν τοὺς
ὑπηκόους μαθόντας, ὅτι ξένων ἐπιθυμήσειεν καὶ
ἀλλοτρίων αὐτοῖς ἐθῶν, οὐκ ἀνέξεσθαί τε βασιλευόν-
40 τος αὐτῶν Ἰουδαίου. καὶ ἡ μὲν ταῦτ᾿ ἔλεγεν καὶ
παντοίως⁷ ἐκώλυεν. ὁ δ᾿ εἰς τὸν Ἀνανίαν τοὺς
λόγους ἀνέφερεν. τοῦ δὲ τῇ μητρὶ συμφάσκοντος⁸
καὶ συναπειλήσαντος ὡς εἰ μὴ πείθοι⁹ καταλιπὼν¹⁰
41 ἄπεισιν· δεδοικέναι γὰρ ἔλεγεν,¹¹ μὴ τοῦ πράγματος
ἐκδήλου πᾶσιν γενομένου κινδυνεύσειε τιμωρίαν
ὑποσχεῖν ὡς αὐτὸς αἴτιος τούτων καὶ διδάσκαλος
τῷ βασιλεῖ ἀπρεπῶν ἔργων¹² γενόμενος, δυνάμενον
δ᾿ αὐτὸν ἔφη καὶ χωρὶς τῆς περιτομῆς τὸ θεῖον

¹ om. Lat.
² ἐδυσχέρανεν . . . μὴ δεδεμένους] om. MW.
³ codd. Lat. E : Ἀρτάβανον Hudson.
⁴ E : πειθόμενος codd. Lat.
⁵ χαίρειν . . . ἑαυτοῦ] E : om. codd. Lat.
⁶ codd. E : περιτέμνοιτο Hudson ; τὴν σάρκα post περιτέμοιτο add. A (-ος εἰ μὴ περιτέμοιτο τὴν σάρκα i. ras., Ἰουδαῖ
suppl. m. 2 A).   ⁷ A : τέως MWE : omnino Lat.
⁸ E : συμπάσχοντος A : συγκατασχόντος M : συνκατασχόντος
W : dixit Lat.

20

to kill them or to keep them in chains, and yet thinking it hazardous to keep them with him if they were
not imprisoned—cherishing resentment as they must
—he sent some of them with their children to
Claudius Caesar in Rome as hostages, and others to
Artabanus [a] the Parthian king with the same excuse.

(4) When Izates had learned that his mother was
very much pleased with the Jewish religion, he was
zealous to convert to it himself ; and since he considered that he would not be genuinely a Jew unless
he was circumcised, he was ready to act accordingly.
When his mother learned of his intention, however,
she tried to stop him by telling him that it was a
dangerous move. For, she said, he was a king ; and
if his subjects should discover that he was devoted
to rites that were strange and foreign to themselves,
it would produce much disaffection and they would
not tolerate the rule of a Jew over them. Besides
this advice she tried by every other means [b] to hold
him back. He, in turn, reported her arguments to
Ananias. The latter expressed agreement with the
king's mother and actually threatened that if he
should be unable to persuade Izates, he would abandon him and leave the land. For he said that he was
afraid that if the matter became universally known,
he would be punished, in all likelihood, as personally
responsible because he had instructed the king in un-
seemly practices. The king could, he said, worship ✗

Helena urges Izates not to be circumcised.

Conflicting Jewish views on the necessity of circumcision.

---

[a] *Cf. Ant.* xviii. 48-52, 96-104, 250, 325-338, 353 ; xx. 54-69.   [b] Variant " for a time."

---

[9] MW : πείθοιτο E et ex corr. A.
[10] καταλιπὼν] καταλιπεῖν αὐτὸν ed. pr.
[11] ἔλεγεν] cui mater ait Lat.
[12] καὶ διδάσκαλος . . . ἔργων] om. E.

σέβειν, εἴγε πάντως κέκρικε ζηλοῦν τὰ πάτρια τῶν
Ἰουδαίων· τοῦτ' εἶναι κυριώτερον τοῦ περιτέμνε-
42 σθαι· συγγνώμην δ' ἕξειν αὐτῷ καὶ τὸν θεὸν φήσαν-
τος μὴ πράξαντι τὸ ἔργον δι' ἀνάγκην καὶ τὸν ἐκ
τῶν ὑπηκόων φόβον, ἐπείσθη μὲν τότε τοῖς λόγοις
43 ὁ βασιλεύς. μετὰ ταῦτα δέ, τὴν γὰρ ἐπιθυμίαν οὐκ
ἐξεβεβλήκει παντάπασιν, Ἰουδαῖός τις ἕτερος ἐκ
τῆς Γαλιλαίας ἀφικόμενος Ἐλεάζαρος ὄνομα πάνυ
περὶ τὰ πάτρια δοκῶν ἀκριβὴς¹ εἶναι προετρέψατο
44 πρᾶξαι τοὖργον. ἐπεὶ γὰρ εἰσῆλθεν ἀσπασόμενος

---

¹ AW : εὐσεβὴς M : eruditum Lat.

ᵃ Many scholars, following J. Derenbourg, *Essai sur
l'histoire et la géographie de la Palestine*, 1867, pp. 225-229
(see the literature cited by B. J. Bamberger, *Proselytism in
the Talmudic Period*, 1939, pp. 48-49), who attempts to see
in the dispute between Ananias and Eleazar a controversy between the schools of Hillel and Shammai, have suggested that
the difference between Ananias and Eleazar as to the necessity of circumcision for conversion is also found in the Talmud,
Yebamot 46 a, where Rabbi Joshua holds the view, akin to
that expressed here by Ananias, that circumcision is not a
sine qua non for conversion—he says that only baptism is
necessary—, whereas Rabbi Eliezer, like Eleazar here (the
similarity in spelling is not significant, since Rabbi Eliezer
did not flourish until the end of the first century and the
beginning of the second), says that circumcision is the *sine
qua non* for conversion. J. Klausner, *From Jesus to Paul*,
1943, pp. 39-40, asserts that the controversy between Joshua
and Eliezer is reflected also in the dispute between Paul and
Barnabas, on the one hand, and James and Peter, on the
other hand, as to whether circumcision is necessary in the
case of pagans who accept Christianity or whether baptism
alone is sufficient. But these proposed parallels to the controversy between Ananias and Eleazar, though tempting,
are unlikely, since Ananias' motives seem to stem not from
his religious beliefs on the question but from caution. Jose-

22

God even without being circumcised if indeed he had
fully decided to be a devoted adherent of Judaism,
for it was this that counted more than circumcision.
He told him, furthermore, that God Himself would
pardon him if, constrained thus by necessity and by
fear of his subjects, he failed to perform this rite.
And so, for the time, the king was convinced by his
arguments. Afterwards, however, since he had not
completely given up his desire, another Jew, named
Eleazar,[a] who came from Galilee and who had a
reputation for being extremely strict when it came to
the ancestral laws, urged him to carry out the rite.
For when he came to him to pay him his respects and

phus elsewhere, for example, in the case of Azizus king of
Emesa (*Ant.* xx. 139) and Polemo king of Cilicia (*Ant.* xx.
145), cites circumcision as necessary for conversion. But circumcision, according to Ananias (so S. Bialoblocki, *Die
Beziehungen des Judentums zu Proselyten und Proselytentum,*
1930, p. 16), is like other commandments in that it may be
omitted when it involves physical danger, *i.e.* when a person
has hemophilia ; Ananias regards Izates' case as similar in
that it too involves danger to life. Eliezer, on the other hand,
insists—and such is the law as recognized in the Talmud,
that only through circumcision may a non-Jew become a
Jew. The controversy between Joshua and Eliezer is presented differently in the Palestinian Talmud, *Kiddushin* iii.
14, where Eliezer says that circumcision alone is sufficient,
whereas Joshua asserts that baptism is also necessary. *Cf.*
Bamberger, pp. 49-51, who ingeniously argues that Joshua
cannot mean that the convert may omit circumcision, since
even if a heathen became a convert after mere baptism, as
indicated by Joshua, he would now be obligated to observe all
the commandments of the Torah, one of which is circumcision. The controversy between Joshua and Eliezer, says
Bamberger, is on the question—which is important for practical purposes—as to the exact moment when conversion
takes place ; Joshua believes that baptism is the determining
act, whereas Eliezer says that circumcision is the determining
act.

23

αὐτὸν[1] καὶ κατέλαβε[2] τὸν Μωυσέος νόμον ἀναγινώ-
σκοντα, "λανθάνεις," εἶπεν, "ὦ βασιλεῦ, τὰ μέγιστα
τοὺς νόμους[3] καὶ δι᾽ αὐτῶν τὸν θεὸν ἀδικῶν· οὐ γὰρ
ἀναγινώσκειν[4] σε δεῖ μόνον αὐτούς, ἀλλὰ καὶ πρό-
45 τερον τὰ προστασσόμενα ποιεῖν ὑπ᾽ αὐτῶν. μέχρι
τίνος ἀπερίτμητος μένεις;[5] ἀλλ᾽ εἰ μήπω τὸν περὶ
τούτου νόμον ἀνέγνως, ἵν᾽ εἰδῇς τίς ἐστιν ἡ ἀσέβεια,
46 νῦν ἀνάγνωθι." ταῦτα ἀκούσας ὁ βασιλεὺς οὐχ
ὑπερεβάλετο τὴν πρᾶξιν, μεταστὰς δ᾽ εἰς ἕτερον
οἴκημα καὶ τὸν ἰατρὸν εἰσκαλεσάμενος τὸ προσ-
ταχθὲν ἐτέλει καὶ μεταπεμψάμενος τήν τε μητέρα
καὶ τὸν διδάσκαλον Ἀνανίαν ἐσήμαινεν[6] αὐτὸν[7]
47 πεπραχέναι τοὐργον. τοὺς δ᾽ ἔκπληξις εὐθὺς ἔλαβεν
καὶ φόβος οὔτι μέτριος,[8] μὴ τῆς πράξεως εἰς ἔλεγ-
χον ἐλθούσης κινδυνεύσειεν μὲν ὁ βασιλεὺς τὴν
ἀρχὴν ἀποβαλεῖν οὐκ ἀνασχομένων τῶν ὑπηκόων
ἄρχειν αὐτῶν ἄνδρα τῶν παρ᾽ ἑτέροις ζηλωτὴν
ἐθῶν, κινδυνεύσειαν δὲ καὶ αὐτοὶ τῆς αἰτίας ἐπ᾽
48 αὐτοῖς ἐνεχθείσης. θεὸς δ᾽ ἦν ὁ κωλύσων ἄρα τοὺς
ἐκείνων φόβους ἐλθεῖν ἐπὶ τέλος· πολλοῖς γὰρ αὐτόν
τε τὸν Ἰζάτην περιπεσόντα κινδύνοις καὶ παῖδας

[1] εἰσῆλθεν . . . αὐτὸν] intrasset ad eum Lat.
[2] ἐπεὶ . . . κατέλαβε] καταλαβὼν γὰρ αὐτὸν E.
[3] τὰ μέγιστα τοὺς νόμους] Moyseos iura Lat.
[4] AM : γινώσκειν W.
[5] codd. E : μενεῖς Dindorf ; μέχρι . . . μένεις] quamdiu
sine circumcisione permanes legibus nequaquam nosceris
oboedire Lat.
[6] Niese : ἐσήμανεν codd. E : ἐσήμηνεν Dindorf.
[7] MW : αὐτὸν ex corr. A : αὑτοῖς E : αὐτὸς Bekker.
[8] οὔτι μέτριος] om. E.

[a] The *Midrash Rabbah on Genesis* xlvi. 10, according to

24

found him reading the law of Moses,[a] he said : " In
your ignorance, O king, you are guilty of the greatest
offence against the law and thereby against God.
For you ought not merely to read the law but also,
and even more, to do what is commanded in it. How
long will you continue to be uncircumcised ? If you
have not yet read the law concerning this matter,
read it now, so that you may know what an impiety
it is that you commit." Upon hearing these words, Izates is
the king postponed the deed no longer. Withdrawing circum-
into another room, he summoned his physician and cised.
had the prescribed act performed. Then he sent for
both his mother and his teacher Ananias and notified
them that he had performed the rite. They were
immediately seized with consternation and fear beyond measure that, if it should be proved that he
had performed the act, the king would risk losing his
throne, since his subjects would not submit to government by a man who was a devotee of foreign practices,
and that they themselves would be in jeopardy since
the blame for his action would be attributed to them.
It was God who was to prevent their fears from being
realized. For although Izates himself and his children
were often threatened with destruction, God pre-

which the circumcision of Izates occurred while his father
was still alive, reports that Izates and his brother Monobazus
were once reading the book of Genesis and came to the verse
"And ye shall be circumcised in the flesh of your foreskin"
(Gen. xvii. 11). Both began to weep and independently
decided on circumcision. Some time later, when they once
again read from Genesis and reached this verse, each lamented
that the other was uncircumcised. They then confided in
each other and informed their mother, who, in turn, told
their father that a sore had broken out on their sons' flesh
and that the physician had ordered circumcision. Thereupon
the father gave his consent to what had already been done

25

τοὺς ἐκείνου διέσωσεν ἐξ ἀμηχάνων πόρον εἰς σωτηρίαν παρασχών, ἐπιδεικνὺς ὅτι τοῖς εἰς αὐτὸν
ἀποβλέπουσιν καὶ μόνῳ πεπιστευκόσιν ὁ καρπὸς
οὐκ ἀπόλλυται ὁ τῆς εὐσεβείας. ἀλλὰ ταῦτα μὲν
ὕστερον ἀπαγγελοῦμεν.

49 (5) Ἑλένη δὲ ἡ τοῦ βασιλέως μήτηρ ὁρῶσα τὰ
μὲν κατὰ τὴν βασιλείαν εἰρηνευόμενα, τὸν δὲ υἱὸν
αὐτῆς μακάριον καὶ παρὰ πᾶσι ζηλωτὸν καὶ τοῖς
ἀλλοεθνέσι διὰ τὴν ἐκ τοῦ θεοῦ πρόνοιαν,[1] ἐπιθυμίαν
ἔσχεν εἰς τὴν Ἱεροσολυμιτῶν πόλιν ἀφικομένη τὸ
πᾶσιν ἀνθρώποις περιβόητον ἱερὸν τοῦ θεοῦ προσ-
κυνῆσαι καὶ χαριστηρίους θυσίας προσενεγκεῖν,
50 ἐδεῖτό τε τοῦ παιδὸς ἐπιτρέψαι. τοῦ δὲ πάνυ προ-
θύμως τῇ μητρὶ παρακαλούσῃ κατανεύσαντος καὶ
πολλὴν παρασκευὴν τῶν εἰς τὴν ἀποστολὴν ἑτοιμα-
σαμένου καὶ χρήματα πλεῖστα δόντος, καταβαίνει
εἰς τὴν Ἱεροσολυμιτῶν πόλιν προπέμποντος ἐπὶ
51 πολὺ τοῦ παιδός.[2] γίνεται δὲ αὐτῆς ἡ ἄφιξις πάνυ
συμφέρουσα τοῖς Ἱεροσολυμίταις[3]· λιμοῦ γὰρ αὐτῶν

[1] καὶ παρὰ . . . πρόνοιαν] et ultra cunctas gentes provi-
dentia divina religiosum Lat.
[2] προπέμποντος . . . παιδός] om. E.
[3] καὶ εἰς τὰ μάλιστα χρησίμη post Ἱεροσολυμίταις add. A.

---

[a] Part of this promise is perhaps fulfilled in §§ 69-91 ; but
we do not hear of the miraculous escape from the dangers
that confronted Izates' children. Nor do we hear of God's
aid to Izates during the period that elapsed between Izates'
conversion, presumably shortly after the beginning of his
reign in 31, and Helena's journey to Jerusalem in 46 or 47.
The Mishnah *Nazir* iii. 6, however, does tell us of one incident
that occurred during this period. Once, when Izates went
to war, Helena vowed to become a Nazirite for seven years
if he should return safely. Her son returned, and she fulfilled the vow. At the conclusion of the seven years she went

served them, opening a path to safety from desperate straits. God thus demonstrated that those who fix their eyes on Him and trust in Him alone do not lose the reward of their piety. But I shall report these events at a later time.[a]

(5) Helena, the mother of the king, saw that peace prevailed in the kingdom and that her son was prosperous and the object of admiration in all men's eyes, even those of foreigners, thanks to the prudence that God gave him. Now she had conceived a desire to go to the city of Jerusalem and to worship at the temple of God, which was famous throughout the world, and to make thank-offerings there. She consequently asked her son to give her leave. Izates was most enthusiastic in granting his mother's request, made great preparations for her journey, and gave her a large sum of money. He even escorted her for a considerable distance, and she completed her journey to the city of Jerusalem. Her arrival[b] was very advantageous for the people of Jerusalem,

Helena's visit to Jerusalem and her gifts for relief of the famine.

to the land of Israel—presumably her journey in 46 or 47—, where she was told that she would have to become a Nazirite for an additional seven years, since residence outside the land of Israel renders one ritually unclean so far as Naziriteship is concerned. She faithfully served the additional seven years, only to become unclean herself at the conclusion of them, and so she started a third period as a Nazirite. It was during this period, in A.D. 55, that Izates died and Helena returned to Adiabene, where she died shortly thereafter.

[b] H. Graetz, " Zeit der Anwesenheit der adiabenischen Königin in Jerusalem, unter der Apostel Paulus," *Monatsschr. f. Gesch. u. Wissen. d. Jud.* xxvi, 1877, pp. 241-255 and 289-306, suggests, though it is only a guess, that Paul was converted to Christianity during Helena's stay in Jerusalem, and that her presence inspired in him a belief that the Messianic age was rapidly approaching and that it was necessary to find some means of converting the heathen.

27

τὴν πόλιν κατὰ τὸν καιρὸν ἐκεῖνον πιεζοῦντος καὶ
πολλῶν ὑπ' ἐνδείας ἀναλωμάτων[1] φθειρομένων ἡ
βασιλὶς Ἑλένη πέμπει τινὰς τῶν ἑαυτῆς, τοὺς μὲν
εἰς τὴν Ἀλεξάνδρειαν πολλῶν[2] σῖτον ὠνησομένους
χρημάτων,[3] τοὺς δ' εἰς Κύπρον ἰσχάδων φόρτον
52 οἴσοντας.[4] ὡς δ' ἐπανῆλθον ταχέως κομίζοντες
τοῖς ἀπορουμένοις διένειμε τροφὴν καὶ μεγίστην
αὐτῆς μνήμην[5] τῆς εὐποιίας ταύτης εἰς τὸ πᾶν
53 ἡμῶν ἔθνος καταλέλοιπε. πυθόμενος δὲ καὶ ὁ παῖς
αὐτῆς Ἰζάτης τὰ περὶ τὸν λιμὸν ἔπεμψε πολλὰ
χρήματα τοῖς πρώτοις τῶν Ἱεροσολυμιτῶν ἃ τοῖς

[1] ἀναλωμάτων] ἀναγκαίων Richards et Shutt : βρωμάτων
coni. Petersen.   [2] E (cf. § 101) : πολὺν codd.
[3] πολλῶν . . . χρημάτων] ut frumenta ex eius pecuniis com-
pararent Lat.
[4] ἰσχάδων φόρτον οἴσοντας] quatenus caricas ex abundanti
deferrent Lat.   [5] εἰς ἀεὶ διαβοωμένην post μνήμην add. A.

[a] Cf. Josephus' account of the great famine in Judaea
during the reign of Herod the Great and of the relief that
Herod, as a kind of second Joseph, secured for his people by
the purchase of grain from Egypt (Ant. xv. 299-316). According to Acts xi. 28, a certain prophet named Agabus
came from Jerusalem to Antioch, where he predicted that
there would be a great famine over all the world—a famine
which, adds the author of Acts, occurred during the reign of
Claudius, and hence appears to be the famine mentioned in
our passage. The famine, to judge from Acts xi. 29-30, was
not worldwide, since the disciples in Antioch sent relief to
Judaea ; and C. C. Torrey, The Composition and Date of
Acts, 1916, p. 21, suggests that Luke, the author of Acts, had
an Aramaic source which spoke of the famine as extending
throughout " the land," where " the land," as commonly,
refers to Palestine, but that he mistakenly rendered it as ὅλη
ἡ οἰκουμένη, " all the earth," just as Luke himself (ii. 1) speaks
of Quirinius as taxing the whole world (πᾶσαν τὴν οἰκουμένην)
instead of all the land (of Palestine). The famine occurred
in A.D. 46 or 47, perhaps in the spring (so K. S. Gapp, " The
Universal Famine under Claudius," Harv. Theol. Rev.

for at that time the city was hard pressed by famine [a] and many were perishing from want of money to purchase what they needed.[b] Queen Helena sent some of her attendants to Alexandria [c] to buy grain for large sums and others to Cyprus [d] to bring back a cargo of dried figs. Her attendants speedily returned with these provisions, which she thereupon distributed among the needy. She has thus left a very great name that will be famous forever among our whole people for her benefaction. When her son Izates learned of the famine, he likewise sent a great sum of money to leaders of the Jerusalemites.[e] The dis-

xxviii, 1935, p. 261 n. 11), if the famine referred to in *Ant.* iii. 320-321 is to be identified with our famine (but see Thackeray's note *ad loc.*).

[b] Lit. " from lack of expenses."

[c] Egypt too had suffered from a famine in 45, according to papyrological evidence cited by Gapp, pp. 258 ff. If, as Gapp, p. 260, theorizes, the famine extended to the spring of 46 or 47, Helena's benefaction was all the greater, since the price of grain in 45, at least, was more than twice as high as had ever been recorded previously in the Roman period. Helena did not send to Syria for grain since, as Orosius, *Hist.* vii. 6. 12, states, the famine extended to all of Syria (but *cf.* Acts xi. 29-30).

[d] See Palestinian Talmud, *Demai* ii. 1, which indicates that fruits from Cyprus were regularly imported into Palestine. *Cf.* A. Reifenberg, " Das antike zyprische Judentum und seine Beziehungen zu Palästina," *Jour. of the Pal. Or. Soc.* xii, 1932, pp. 209-213.

[e] The Talmud (*Baba Bathra* 11 a) records that King Monobazus, Izates' successor, dissipated all his own hoards and the hoards of his fathers " in years of scarcity "—hence not necessarily referring to this famine and not necessarily referring to relief of a famine in Palestine. His brothers and his father's household—according to *Ant.* xx. 75, they had been converted to Judaism—came in a deputation to him and said : " Your father saved money and added to the treasures of his fathers, and you are squandering them." He replied :

29

ἐνδεέσι διανεμηθέντα πολλοὺς τοῦ λιμοῦ σφοδροτά-
της ἀνάγκης ἀνεκτήσατο.¹ ἀλλὰ γὰρ ἃ τοῖς βα-
σιλεῦσιν εἰς τὴν πόλιν ἡμῶν ἀγαθὰ πέπρακται² μετὰ
ταῦτα δηλώσομεν.

54 (iii. 1) Ὁ δὲ τῶν Πάρθων βασιλεὺς Ἀρταβάνης³
αἰσθόμενος τοὺς σατράπας ἐπιβουλὴν ἐπ' αὐτὸν
συντεθεικότας, μένειν παρ' αὐτοῖς ἀσφαλὲς οὐχ
ὁρῶν ἔγνω πρὸς Ἰζάτην ἀπαίρειν, πόρον παρ'
αὐτοῦ βουλόμενος σωτηρίας εὑρέσθαι καὶ κάθοδον
55 εἰς τὴν ἀρχήν, εἰ δυνηθείη. καὶ δὴ ἀφικνεῖται συγ-
γενῶν τε καὶ οἰκετῶν περὶ χιλίους⁴ τὸν ἀριθμὸν
ἐπαγόμενος συντυγχάνει τε τῷ Ἰζάτῃ καθ' ὁδόν.
56 αὐτός τε σαφῶς ἐκεῖνον ἐπιστάμενος, ὑπ' Ἰζάτου
δὲ οὐ γινωσκόμενος, πλησίον καταστὰς πρῶτον μὲν
κατὰ τὸ πάτριον προσεκύνησεν αὐτόν, εἶτα, " βασιλεῦ," φησίν, " μὴ περιίδῃς με τὸν σὸν ἱκέτην⁵ μηδ'
ὑπερηφανήσῃς δεομένου· ταπεινὸς γὰρ ἐκ μετα-
βολῆς γενόμενος καὶ ἐκ βασιλέως ἰδιώτης τῆς σῆς

¹ ἃ τοῖς . . . ἀνεκτήσατο] A : om. MWE.
² καὶ ὅσοι τούτοις ἐκ ταύτης πόροι συνελέγησαν post πέπρακται
add. codex Gallicus teste Hudsono.
³ γρ Ἀρτάβανος i. marg. A : Artabanus Lat. : Ἀρτάβανος
Ant. xviii. 48 sqq.
⁴ AW : δισχιλίους M : mille Lat.
⁵ A : οἰκέτην MW : servum Lat.

" My fathers stored up below and I am storing above [*i.e.* in
heaven] " (trans. by M. Simon in Soncino edition).

ᵃ This promise does not appear to have been fulfilled. H.
Petersen, " Real and Alleged Literary Projects of Josephus,"
Am. Jour. of Philol. lxxix, 1958, p. 273, says that Josephus
probably thought that he had fulfilled this project and refers
to §§ 94-95, which mention the pyramids constructed by
Helena. But though the building of these pyramids was a
blessing to the Jews in that it supplied jobs to construction

tribution of this fund to the needy delivered many
from the extremely severe pressure of famine. But
I shall leave to a later time [a] the further tale of good
deeds performed for our city by this royal pair.

(iii. 1) Artabanus,[b] king of the Parthians, discovering that the satraps had concocted a plot against him
and seeing that it was not safe to remain with them,
decided to make his way to Izates. His object was to
obtain from him some provision for his security as
well as for his restoration to his rule if that should be
possible. He did succeed in reaching him, followed
by about a thousand of his kinsmen and attendants.
He met Izates on the road, as it happened. Now
Artabanus knew him well, but not being recognized
by Izates, he halted beside him and first of all made
obeisance to him according to the native custom.
He then spoke : " O king, be not indifferent to me,
your suppliant, nor scorn my request. For I have
been brought low by a turn of fortune, having exchanged kingship for a private life, and am in need of

*Artabanus,
king of
Parthia,
seeks help
from
Izates.*

workers in Jerusalem, it seems more likely that the good
deeds performed by Izates and Helena and referred to here
involved more direct benefits to the Jews, such as the distribution of food in the famine mentioned in §§ 51-52. From
the Mishnah, *Yoma* iii. 10, we learn of two of the gifts presented by Queen Helena to the temple, namely, a golden
candlestick which was placed over the door of the sanctuary
and a golden tablet on which was written the section from
the Torah (Num. v. 12-31) discussing the suspected adulteress.
According to *B.J.* v. 253 and vi. 355 she built a palace in
Jerusalem. Another detail of Helena's sojourn in the Holy
Land is supplied by the Talmud, *Sukkah* 2 b, which records
that she had a *sukkah* built for the Feast of Tabernacles in
Lydda which was higher than twenty cubits and that the
elders frequented it.

   [b] Artabanus III ; *cf. Ant.* xviii. 48-52, 96-104, 250, 325-
338, 353 ; xx. 37.

31

JOSEPHUS

57 ἐπικουρίας¹ χρῄζω. βλέψον οὖν εἰς τὸ τῆς τύχης
ἄστατον καὶ κοινὴν εἶναι² νόμισον καὶ ὑπὲρ σαυτοῦ
πρόνοιαν³· ἐμοῦ⁴ γὰρ ἀνεκδικήτου περιοφθέντος
ἔσονται θρασύτεροι πολλοὶ καὶ κατὰ τῶν ἄλλων
58 βασιλέων.᾽᾽ ὁ μὲν ταῦτ᾽ ἔλεγεν δακρύων καὶ τῇ
κεφαλῇ κάτω νεύων, ὁ δὲ Ἰζάτης ὡς ἤκουσε τοὔ-
νομα καὶ εἶδεν ἱκέτην αὐτῷ παρεστῶτα καὶ ποτνιώ-
μενον⁵ τὸν Ἀρταβάνην, κατεπήδησεν ἀπὸ τοῦ ἵπ-
59 που ὀξέως⁶ καί, ʽʽ θάρσησον,ʼʼ εἶπεν, ʽʽ ὦ βασιλεῦ,
μηδέ σε συγχείτω τὸ παρὸν ὡς ἀνήκεστον· ταχεῖα
γὰρ ἔσται τῆς λύπης⁷ ἡ μεταβολή. φίλον δέ με καὶ
σύμμαχον εὑρήσεις κρείττω τῆς ἐλπίδος· ἢ γὰρ εἰς
τὴν Πάρθων σε καταστήσω βασιλείαν πάλιν ἢ τῆς
ἐμῆς ἐκστήσομαι.ʼʼ⁸
60 (2) Ταῦτα εἰπὼν ἀνεβίβαζεν τὸν Ἀρταβάνην ἐπὶ
τὸν ἵππον, παρείπετο δ᾽ αὐτὸς πεζὸς τιμὴν ἀπονέ-
μων ταυτηνὶ ὡς⁹ ἂν μείζονι βασιλεῖ. θεασάμενος
δ᾽ Ἀρταβάνης βαρέως ἤνεγκεν καὶ τὴν ἐφεστῶσαν
αὐτῷ τύχην καὶ τιμὴν¹⁰ ἐπωμόσατο¹¹ καταβήσεσθαι
61 μὴ ᾽κείνου πάλιν ἀναβάντος καὶ προηγουμένου. ὁ
δὲ πεισθεὶς ἐπὶ τὸν ἵππον ἥλατο καὶ ἀγαγὼν αὐτὸν
εἰς τὴν βασιλείαν πᾶσαν τιμὴν ἀπένειμεν ἔν τε
συνεδρίαις καὶ ταῖς περὶ τὰς ἑστιάσεις προκατα-
κλίσεσιν, οὐκ εἰς τὸ παρὸν αὐτοῦ τῆς τύχης ἀπο-
βλέπων, ἀλλ᾽ εἰς τὸ πρότερον ἀξίωμα, καί τι καὶ

¹ solatium Lat.
² τὴν συμφορὰν τὴν ἐμὴν post εἶναι add. A.
³ πρόνοιαν] MW : πρόνοιαν ἥγησαι A ; καὶ κοινὴν . . . πρό-
νοιαν] et hanc scito esse communem et tui similiter habe curam
Lat.
⁴ MW : λιμοῦ A.
⁵ καὶ ποτνιώμενον] A : om. MWE.

32

your help. Cast an eye, therefore, at the instability
of fortune and consider that forethought for me is
forethought for you also ; for if I am disregarded and
left unavenged many will be bolder to attack other
kings as well." This he said with tears in his eyes
and with bowed head. When Izates heard his name
and beheld Artabanus standing beside him as a suppliant and lamenting his fate, he leapt down quickly
from his horse and said : " Take heart, O king, and
be not confounded by your present condition as
though it were past cure ; for there will be a sudden
change to end your sadness. You will find me as
friend and ally better than you expected. For either
I will restore you to the throne of Parthia or I will
abandon my own."

(2) So saying he aided Artabanus in mounting his
horse and himself attended him on foot, according
him this honour since he was the greater king. But
when Artabanus beheld this, he was distressed and
swore by the misfortune that had come upon him
and by the honour accorded him that he would dis-
mount unless Izates remounted and preceded him.
The latter complied, leapt on his horse, and brought
him to his kingdom, where he assigned him every
honour at his [a] councils and gave him the chief seat
at banquets ; for Izates had regard not for his present
fortune but for his former dignity ; moreover, he took

---

[a] Izates'.

---

[6] A : mox Lat. : om. MWE.
[7] λύπης] MW : παρούσης λύπης A.
[8] A : στήσομαι MW : constituam Lat.
[9] ταυτηνὶ ὡς] ταύτην μεγίστην ὡς i. ras. 8-9 litt. m. 2 A :
ταύτην ὡς E.
[10] καὶ τιμὴν] om. E.
[11] ἐπωμόσατο] ἐπωμόσατο ἡμὴν E.

λογισμῷ διδούς,¹ ὡς κοιναὶ τοῖς ἀνθρώποις αἱ
62 μεταβολαὶ τῆς τύχης. γράφει τε πρὸς τοὺς Πάρ-
θους πείθων αὐτοὺς τὸν Ἀρταβάνην ὑποδέξασθαι,
πίστιν προτείνων τῆς τῶν πεπραγμένων ἀμνηστίας
63 δεξιὰν καὶ ὅρκους καὶ μεσιτείαν τὴν αὐτοῦ.² τῶν
δὲ Πάρθων δέξασθαι μὲν αὐτὸν θέλειν οὐκ ἀρνου-
μένων, μὴ δύνασθαι δὲ λεγόντων διὰ τὸ τὴν ἀρχὴν
ἑτέρῳ πεπιστευκέναι, Κίνναμος³ δ' ἦν ὄνομα τῷ
παρειληφότι, καὶ δεδοικέναι, μὴ στάσις αὐτοὺς ἐκ
64 τούτου καταλάβῃ,⁴ μαθὼν τὴν προαίρεσιν αὐτῶν⁵
ὁ Κίνναμος ταύτην αὐτὸς γράφει τῷ Ἀρταβάνῃ,
τέθραπτο γὰρ ὑπ' αὐτοῦ καὶ φύσει δ' ἦν καλὸς
καὶ⁶ ἀγαθός, παρακαλῶν αὐτῷ πιστεύσαντα παρα-
65 γενέσθαι τὴν ἀρχὴν ἀποληψόμενον⁷ τὴν αὐτοῦ. καὶ
ὁ Ἀρταβάνης πιστεύσας παρῆν. ὑπαντᾷ δ' αὐτῷ
ὁ Κίνναμος καὶ προσκυνήσας βασιλέα τε προσαγο-
ρεύσας περιτίθησιν αὐτοῦ τῇ κεφαλῇ τὸ διάδημα
ἀφελὼν τῆς ἑαυτοῦ.
66 (3) Καὶ Ἀρταβάνης οὕτω διὰ Ἰζάτου⁸ πάλιν⁹
εἰς τὴν ἀρχὴν καθίσταται πρότερον αὐτῆς ἐκπεσὼν
διὰ τοὺς μεγιστᾶνας.¹⁰ οὐκ ἐγένετο μὴν ἀμνήμων
τῶν εἰς αὐτὸν εὐεργεσιῶν, ἀλλ' ἀντιδωρεῖται τὸν
67 Ἰζάτην ταῖς μεγίσταις τιμαῖς παρ' αὐτοῖς· τήν τε

¹ καί τι . . . διδούς] eumque ratione frequenter consolatus
est Lat.
² δεξιὰν . . . αὐτοῦ] iuramenta Lat.
³ A : Κιννάμωμος MW : Cinnamum Lat.
⁴ Κίνναμος . . . καταλάβῃ] oin. E.

34

into consideration the fact that changes of fortune are the lot of all men. He wrote to the Parthians urging them to welcome back Artabanus, offering his right hand and oaths and his mediation as security that Artabanus would not hold against them what they had done. The Parthians answered that they were not unwilling to receive him, but were unable to do so because they had already entrusted the government to another—Cinnamus [a] was the name of the one who had acceded to it—and they were afraid that to do so would subject them to civil war. Cinnamus, on learning of their policy, himself wrote to Artabanus—for he had been brought up by him and was by disposition a thorough gentleman—inviting him to put faith in him and come back to receive his office. Artabanus trusted him and came. Cinnamus met him and after doing obeisance and addressing him as king removed the diadem from his own head and placed it on that of Artabanus.

(3) Thus, through the aid of Izates,[b] Artabanus was again established on his throne, after having been previously expelled from it by action of the great nobles. Nor was he unmindful of Izates' benefactions to him, but repaid him with the highest of honours that they recognize. For he permitted him

Izates persuades the Parthians to reinstate Artabanus.

Izates is rewarded.

[a] c. A.D. 37. On the name Κίνναμος cf. McCown-Albright, in *Bull. of the Am. Sch. of Or. Res.* lxvi, Apr. 1937, p. 20.

[b] For " through the aid of Izates " two of the mss. and the Epitome have " after six years."

[5] E Lat. et i. marg. A : αὐτοῦ codd.
[6] φύσει δ' ἦν καλὸς καὶ] ἦν γὰρ E.
[7] πιστεύσαντα . . . ἀπολημψόμενον] ληψόμενον W.
[8] διὰ 'Ιζάτου] A : δι' ἐξαετοῦς (ἐξ ex ἰζ corr. M) MWE : per Iazatem Lat.
[9] πάλιν] A : πάλιν χρόνου MW : χρόνου πάλιν E.
[10] πρότερον . . . μεγιστᾶνας] om. E.

γὰρ τιάραν ὀρθὴν ἐπέτρεψεν αὐτῷ φορεῖν καὶ ἐπὶ
κλίνης χρυσῆς καθεύδειν, ἅπερ μόνων ἐστὶ γέρα καὶ
68 σημεῖα τῶν Πάρθων βασιλέων. ἔδωκεν δὲ καὶ
χώραν πολλὴν αὐτῷ κἀγαθὴν τοῦ τῶν Ἀρμενίων
βασιλέως ἀποτεμόμενος, Νίσιβις δέ ἐστιν ὄνομα τῇ
γῇ, καὶ ἐν αὐτῇ πρότερον Μακεδόνες ἐκτίσαντο
πόλιν Ἀντιόχειαν, ἣν Ἐπιμυγδονίαν[1] προσηγόρευ-
σαν. ταύταις μὲν δὴ ταῖς τιμαῖς ὁ Ἰζάτης ὑπὸ τοῦ
τῶν Πάρθων βασιλέως ἐτιμήθη.

69 (4) Μετ' οὐ πολὺν δὲ χρόνον Ἀρταβάνης τελευτᾷ
τὴν βασιλείαν τῷ παιδὶ Οὐαρδάνῃ[2] καταλιπών.
οὗτος δὴ πρὸς τὸν Ἰζάτην ἀφικόμενος ἔπειθεν
αὐτὸν μέλλων πρὸς Ῥωμαίους πόλεμον ἐκφέρειν
70 συστρατεύεσθαι καὶ συμμαχίαν ἑτοιμάζειν. οὐ μὴν
ἔπειθεν· ὁ γὰρ Ἰζάτης τὴν Ῥωμαίων δύναμίν τε

---

[1] Ἐπιμυγδονίαν] AM : ἐπὶ Μυγδονίαν W : Μυγδονίαν E : In-
mygdoniam Lat. [2] Partadani Lat.

---

[a] Aristophanes, *Birds* 487, likewise mentions the upright
tiara (κυρβασία) of the Persian kings. *Cf.* Xenophon, *Anab.*
ii. 5. 23, where Tissaphernes says : " The King alone may
wear upright the tiara that is upon the head, but another,
too, with your help, might easily so wear the one that is upon
the heart." He thus indicates that with the aid of the Greeks
he would possess an authority virtually or perhaps even actually royal ; in the latter case this would be a hint of revolt.

[b] Apparently to be distinguished from the Nisibis of *Ant.*
xviii. 312 and 379. J. Sturm, " Nisibis," no. 3, Pauly-
Wissowa, xvii[1], 1936, p. 757, asserts that this Nisibis is also
to be distinguished from the more famous Nisibis in north-
eastern Babylonia ; but the surname (Epi)mygdonia seems
to argue for identifying the two. A district named Nisibis is,
however, otherwise unknown.

[c] *Cf.* Polybius v. 51. 1 and Strabo xvi. 747, who refer to it as
Antiocheia in Mygdonia. See J. Sturm, " Nisibis," Pauly-
Wissowa, xvii[1], 1936, pp. 727-730. [d] About A.D. 38.

[e] Tacitus, *Ann.* xi. 8, says that Artabanus was succeeded

to wear his tiara upright [a] and to sleep on a bed of gold—privileges and symbols that belong only to the kings of the Parthians. He furthermore gave him an extensive and productive territory which he carved from that of the king of Armenia. The district is called Nisibis,[b] and in it the Macedonians had in days of old founded the city of Antioch which they surnamed Epimygdonia.[c] Such were the honours that Izates received from the king of the Parthians.

(4) Not long afterwards [d] Artabanus died, leaving his kingdom to his son Vardanes.[e] The latter, contemplating war on the Romans, came to Izates and urged him to take part in the campaign and to prepare an auxiliary force. He failed, however, to convince him. For Izates, knowing well the might and

Vardanes, Artabanus' successor, fails to enlist Izates for war against the Romans.

by Gotarzes II, who was, in turn, succeeded by his brother Vardanes. Josephus has Gotarzes (Cotardes) succeed Vardanes. J. G. C. Anderson, in *Camb. Anc. Hist.* x, 1934, p. 754 n. 1, therefore, contends that Josephus' account is inaccurate. But actually there is no necessary contradiction between Tacitus and Josephus, since, upon the murder of Vardanes, Gotarzes once again assumed the throne (Tac. *Ann.* xi. 10). Hence, Josephus merely omits Gotarzes' first tenure—an omission which, in view of the greater brevity of Josephus' account, is quite understandable. Moreover, since the first tenure of Gotarzes was almost immediately disputed by Vardanes and since, after Vardanes' arrival, Gotarzes withdrew his claim to the throne and came to an agreement with him (Tac. *Ann.* xi. 9), Josephus may have thought it proper to omit Gotarzes' first tenure as not really a reign but as a pretension to the throne. The numismatic evidence for 44/45–45/46 indicates merely that Tacitus has the more complete account in describing the struggle for the Parthian throne for this period. Thus in Seleucia we find the coins of Gotarzes, then a month later those of Vardanes, then six months later those of Gotarzes, then three months later Vardanes again, then nine months later those of Gotarzes again (see R. H. McDowell, *Coins from Seleucia on the Tigris*, 1935, pp. 189-190).

καὶ τύχην ἐπιστάμενος ἀδυνάτοις αὐτὸν ἐνόμιζεν
71 ἐπιχειρεῖν. ἔτι γε πεπομφὼς πέντε μὲν τὸν ἀριθμὸν
υἱοὺς τὴν ἡλικίαν νέους γλῶτταν τὴν παρ' ἡμῖν
πάτριον καὶ παιδείαν ἀκριβῶς μαθησομένους, τήν
τε μητέρα προσκυνήσουσαν τὸ ἱερόν, ὡς προεῖπον,
ὀκνηρότερος ἦν καὶ τὸν Οὐαρδάνην¹ ἐκώλυεν συνεχῶς διηγούμενος τὰς Ῥωμαίων δυνάμεις² τε καὶ
πράξεις, διὰ τούτων οἰόμενος αὐτὸν φοβήσειν καὶ
παύσειν ἐπιθυμοῦντα τῆς ἐπ' αὐτοὺς στρατείας.
72 παροξυνθεὶς δ' ἐπὶ τούτοις ὁ Πάρθος πόλεμον εὐθὺς³
πρὸς Ἰζάτην κατήγγειλεν. οὐ μὴν ἔλαβεν οὐδὲ τῆς
ἐπὶ τούτῳ στρατείας ὄνησιν τοῦ θεοῦ τὰς ἐλπίδας
73 αὐτοῦ πάσας ὑποτεμόντος· μαθόντες γὰρ οἱ Πάρθοι
τὴν διάνοιαν τοῦ Οὐαρδάνου καὶ ὡς ἐπὶ Ῥωμαίους
στρατεύειν ἔκρινεν, αὐτὸν μὲν ἀναιροῦσιν, τὴν ἀρχὴν
74 δὲ τῷ ἀδελφῷ Κοτάρδῃ⁴ παρέδοσαν. καὶ τοῦτον

¹ Bardanem hic et infra Lat.
² δυνάμεις] εὐτυχεῖς | δυνάμεις A.
³ om. E.
⁴ Spanheim : Ἴκοτάρδη (ῖ i. ras. ο ex ω corr. A) AE : Κα-
τάρδη MW : Cotardi Lat. : Γοτάρζῃ Hudson.

─────────────────────────

ᵃ §§ 49 ff.
ᵇ Izates' defiance of Vardanes is all the more remarkable
in view of the terror that he had inspired in his enemies
generally. *Cf.* Tacitus' tribute to his ability (*Ann.* xi. 10):
" He might have been one of the illustrious few among aged
princes, had he sought to be loved by his subjects as much as
to be feared by his foes."
ᶜ Tacitus, *Ann.* xi. 10, says that despite the many victories
won by Vardanes and despite the erection of monuments by
the Parthians in tribute to his triumphs, the Parthians rebelled against distant service and against his haughty and
autocratic attitude towards them after his return homeward.
A plot was arranged, and they slew him while hunting.

fortune of the Romans, thought that Vardanes was
attempting the impossible. Moreover, he was the
more reluctant because he had sent five sons of tender
age to get a thorough knowledge of our native language and culture, besides his mother who had gone
to worship in the temple, as I have said already.[a] He
therefore dissuaded Vardanes by constantly describing the resources and achievements of the Romans,
supposing that such accounts would be enough to
frighten him and curb his will to make war on them.
The Parthian, however, exasperated at this, forthwith declared war on Izates.[b] Nevertheless, he did
not derive any advantage from his campaign against
Izates, since God cut short all his expectations. For
the Parthians, on hearing of Vardanes' intention and
of his decision to march against the Romans, put him
to death [c] and delivered the government to his
brother Cotardes.[d] Not long afterwards he too was

Firdousi's tenth-century epic poem *Shāhnāma*, or " Book of
Kings," containing a complete history of Persia, preserves a
tradition that Farud (= Vardanes) was actually killed by
Bizan and Rahan, both of whom were related to Gudarz
(= Gotarzes). See J. C. Coyajee, " The House of Gotarzes,"
Jour. and Proc. of the Asiatic Soc. of Bengal, N.S. xxviii,
1932, p. 211.

[d] *i.e.* Gotarzes. Tacitus, *Ann.* xii. 10, depicts Gotarzes as
ruthless in his dealings with both the nobility and the common
people. " Already," he says, " brothers, relatives, and distant
kin had been swept off by murder after murder ; wives actually pregnant and tender children were added to Gotarzes'
victims, while, slothful at home and unsuccessful in war, he
made cruelty a screen for his feebleness." Josephus omits
the rivalry for the throne between Gotarzes and Meherdates
after the murder of Vardanes. In this rivalry, according to
Tacitus, *Ann.* xii. 13, Izates allied himself with Meherdates,
but secretly favoured Gotarzes, and deserted to the latter's
side before the crucial battle between the two contenders for
the throne.

δὲ μετ' οὐ πολὺν χρόνον ἐξ ἐπιβουλῆς τελευτήσαντα διαδέχεται Οὐολογέσης[1] ὁ ἀδελφός, ὃς δὴ
καὶ τοῖς ὁμοπατρίοις δυσὶν ἀδελφοῖς δυναστείας
ἐπίστευσεν, Πακόρῳ μὲν τῷ καὶ[2] πρεσβυτέρῳ τὴν
Μήδων, Τιριδάτῃ δὲ τῷ νεωτέρῳ τὴν Ἀρμενίαν.
75 (iv. 1) Ὁ δὲ τοῦ βασιλέως ἀδελφὸς Μονόβαζος
καὶ οἱ συγγενεῖς θεωροῦντες τὸν Ἰζάτην διὰ τὴν
πρὸς τὸν θεὸν εὐσέβειαν[3] ζηλωτὸν παρὰ πᾶσιν
ἀνθρώποις γεγενημένον ἔσχον ἐπιθυμίαν καὶ αὐτοὶ
τὰ πάτρια καταλιπόντες ἔθεσι χρῆσθαι τοῖς Ἰου-
76 δαίων.[4] γίνεται δ' ἡ πρᾶξις αὐτῶν κατάφωρος τοῖς
ὑπηκόοις,[5] κἀπὶ τούτῳ χαλεπήναντες οἱ μεγιστᾶνες[6]
οὐκ ἐφανέρουν μὲν τὴν ὀργήν, κατὰ νοῦν δὲ ἔχοντες

[1] ed. pr. : Οὐολιγέσης A : Οὐολιγαίσης MW : Οὐλελέσης E :
Vologesis Lat. : Οὐλογάσης Hudson.

[2] καὶ] om. I. Levy (Mélanges Dussaud, 1939, p. 547).

[3] καὶ τὴν ἐνοῦσαν αὐτῷ τῶν ἠθῶν χρηστότητα post εὐσέβειαν
add. E.

[4] καὶ τὴν ἔφεσιν εἰς πέρας ἐξήνεγκαν post Ἰουδαίων add. E.

[5] γίνεται . . . ὑπηκόοις] horum nisus subiectis fuit valde
gravissimus Lat.

[6] καὶ ὀργίλως διατεθέντες post μεγιστᾶνες add. E.

---

[a] Tacitus, *Ann.* xii. 14, mentions no conspiracy, but says
merely that Gotarzes fell ill and died.

[b] Vologeses, according to Tacitus, *Ann.* xii. 14, was the
son of Vonones.

[c] This is the common spelling, but the name appears as
"Volagases" on his coins. *Cf. B.J.* vii. 105, where a delegation from him brings Vespasian a golden crown in recognition of his victory over the Jews. *Cf.* also *B.J.* vii. 237 and
242. Josephus' account omits the reign of Vonones, who,
according to Tacitus, *Ann.* xii. 14, succeeded Gotarzes. But
Tacitus himself remarks that Vonones' reign was short and
inglorious, and since Josephus is giving an abbreviated
account of the complicated dynastic struggles of the Parthians,
it is not remarkable that he should have omitted Vonones, for

slain by a conspiracy *a* and was succeeded by his
brother *b* Vologeses,*c* who thereupon assigned to his
two brothers *d* by the same father positions of power.
To the elder, Pacorus,*e* he gave Media and to the
younger, Tiridates,*f* Armenia.

(iv. 1) Izates' brother Monobazus *g* and his kinsmen, seeing that the king because of his pious worship
of God *h* had won the admiration of all men, became
eager to abandon their ancestral religion and to
adopt the practices of the Jews.*i* Their action, however, was detected and exposed to their subjects.
The high nobles, though they were angry at this, did
not reveal their anger but stored it in their hearts and

Monobazus, brother of Izates, and his kinsmen plan conversion to Judaism.

whose reign no coins have yet been found, as N. C. Debe-
voise, *A Political History of Parthia*, 1938, p. 174, notes.

d Tacitus, *Ann.* xii. 44, also remarks that Vologeses obtained the throne with the consent of his brothers.

e According to Tacitus, *Ann.* xv. 2, Pacorus was already
in possession of Media when Vologeses became king. *Cf.*
B.J. vii. 247, where he flees from his country upon the ad-
vance of the Alani, a Scythian tribe.

f *Cf.* the impressive scene in Dio lxii (lxiii). 4 ff., in which
Nero proclaims him king of Armenia. Tacitus, *Ann.* xii.
50-51, tells of Vologeses' unsuccessful attempt to place Tiridates on the throne through an invasion of Armenia. *Cf.*
Ann. xv. 2, where, after Tiridates has egged him on, Vologeses
defends his irresolution in not pressing for Armenia, which,
he admits, is only a third-rate kingdom (not, as stated here
in Josephus, a position of power). In *B.J.* vii. 249, Tiridates,
who has managed to win the rule of Armenia, is defeated by
the Alani.

g *Cf.* Mishnah, *Yoma* iii. 10, which records the lavish gift
that he later gave for the temple in Jerusalem, namely, golden
handles for the vessels used on the Day of Atonement.

h The Epitome adds " and goodness of heart in all his
ways." But the additions of the Epitome in this and in the
following section are quite clearly interpolations, as indicated
by Niese, in his preface to vol. iii, p. xxxvii.

i The Epitome adds " They carried out this project fully."

καιρὸν ἐπιτήδειον ἐζήτουν δίκην εἰσπράξασθαι
77 σπεύδοντες[1] παρ᾽ αὐτῶν. καὶ δὴ γράφουσιν πρὸς
Ἀβίαν τὸν Ἀράβων βασιλέα χρήματα πολλὰ δώσειν ὑπισχνούμενοι στρατεύσασθαι θελήσαντι κατὰ
τοῦ παρ᾽ αὐτοῖς βασιλέως, ἐπηγγέλλοντο δὲ καὶ
περὶ τὴν πρώτην συμβολὴν ἐγκαταλείψειν τὸν βα-
σιλέα· θέλειν γὰρ αὐτὸν τιμωρήσασθαι μισήσαντα
τὰ παρ᾽ αὐτοῖς ἔθη· καὶ ὅρκοις τὴν πρὸς ἀλλήλους
78 ἐνδησάμενοι πίστιν σπεύδειν[2] παρεκάλουν. πείθεται δὲ ὁ Ἄραψ, καὶ πολλὴν ἐπαγόμενος δύναμιν
ἧκεν ἐπὶ τὸν Ἰζάτην. μελλούσης δὲ τῆς πρώτης
συμβολῆς πρὶν εἰς χεῖρας ἐλθεῖν καταλείπουσιν τὸν
Ἰζάτην ἐκ συνθήματος πάντες ὡς πανικῷ δείματι
κατασχεθέντες,[3] καὶ τὰ νῶτα τοῖς πολεμίοις ἐντρέ-
79 ψαντες ἔφευγον. οὐ μὴν ὁ Ἰζάτης κατεπλάγη,
νοήσας δὲ προδοσίαν ὑπὸ τῶν μεγιστάνων γεγενῆσθαι καὶ αὐτὸς εἰς τὸ στρατόπεδον[4] ὑπεχώρησεν,
καὶ τὴν αἰτίαν ζητήσας ὡς ἔμαθεν συντεταγμένους
πρὸς τὸν Ἄραβα, τοὺς μὲν αἰτίους ἀναιρεῖ, τῇ δ᾽
80 ἐπιούσῃ συμβαλὼν πλείστους μὲν ἀπέκτεινε, πάντας
δὲ φυγεῖν ἠνάγκασεν, αὐτὸν δὲ τὸν βασιλέα διώκων
εἴς τι φρούριον συνήλασεν Ἄρσαμον καλούμενον,
καὶ προσμαχεσάμενος καρτερῶς εἷλε[5] τὸ φρούριον
διαρπάσας τε τὴν ἐν αὐτῷ λείαν πᾶσαν, πολλὴ δὲ
ἦν, ὑπέστρεψεν εἰς τὴν Ἀδιαβηνὴν τὸν Ἀβίαν οὐ
καταλαβὼν ζῶντα· περικαταλαμβανόμενος γὰρ ἑαυτὸν ἀνεῖλεν πρὶν εἰς χεῖρας συγκλεισθῇ τοῦ Ἰζάτου.[6]
81 (2) Ἀποτυχόντες δὲ οἱ τῶν Ἀδιαβηνῶν μεγι-

---

[1] σπεύδοντες] om. E.   [2] σπεύδειν] σπεύδειν τομῶς E.
[3] ὡς πανικῷ δείματι κατασχεθέντες] om. E : velut uno vincti
funiculo Lat.
[4] εἰς τὸ στρατόπεδον] cum exercitu Lat.
[5] καὶ προσμαχεσάμενος καρτερῶς εἷλε] ἑλών τε E.

42

eagerly sought a convenient opportunity to make
them pay the penalty for their act. Consequently Defeat of
they wrote to Abias king of the Arabs, promising him Abias, king
of the
large sums if he would consent to take the field against Arabs,
their king. They further offered to abandon the when he
attacks
king at the first onset, for they wished to punish Izates.
him because he had come to hate their way of life.
Having bound themselves to mutual loyalty by oaths,
they exhorted Abias to make haste. The Arab king
consented and came marching with a great army
against Izates. When the first engagement was just
about to take place and before they came to blows,
the high nobles, at a prearranged signal, deserted
Izates, pretending to be possessed by panic, and,
turning their backs to the enemy, took to flight.
Izates, however, was not panic-stricken, but per-
ceiving that there had been treachery on the part of
the high nobles, personally withdrew to the camp.
On inquiring into the cause of the flight and on
learning that they had joined forces with the Arab,
he put the guilty parties to death. On the morrow,
joining battle, he slew a great number of the enemy
and compelled the rest to flee. The king himself he
pursued and hemmed into a certain fortress called
Arsamus, which he captured by assault after a stub-
born fight. When he had plundered it of all the booty
that it contained—and it was much—he returned to
Adiabene. He did not take Abias alive ; for the
latter, being surrounded on all sides, killed himself
before he was quite trapped and in the hands of
Izates.

(2) Foiled in their first attempt, when God de- Vologeses,
king of

---

⁶ πρὶν . . . Ἰζάτου] A (litt. πρὶν . . . πάλιν Οὐο i. ras.
m. 2 A) : om. MWE.

στάνες τῆς πρώτης ἐπιχειρήσεως παραδόντος αὐτοὺς τοῦ θεοῦ τῷ βασιλεῖ οὐδ' ὡς ἠρέμουν, ἀλλὰ
γράφουσιν πάλιν Οὐολογέσῃ, βασιλεὺς δὲ Πάρθων
οὗτος ἦν, παρακαλοῦντες ἀποκτεῖναι μὲν τὸν Ἰζάτην, καταστῆσαι δ' αὐτοῖς ἕτερον δυνάστην καὶ
τῷ γένει Πάρθον· μισεῖν γὰρ ἔλεγον τὸν ἑαυτῶν
βασιλέα καταλύσαντα μὲν τὰ πάτρια,¹ ξένων δ'
82 ἐραστὴν ἐθῶν γενόμενον. ταῦτα ἀκούσας ὁ Πάρθος
ἐπήρθη πρὸς τὸν πόλεμον, καὶ προφάσεως δικαίας
μηδεμίαν ἀφορμὴν ἔχων τὰς ὑπὸ τοῦ πατρὸς αὐτῷ
δοθείσας τιμὰς ἔπεμψεν ἀπαιτῶν, ἀπειθήσαντι δὲ
83 πόλεμον κατήγγελλεν. ταράσσεται δὲ τὴν ψυχὴν
οὐχὶ μετρίως ὁ Ἰζάτης, ὡς ἤκουσεν ταῦτα, κατά-
γνωσιν μὲν φέρειν αὐτῷ νομίσας τὸ τῶν δωρεῶν
84 ἐξίστασθαι δοκεῖν² διὰ φόβον τοῦτο πράξας. εἰδὼς
δέ, ὅτι καὶ ἀπολαβὼν ὁ Πάρθος τὰς τιμὰς οὐκ ἂν
ἠρεμήσειεν, ἔκρινεν ἐπιτρέψαι τῷ κηδεμόνι θεῷ
85 τὸν ὑπὲρ τῆς ψυχῆς κίνδυνον, καὶ τοῦτον μέγιστον
ἡγησάμενος ἔχειν σύμμαχον κατατίθεται μὲν τὰ
τέκνα καὶ τὰς γυναῖκας εἰς τὰ τῶν φρουρίων ἀσφα-
λέστατα, τὸν σῖτον δὲ πάντα μὲν³ εἰς τὰς βάρεις⁴
καὶ⁵ ἐμπίπρησιν τόν τε χόρτον καὶ τὰς νομάς,⁶
ταῦτά τε προευτρεπισάμενος ἐξεδέχετο τοὺς πολε-
86 μίους. παραγενομένου δὲ τοῦ Πάρθου μετὰ πολλῆς
δυνάμεως πεζῶν τε καὶ ἱππέων θᾶττον ἐλπίδος,
ὤδευσε γὰρ συντόνως, βαλλομένου τε χάρακα πρὸς
τῷ ποταμῷ τῷ τὴν Ἀδιαβηνὴν καὶ τὴν Μηδίαν
ὁρίζοντι, τίθησι καὶ ὁ Ἰζάτης τὸ στρατόπεδον οὐκ
ἄπωθεν ἔχων περὶ αὐτὸν ἱππεῖς τὸν ἀριθμὸν ἑξα-

¹ καταλύσαντα . . . πάτρια] om. E.
² AW : om. ME : δοκοῦντι Ernesti.

livered them over to the king, the nobles of Adiabene
did not even then keep quiet, but wrote another
letter, this time to Vologeses king of the Parthians,
urging him to put Izates to death and to appoint
for them another overlord, of Parthian descent ; for,
they said, they had come to loathe their own king,
who had overthrown their traditions and had become
enamoured of foreign practices. The Parthian king
was swayed by their words to seek a war ; but having
no honest pretext, he sent a message demanding the
return of those awards of honour that his father had
bestowed on Izates, and threatened to declare war
on him if he refused. Izates was sorely perturbed in
his mind when he received this message, for he
thought that to surrender the gifts would bring him
into contempt since it would appear that he had done
so through fear. Besides, he knew that the Parthian
would not refrain from action even if he recovered
the awards, and so he decided, in his present danger,
to commit himself to God the protector. Reflecting
that he had in God the greatest of allies, he deposited
his children and wives in the most secure of his fortresses, stored all the grain in towers, and burnt over
the grass for pasturage. After these preliminary
moves he awaited the enemy. The Parthian arrived
with a large force of infantry and cavalry sooner than
was expected, for he had recourse to forced marches,
and threw up a palisaded camp at the river that is
the boundary between Adiabene and Media. Izates
also, who had with him six thousand horsemen,

---

³ μὲν] MW : μὲν τὸν A.
⁴ lacunam post βάρεις indicat Niese.
⁵ ed. pr. : om. codd. E.
⁶ εἰς τὰς . . . νομάς] in munitissimis locis cunctaque frumenta et foenum et pabula congregavit Lat.

87 κισχιλίους.¹ ἀφικνεῖται δὲ πρὸς τὸν Ἰζάτην ἄγ-
γελος παρὰ τοῦ Πάρθου πεμφθείς, ὃς τὴν Πάρθων
δύναμιν ὅση τίς ἐστιν ἤγγελλεν ἀπὸ Εὐφράτου πο-
ταμοῦ μέχρι Βάκτρων τοὺς ὅρους αὐτῆς τιθέμε-
νος καὶ τοὺς ὑπηκόους αὐτῆς βασιλέας καταλέγων.
88 ἠπείλει δὲ δώσειν αὐτὸν δίκας ἀχάριστον περὶ
δεσπότας τοὺς ἑαυτοῦ γενόμενον, καὶ ῥύεσθαι τῶν
βασιλέως αὐτὸν χειρῶν οὐδὲ τὸν θεὸν ὃν σέβει
89 δυνήσεσθαι. ταῦτα τοῦ ἀγγέλου φράσαντος ὁ
Ἰζάτης εἰδέναι μὲν τὴν Πάρθων δύναμιν ἔφη πολὺ
τῆς αὐτοῦ διαφέρουσαν, γινώσκειν δ' οὖν ἔτι μᾶλλον πάντων ἀνθρώπων ἔλεγεν κρείσσω τὸν θεόν.
καὶ τοιαύτην δοὺς τὴν ἀπόκρισιν ἐπὶ τὴν ἱκετείαν
ἐτρέπετο τοῦ θεοῦ, χαμαί τε ῥίψας αὐτὸν καὶ
σποδῷ τὴν κεφαλὴν καταισχύνας μετὰ γυναικὸς²
καὶ τέκνων ἐνήστευεν ἀνακαλῶν τὸν θεὸν καὶ λέγων,
90 " εἰ μὴ μάτην, ὦ δέσποτα κύριε, τῆς σῆς ἐγενόμην³
χρηστότητος, τῶν πάντων δὲ δικαίως μόνον καὶ
πρῶτον ἥγημαι κύριον,⁴ ἐλθὲ σύμμαχος οὐχ ὑπὲρ
ἐμοῦ μόνον ἀμυνούμενος τοὺς πολεμίους, ἀλλ' ὅτι
91 καὶ τῆς σῆς δυνάμεως κατατετολμήκασιν."⁵ ὁ μὲν

¹ ἔχων . . . ἑξακισχιλίους] AM : om. W.
² γυναικῶν E Lat.
³ τῆς σῆς ἐγενόμην] Warmington : τῆς σῆς ἐγενόμην codd. :
τῆς σῆς ἐγενόμην <κοινωνὸς> Richards et Shutt : <προστάτης>
τῆς σῆς ἐγενόμην Petersen.
⁴ τῶν πάντων . . . κύριον] τὸν τῶν πάντων δὲ δικαίως μόνον
δεσπότην καὶ πρῶτον ἥγημαι προνοητὴν καὶ κύριον i. marg. A.
⁵ ἀλλ' ὅτι . . . κατατετολμήκασιν] sed quia etiam contra
tuam virtutem cum nefanda praesumptione locuti sunt Lat. ;
καὶ μεγαλορρήμονα γλῶσσαν ἐπαφιέναι οὐ πεφρίκασιν post κατατετολμήκασιν add. ed. pr.

ᵃ In the northern part of modern Afghanistan and in
Russian Turkestan.

pitched his camp not far off. A messenger sent by the Parthian made his way to Izates and reported to him the extent of the Parthian empire, declaring that it was bounded by the river Euphrates and went from there to Bactria.[a] He also called the roll of kings subject to it. Then he threatened that Izates would pay the penalty for ingratitude to his masters, and that even the God whom he worshipped would be unable to deliver him from the king's hands. After the messenger had spoken these words, Izates replied that he was aware that the Parthian empire was far larger than his own, but for all that he was even more certain that God is mightier than all mankind. After giving this reply, he gave himself to supplicating God's favour. He flung himself on the ground and befouled his head with ashes; he fasted, together with his wife and children, calling upon God with these words : " If it is not in vain, O sovereign Lord, that I have had a taste of Thy goodness,[b] and that I have made it my belief that Thou art the first and only rightful Lord of all, come to my aid not only for my sake to defend me from my enemies, but also because it is Thy power that they have had the audacity to challenge." [c] Thus he

Izates'
prayer and
his deliver-
ance from
the Par-
thians.

[b] Richards and Shutt emend to " I have become a partner in Thy goodness." Prof. Petersen suggests " I have become the champion of Thy goodness."

[c] The *editio princeps* adds " and have not shuddered to utter grandiloquent words." The prayer of Izates bears similarities to the prayer of Hezekiah (2 Kings xix. 15-19) when he was attacked by Sennacherib, particularly in its emphasis on imploring God to show the gentiles that they may not attack or taunt Him with impunity. Both Sennacherib (2 Kings xix. 36) and Vologeses are later forced to depart without carrying out their attacks on the Jewish king.

JOSEPHUS

ταῦτ' ἐποτνιᾶτο δακρύων καὶ ὀδυρόμενος, ἐπήκοος
δὲ ὁ θεὸς ἐγίνετο, καὶ κατ' ἐκείνην εὐθὺς τὴν νύκτα[1]
δεξάμενος Οὐολογέσης ἐπιστολάς, ἐν αἷς ἐγέγραπτο
Δαῶν[2] καὶ Σακῶν[3] χεῖρα μεγάλην καταφρονήσασαν
αὐτοῦ τῆς ἀποδημίας ἐπιστρατευσαμένην διαρπάζειν τὴν Παρθυηνῶν, ἄπρακτος ἀνέζευξεν εἰς τοὔ-
πίσω. καὶ Ἰζάτης οὕτω κατὰ θεοῦ πρόνοιαν τὰς
ἀπειλὰς τοῦ Πάρθου διαφεύγει.

92   (3) Μετ' οὐ πολὺν δὲ χρόνον πεντηκοστὸν μὲν καὶ
πέμπτον ἀπὸ γενεᾶς πληρώσας ἔτος τέταρτον δὲ
πρὸς εἰκοστῷ δυναστεύσας, καταλιπὼν παῖδας ἄρ-
ρενας εἰκοσιτέσσαρας καὶ θυγατέρας εἰκοσιτέσ-
93 σαρας[4] καταστρέφει τὸν βίον.[5] τὴν μέντοι διαδοχὴν
τῆς ἀρχῆς τὸν ἀδελφὸν Μονόβαζον ἐκέλευεν παραλαβεῖν, ἀμειβόμενος αὐτὸν ὅτι κατὰ τὴν ἀποδημίαν
αὐτοῦ μετὰ τὸν τοῦ πατρὸς θάνατον πιστῶς φυλά-
94 ξειεν αὐτῷ τὴν δυναστείαν. ἡ δὲ μήτηρ Ἑλένη τὸν
τοῦ παιδὸς θάνατον ἀκούσασα βαρέως μὲν ἤνεγκεν
ὡς εἰκὸς μητέρα στερομένην εὐσεβεστάτου παιδός,
παραμυθίαν δ' ὅμως εἶχεν τὴν διαδοχὴν ἀκούσασα
εἰς τὸν πρεσβύτερον αὐτῆς υἱὸν ἤκουσαν, καὶ πρὸς

---

[1] ἐν ᾗ ταῦτα ἐκεῖνος ἐδεῖτο post νύκτα i. marg. add. A.
[2] Hudson : Δακῶν AME : Δοκῶν W : Dacus (h. e. Δακὸν)
Lat.
[3] A'MWE : Ἰσακῶν ex corr. A : Isacus (h.e. Ἴσακον) Lat.
[4] καὶ θυγατέρας εἴκοσι τέσσαρας] A : om. MW : καὶ θυγατέρας τοσαύτας E.
[5] καταστρέφει τὸν βίον] E et ut vid. Lat. : om. codd.

---

[a] These nomadic Scythian tribes are also coupled in *Ant.*
xviii. 100.
[b] On twenty-four as a round number in the Biblical and

cried aloud with tears and lamentation, and God hearkened to him. And on that very night Vologeses received letters in which it was written that a great force of Dahae and Sacae,[a] presuming on his absence from home, had invaded and were ravaging the Parthian territory. He consequently retreated in frustration. Thus by the providence of God Izates escaped the threats of the Parthian.

(3) Not long afterwards Izates passed away, having completed fifty-five years of his life and having been monarch for twenty-four ; he left twenty-four sons and twenty-four daughters.[b] His orders were that his brother Monobazus should succeed to the throne. Thus Monobazus was rewarded for faithfully keeping the throne for his brother during the latter's absence from home after his father's death. His mother Helena was sorely distressed by the news of her son's death, as was to be expected of a mother bereft of a son so very religious. She was, however, consoled on hearing that the succession had passed to her eldest

Death of Izates and Helena and their burial near Jerusalem.

Talmudic traditions see the index to L. Ginzberg, *Legends of the Jews*, vii, 1938, p. 484, who cites, among other examples, the twenty-four descendants of Korah who were destined to compose psalms and sing them in the temple. Other examples are the twenty-four (or twenty-two) blessings that God bestowed on Adam, the twenty-four days that Joseph stayed in prison, the twenty-four species of cedar, the twenty-four vines above the throne of Solomon, the twenty-four kinds of disease inflicted on the Egyptians, the twenty-four sects into which Israel was divided before it was exiled, and the twenty-four generations during which it is said that one cannot trust a proselyte. To this list should be added the twenty-four thousand myriad *denarii* spent by Rabbi Judah the Prince on a wedding feast for his son (Bab. *Nedarim* 50 b). On equal numbers of sons and daughters *cf.* the judge Ibzan of Bethlehem, who had thirty sons and thirty daughters (Judges xii. 9).

JOSEPHUS

αὐτὸν ἔσπευδεν. παραγενομένη δὲ εἰς τὴν Ἀδιαβηνὴν οὐ πολὺν Ἰζάτῃ τῷ παιδὶ χρόνον ἐπεβίωσεν,
ἀλλὰ τῷ γήρᾳ καὶ τῷ τῆς λύπης ἀλγήματι πιεζο-
95 μένη ταχέως ἀπέψυξεν.¹ ὁ δὲ Μονόβαζος τά τε
ἐκείνης ὀστᾶ καὶ τὰ τοῦ ἀδελφοῦ πέμψας εἰς Ἱεροσόλυμα θάψαι προσέταξεν ἐν ταῖς πυραμίσιν, ἃς ἡ
μήτηρ κατεσκευάκει τρεῖς τὸν ἀριθμὸν τρία στάδια
96 τῆς Ἱεροσολυμιτῶν πόλεως ἀπεχούσας. ἀλλὰ
Μονόβαζος μὲν ὁ βασιλεὺς ὅσα κατὰ τὸν τῆς ζωῆς
χρόνον ἔπραξεν, ὕστερον ἀπαγγελοῦμεν.

¹ ἀλλὰ . . . ἀπέψυξεν] A (in ras. m. 2 A) : om. MWE.

---

[a] The clause " for . . . last " is found in only one ms.,
the Ambrosian, and there only over an erasure. Niese, in the
preface to vol. iii of his edition, p. xxxiii, has no doubt that
it is not genuine, but the Ambrosian is definitely our best ms.
for Books XVIII-XX, and one should be slow to depart
from it.

[b] Presumably for Helena and her two sons, Izates and
Monobazus. Helena's " monuments " are mentioned in
B.J. v. 55 and 147 ; her tomb as such is noted as a landmark
in *B.J.* v. 119. Most archaeologists place these pyramids at
the Tombs of the Kings, where F. de Saulcy in 1865 found
an unopened sarcophagus containing a body which crumbled
when exposed to the air. The inscription on the sarcophagus
is said to have contained letters of Aramaic or Palmyrene
script, with two of the words meaning " Helena the Queen."
N. P. Clarke, " Helena's Pyramids," *Pal. Explor. Quart.*
lxx, 1938, pp. 88-89, objects to placing the pyramids at the
Tombs of the Kings because this site is about four and a half
furlongs from the Damascus Gate or from Herod's Gate (from
which Josephus apparently measured), whereas Josephus in
our passage says that the distance is three furlongs. Clarke
argues that the distance must have been well known ; but why
quibble over a furlong and a half when the inscription on the
sarcophagus makes it clear that Helena was buried at the
Tombs of the Kings? Clarke, p. 103, holds that before Titus
attacked the third wall of Jerusalem he levelled the whole
place in front of it, including Helena's pyramids, and that

50

son and hastened to join him. She arrived in Adiabene but did not long survive her son Izates, for, weighed down with age and with the pain of her sorrow, she quickly breathed out her last.[a] Monobazus sent her bones and those of his brother to Jerusalem with instructions that they should be buried in the three pyramids [b] that his mother had erected at a distance of three furlongs from the city of Jerusalem. As for the acts of King Monobazus during his lifetime, I shall narrate them later.[c]

after the war, her relatives reinterred the queen in the Tombs of the Kings. Pausanias, then, who mentions (viii. 16. 5) Helena's tomb, did not see the pyramids but the Tombs of the Kings, according to Clarke.

[c] Such an account is not to be found in Josephus' extant works, unless perhaps Josephus has in mind the brief mention of the participation of the family of Monobazus in the revolt in 66 (*B.J.* ii. 520, iv. 567, and vi. 356). Petersen, *op. cit.* pp. 273-274, theorizes that Josephus intended to fulfil this promise, together with the promises contained in §§ 144, 147, and perhaps 53, in his *Vita*, but that he modified his original plan through his desire to present an *apologia pro vita sua*. But the *Vita*, at least as we have it, seems to have been apologetic from the start, and contains no evidence of a plan to fulfil these projects. Josephus could, to be sure, have fulfilled these projects in the *Vita*, since he wrote it later, but only by digressing. We obtain one clue to the events of Monobazus' reign from Tacitus, *Ann.* xv. 1 (*cf.* xv. 14), which records his appeal to Vologeses the Parthian king for aid against Tigranes, whom the Romans had appointed to rule Armenia and who was, in 62, ravaging the territory of Adiabene. The Talmud, *Menaḥot* 32 b, relates that the members of the house of Monobazus were so pious that they carried a mezuzah with them and set it up in the inns where they stayed, even though a mezuzah is not required for such temporary dwelling-places. Not long after the reign of Monobazus, Adiabene was conquered by Trajan and made part of the Roman province of Assyria. In the Talmudic literature (*e.g. Shabbath* 68 b) there is reference several times

51

97 (v. 1) Φάδου δὲ τῆς Ἰουδαίας ἐπιτροπεύοντος
γόης τις ἀνὴρ Θευδᾶς¹ ὀνόματι πείθει τὸν πλεῖστον
ὄχλον ἀναλαβόντα τὰς κτήσεις ἕπεσθαι πρὸς τὸν
Ἰορδάνην ποταμὸν αὐτῷ· προφήτης γὰρ ἔλεγεν
εἶναι, καὶ προστάγματι τὸν ποταμὸν σχίσας δίοδον
98 ἔχειν² ἔφη παρέξειν αὐτοῖς ῥᾳδίαν. καὶ ταῦτα

¹ Theodas Lat.
² A : om. MWE Eus. et fort. Lat.

to a second-century disciple of Rabbi Akiba who is named
Monobaz and who is generally regarded (*cf.*, *e.g.*, B. J. Bamberger, *Proselytism in the Talmudic Period*, 1939, p. 228) as
a descendant of King Monobazus.

ᵃ *Cf. Ant.* xix. 363-xx. 8 and xx. 14.

ᵇ The term γόης, which is here used, refers to a sorcerer or
a wizard (later a juggler or a cheat) in classical Greek literature (*cf.*, *e.g.*, Herodotus iv. 105, who says that the Neuri, who
were neighbours of the Scythians, may be wizards (γόητες),
since all of them are said to turn into wolves once a year).
The term is not found in the Septuagint, but in 2 Maccabees
xii. 24 we read that Timotheus, who had fallen into the hands
of Dositheus and Sosipater, entreated them with much craft
(μετὰ πολλῆς γοητείας) to release him, threatening to harm
their parents and brothers, who were in his power, if they
did not do so. The word γόης is used in our sense in the only
occurrence of the term in the New Testament, 2 Timothy
iii. 13, where we read that all believers will be persecuted,
" while evil men and impostors (γόητες) will go on from bad
to worse, deceivers and deceived." In Philo, *Spec. Leg.* i.
315, the term is used in the sense of false prophet and is the
very antithesis of προφήτης : " If anyone cloaking himself
under the name and guise of a prophet and claiming to be
possessed by inspiration lead us on to the worship of the gods
recognized in the different cities, we ought not to listen to
him and be deceived by the name of a prophet. For such a
one is no prophet, but an impostor [γόης], since his oracles
and pronouncements are falsehoods invented by himself."

(v. 1) During the period when Fadus *a* was pro- The false
curator of Judaea, a certain impostor *b* named Theu- prophet
das *c* persuaded the majority of the masses *d* to take executed by
up their possessions and to follow him to the Jordan Fadus.
River. He stated that he was a prophet and that at
his command the river would be parted and would
provide them an easy passage. With this talk he

See Delling, *s.v. γόης*, in G. Kittel's *Theologisches Wörterbuch
zum Neuen Testament*, i, 1933, pp. 237-238.

c *Cf.* Acts v. 36.

d About four hundred according to Acts v. 36. The view
that Luke, the author of Acts, used Josephus is propounded
at length by M. Krenkel, *Josephus und Lucas*, 1894, and
accepted by P. W. Schmiedel, " Theudas," *Ency. Bibl.* iv,
1903, pp. 5051-5056, and by F. C. Burkitt, *The Gospel History
and Its Transmission*, 1906, pp. 106-108. But Luke, as C. C.
Torrey, *The Composition and Date of Acts*, 1916, p. 71, and
H. St. J. Thackeray, *Selections from Josephus*, 1919, p. 194,
rightly remark, must have had access to a source other than
Josephus, since he is precise in the number, whereas Josephus
is not. Though the identity of names is striking, it is, of
course, perfectly possible that two different people named
Theudas are referred to. Moreover, as A. C. Headlam,
" Theudas," *Hastings' Dict. of the Bible*, iv, 1903, p. 750,
notes, there is a chronological discrepancy between Josephus
and Acts, since the reference to Theudas in Acts is found in
a speech which Gamaliel must have made before A.D. 37,
whereas the revolt mentioned by Josephus occurred in A.D.
45 or 46. Moreover, whereas Josephus, in § 102, almost
immediately after he recounts the incident of Theudas, mentions the crucifixion of the *sons* of Judas the Galilaean,
Gamaliel says that after Theudas Judas the Galilaean arose
in the days of the census. Because of these discrepancies,
therefore, some have contended that the Theudas referred to
in Acts is not the same as the Theudas mentioned by Josephus. But, as Schmiedel, p. 5051, points out, the name
Theudas is relatively uncommon and the Theudas who is
cited by Gamaliel in Acts must have created a major disturbance if the illustration is to have any effectiveness ; hence
Josephus is not likely to have passed it over.

λέγων πολλοὺς ἠπάτησεν. οὐ μὴν εἴασεν αὐτοὺς
τῆς ἀφροσύνης ὄνασθαι Φᾶδος, ἀλλ' ἐξέπεμψεν ἴλην
ἱππέων ἐπ' αὐτούς, ἥτις ἀπροσδόκητος ἐπιπεσοῦσα
πολλοὺς μὲν ἀνεῖλεν, πολλοὺς δὲ ζῶντας ἔλαβεν,
αὐτὸν δὲ τὸν Θευδᾶν ζωγρήσαντες ἀποτέμνουσι τὴν
99 κεφαλὴν καὶ κομίζουσιν εἰς Ἱεροσόλυμα. τὰ μὲν
οὖν συμβάντα τοῖς Ἰουδαίοις κατὰ τοὺς Κουσπίου
Φάδου τῆς ἐπιτροπῆς χρόνους ταῦτ' ἐγένετο.

100 (2) Ἦλθε δὲ Φάδῳ διάδοχος Τιβέριος Ἀλέξανδρος Ἀλεξάνδρου παῖς τοῦ καὶ ἀλαβαρχήσαντος[1]
ἐν Ἀλεξανδρείᾳ γένει τε[2] καὶ πλούτῳ πρωτεύσαντος
τῶν ἐκεῖ καθ' αὑτόν. διήνεγκε καὶ τῇ πρὸς τὸν
θεὸν εὐσεβείᾳ τοῦ παιδὸς Ἀλεξάνδρου· τοῖς γὰρ
101 πατρίοις οὐκ ἐνέμεινεν οὗτος ἔθεσιν. ἐπὶ τούτου
δὲ καὶ τὸν μέγαν λιμὸν κατὰ τὴν Ἰουδαίαν συνέβη
γενέσθαι, καθ' ὃν καὶ ἡ βασίλισσα Ἑλένη πολλῶν
χρημάτων ὠνησαμένη σῖτον ἀπὸ τῆς Αἰγύπτου
102 διένειμεν τοῖς ἀπορουμένοις, ὡς προεῖπον. πρὸς
τούτοις δὲ καὶ οἱ παῖδες Ἰούδα τοῦ Γαλιλαίου
ἀνήχθησαν[3] τοῦ τὸν λαὸν ἀπὸ Ῥωμαίων ἀποστή-
σαντος Κυρινίου τῆς Ἰουδαίας τιμητεύοντος, ὡς ἐν

---

[1] ἀλαβαρχήσαντος] alabarchis id est princeps salis Lat.
[2] γένει τε] A : om. MWE.
[3] A : ἀνηρέθησαν MWE et i. marg. A : om. Lat.

---

[a] Either 500 or 1000 men. *Cf. Ant.* xix. 365.
[b] According to Acts v. 36, Theudas himself was slain and
his followers were scattered.
[c] Nephew of the philosopher Philo. Procurator *c.* 46–48.
In *B.J.* ii. 220 Josephus says that he, like Cuspius Fadus,
kept the nation at peace by avoiding interference in Jewish
customs. Alexander later (63) served under Corbulo in
Armenia (Tac. *Ann.* xv. 28) and as prefect of Egypt (*cf. B.J.*
ii. 309 and 492-498). When Vespasian was proclaimed
emperor, Alexander required the legions and the people to

deceived many. Fadus, however, did not permit
them to reap the fruit of their folly, but sent against
them a squadron [a] of cavalry. These fell upon them
unexpectedly, slew many of them and took many
prisoners. Theudas himself was captured, whereupon
they cut off his head and brought it to Jerusalem.[b]
These, then, are the events that befell the Jews
during the time that Cuspius Fadus was procurator.

(2) The successor of Fadus was Tiberius Alex- Tiberius
ander,[c] the son of that Alexander [d] who had been Alexander
is appointed
alabarch in Alexandria and who surpassed all his procurator.
fellow citizens both in ancestry and in wealth. He
was also superior to his son Alexander in his religious
devotion, for the latter did not stand by the practices
of his people. It was in the administration of Tiberius
Alexander [e] that the great famine occurred in Judaea,
during which Queen Helena bought grain from Egypt
for large sums and distributed it to the needy, as I
have stated above.[f] Besides this James and Simon, Crucifixion
the sons of Judas the Galilaean, were brought up for of the sons
of Judas the
trial [g] and, at the order of Alexander, were crucified. Galilaean.
This was the Judas [h] who, as I have explained above,[i]

take an oath of allegiance to him (*B.J.* iv. 616-617). Later
he held a military command under Titus (*B.J.* v. 45-46, etc.).
    [d] *Cf. Ant.* xviii. 159-160, 259 ; and xix. 276-277.
    [e] This is based on the reading of the Epitome. The MSS.,
however, read ἐπὶ τούτοις, which can mean, as remarked by
Kirsopp Lake, in Foakes Jackson and Kirsopp Lake, *op. cit.*
v. 454, either " under these circumstances " or " in their [*i.e.*
Fadus and Tiberius Alexander's] time." If the latter is the
meaning, the famine might have begun in 45.   [f] § 51.
    [g] Variant " were put to death."
    [h] As noted above, Luke, like Josephus, mentions Judas
(Acts v. 37) after the incident of Theudas. But his source is
probably not Josephus, since he says that it was Judas who
perished, whereas Josephus says that it was Judas' sons who
were put to death.   [i] *Ant.* xviii. 4 ff.

τοῖς πρὸ τούτων δεδηλώκαμεν, Ἰάκωβος καὶ Σίμων, οὓς ἀνασταυρῶσαι προσέταξεν Ἀλέξανδρος.
103 ὁ δὲ τῆς Χαλκίδος βασιλεὺς Ἡρώδης μεταστήσας
τῆς ἀρχιερωσύνης Ἰώσηπον τὸν τοῦ Καμεὶ¹ τὴν
διαδοχὴν τῆς τιμῆς Ἀνανίᾳ τῷ τοῦ Νεδεβαίου²
δίδωσιν. Τιβερίῳ δὲ Ἀλεξάνδρῳ Κουμανὸς ἀφ-
104 ίκετο διάδοχος. καὶ τελευτᾷ τὸν βίον Ἡρώδης ὁ
τοῦ μεγάλου βασιλέως Ἀγρίππα ἀδελφὸς ὀγδόῳ
τῆς Κλαυδίου Καίσαρος ἀρχῆς ἔτει, καταλιπὼν
τρεῖς υἱοὺς Ἀριστόβουλον μὲν ὑπὸ τῆς πρώτης
αὐτῷ τεχθέντα γυναικός, ἐκ Βερενίκης δὲ τῆς τἀδελφοῦ θυγατρὸς Βερενικιανὸν καὶ Ὑρκανόν. τὴν
δ’ ἀρχὴν αὐτοῦ Καῖσαρ Κλαύδιος Ἀγρίππᾳ τῷ
νεωτέρῳ δίδωσιν.
105 (3) Στάσεως δ’ ἐμπεσούσης τῇ τῶν Ἱεροσολυμιτῶν πόλει Κουμανοῦ τὰ κατὰ τὴν Ἰουδαίαν πράγματα διοικοῦντος ἐφθάρησαν ὑπὸ ταύτης πολλοὶ τῶν

¹ coni. (cf. § 16): Καμοιδὶ, οἱ ex ωι corr., i. marg. γρ ἐν ἄλλοις Κεμεδὶ γρ δὲ ἐν ἄλλοις Καμύδου A: Καμύδου MW: Κεμεδῆ
E: Cami Lat.
² AE (δεβαίου i. ras. m. 1 A): Νεβεδαίου MW: Nibedei
Lat.

ᵃ mss. Camoedi, Camudus, Camede. *Cf.* § 16. But the
Latin version reads Cami, and in § 16 above the name is
Camei.
ᵇ *Cf.* §§ 131 and 205 ff. His murder by brigands in 66 is
described in *B.J.* ii. 441. The Talmud, *Pesaḥim* 57 a, which
calls him Johanan the son of Narbai (or Nadbai), praises
him by noting that during his administration the law that
sacrifices must not be left after the time prescribed for consuming them was always observed. On the other hand, it
cites his huge appetite, remarking that he—a marginal note
says his household—consumed three hundred calves, drank
three hundred barrels of wine, and ate forty *se'ah* of young
birds as a dessert for a single meal. He is perhaps to be

had aroused the people to revolt against the Romans while Quirinius was taking the census in Judaea. Herod, king of Chalcis, now removed Joseph, the son of Camei,[a] from the high priesthood and assigned the office to Ananias,[b] the son of Nedebaeus, as successor. Cumanus [c] also came as successor to Tiberius Alexander. [d] Herod, the brother of the great king Agrippa, died in the eighth year of the reign of Claudius Caesar.[e] He left three sons—Aristobulus, born to him by his first wife,[f] and Berenicianus and Hyrcanus, born to him by Berenice, his brother's daughter. Claudius Caesar assigned Herod's kingdom to the younger Agrippa.

Cumanus is appointed procurator.

Agrippa II succeeds Herod of Chalcis.

(3) [g] While Cumanus was administering affairs in Judaea, an uprising occurred in the city of Jerusalem as a result of which many of the Jews lost their lives.

The Jewish calamity during Passover because of a Roman soldier's lewdness.

identified with the Hanin ben Matron whose assassination by Judah the brother of Menahem (perhaps the Menahem who, according to *B.J.* ii. 434, was in command of the rebels against Rome) is mentioned at the end of the Midrashic work *Shir Hashirim Zuta*. S. Lieberman, *Greek in Jewish Palestine*, 1942, p. 181 n. 188, suggests that " ben Matron " may be Μέτριος, " the moderate," and thinks that this would be biting irony in allusion to his gluttony. Or, as he also suggests, the term may be taken literally in allusion to his opposition to the extremists who favoured war with the Romans (*cf. B.J.* ii. 455, which speaks of the moderates, οἱ μέτριοι). Ananias is mentioned in the New Testament as the high priest who orders that Paul be struck by those standing near him (Acts xxiii. 2-5) and as one of those who accuse Paul before the Roman governor (Acts xxiv. 1).

[c] Ventidius Cumanus, procurator A.D. 49. According to Tacitus, *Ann.* xii. 54, who assails him for his wickedness, be was governor of Galilee alone.

[d] *Cf.* the parallel passage, *B.J.* ii. 221.

[e] A.D. 49.

[f] Mariamme.

[g] With §§ 105-137 *cf.* the parallel passage, *B.J.* ii. 223-247.

Ἰουδαίων. καὶ πρότερον ἀφηγήσομαι τὴν αἰτίαν,
106 δι' ἣν ταῦτα συνέβη· τῆς πάσχα προσαγορευομένης
ἑορτῆς ἐνστάσης, καθ' ἣν ἔθος ἐστὶν ἡμῖν ἄζυμα
προσφέρεσθαι, πολλοῦ καὶ πανταχόθεν πλήθους
συναχθέντος ἐπὶ τὴν ἑορτὴν δείσας ὁ Κουμανός, μὴ
νεώτερόν τι παρὰ τούτων προσπέσῃ,[1] κελεύει τῶν
στρατιωτῶν μίαν τάξιν ἀναλαβοῦσαν τὰ ὅπλα ἐπὶ
τῶν τοῦ ἱεροῦ στοῶν ἑστάναι καταστελοῦντας τὸν
107 νεωτερισμόν, εἰ ἄρα τις γένοιτο. τοῦτο δὲ καὶ οἱ
πρὸ αὐτοῦ τῆς Ἰουδαίας ἐπιτροπεύσαντες ἐν ταῖς
108 ἑορταῖς ἔπραττον. τετάρτῃ δὲ ἡμέρᾳ τῆς ἑορτῆς
στρατιώτης τις ἀνακαλύψας ἐπεδείκνυε τῷ πλήθει
τὰ αἰδοῖα, καὶ πρὸς τοῦτο θεασαμένων ὀργὴ καὶ
θυμὸς ἦν οὐχ ἑαυτοὺς ὑβρίσθαι λεγόντων, ἀλλὰ τὸν
θεὸν ἠσεβῆσθαι· τινὲς δὲ τῶν θρασυτέρων τὸν
Κουμανὸν ἐβλασφήμουν ὑπ' αὐτοῦ τὸν στρατιώτην
109 καθεῖσθαι[2] λέγοντες. Κουμανὸς δ' ἀκούσας καὶ
αὐτὸς οὐ μετρίως ἐρεθίζεται πρὸς τὰς βλασφημίας,
παρῄνει μέντοι παύσασθαι νεωτέρων ἐπιθυμοῦντας
110 πραγμάτων μηδὲ στάσεις ἐξάπτειν ἐν ἑορτῇ.[3] μὴ
πείθων δέ, μᾶλλον γὰρ ἐπέκειντο βλασφημοῦντες,
κελεύει τὸ στράτευμα πᾶν τὰς πανοπλίας ἀναλαβὸν
ἥκειν εἰς τὴν Ἀντωνίαν, φρούριον δ' ἦν τοῦτο,
καθάπερ καὶ πρότερον εἴπομεν, ἐπικείμενον τῷ
111 ἱερῷ. παραγενομένους δὲ τοὺς στρατιώτας θεασά-

[1] μὴ . . . προσπέσῃ] ne quae per multitudinem turba aut
resultatio nasceretur Lat.
[2] E : καθίστασθαι codd.
[3] ἐν ἑορτῇ] καὶ ταραχάς E.

---

[a] A τάξις is a contingent of 128 men.
[b] On the tumult prevailing in Jerusalem during the festivals see Matt. xxvi. 5, cited by Whiston.

I shall first narrate the cause that brought about this uprising. When the festival called Passover was at hand, at which it is our custom to serve unleavened bread, a large multitude from all quarters assembled for it. Cumanus, fearing that their presence might afford occasion for an uprising, ordered one company [a] of soldiers to take up arms and stand guard on the porticoes of the temple so as to quell any uprising that might occur. This had been in fact the usual practice of previous procurators of Judaea at the festivals.[b] On the fourth day of the festival, one of the soldiers uncovered his genitals and exhibited them to the multitude—an action which created anger and rage in the onlookers, who said that it was not they who had been insulted, but that it was a blasphemy against God. Some of the bolder ones also reviled Cumanus, asserting that the soldier had been prompted by him. Cumanus, when informed, was himself not a little provoked at the insulting remarks, but still merely admonished them to put an end to this lust for revolution and not to set disorders ablaze during the festival. Failing, however, to persuade them, for they only attacked him with more scurrilities,[c] he ordered the whole army to take full armour and come to Antonia ; this was, as I have said before,[d] a fortress overlooking the temple. The crowd, seeing the arrival of the soldiers, was frightened

[c] Josephus here omits a detail which is supplied by the parallel passage, *B.J.* ii. 225-226, namely, that some of the more hot-headed young revolutionaries in the crowd actually started a fight and, picking up stones, threw them at the soldiers. It was then that Cumanus sent for reinforcements, who, upon their arrival, created panic among the Jews.

[d] *Ant.* xv. 403-409. *Cf.* also *Ant.* xiii. 307, xv. 292, xviii. 91, and xx. 6.

μενον τὸ πλῆθος καὶ φοβηθὲν φεύγειν ὥρμησεν, τῶν
δ' ἐξόδων στενῶν οὐσῶν διώκεσθαι νομίζοντες ὑπὸ
τῶν πολεμίων καὶ συνωθούμενοι κατὰ τὴν φυγὴν
πολλοὺς ἀλλήλοις ἐν τοῖς στενοῖς θλιβόμενοι δι-
112 έφθειρον. δύο γοῦν μυριάδες¹ ἐξηριθμήθησαν τῶν
κατὰ τὴν στάσιν ἐκείνην φθαρέντων. πένθος δ' ἦν
τὸ λοιπὸν ἀντὶ τῆς ἑορτῆς, καὶ πάντες ἐκλαθόμενοι
τῶν εὐχῶν καὶ τῶν θυσιῶν ἐπὶ θρήνους καὶ κλαυθ-
μοὺς ἐτράποντο. τοιαῦτα μὲν ἑνὸς ἀσέλγεια στρα-
τιώτου παθήματα γενέσθαι παρεσκεύασεν.

113   (4) Οὔπω δ' αὐτῶν τὸ πρῶτον πένθος ἐπέπαυτο
καὶ κακὸν ἄλλο προσέπιπτεν· τῶν γὰρ ἀφεστώτων
ἐπὶ νεωτερισμῷ τινες² κατὰ τὴν δημοσίαν ὁδὸν ὡς
ἑκατὸν σταδίων ἄπωθεν τῆς πόλεως Στέφανον Καίσαρος δοῦλον ὁδοιποροῦντα λῃστεύσαντες ἅπασαν
114 αὐτοῦ τὴν κτῆσιν διαρπάζουσιν. ἀκούσας δὲ τὸ
πραχθὲν ὁ Κουμανὸς εὐθὺς πέμπει στρατιώτας, κελεύσας αὐτοῖς τὰς πλησίον κώμας³ διαρπάσαι, τοὺς
δ' ἐπιφανεστάτους αὐτῶν δήσαντας ἐπ' αὐτὸν ἄγειν
115 λόγον τῶν τετολμημένων εἰσπράξαντας.⁴ τῆς δὲ πορθήσεως γενομένης⁵ τῶν κωμῶν⁶ τῶν στρατιωτῶν τις⁷
τοὺς Μωυσέως νόμους ἔν τινι κώμῃ λαβὼν κειμέ-
νους⁸ προκομίσας εἰς τὴν πάντων ὄψιν διέσχισεν⁹ ἐπι-

¹ δύο . . . μυριάδες] ὑπὲρ τοὺς μυρίους (vel ὑπὲρ τρισμυρίους)
B.J. ii. 227 : τρεῖς μυριάδας Eus.
² τῶν γὰρ . . . τινες] quidam enim qui ex illa turba fugi-
entes evaserant Lat.
³ MW : χώρας AE : vicos Lat.
⁴ λόγον . . . εἰσπράξαντας] A : om. MWE.
⁵ πορθήσεως γενομένης] πορθήσεως τῶν χωρίων ὑπὸ τῶν πεμ-
φθέντων στρατιωτῶν γινομένης E.
⁶ τῶν κωμῶν] A : om. MWE.
⁷ τῶν στρατιωτῶν τις] ἀτάσθαλός τις ἐξ αὐτῶν νεανίας E.

and started to flee. But since the exits were narrow, they, supposing that they were being pursued by the enemy, pushed together in their flight and crushed to death many of their number who were caught in the narrow passages. Indeed, the number of those who perished in that disturbance was computed at twenty thousand.[a] So there was mourning henceforth instead of feasting ; and all, utterly oblivious of prayers and sacrifices, turned to lamentation and weeping. Such were the calamities produced by the indecent behaviour of a single soldier.

(4) Their first mourning had not yet ceased when another calamity befell them. For some of the seditious revolutionaries robbed Stephen, a slave of Caesar, as he was travelling on the public highway [b] at a distance of about one hundred furlongs [c] from the city, and despoiled him of all his belongings. When Cumanus heard of this, he at once dispatched soldiers with orders to plunder the neighbouring villages and to bring before him their most eminent men [d] in chains so that he might exact vengeance for their effrontery. After the sacking of the villages, one of the soldiers,[e] who had found a copy of the laws of Moses that was kept in one of the villages, fetched it out where all could see and tore it in two while he

Cumanus executes a soldier for destroying a copy of the law.

---

[a] In the parallel passage, *B.J.* ii. 227, the number is given as more than thirty thousand according to some MSS., and as more than ten thousand according to others.

[b] *B.J.* ii. 228 supplies the detail that this was the public road leading up to Bethhoron.   [c] About twelve miles.

[d] *B.J.* ii. 229 : " with orders to bring up the inhabitants to him in chains."

[e] The Epitome has " one of them, a rash young man."

---

[8] κειμένους] σεβασμίως κειμένους E.
[9] διέσχισεν] ἀναιδῶς διέσχισεν E.

116 βλασφημῶν καὶ πολλὰ κατακερτομῶν.¹ Ἰουδαῖοι
δὲ ταῦτα ἀκούσαντες καὶ πολλοὶ συνδραμόντες
καταβαίνουσιν εἰς Καισάρειαν, ἐκεῖ γὰρ ἐτύγχανεν
ὁ Κουμανὸς ὤν, ἱκετεύοντες μὴ αὐτοὺς ἀλλὰ τὸν θεὸν
οὗπερ οἱ νόμοι καθυβρίσθησαν ἐκδικῆσαι· ζῆν γὰρ
οὐχ ὑπομένειν τῶν πατρίων αὐτοῖς² οὕτως περι-
117 υβρισμένων. καὶ Κουμανὸς δείσας, μὴ πάλιν νεωτερίσειεν τὸ πλῆθος, συμβουλευσάντων καὶ τῶν
φίλων τὸν ἐνυβρίσαντα τοῖς νόμοις στρατιώτην πελε-
κίσας ἔπαυσεν τὴν στάσιν ἐκ δευτέρου μέλλουσαν
ἐξάπτεσθαι.

118 (vi. 1) Γίνεται δὲ καὶ Σαμαρείταις πρὸς Ἰουδαίους ἔχθρα δι᾽ αἰτίαν τοιαύτην· ἔθος ἦν τοῖς
Γαλιλαίοις ἐν ταῖς ἑορταῖς εἰς τὴν ἱερὰν πόλιν παρα-
γινομένοις ὁδεύειν διὰ τῆς Σαμαρέων χώρας. καὶ
τότε καθ᾽ ὁδὸν αὐτοῖς κώμης Γιναῆς³ λεγομένης
τῆς ἐν μεθορίῳ κειμένης Σαμαρείας τε καὶ τοῦ
μεγάλου πεδίου τινὲς συνάψαντες μάχην πολλοὺς

¹ καὶ ἀκρατῶς καθυλακτῶν post κατακερτομῶν add. E.
² τῶν πατρίων αὐτοῖς] τῶν πατρίων αὐτοῖς νόμων i. ras. m. 2,
i. marg. νόμων suppl. A : τῶν πατρίων καὶ νομίμων αὐτοῖς E :
leges patrias Lat.
³ E : Ναναῆς, να i. ras. maiore, η ex ι corr. A : τῆς Ναῖς
MW : Ginais Lat. : Γήμαν B.J. ii. 232.

ᵃ The Epitome adds " and indulged in uncontrolled
clamour like a dog's barking." B.J. ii. 229 adds that he
threw the copy into a fire.

ᵇ Without referring to this incident in particular, Tacitus,
Ann. xii. 54, mentions the long-standing feud between the
Jews and the Samaritans which, he says, because of the con-
tempt of both peoples for the procurators Cumanus and
Felix, now erupted in plunder and occasional battles.

ᶜ Gema in the parallel passage, B.J. ii. 232 ; modern
Jenin. This village is called Ginaea in B.J. iii. 48, where it is
said to be on the northern boundary of Samaria. Thackeray,

uttered blasphemies and railed violently.[a] The Jews,
on learning of this, collected in large numbers, went
down to Caesarea, where Cumanus happened to be,
and besought him to avenge not them but God,
whose laws had been subjected to outrage. For,
they said, they could not endure to live, since their
ancestral code was thus wantonly insulted. Cumanus,
alarmed at the thought of a fresh revolution of the
masses, after taking counsel with his friends, beheaded the soldier who had outraged the laws and
thus prevented the uprising when it was on the verge
of breaking out a second time.

(vi. 1) Hatred also arose between the Samaritans
and the Jews for the following reason.[b] It was the
custom of the Galilaeans at the time of a festival to
pass through the Samaritan territory on their way to
the Holy City. On one occasion, while they were
passing through, certain of the inhabitants of a village
called Ginaë,[c] which was situated on the border
between Samaria and the Great Plain,[d] joined battle
with the Galilaeans and slew a great number[e] of them.

Cumanus' failure to act in the quarrel between the Jews and the Samaritans

in his note on *B.J.* ii. 232, refers to Luke ix. 52-56, which
illustrates the hostility shown by the Samaritans towards the
Jews on their way to Jerusalem.

[d] The Plain of Esdraelon between Samaria and Galilee.

[e] The parallel passage, *B.J.* ii. 232, in some of the MSS.,
says that one Galilaean was slain, while in other MSS., perhaps
to make the passage agree with ours, the statement reads
that many were slain. But the slaying of a single person,
even by the hated Samaritans, would not, in all probability,
have aroused so much indignation. M. Aberbach, " The
Conflicting Accounts of Josephus and Tacitus concerning
Cumanus' and Felix' Terms of Office," *Jewish Quart. Rev.*
xl, 1949-1950, p. 1 n. 1, suggests the possibility that Josephus'
dependence in the *Bellum* on official Roman sources, which
were often anti-Jewish, explains the reduction of the slain to
only one.

119 αὐτῶν ἀναιροῦσιν. πυθόμενοι δὲ τὰ πραχθέντα τῶν
Γαλιλαίων¹ οἱ πρῶτοι πρὸς Κουμανὸν ἀφίκοντο καὶ
παρεκάλουν αὐτὸν μετιέναι² τῶν ἀνῃρημένων τὸν
φόνον. ὁ δὲ χρήμασι πεισθεὶς³ ὑπὸ τῶν Σαμαρέων
120 τὴν ἐκδίκησιν⁴ ὠλιγώρησεν. ἀγανακτήσαντες δὲ
ἐπὶ τούτῳ Γαλιλαῖοι τὸ πλῆθος τῶν Ἰουδαίων ἔπειθον ἐφ' ὅπλα⁵ χωρῆσαι καὶ τῆς ἐλευθερίας ἀντέχε-
σθαι· δουλείαν γὰρ καὶ καθ' αὑτὴν μὲν πικρὰν
ἔλεγον εἶναι, τὴν ἐφ' ὕβρει δὲ παντάπασιν ἀφόρητον.
121 τῶν δ' ἐν τέλει καταπραΰνειν αὐτοὺς καὶ συστέλλειν τὴν ταραχὴν⁶ πειρωμένων καὶ πείσειν τὸν Κουμανὸν ἐπαγγελλομένων δίκας εἰσπράξασθαι παρὰ
τῶν ἀνῃρηκότων, ἐκείνοις μὲν οὐ προσέσχον, ἀναλαβόντες δὲ τὰ ὅπλα καὶ βοηθεῖν Ἐλεάζαρον τὸν τοῦ
Δειναίου παρακαλέσαντες, λῃστὴς δ' οὗτος ἦν ἔτη
πολλὰ τὴν διατριβὴν ἐν ὄρει πεποιημένος, κώμας
τινὰς τῶν Σαμαρέων ἐμπρήσαντες διαρπάζουσι.
122 Κουμανὸς δὲ τῆς πράξεως εἰς αὐτὸν ἀφικομένης
ἀναλαβὼν τὴν τῶν Σεβαστηνῶν ἴλην καὶ πεζῶν

---

¹ τινὲς καὶ μᾶλλον post Γαλιλαίων add. M.
² Cocceji : μετεῖναι codd. E : ut : ... inquireret Lat.
³ πεισθεὶς] πολλοῖς ἀποτυφλωθεὶς E.
⁴ τὴν ἐκδίκησιν] ΑΕ : om. MW.
⁵ ὅπλα] ὅπλα καὶ φόνους E.
⁶ καὶ συστέλλειν τὴν ταραχὴν] ΑΕ : om. MW.

ᵃ B.J. ii. 233 gives, as the reason for the dismissal of the
petition, Cumanus' concern with other affairs that he deemed
more important.

ᵇ B.J. ii. 234 supplies the detail that the masses in Jerusalem abandoned the celebration of the festival and dashed
off to Samaria, even though they were without generals.

ᶜ The Epitome adds " and slaughter." The parallel pas-

The leaders of the Galilaeans, hearing of the occurrence, came to Cumanus and besought him to seek out the murderers of those who had been slain. He, however, having been bribed by the Samaritans, neglected to avenge them.[a] The Galilaeans, indignant at this, urged the Jewish masses to resort to arms and to assert their liberty ; for, they said, slavery was in itself bitter, but when it involved insolent treatment, it was quite intolerable. Those in authority tried to mollify them and reduce the disorder, and offered to induce Cumanus to punish the murderers. The masses,[b] however, paid no heed to them, but taking up arms [c] and inviting the assistance of Eleazar [d] son of Deinaeus—he was a brigand who for many years had had his home in the mountains—they fired and sacked certain villages[e] of the Samaritans.[f] When the affair came to Cumanus' ears, he took over the squadron of the Sebastenians [g] and four units [h] of

sage, *B.J.* ii. 233, says that the Jews took up arms even before their leaders went to Cumanus.

[d] *B.J.* ii. 235 adds another leader, Alexander. Eleazar is to be identified with the Ben Dinai who, according to the *Midrash Rabbah on Song of Songs* ii. 18, prematurely tried to free the Jews. According to the Mishnah, *Soṭah* ix. 9, he inspired so many murders that the sacrifice of atonement for an unknown murderer was discontinued, and he began to be called Ben Harazḥan (" the murderer "). *Cf.* below, § 161.

[e] These villages bordered on the toparchy of Acrabatene, southeast of Shechem (*B.J.* ii. 235).

[f] *B.J.* ii. 235 adds that the Jews massacred the Samaritan inhabitants without distinction of age.

[g] *Cf. Ant.* xix. 365, which indicates that they were a cavalry unit composed of either 500 or 1000 men.

[h] Since Josephus, *Ant.* xix. 365, speaks of the cavalry unit and the five cohorts (σπεῖραι) of Sebastenians, the term here used, τάγματα, which is a general term for army units of various sizes, probably refers to cohorts, each of which had a strength of 500 to 600 men.

τέσσαρα τάγματα τούς τε Σαμαρεῖς καθοπλίσας
ἐξῆλθεν ἐπὶ τοὺς Ἰουδαίους, καὶ συμβαλὼν[1] πολλοὺς μὲν αὐτῶν ἀπέκτεινεν πλείους δὲ ζῶντας
123 ἔλαβεν. οἱ δὲ πρῶτοι κατὰ τιμὴν καὶ γένος τῶν
Ἱεροσολυμιτῶν, ὡς εἶδον εἰς οἷον κακῶν μέγεθος
ἥκουσιν, μετενδυσάμενοι σάκκους καὶ σποδοῦ τὰς
κεφαλὰς ἀναπλήσαντες παντοῖοι τοὺς ἀφεστῶτας
παρακαλοῦντες ἦσαν καὶ πείθοντες πρὸ ὀφθαλμῶν
θεμένους κατασκαφησομένην μὲν αὐτῶν τὴν πα-
τρίδα, τὸ δὲ ἱερὸν πυρποληθησόμενον, αὐτῶν δὲ καὶ
γυναικῶν σὺν τέκνοις ἀνδραποδισμοὺς ἐσομένους,
μεταθέσθαι τὸν λογισμὸν καὶ τὰ ὅπλα ῥίψαντας
ἠρεμεῖν εἰς τὸ λοιπὸν ἀποχωρήσαντας εἰς τὰ αὐτῶν.
124 ταῦτα δὲ εἰπόντες ἔπεισαν. καὶ οἱ μὲν διελύθησαν,
οἱ λησταὶ δὲ ἐπὶ τοὺς ἐχυροὺς τόπους πάλιν ἀπῆλ-
θον. ἐξ ἐκείνου τε ἡ σύμπασα Ἰουδαία ληστηρίων
ἐπληρώθη.

125 (2) Σαμαρέων δὲ οἱ πρῶτοι πρὸς Οὐμμίδιον[2]
Κοδράτον[3] τῆς Συρίας προεστηκότα κατὰ τὸν καιρὸν
ἐκεῖνον ἐν Τύρῳ τυγχάνοντα παραγενόμενοι κατηγόρουν τῶν Ἰουδαίων, ὡς τὰς κώμας αὐτῶν ἐμ-
126 πρήσειαν καὶ διαρπάσειαν, καὶ περὶ μὲν ὧν αὐτοὶ
πεπόνθασιν οὐχ οὕτως ἀγανακτεῖν ἔφασκον, ὡς ὅτι
Ῥωμαίων καταφρονήσειαν, ἐφ' οὓς κριτὰς ἐχρῆν
αὐτοὺς εἴπερ ἠδίκουν[4] παραγενέσθαι, ἢ νῦν ὡς οὐκ
ἐχόντων ἡγεμόνας Ῥωμαίους καταδραμεῖν· ἥκειν

---

[1] E : συλλαβὼν codd. : facta . . . congressione Lat.
[2] Hudson ex B.J. ii. 239 : Νουμίδιον (Νουμήδιον W) codd.
E Lat.
[3] Κοναδράτον E : Quadratum Lat.

infantry and armed the Samaritans. He then marched
out against the Jews and, in an encounter, slew many,
but took more alive. Thereupon those who were by
rank and birth the leaders of the inhabitants of Jerusalem, when they saw to what depth of calamity they
had come, changed their robes for sackcloth and de-
filed their heads with ashes and went to all lengths
entreating the rebels. They urged them to picture
to themselves that their country would be rased to
the ground, their temple consigned to the flames, and
they themselves with their wives and children reduced to slavery. They therefore besought them to
think again, to throw down their arms, to return to
their homes, and to lead a quiet life in the future.
With these words they prevailed. The people dis-
persed and the brigands returned to their strong-
holds. From that time the whole of Judaea was
infested with bands of brigands.

(2) The leaders of the Samaritans met with Ummidius Quadratus,[a] the governor of Syria, who at
that time was at Tyre, and accused the Jews of firing
and sacking their villages. They professed to be
indignant not so much because of the treatment that[4]
they themselves had received as because of the contempt that the Jews had shown for the Romans. For
the Jews, they said, should have appealed to the
Romans to decide the matter, if indeed the Samaritans
had done them an injustice, and not, as they had now
done, have overrun the Samaritan country, as though
they did not have the Romans as their governors.

The
Samaritans
appeal to
the gover-
nor of
Syria, who
refers the
case to the
emperor.

[a] Tacitus, *Ann.* xii. 54, says that but for Quadratus the
armed conflict between the Samaritans and the Jews would
have spread throughout Galilee and Samaria.

---

[4] $\dot{\eta}\delta\iota\kappa o\hat{v}\nu\tau o$ E.

127 οὖν ἐπ' αὐτὸν ἐκδικίας τευξόμενοι.¹ ταῦτα μὲν οὖν
οἱ Σαμαρεῖς κατηγόρουν. Ἰουδαῖοι δὲ καὶ τῆς
στάσεως καὶ τῆς μάχης αἰτίους γεγονέναι Σαμα-
ρεῖς² ἔφασαν, πρὸ πάντων δὲ Κουμανὸν δώροις ὑπ'
αὐτῶν φθαρέντα καὶ παρασιωπήσαντα τὸν τῶν ἀνῃ-
128 ρημένων φόνον. καὶ Κουαδρᾶτος ἀκούσας ὑπερτί-
θεται τὴν κρίσιν, εἰπὼν ἀποφανεῖσθαι, ἐπειδὰν εἰς
τὴν Ἰουδαίαν παραγενόμενος ἀκριβέστερον ἐπιγνῷ
129 τὴν ἀλήθειαν. καὶ οἱ μὲν ἀπῄεσαν ἄπρακτοι. μετ'
οὐ πολὺν δὲ χρόνον ὁ Κουαδρᾶτος ἧκεν εἰς Σα-
μάρειαν, ἔνθα διακούσας αἰτίους τῆς ταραχῆς ὑπέ-
λαβε γεγονέναι τοὺς Σαμαρεῖς.³ Σαμαρέων⁴ δὲ καὶ
Ἰουδαίων οὕστινας⁵ νεωτερίσαντας ἔμαθεν⁶ ἀνε-
σταύρωσεν οὓς Κουμανὸς ἔλαβεν αἰχμαλώτους⁷
130 κἀκεῖθεν εἰς κώμην τινὰ παραγενόμενος Λύδδαν.
πόλεως τὸ μέγεθος οὐκ ἀποδέουσαν καθίσας ἐπὶ
βήματος κἀκ δευτέρου τῶν Σαμαρέων διακούσας
διδάσκεται παρά τινος Σαμαρέως, ὅτι τῶν Ἰουδαίων τις πρῶτος ὄνομα Δόητος⁸ καί τινες σὺν αὐτῷ

¹ ἐφ' οὓς . . . τευξόμενοι] ad quorum iudicium debuerant
pro sua vel si qua fuisset laesione concurrere, nunc autem
quasi Romanos iudices non haberent haec ab eis acta dicebant
et propterea vindictam fieri postulabant Lat.

² κατηγόρουν . . . Σαμαρεῖς] A : om. MW.

³ αἰτίους . . . Σαμαρεῖς] i. ras. m. 2 A.

⁴ τοὺς Σαμαρεῖς. Σαμαρέων] A : Σαμαρέων MW : Σαμαρεῖς
ὡς E.

⁵ Ἰουδαίων οὕστινας] Ἰουδαίους τινὰς E.

⁶ ἔνθα . . . ἔμαθεν] ubi auctores seditionis audiens et quos-
dam Samaritanorum ac Iudaeorum indisciplinatos inveniens
Lat.

⁷ Λύδδαν] Λύδδαν λεγομένην E : nomine Liddam Lat.

⁸ A : Δόρτος MW : Δόϊτος E : Doitus Lat.

ᵃ Included in the Jewish delegation (so B.J. ii. 240) was
the high priest Jonathan son of Ananus, who was later put to

Therefore, said the Samaritans, they had come to
Quadratus to obtain redress. Such were the accusations of the Samaritans. The Jews,[a] on the other
hand, said that the Samaritans were responsible for
the factional strife and the fighting, but in the
highest degree Cumanus, who had been bribed by
them to pass over in silence the murder of the Jewish
victims. After the hearing, Quadratus deferred
judgement, saying that he would announce his decision when he had reached Judaea and had gained
a more accurate understanding of the case. Thus
the Samaritans departed without attaining their
object. Not long afterwards Quadratus reached
Samaria,[b] where, after a full hearing, he came to the
conclusion that the Samaritans had been responsible
for the disorder. He then crucified those of the
Samaritans [c] and of the Jews who, he had learned,
had taken part in the rebellion and whom Cumanus
had taken prisoner. From there he came to Lydda,[d]
a village that was in size not inferior to a city, and sat
on the judgement seat, where he gave a second
thorough hearing to the case of the Samaritans.
Here he was informed by a certain Samaritan that a
leader of the Jews named Doëtus,[e] together with

death by brigands at the instigation of the procurator Felix
(*Ant.* xx. 162-164). [b] Caesarea, according to *B.J.* ii. 241.
  [c] The Epitome speaks of his crucifying the Jews only.
Tacitus, *Ann.* xii. 54, also, after mentioning the constant
quarrels between the Samaritans and the Jews, says that
Quadratus put to death those of the Jews who had been
daring enough to slay Roman soldiers. But the parallel
passage, *B.J.* ii. 241, says that Quadratus crucified all the
prisoners—presumably both Jews and Samaritans—taken
by Cumanus.
  [d] Modern *Lud*, between Jerusalem and Tel Aviv.
  [e] Variants " Dortus," " Doïtus."

νεωτερισταὶ τέσσαρες τὸν ἀριθμὸν πείσειαν τὸν
131 ὄχλον ἐπὶ τῇ ῾Ρωμαίων ἀποστάσει. κἀκείνους μὲν
ὁ Κουαδρᾶτος ἀνελεῖν προσέταξεν, τοὺς δὲ περὶ
᾿Ανανίαν τὸν ἀρχιερέα καὶ τὸν στρατηγὸν ῎Ανανον
δήσας εἰς ῾Ρώμην ἀνέπεμψεν περὶ τῶν πεπραγ-
132 μένων λόγον ὑφέξοντας Κλαυδίῳ Καίσαρι. κελεύει
δὲ καὶ τοῖς τῶν Σαμαρέων πρώτοις καὶ[1] τοῖς ᾿Ιου-
δαίοις[2] Κουμανῷ τε τῷ ἐπιτρόπῳ καὶ Κέλερι,
χιλίαρχος δ᾽ ἦν οὗτος, ἐπ᾽ ᾿Ιταλίας[3] ἀπιέναι[4] πρὸς
τὸν αὐτοκράτορα κριθησομένους ἐπ᾽ αὐτοῦ περὶ τῶν
133 πρὸς ἀλλήλους ζητήσεων. αὐτὸς δὲ δείσας, μὴ τὸ
πλῆθος πάλιν τῶν ᾿Ιουδαίων νεωτερίσειεν, εἰς τὴν
τῶν ῾Ιεροσολυμιτῶν πόλιν ἀφικνεῖται· καταλαμβάνει δ᾽ αὐτὴν εἰρηνευομένην καὶ πάτριον ἑορτὴν
τῷ θεῷ τελοῦσαν. πιστεύσας οὖν μηδένα νεωτερισ-
μὸν παρ᾽ αὐτῶν γενήσεσθαι[5] καταλιπὼν ἑορτάζοντας
ὑπέστρεψεν εἰς ᾿Αντιόχειαν.

134 (3) Οἱ περὶ Κουμανὸν δὲ καὶ τοὺς πρώτους τῶν
Σαμαρέων ἀναπεμφθέντες εἰς ῾Ρώμην λαμβάνουσι
παρὰ τοῦ αὐτοκράτορος ἡμέραν, καθ᾽ ἣν περὶ τῶν
πρὸς ἀλλήλους ἀμφισβητήσεων λέγειν ἔμελλον.
135 σπουδὴ δὲ μεγίστη τῷ Κουμανῷ καὶ τοῖς Σα-

[1] τοῖς τῶν Σαμαρέων πρώτοις καί] om. E.
[2] καὶ τοῖς ᾿Ιουδαίοις] A : om. MW : τοῖς ᾿Ιουδαίων E Lat.
[3] ἐπ᾽ ᾿Ιταλίας] Lowthius : ἐπὶ τῆς βίας codd. E ; χιλίαρχος
. . . ᾿Ιταλίας] millenario et violentiarum inhibitori Lat.
[4] Hudson : ἀπεῖναι codd. E : ut . . . pergerent Lat.
[5] MW : γεγενῆσθαι AE : generari Lat.

---

[a] According to *B.J.* ii. 242, Cumanus beheaded eighteen
Jews who, according to information given him, had partici-
pated in the fighting.
[b] *Cf.* § 103.
[c] Or perhaps better " superintendent." Presumably the
reference is to the captain who had custody of the temple, a

four other revolutionaries, had instigated the mob to
revolt against the Romans. These *a* also Quadratus
ordered to be put to death. As for the high priest
Ananias *b* and the captain *c* Ananus *d* and their
followers, he put them in chains and sent them up to
Rome to render an account of their actions to Claudius
Caesar. He further ordered the leaders of the Samaritans, those of the Jews, Cumanus the procurator, and
Celer, *e* a military tribune, to set off to Italy to get a
decision in the imperial court concerning the matters
in dispute between them. He himself, fearing a
fresh revolution on the part of the Jewish people,
visited the city of Jerusalem, which he found at
peace and observing one of the traditional religious
festivals. *f* Having satisfied himself, therefore, that
there would be no revolt on their part, he left them
celebrating the festival and returned to Antioch.

(3) Cumanus and the leaders of the Samaritans
with their companions who had been sent to Rome
were assigned a day by the emperor on which they
were to state their case in the matters at issue involving them. Caesar's freedmen and friends dis-

Claudius,
thanks to
Agrippa's
influence,
decides in
favour of
the Jews.

position mentioned in *B.J.* vi. 294, as well as in Luke xxii. 4,
52 ; Acts iv. 1, v. 24, 26. He is the *sagan*, second in rank to
the high priest. *Cf.* Mishnah, *Yoma* iii. 1.
   d The son of Ananias the high priest, according to *B.J.* ii.
243, which also adds that the delegation included the high
priest Jonathan.
   e In view of the drastic punishment inflicted on Celer,
whose crime is nowhere indicated, Aberbach, *op. cit.* p. 12,
suggests that he may have been the soldier (§§ 108-112) whose
lewdness had prompted such calamity for the Jews. But
Josephus normally, though not always, gives cross-references
and certainly would be expected to do so in so notorious a
case as this ; moreover, Josephus never calls a military
tribune a mere soldier.
   f Passover, according to *B.J.* ii. 244.

JOSEPHUS

μαρεῦσιν ἦν παρὰ τῶν Καίσαρος ἀπελευθέρων καὶ
φίλων, κἂν περιεγένοντο τῶν Ἰουδαίων, εἰ μή περ
Ἀγρίππας ὁ νεώτερος ἐν τῇ Ῥώμῃ τυγχάνων
κατασπευδομένους ἰδὼν τοὺς τῶν Ἰουδαίων πρώτους ἐδεήθη πολλὰ τῆς τοῦ αὐτοκράτορος γυναικὸς
Ἀγριππίνης πεῖσαι τὸν ἄνδρα διακούσαντα[1] πρε-
πόντως τῇ ἑαυτοῦ δικαιοσύνῃ τιμωρήσασθαι τοὺς
136 αἰτίους τῆς ἀποστάσεως. καὶ Κλαύδιος τῇ δεήσει
ταύτῃ προευτρεπισθεὶς καὶ διακούσας, ὡς εὗρε τῶν
κακῶν ἀρχηγοὺς τοὺς Σαμαρείτας γενομένους, τοὺς
μὲν ἀναβάντας πρὸς αὐτὸν ἐκέλευσεν ἀναιρεθῆναι,
τῷ Κουμανῷ δὲ φυγὴν ἐπέβαλεν, Κέλερα δὲ τὸν
χιλίαρχον ἐκέλευσεν ἀγαγόντας εἰς τὰ Ἱεροσόλυμα
πάντων ὁρώντων ἐπὶ τὴν πόλιν πᾶσαν σύραντας
οὕτως ἀποκτεῖναι.
137 (vii. 1) Πέμπει δὲ καὶ Κλαύδιος[2] Φήλικα Πάλ-

[1] A : δικάσαντα MWE : causam audiens Lat.
[2] E : Κλαύδιον codd.

ᵃ The granddaughter of Antonia, whose friendship for
Agrippa I (*Ant.* xviii. 143) may well have been recalled by
Agrippa II's entreaties to her.

ᵇ Suetonius, *Claud.* 15, to be sure, asserts that he rendered
judgements after having heard only one party to a suit;
and Seneca, *Apoc.* 12. 3, goes so far as to say that he did so
without hearing either party. But V. M. Scramuzza, *The
Emperor Claudius*, 1940, pp. 46-47, rightly defends Claudius
against these charges by suggesting that since the courts
were cluttered with trivial cases Claudius decided to follow
the court procedure later recognized in the Code of Justinian,
awarding the decision to the party present at a trial if the
other party did not appear.

ᶜ Aberbach, *op. cit.* pp. 11-12, plausibly suggests that the
Jewish cause may have had another strong ally in Pallas,
whose influence over Claudius was particularly strong at this
time, and who acted in secret. There may well be a con-

72

played the greatest partiality for Cumanus and the Samaritans, and they would have got the better of the Jews, had not Agrippa the Younger, who was in Rome and saw that the Jewish leaders were losing the race for influence, urgently entreated Agrippina,[a] the wife of the emperor, to persuade her husband to give the case a thorough hearing in a manner befitting his respect for law [b] and to punish the instigators of the revolt.[c] Claudius was favourably impressed by this petition. He then heard the case through, and, on discovering that the Samaritans were the first to move in stirring up trouble, he ordered those of them who had come before him to be put to death,[d] condemned Cumanus to exile, and ordered Celer the tribune to be taken to Jerusalem, where he was to be dragged around the whole city in a public spectacle and then put to death.

(vii. 1) Claudius now sent Felix,[e] the brother of

Felix is appointed procurator.

nexion, as indicated by Aberbach, between Pallas' assistance in this case and the championing by the high priest Jonathan of the candidacy of Felix, Pallas' brother, for the procuratorship of Judaea shortly thereafter.

[d] Three Samaritans were executed (*B.J.* ii. 245).

[e] This is the reading of the Epitome. The MSS. read " He now sent Claudius Felix." But Tacitus, *Hist.* v. 9, calls him Antonius Felix, and he is so called also in an inscription (*C.I.L.* v. 34). See Schürer, i. 571-572 n. 18, who, therefore, defends the emendation Κλαύδιος. Like his brother Pallas, he probably, as P. von Rohden, " Antonius " no. 54, Pauly-Wissowa, i, 1894, p. 2617, suggests, was freed by Claudius' mother Antonia. Suetonius, *Claud.* 28, mentions Claudius' high regard for him. He was named procurator *c.* A.D. 52, and it is he before whom Paul is accused in Acts xxiv. 1 ff. Josephus' account of Felix appears to contradict that of Tacitus, *Ann.* xii. 54, who states that while Cumanus was in charge of Galilee, Felix was already governing Samaria. Acts xxiv. 10, as noted by Kirsopp Lake, *op. cit.* p. 465, perhaps offers some support for Tacitus' account, for Paul

λαντος ἀδελφὸν τῶν κατὰ τὴν Ἰουδαίαν προστησό-
138 μενον πραγμάτων. τῆς δ' ἀρχῆς δωδέκατον[1] ἔτος
ἤδη πεπληρωκὼς δωρεῖται τὸν Ἀγρίππαν τῇ Φιλίππου τετραρχίᾳ καὶ Βαταναίᾳ προσθεὶς αὐτῷ τὴν
Τραχωνῖτιν σὺν Ἀβέλᾳ[2]· Λυσανία δ' αὕτη γεγόνει
τετραρχία· τὴν Χαλκίδα δ' αὐτὸν ἀφαιρεῖται δυνα-
139 στεύσαντα ταύτης ἔτη τέσσαρα. λαβὼν δὲ τὴν
δωρεὰν παρὰ τοῦ Καίσαρος Ἀγρίππας ἐκδίδωσι
πρὸς γάμον Ἀζίζῳ τῷ Ἐμεσῶν βασιλεῖ περιτέμνε-
σθαι θελήσαντι Δρούσιλλαν τὴν ἀδελφήν· Ἐπιφανὴς
γὰρ ὁ Ἀντιόχου τοῦ βασιλέως παῖς παρῃτήσατο

[1] decimum Lat.
[2] A : συνέβαλε M : συνέβαλλε W : σὺν Ἀβέλᾳ E : una cum Abela Lat.

---

remarks that Felix had been " a judge of this nation " for many years. Cumanus and Felix, according to Tacitus, shared in the spoils collected by the brigands and were unsuccessful in quelling disturbances. Thereupon Ummidius Quadratus, the governor of Syria, brought them to account, sentencing Cumanus, while actually exhibiting Felix as one of the judges. Aberbach, pp. 4-6, in an ingenious attempt to reconcile the accounts of Josephus and Tacitus, suggests that Cumanus was actually procurator of Judaea and Samaria when the disturbance described in §§ 118-124 occurred, while Felix was in charge of Galilee, in which Josephus, until the events of 66, was less interested. But Josephus describes the dispatch of Felix by Claudius to become procurator in the same terms in which he describes the dispatch of other procurators (e.g. Porcius Festus, § 182), and it seems hard to believe that, if Felix was already serving in Palestine, Josephus should not have mentioned that fact but should say that Claudius " sent " (" sent forth," *B.J.* ii. 247) him to take charge of Judaea. On the other hand, Josephus, who normally speaks of a person as being sent to be procurator of *Judaea*, says (*B.J.* ii. 247) that Felix was sent to be procurator

Pallas,[a] to take charge of matters in Judaea. When he had completed the twelfth year of his reign,[b] he granted to Agrippa the tetrarchy of Philip [c] together with Batanaea, adding thereto Trachonitis [d] and Lysanias' former tetrarchy of Abila [e]; but he deprived him of Chalcis, after he had ruled it for four years. After receiving this gift from the emperor, Agrippa gave his sister Drusilla [f] in marriage to Azizus king of Emesa, who had consented to be circumcised. Epiphanes, son of King Antiochus, had

of Judaea, Samaria, Galilee, and Peraea ; this would not necessarily be inconsistent with his having served as procurator of one of these districts previously.

[a] A freedman of Antonia (cf. Ant. xviii. 182, where he is mentioned as the most trustworthy of Antonia's slaves) and a favourite of the emperor Claudius. He championed the cause of Agrippina, whose lover he supposedly was. In January 52, shortly before the appointment of Felix, Pallas had reached the pinnacle of his power when he was awarded the *ornamenta praetoria* and a large sum of money by the senate. Cf. Pliny, *Hist. Nat.* vii. 29. 2 and viii. 16. 3 ; and Suet. *Claud.* 28. Nero ordained his death in 62 allegedly because of his wealth.

[b] A.D. 53.

[c] Cf. Ant. xviii. 27-28, 106, etc. According to B.J. ii. 247, Agrippa was also presented with the tetrarchy of Varus.

[d] Luke iii. 1 speaks of Trachonitis as part of Philip's tetrarchy, and hence J. W. Hunkin, " St. Luke and Josephus," *Church Quart. Rev.* lxxxviii, 1919, p. 100, seems justified in concluding that Luke did not have this passage of the *Antiquities* before him.

[e] Or Abela, north-west of Damascus. Cf. Ant. xix. 275. It is the Abilene of which Lysanias was tetrarch under Tiberius, according to Luke iii. 1. Cf. Schürer, i. 716-720.

[f] Cf. Ant. xviii. 132 for her place in the genealogy of the house of Herod. In Ant. xix. 354 she is mentioned as being six years old at the death of her father, Agrippa I. She is identified in Acts xxiv. 24 as Felix's Jewish wife. She is presumably one of the three queens whom Felix married, according to Suetonius, *Claud.* 28.

τὸν γάμον μὴ βουληθεὶς τὰ Ἰουδαίων ἔθη μεταλα-
βεῖν καίπερ τοῦτο ποιήσειν προϋπεσχημένος αὐτῆς
140 τῷ πατρί. καὶ Μαριάμμην δ' ἐξέδωκεν Ἀρχελάῳ
τῷ Ἑλκίου παιδὶ πρότερον ὑπὸ Ἀγρίππα τοῦ
πατρὸς[1] ἁρμοσθεῖσαν αὐτῷ, καὶ γίνεται θυγάτηρ
αὐτοῖς ὄνομα Βερενίκη.

141 (2) Διαλύονται δὲ τῇ Δρουσίλλῃ πρὸς τὸν Ἄζιζον
οἱ γάμοι μετ' οὐ πολὺν χρόνον τοιαύτης ἐμπεσούσηε
142 αἰτίας· καθ' ὃν χρόνον τῆς Ἰουδαίας ἐπετρόπευς
Φῆλιξ θεασάμενος ταύτην, καὶ γὰρ ἦν κάλλει πασῶν
διαφέρουσα, λαμβάνει τῆς γυναικὸς ἐπιθυμίαν, καὶ
Ἄτομον[2] ὀνόματι τῶν ἑαυτοῦ φίλων Ἰουδαῖον,
Κύπριον δὲ τὸ γένος, μάγον εἶναι σκηπτόμενον
πέμπων πρὸς αὐτὴν ἔπειθεν τὸν ἄνδρα καταλιποῦ-
σαν αὐτῷ γήμασθαι, μακαρίαν ποιήσειν ἐπαγγελ-

---

[1] MWE Lat. Phot. : παιδὸς A.
[2] AE : Σίμωνα MW Lat. et i. marg. A.

---

[a] Or " had excused himself from marrying her."
[b] See *Ant*. xix. 355.
[c] See *Ant*. xix. 355.
[d] According to Tacitus, *Hist*. v. 9, Felix was now married
to Drusilla (not the Drusilla whom he married in § 143 ; *cf*.
Stein, " Drusilla " no. 2, Pauly-Wissowa, v, 1905, p. 1741,
who suggests that there is some confusion), the granddaughter of Antony and Cleopatra, and hence he was the
grandson-in-law, as Claudius was the grandson, of Antony.
Tacitus also mentions that Felix indulged in " every kind of
barbarity and lust."
[e] This is the reading of the best ms. and of the Epitome.
The other two major mss., a marginal notation in the best
ms., and the Latin version have the name as Simoń. Who is
this Atomus or Simon ? M. Krenkel, *Josephus und Lukas*,
1894, pp. 178 ff., identifies him with the apostle Paul, who
was regarded as the false Simon as opposed to Simon Peter
and who was called a Samaritan because he declared that the

rejected the marriage [a] since he was not willing to
convert to the Jewish religion, although he had previously [b] contracted with her father to do so. Agrippa
also gave his daughter Mariamme in marriage to
Archelaus,[c] the son of Helcias, to whom his father
had previously betrothed her. Of this marriage there
was born a daughter named Berenice.

(2) Not long afterwards Drusilla's marriage to
Azizus was dissolved under the impact of the following circumstances. At the time when Felix was procurator of Judaea, he beheld her ; and, inasmuch as
she surpassed all other women in beauty, he conceived a passion for the lady.[d] He sent to her one of
his friends,[e] a Cyprian Jew named Atomus, who
pretended to be a magician,[f] in an effort to persuade
her to leave her husband and to marry Felix. Felix
promised to make her supremely happy [g] if she did

Felix,
through a
Cyprian
magician,
induces
Agrippa's
sister
Drusilla to
marry him.

Mosaic law had been abrogated ; but, as P. W. Schmiedel'
"Simon Magus," *Ency. Bibl.* iv, 1903, p. 4556, and H·
Waitz, "Simon Magus in der altchristlichen Literatur,"
Zeitsch. f. d. Neutest. Wiss. v, 1904, p. 127, note, there is no
evidence that Paul was so called, nor was Paul a Cyprian, as
the magician here is said to be. Waitz, in turn, suggests (p.
128) an identification with Simon the Church Father, but the
latter was a Samaritan and not a Cyprian. The name Simon
is extremely common during this period, and magicians were
plentiful.

[f] On Jewish magicians, S. W. Baron, *A Social and Religious History of the Jews,* ii[2], 1952, p. 21, cites Lucian,
Tragodopodagra, verse 173, who satirically refers to a
sufferer from podagra who, having tried every remedy, re-
sorts to the incantations of a Jew. *Cf.* Baron ii. 336 n. 25,
who notes the belief, found in Jub. x. 10-15, that Noah had
acquired the art of magic healing from the angels and had
transmitted it to his son Shem.

[g] In all probability, as noted by Thackeray, *Selections
from Josephus,* p. 95 n. 2, there is here a play on the name
Felix, meaning " happy."

143 λόμενος μὴ ὑπερηφανήσασαν αὐτόν.[1] ἡ δὲ κακῶς
πράττουσα καὶ φυγεῖν τὸν ἐκ τῆς ἀδελφῆς Βερενίκης βουλομένη φθόνον· διὰ γὰρ τὸ κάλλος παρ’
ἐκείνης ἐν οὐκ ὀλίγοις ἐβλάπτετο,[2] παραβῆναί τε τὰ
πάτρια νόμιμα πείθεται καὶ τῷ Φήλικι γήμασθαι.[3]
τεκοῦσα δ’ ἐξ αὐτοῦ παῖδα προσηγόρευσεν Ἀγρίπ-
144 παν. ἀλλ’ ὃν μὲν τρόπον ὁ νεανίας οὗτος σὺν τῇ
γυναικὶ κατὰ τὴν ἐκπύρωσιν τοῦ Βεσβίου ὄρους ἐπὶ
τῶν Τίτου Καίσαρος χρόνων ἠφανίσθη, μετὰ ταῦτα
δηλώσω.

145 (3) Βερενίκη δὲ μετὰ τὴν Ἡρώδου τελευτήν, ὃς
αὐτῆς ἀνὴρ καὶ θεῖος ἐγεγόνει, πολὺν χρόνον ἐπι-
χηρεύσασα, φήμης ἐπισχούσης, ὅτι τἀδελφῷ συνείη,[4]
πείθει Πολέμωνα, Κιλικίας[5] δὲ ἦν οὗτος βασιλεύς,
περιτεμόμενον ἀγαγέσθαι πρὸς γάμον αὐτήν· οὕτως
146 γὰρ ἐλέγξειν ᾤετο ψευδεῖς τὰς διαβολάς. καὶ ὁ

---

[1] μὴ ὑπερηφανήσασαν αὐτόν] om. E.
[2] διὰ γὰρ . . . ἐβλάπτετο] ed. pr. : αὐτῇ (αὐτῇ MW) διὰ τὸ
κάλλος παρεκάλει παρ’ ἐκείνης οἰόμενος (γρ ὑποπτευόμενος i. marg.
A), οὐκ ἐν (ἐν οὐκ MW) ὀλίγοις ἔβλαπτεν (βλάπτεσθαι Mathieu-
Herrmann) codd.
[3] ἡ δὲ . . . γήμασθαι] illa vero non bene faciens declinare
volens invidiam Berenicae sororis propter pulchritudinem
suam transcendere paternas sollemnitates flexa est et Felicis
nuptias est secuta Lat.
[4] A : γρ συνοικεῖ i. marg. A : συνῄει MWE : coiret Lat.
[5] Lyciae Lat.

---

[a] The clause " for Drusilla . . . beauty " is corrupt in
the mss. ; the text here adopted follows the *editio princeps*.
Mathieu-Herrmann, emending the text of the mss. slightly,
translate : " Felix invited her by reason of her beauty,
which she believed exposed her to much torment by Berenice."
[b] A.D. 79.
[c] There is no further mention of this in the extant works
of Josephus.

not disdain him. She, being unhappy and wishing to escape the malice of her sister Berenice—for Drusilla was exceedingly abused by her because of her beauty [a]—, was persuaded to transgress the ancestral laws and to marry Felix. By him she gave birth to a son whom she named Agrippa. How this youth and his wife disappeared at the time of the eruption of Mount Vesuvius in the times of Titus Caesar,[b] I shall describe later.[c]

(3) After the death of Herod, who had been her uncle and husband, Berenice lived for a long time as a widow. But when a report gained currency that she had a liaison with her brother,[d] she induced Polemo,[e] king of Cilicia, to be circumcised and to take her in marriage ; for she thought that she would demonstrate in this way that the reports were false.

Berenice, after Herod's death, marries Polemo, king of Cilicia.

[d] Juvenal vi. 156-160 likewise alludes to this report when he speaks of the famous diamond that the " barbarian " Agrippa gave to his " unchaste " sister. G. H. Macurdy, " Julia Berenice," *Am. Jour. of Philol.* lvi, 1935, p. 251, plausibly suggests that the rumour may have originated because Berenice presided over the court of Agrippa, who was never married. Suetonius (*Tit.* 7), Tacitus (*Hist.* ii. 2), and Dio (lxvi. 15 and 18); all of whom speak of Titus' love for her, do not mention the alleged incest with Agrippa. *Cf.* R. M. Haywood, " A Note on the Dialogus of Tacitus," *Class. Weekly* xxxvi, 1942-1943, p. 255, who suggests that Maternus' Medea (Tac. *Dial.* 3) is Berenice, whom Titus wished to marry. The idea of such a marriage with a foreigner was regarded with repugnance by the Romans. The rumour of the incest between Agrippa and Berenice is perhaps an indication that Agrippa, with whom Josephus had kept up a long correspondence while in Rome (*Vita* 364-367), was dead by 93/94, when these words were written (*Ant.* xx. 267) : so Macurdy, p. 250, and J. A. Crook, " Titus and Berenice," *Am. Jour. of Philol.* lxxii, 1951, p. 163 n. 9.

[e] Not the Polemo of *Ant.* xix. 338. See D. Magie, *Roman Rule in Asia Minor*, ii, 1950, p. 1407.

Πολέμων ἐπείσθη μάλιστα διὰ τὸν πλοῦτον αὐτῆς·
οὐ μὴν ἐπὶ πολὺ συνέμεινεν ὁ γάμος, ἀλλ᾽ ἡ Βερενίκη δι᾽ ἀκολασίαν, ὡς ἔφασαν, καταλείπει τὸν
Πολέμωνα. ὁ δ᾽ ἅμα τοῦ τε γάμου καὶ τοῦ τοῖς
147 ἔθεσι τῶν Ἰουδαίων ἐμμένειν ἀπήλλακτο. τῷ αὐτῷ
δὲ καιρῷ καὶ Μαριάμμη παραιτησαμένη τὸν Ἀρ-
χέλαον συνῴκησε Δημητρίῳ τῶν ἐν Ἀλεξανδρείᾳ
Ἰουδαίων πρωτεύοντι γένει τε καὶ πλούτῳ· τότε δὴ
καὶ τὴν ἀλαβαρχίαν αὐτὸς εἶχεν. γενόμενον δ᾽
αὐτῇ παιδίον ἐξ ἐκείνου Ἀγριππῖνον¹ προσηγόρευσεν. ἀλλὰ περὶ μὲν ἑκάστου τούτων μετὰ ἀκρι-
βείας ὕστερον ἀπαγγελοῦμεν.

148 (viii. 1) Τελευτᾷ δὲ Κλαύδιος Καῖσαρ βασιλεύσας ἔτη δεκατρία καὶ μῆνας ὀκτὼ πρὸς ἡμέραις
εἴκοσι, καὶ λόγος ἦν παρά τινων, ὡς ὑπὸ τῆς γυ-

¹ Ἀγριππῖνον] Agrippae vocabulo Lat.

ᵃ Such a conversion is invalid according to Jewish law.
See the Babylonian Talmud, *Gerim* i. 7 : " Whoever converts
for the sake of marriage, fear, or love is not a proselyte . . . ,
and whoever does not convert for the sake of Heaven is not
a proselyte."
ᵇ On the office of alabarch see note on *Ant.* xviii. 159.
ᶜ There is no such account extant.
ᵈ For §§ 148-178 *cf.* the parallel passage, *B.J.* ii. 248-270.
ᵉ A.D. 54.
ᶠ This is exact, since Suetonius, *Calig.* 58, gives the date
of Gaius' death as 24 January, A.D. 41 ; and Suetonius
(*Claud.* 45), Tacitus (*Ann.* xii. 69), Seneca (*Apoc.* 2), and
Dio (lx. 34. 3) give the date of Claudius' death as 13 October,
A.D. 54.
ᵍ Tacitus, who has a detailed account (*Ann.* xii. 66-67) of
Claudius' death, says definitely that Agrippina attempted to
kill him with a slowly acting poison which was inserted by a
certain Halotus, Claudius' official taster, in mushrooms, one
of the emperor's favourite foods. After administering this
poison, she availed herself of the aid of a physician named

Polemo was prevailed upon chiefly on account of her wealth.[a] The marriage did not, however, last long, for Berenice, out of licentiousness, according to report, deserted Polemo. And he was relieved simultaneously of his marriage and of further adherence to the Jewish way of life. At the same time Mariamme took leave of Archelaus and married Demetrius, an Alexandrian Jew who stood among the first in birth and wealth. He also held at that time the office of alabarch.[b] By him she had a son whom she called Agrippinus. But I shall report fully on each of these persons hereafter.[c]

(viii. 1) [d] Claudius Caesar now died [g] after a reign of thirteen years, eight months, and twenty days.[f] It was reported by some [g] that he had been poisoned

Xenophon who put into Claudius' throat a feather smeared with a rapid poison. Suetonius, *Claud.* 44, says that most people think that Claudius was poisoned, but that there is a difference of opinion as to when and by whom. Some, he says, assert that Halotus administered the drug, others that Agrippina herself did so at a banquet by poisoning a dish of mushrooms. Dio lxi. 34. 2-3 says definitely that Claudius died during the night after he had eaten the mushroom in which Agrippina had arranged to have poison placed. But V. M. Scramuzza, *The Emperor Claudius*, 1940, pp. 92-93, concludes that while the report that Agrippina poisoned Claudius can be neither proved nor disproved, there was a uniform tradition insinuating that every Julio-Claudian emperor had died by foul means. As Scramuzza remarks, we are even asked to believe, to judge from Tacitus' innuendoes, that Augustus, who had been married happily to Livia for fifty years, was put to death by her. On the various versions of Claudius' death see W. Kroll, "De Claudii morte," *Raccolta Ramorino*, 1925, pp. 197-198 ; A. Momigliano, "Osservazioni sulle fonti per la storia di Caligola, Claudio, Nerone," *Rend. d. Accad. d. Lincei* viii, 1932, pp. 293 ff. ; and R. A. Pack, "Seneca's Evidence on the Deaths of Claudius and Narcissus," *Class. Weekly* xxxvi, 1942-1943, pp. 150-151

(margin notes:)

Death of Claud

ναικὸς Ἀγριππίνης φαρμάκοις ἀνῄρητο. ταύτης
πατὴρ μὲν ἦν Γερμανικὸς ὁ Καίσαρος ἀδελφός, ἀνὴρ
δὲ γενόμενος¹ Δομέτιος Ἠνόβαρβος² ὁ τῶν ἐπισή-
149 μων κατὰ τὴν Ῥωμαίων πόλιν. οὗ τελευτήσαντος
χηρεύουσαν αὐτὴν ἐπὶ πολὺν χρόνον Κλαύδιος
ἄγεται πρὸς γάμον ἐπαγομένην καὶ παῖδα Δομέτιον
ὁμώνυμον τῷ πατρί. προανῄρήκει δὲ τὴν γυναῖκα
Μεσσαλῖναν διὰ ζηλοτυπίαν, ἐξ ἧς αὐτῷ καὶ παῖ-
150 δες ἐγεγόνεσαν Βρεττανικός τε καὶ Ὀκταουία.³ ἦν
γὰρ Ἀντωνία ἤδη καὶ⁴ πρεσβυτάτη τῶν ἀδελφῶν,
ἣν ἐκ Πετίνης τῆς πρώτης γυναικὸς εἶχεν. καὶ δὴ
τὴν Ὀκταουίαν ἥρμοσεν τῷ Νέρωνι· τοῦτο γὰρ
ὕστερον αὐτὸν ἐκάλεσεν εἰσποιησάμενος υἱὸν ὁ
Καῖσαρ.
151 (2) Δεδοικυῖα δ' ἡ Ἀγριππῖνα, μὴ ὁ Βρεττανικὸς

¹ Γερμανικὸς . . . γενόμενος] WE (ὁ om. W) : Γερμανικὸς
Τιβερίου Καίσαρος ἀδελφὸς ἀνὴρ δὲ γενόμενος, litt. σ Τιβερίου . . .
γενόμενος i. ras. m. 2 paulo spatiosius scriptae A : Γερμανικὸς
Καίσαρος ἀδελφὸς M : Germanicus Caesaris frater vir autem
eius Lat.
² Δομέτιος Ἠνόβαρβος] ed. pr. : Δομέτιος ἦν ὁ βάρβαρος A :
Καίσαρος ἀδελφὸς Δομέτιος ἦν ὁ βάρβαρος W : Δομέτιος βάρβαρος
M : ἦν Δομέτιος ὁ βάρβαρος E : Dometius Barbarus Lat.
³ Ὀκταουία] Hudson ex Lat. : Ὀκταούϊος καὶ Ὀκταουΐα
codd. E.
⁴ ἦν γὰρ Ἀντωνία ἤδη καὶ] Post : ἦν γὰρ Ἀντωνιανὴ καὶ A :
ἡ καὶ MW : om. E : ἦν δὲ καὶ αὐτῷ Ἀντωνία Hudson : ἦν γὰρ
καὶ Ἀντωνία ἡ coni. Niese.

ª On his universal popularity see *Ant.* xviii. 206-209.
ᵇ Gnaeus Domitius Ahenobarbus, son of Lucius Domitius
Ahenobarbus, who was consul in 16 B.C., and of Antonia, the
daughter of Marcus Antonius and Octavia (the sister of
Augustus). His grandfather and great-grandfather had
also been consuls. He married Agrippina in 28, and in 32
he served as consul. He died in 40.

by his wife Agrippina. Her father was Germanicus,[a] the brother of the emperor, and her previous husband had been Domitius Ahenobarbus,[b] who was one of the prominent men in the city of Rome. On Domitius' death she remained a widow for a long time until Claudius married her. She brought with her a boy Domitius, who had the same name as his father. Claudius, smitten by jealousy,[c] had previously put to death his wife Messalina,[d] by whom he had had two children, Britannicus and Octavia. He already had had another child, actually his eldest, Antonia, born to him by his first wife Petina.[e] Moreover, he betrothed Octavia to Nero ; for so the emperor called Domitius later, when he had adopted[f] him as a son.[g]

(2) Agrippina, fearing that Britannicus on coming

How Nero became emperor. His barbarities.

[c] Tacitus, *Ann.* xi. 26, reports that Messalina, " now grown weary of the very facility of her adulteries, was rushing into strange excesses," when Gaius Silius proposed marriage to her. Messalina agreed, and the marriage contract was actually signed before witnesses (Tac. *Ann.* xi. 27 ; so also Suet. *Claud.* 26). Messalina, according to A. Momigliano, *Claudius*, 1934, pp. 76 and 120, would not have risked a second marriage unless, as is implied by Tacitus, she meant to start a revolution against Claudius ; hence it is significant that her second husband, Silius, was a notable aristocrat who probably favoured the establishment of a true senatorial principate.

[d] Valeria Messalina. A.D. 48.

[e] Aelia Paetina, according to Suetonius, *Claud.* 26, was actually Claudius' second wife, his first wife having been Plautia Urgulanilla.

[f] *Cf.* Tac. *Ann.* xii. 25-26. Scramuzza, *op. cit.* p. 91, makes the sound suggestion that this adoption was dictated partly by Claudius' desire to heal the rift with the party of Germanicus, who was Nero's grandfather.

[g] A.D. 50, when Nero was twelve years old (Tac. *Ann.* xii. 25). R. M. Geer, " Notes on the Early Life of Nero," *Trans. of the Am. Philol. Assoc.* lxii, 1931, p. 63, after examining the possible forms of adoption, suggests that it was irregular.

ἀνδρωθεὶς αὐτὸς παρὰ τοῦ πατρὸς τὴν ἀρχὴν παρα-
λάβοι, τῷ δὲ αὐτῆς παιδὶ προαρπάσαι βουλομένη
τὴν ἡγεμονίαν τά τε περὶ τὸν θάνατον τοῦ Κλαυδίου,
152 καθάπερ ἦν λόγος, διεπράξατο, καὶ παραχρῆμα
πέμπει τὸν τῶν στρατευμάτων ἔπαρχον Βοῦρρον
καὶ σὺν αὐτῷ τοὺς χιλιάρχους τῶν τε ἀπελευθέρων
τοὺς πλεῖστον δυναμένους ἀπάξοντας εἰς τὴν παρ-
εμβολὴν τὸν Νέρωνα καὶ προσαγορεύσοντας αὐτὸν
153 αὐτοκράτορα. Νέρων δὲ τὴν ἀρχὴν οὕτως παρα-
λαβὼν Βρεττανικὸν μὲν ἀδήλως τοῖς πολλοῖς
ἀναιρεῖ διὰ φαρμάκων, φανερῶς δ' οὐκ εἰς μακρὰν[1]
τὴν μητέρα τὴν ἑαυτοῦ φονεύει, ταύτην ἀμοιβὴν
ἀποτίσας αὐτῇ οὐ μόνον τῆς γενέσεως ἀλλὰ καὶ τοῦ
ταῖς ἐκείνης μηχαναῖς τὴν Ῥωμαίων ἡγεμονίαν
παραλαβεῖν. κτείνει δὲ καὶ τὴν Ὀκταουίαν, ᾗ
συνῴκει, πολλούς τε ἐπιφανεῖς ἄνδρας ὡς ἐπ' αὐτὸν
ἐπιβουλὰς συντιθέντας.

154 (3) Ἀλλὰ περὶ μὲν τούτων ἐῶ πλείω γράφειν·
πολλοὶ γὰρ τὴν περὶ Νέρωνα συντετάχασιν ἱστο-
ρίαν, ὧν οἱ μὲν διὰ χάριν εὖ πεπονθότες ὑπ' αὐτοῦ
τῆς ἀληθείας ἠμέλησαν, οἱ δὲ διὰ μῖσος καὶ τὴν
πρὸς αὐτὸν ἀπέχθειαν οὕτως ἀναιδῶς ἐνεπαρῴνησαν
τοῖς ψεύσμασιν, ὡς ἀξίους αὐτοὺς εἶναι καταγνώ-

---

[1] φανερῶς δ' οὐκ εἰς μακρὰν] om. Lat.

[a] Britannicus was now fourteen years old.
[b] So also Dio Cassius lxi. 1. 1. But Scramuzza, *op. cit.* p. 91,
says that Josephus and Dio, who thought in terms of Hellenistic kingship, where the succession was from father to son,

to manhood[a] might fall heir[b] to his father's office,
and wishing to forestall this by snatching the empire
for her own child, contrived, according to report, the
death of Claudius. She also immediately sent Burrus,[c]
the prefect of the praetorian guard, and with him
the military tribunes and the most influential of the
freedmen to conduct Nero to the camp and to pro-
claim him emperor.[d] Nero, having thus succeeded to
the throne, brought about the death of Britannicus
by poison,[e] keeping it hidden from the public. Not
long afterwards he openly murdered his own mother.[f]
This was the compensation that he paid her not only
for giving birth to him but also for having obtained
for him, through her devices, the Roman imperial
throne. He also put to death Octavia,[g] to whom he
was married, as well as many illustrious men, on the
charge that they had conspired against him.

(3) On these matters, however, I forbear to write
more. For many historians have written the story
of Nero, of whom some,[h] because they were well
treated by him, have out of gratitude been careless
of truth, while others from hatred and enmity towards
him have so shamelessly and recklessly revelled in

are mistaken in their view that the succession would belong
to Claudius' son Britannicus, since " there was no such thing
as hereditary right to the throne in the constitution of the
Roman Empire, least of all a right by natural heredity."

[c] Sextus Afranius Burrus. Tacitus speaks of him at
length in *Ann.* xiii. 2 ff.

[d] So also Tac. *Ann.* xii. 69.

[e] A.D. 55. *Cf.* Tac. *Ann.* xiii. 16.

[f] *Cf.* Tac. *Ann.* xiv. 1-13.

[g] *Cf.* Tac. *Ann.* xiv. 60-64.

[h] As A. Momigliano, in *Camb. Anc. Hist.* x, 1934, p. 702,
notes, we do not know the name of even one of those historians
who looked favourably upon Nero. Hence, our accounts of
his reign are one-sided.

(marginal note:) Various attitudes of historians towards Nero.

155 σεως. καὶ θαυμάζειν οὐκ ἔπεισί μοι τοὺς περὶ
Νέρωνος ψευσαμένους, ὅπου μηδὲ τῶν πρὸ αὐτοῦ
γενομένων γράφοντες τὴν ἀλήθειαν τῆς ἱστορίας
τετηρήκασιν, καίτοι πρὸς ἐκείνους αὐτοῖς οὐδὲν
μῖσος ἦν ἅτε μετ᾽ αὐτοὺς πολλῷ χρόνῳ γενομένοις.
156 ἀλλὰ γὰρ τοῖς μὲν οὐ προνοουμένοις τῆς ἀληθείας
ἐξέστω γράφειν ὡς θέλουσιν, τούτῳ γὰρ χαίρειν
157 ἐοίκασιν, ἡμεῖς δὲ σκοπὸν προθέμενοι τὴν ἀλήθειαν
τὰ μὲν ἀπηρτημένα τῆς προκειμένης ἡμῖν πραγ-
ματείας ἐπ᾽ ὀλίγον μνήμης ἀξιοῦμεν, τὰ δ᾽ ἡμῖν[1]
τοῖς Ἰουδαίοις συμπεσόντα δηλοῦμεν οὐ παρέργως
μήτε τὰς συμφορὰς[2] μήτε τὰς ἁμαρτίας διασαφεῖν
ὀκνοῦντες. ἐπανάξω[3] τοίνυν τὸν λόγον[4] ἐπὶ τὴν τῶν
οἰκείων πραγμάτων διήγησιν.

158 (4) Τῷ γὰρ πρώτῳ τῆς Νέρωνος ἀρχῆς ἔτει τελευτήσαντος τοῦ Ἐμέσων δυνάστου[5] Ἀζίζου Σόε-
μος[6] ἀδελφὸς τὴν ἀρχὴν διαδέχεται. τὴν δὲ τῆς
μικρᾶς Ἀρμενίας προστασίαν Ἀριστόβουλος Ἡρώδου τῆς Χαλκίδος βασιλέως παῖς ὑπὸ Νέρωνος ἐγ-
159 χειρίζεται. καὶ τὸν Ἀγρίππαν δὲ δωρεῖται μοίρᾳ
τινὶ τῆς Γαλιλαίας ὁ Καῖσαρ Τιβεριάδα καὶ Ταρι-
χέας[7] ὑπακούειν αὐτῷ κελεύσας,[8] δίδωσι δὲ καὶ

---

[1] AM : ὑμῖν W.
[2] μήτε τὰς συμφορὰς] AM : om. W.
[3] AE (sed in Busb. utrum ἐπανήξω an ἐπανάξω scriptum sit certo distingui non potest): ἐπανέξω E (cod. Laur.): ἐπανήξω MW : revertar Lat.   [4] τὸν λόγον] AE : om. MW.
[5] A : βασιλέως MW : rege Lat.
[6] E : ὁ ἐμὸς A : ἐμὸς MW : meus Lat.
[7] MW : Ταριχαίας, αι i. ras. A : Taricae Lat.
[8] ὑπακούειν αὐτῷ κελεύσας] om. E.

---

[a] A.D. 54.   [b] Cf. § 139.
[c] C. Julius Sohaemus. This Sohaemus, according to
Anderson, in *Camb. Anc. Hist.* x, 1934, p. 758 n. 3, and Magie,

falsehoods as to merit censure. Nor can I be surprised at those who have lied about Nero, since even
when writing about his predecessors they have not
kept to the facts of history. Surely they had no
hatred for those emperors, since they lived long after
them. Nevertheless, we must let those who have no
regard for the truth write as they choose, for that is
what they seem to delight in. But I, who have set
as my target the truth, see no reason to give more
than brief mention to matters unconnected with my
proposed theme. On the other hand, my exposition
of the fate of my own people, the Jews, is not merely
incidental ; and in my treatment I do not hesitate
to give a full account either of our misfortunes or
of our mistakes. I shall accordingly return to the
narrative of our own affairs.

(4) In the first year *a* of Nero's reign, Azizus,*b* the
overlord of Emesa, died and was succeeded on the
throne by his brother Sohaemus.*c* The government
of Armenia Minor was placed by Nero in the hands
of Aristobulus,*d* son of Herod, king of Chalcis. The
emperor also bestowed on Agrippa a certain portion of
Galilee, giving orders to the cities of Tiberias and
Tarichaeae *e* to submit to him. He also gave him

Tiberias, Tarichaeae, and Julias are given to Agrippa by Nero.

op. cit. ii. 1412 n. 41, is hardly to be identified with the Sohaemus, a prince of Emesa to whom as a client-king Sophene,
a district adjoining Armenia, was given by Nero (Tac. *Ann.*
xiii. 7). The two districts, Sophene and Emesa, are too far
apart to make the identity of the two men likely. So also
Stein, " Sohaemus " no. 4, Pauly-Wissowa, 2. Reihe, iii,
1929, p. 797.

d On Aristobulus *cf. Ant.* xviii. 134, 137 ; xx. 13, 104;
and *B.J.* ii. 221, 252. Tacitus, *Ann.* xiii. 7, also reports that
Nero entrusted Armenia Minor to Aristobulus.

e A city in Galilee frequently mentioned by Josephus,
particularly in his *Vita*, 96, 127, etc.

Ἰουλιάδα πόλιν τῆς Περαίας καὶ κώμας τὰς περὶ
αὐτὴν δεκατέσσαρας.[1]

160 (5) Τὰ δὲ κατὰ τὴν Ἰουδαίαν πράγματα πρὸς τὸ
χεῖρον ἀεὶ τὴν ἐπίδοσιν ἐλάμβανεν· λῃστηρίων γὰρ
ἡ χώρα πάλιν ἀνεπλήσθη καὶ γοήτων ἀνθρώπων, οἳ
161 τὸν ὄχλον ἠπάτων. ἀλλὰ τούτους μὲν ὁ Φῆλιξ
πολλοὺς καθ᾽ ἑκάστην ἡμέραν σὺν τοῖς λῃσταῖς
λαμβάνων ἀνῄρει, καὶ Ἐλεάζαρον δὲ τὸν Διναίου
παῖδα τὸν συστησάμενον τῶν λῃστῶν τὸ σύνταγμα
δι᾽ ἐνέδρας εἷλεν ζῶντα· πίστιν γὰρ αὐτῷ προτείνας
ὑπὲρ τοῦ μηδὲν πείσεσθαι κακὸν πείθει πρὸς αὐτὸν
162 ἀφικέσθαι καὶ δήσας ἀνέπεμψεν εἰς Ῥώμην. ἔχων
δὲ καὶ ἀπεχθῶς πρὸς τὸν ἀρχιερέα Ἰωνάθην ὁ
Φῆλιξ διὰ τὸ πολλάκις ὑπ᾽ αὐτοῦ νουθετεῖσθαι περὶ
τοῦ κρειττόνως προΐστασθαι τῶν κατὰ τὴν Ἰουδαίαν πραγμάτων, μὴ καὶ μέμψιν αὐτὸς ὀφλοίη
παρὰ τοῖς πλήθεσιν αἰτησάμενος ἐκεῖνον παρὰ τοῦ
Καίσαρος πεμφθῆναι τῆς Ἰουδαίας ἐπίτροπον, πρό-
φασιν ἐπενόει δι᾽ ἧς μεταστήσεται τὸν συνεχῶς
ὀχληρὸν αὐτῷ γινόμενον· βαρὺ γὰρ τοῖς ἀδικεῖν
163 θέλουσιν τὸ συνεχῶς νουθετοῦν. καὶ δὴ διὰ τοιαύτης αἰτίας ὁ Φῆλιξ τὸν πιστότατον τῶν Ἰωνάθου
φίλων Ἱεροσολυμίτην τὸ γένος Δωρᾶν ὀνόματι
πείθει πολλὰ χρήματα δώσειν ὑπισχνούμενος ἐπ-

---

[1] δεκατέσσαρας] A : τεσσαρεσκαίδεκα MW : δέκα Phot.

[a] Betharamphtha, east of the Jordan. *Cf. Ant.* xviii. 27,
where it is said to have been named after Julia (Livia), the
wife of the emperor Augustus.

[b] In the parallel passage, *B.J.* ii. 252, Nero is reported to
have given Agrippa four cities with their districts, namely,
Abila (not mentioned in our passage) and Julias in Peraea
and Tarichaeae and Tiberias in Galilee.

Julias,[a] a city in Peraea, and the fourteen villages that
go with it.[b]

(5) In Judaea matters were constantly going from
bad to worse. For the country was again infested
with bands of brigands and impostors who deceived
the mob. Not a day passed, however, but that Felix
captured and put to death many of these impostors
and brigands. He also, by a ruse, took alive Eleazar [c]
the son of Dinaeus, who had organized the company
of brigands ; for by offering a pledge that he would
suffer no harm, Felix induced him to appear before
him. Felix then imprisoned him and dispatched him
to Rome. Felix also bore a grudge against Jonathan [d]
the high priest because of his frequent admonition to
improve the administration of the affairs of Judaea.
For Jonathan feared that he himself might incur the
censure of the multitude in that he had requested
Caesar to dispatch Felix as procurator of Judaea.
Felix accordingly devised a pretext that would remove from his presence one who was a constant
nuisance to him ; for incessant rebukes are annoying
to those who choose to do wrong. It was such reasons
that moved Felix to bribe Jonathan's most trusted
friend, a native of Jerusalem named Doras, with a
promise to pay a great sum, to bring in brigands [e] to

*Felix puts
down the
brigands
and
impostors.*

*Felix has
the high
priest
Jonathan
murdered
by sicarii.*

[c] Cf. § 121. According to B.J. ii. 253, Eleazar had ravaged
the country for twenty years.

[d] His appointment as high priest is reported in Ant. xviii.
95 and his removal in Ant. xviii. 123. In Ant. xix. 313-316,
where Agrippa I offers to restore the high priesthood to him,
he declines and recommends his brother Matthias.

[e] In B.J. ii. 254 Josephus distinguishes between the old
brigands, of whom Felix successfully cleared the country,
and a new species, the so-called sicarii, " who committed
murders in broad daylight in the heart of the city." Jonathan, he says (B.J. ii. 256), was the first victim of the sicarii.

αγαγεῖν τῷ Ἰωνάθῃ τοὺς λῃστὰς¹ ἀναιρήσοντας,
κἀκεῖνος ὑπακούσας ἐμηχανήσατο διὰ τῶν λῃστῶν
164 πραχθῆναι τοιούτῳ τρόπῳ τὸν φόνον· ἀνέβησάν
τινες αὐτῶν εἰς τὴν πόλιν ὡς προσκυνήσοντες τὸν
θεὸν ὑπὸ τὰς ἐσθῆτας ἔχοντες ξιφίδια καὶ συνανα-
165 μιγέντες τῷ Ἰωνάθῃ κτείνουσιν αὐτόν. ἀνεκδικήτου δὲ τούτου τοῦ φόνου μεμενηκότος μετὰ πάσης
τὸ λοιπὸν ἀδείας ἀναβαίνοντες ἐν ταῖς ἑορταῖς² οἱ
λῃσταὶ καὶ τὸν σίδηρον ὁμοίως κεκρυμμένον ἔχοντες
συναναμιγνύμενοι τοῖς πλήθεσιν ἀνῄρουν μέν τινας
ἑαυτῶν ἐχθρούς, οὓς δ' ἐπὶ χρήμασιν ἄλλοις ὑπηρε-
τοῦντες, οὐ μόνον κατὰ τὴν ἄλλην πόλιν ἀλλὰ καὶ
κατὰ τὸ ἱερὸν ἐνίους· καὶ γὰρ ἐκεῖ σφάττειν ἐτόλ-
166 μων, οὐδ' ἐν τούτῳ δοκοῦντες ἀσεβεῖν. διὰ τοῦτ'
οἶμαι καὶ τὸν θεὸν μισήσαντα τὴν ἀσέβειαν³ αὐτῶν
ἀποστραφῆναι μὲν ἡμῶν τὴν πόλιν, τὸ δὲ ἱερὸν
οὐκέτι καθαρὸν οἰκητήριον αὐτῷ κρίναντα Ῥωμαίους ἐπαγαγεῖν ἡμῖν καὶ τῇ πόλει καθάρσιον πῦρ
καὶ δουλείαν ἐπιβαλεῖν σὺν γυναιξὶν καὶ τέκνοις
σωφρονίσαι ταῖς συμφοραῖς βουλόμενον ἡμᾶς.

167   (6) Τὰ μὲν οὖν τῶν λῃστῶν ἔργα τοιαύτης ἀνοσιό-
τητος ἐπλήρου τὴν πόλιν, οἱ δὲ γόητες καὶ ἀπα-
τεῶνες ἄνθρωποι τὸν ὄχλον ἔπειθον αὐτοῖς εἰς τὴν
168 ἐρημίαν ἕπεσθαι· δείξειν γὰρ ἔφασαν ἐναργῆ τέρατα
καὶ σημεῖα κατὰ τὴν τοῦ θεοῦ πρόνοιαν γινόμενα.
καὶ πολλοὶ πεισθέντες τῆς ἀφροσύνης τιμωρίας

¹ susp. Niese.   ² ἐν ταῖς ἑορταῖς] om. E.
³ μισήσαντα τὴν ἀσέβειαν] om. Lat.

ᵃ The panic created by these brigands, says Josephus,
B.J. ii. 256-257, was even more alarming than the actual
murders that they committed ; and people " would not even
trust their friends when they approached."

attack Jonathan and kill him. Doras agreed and contrived to get him murdered by the brigands in the following way. Certain of these brigands went up to the city as if they intended to worship God. With daggers concealed under their clothes, they mingled with the people about Jonathan and assassinated him. As the murder remained unpunished, from that time forth the brigands with perfect impunity used to go to the city during the festivals and, with their weapons similarly concealed, mingle with the crowds.[a] In this way they slew some because they were private enemies, and others because they were paid to do so by someone else. They committed these murders not only in other parts of the city but even in some cases in the temple ; for there too they made bold to slaughter their victims, for they did not regard even this as a desecration. This is the reason why, in my opinion,[b] even God Himself, for loathing of their impiety, turned away from our city and, because He deemed the temple to be no longer a clean dwelling place for Him, brought the Romans upon us and purification by fire upon the city, while He inflicted slavery upon us together with our wives and children ; for He wished to chasten us by these calamities.

(6) With such pollution did the deeds of the brigands infect the city. Moreover, impostors and deceivers called upon the mob to follow them into the desert. For they said that they would show them unmistakable marvels and signs that would be wrought in harmony with God's design. Many were, in fact, persuaded and paid the penalty of their folly ; for

Impostors lead Jews into the desert. The false prophet from Egypt.

[b] Similar sentiments are expressed by Josephus, *B.J.* iv. 323, v. 19, and elsewhere.

ὑπέσχον· ἀναχθέντας γὰρ αὐτοὺς Φῆλιξ ἐκόλασεν.
169 ἀφικνεῖται δέ τις ἐξ Αἰγύπτου κατὰ τοῦτον τὸν
καιρὸν εἰς Ἱεροσόλυμα προφήτης εἶναι λέγων καὶ
συμβουλεύων τῷ δημοτικῷ πλήθει σὺν αὐτῷ πρὸς
ὄρος τὸ προσαγορευόμενον Ἐλαιῶν, ὃ τῆς πόλεως
170 ἄντικρυς κείμενον ἀπέχει στάδια πέντε· θέλειν γὰρ
ἔφασκεν αὐτοῖς ἐκεῖθεν ἐπιδεῖξαι, ὡς κελεύσαν-
τος αὐτοῦ πίπτοι τὰ τῶν Ἱεροσολυμιτῶν τείχη, δι'
ὧν καὶ τὴν εἴσοδον αὐτοῖς παρέξειν ἐπηγγέλλετο.
171 Φῆλιξ δ' ὡς ἐπύθετο ταῦτα, κελεύει τοὺς στρατιώτας ἀναλαβεῖν τὰ ὅπλα καὶ μετὰ πολλῶν ἱππέων τε
καὶ πεζῶν[1] ὁρμήσας ἀπὸ τῶν Ἱεροσολύμων[2] προσ-
βάλλει τοῖς περὶ τὸν Αἰγύπτιον, καὶ τετρακοσίους
μὲν αὐτῶν ἀνεῖλεν, διακοσίους δὲ ζῶντας ἔλαβεν.
172 ὁ δ' Αἰγύπτιος αὐτὸς διαδρὰς ἐκ τῆς μάχης ἀφανὴς
ἐγένετο. πάλιν δ' οἱ λησταὶ τὸν δῆμον εἰς τὸν πρὸς
Ῥωμαίους πόλεμον ἠρέθιζον μηδὲν ὑπακούειν αὐτοῖς
λέγοντες,[3] καὶ τὰς τῶν ἀπειθούντων κώμας ἐμπι-
πράντες διήρπαζον.

[1] μετὰ πολλῶν ἱππέων τε καὶ πεζῶν] μετ' αὐτῶν E ; τε καὶ πεζῶν] om. Lat.
[2] ἀπὸ τῶν Ἱεροσολύμων] om. E.   [3] θέλοντες E.

[a] For the pattern of the story of the Egyptian prophet see R. Grant, " The Coming of the Kingdom," *Jour. of Bibl. Lit.* lxvii, 1948, p. 300. R. T. Herford, *Christianity in Talmud and Midrash*, 1903, p. 345 n. 1, suggests the possibility that the Egyptian false prophet is the Ben Stada described in the Talmud (*Shabbat* 104 b) as having brought sorcery from Egypt " in a cut upon his flesh," *i.e.* with the magic formulas tattooed or inserted into his flesh, which had been cut open. Two witnesses, according to Bab. *Sanhedrin* 67 a, heard him at Lydda and brought him to the Jewish tribunal ; and as a result, he was stoned. On the later confusion resulting in the identification of Ben Stada with Jesus of Nazareth see J. Derenbourg, *Essai sur l'histoire et la géographie de la Pales-*

they were brought before Felix and he punished
them. At this time there came to Jerusalem from
Egypt a man who declared that he was a prophet [a]
and advised the masses [b] of the common people to go
out with him to the mountain called the Mount of
Olives, which lies opposite the city at a distance of
five furlongs. For he asserted that he wished to
demonstrate from there that at his command Jerusalem's walls would fall down, through which he
promised to provide them an entrance into the city.[c]
When Felix heard of this he ordered his soldiers to
take up their arms. Setting out from Jerusalem
with a large force of cavalry and infantry, he fell upon
the Egyptian and his followers, slaying four hundred
of them and taking two hundred prisoners.[d] The
Egyptian himself escaped from the battle and disappeared. And now the brigands [e] once more incited the populace to war with Rome, telling them
not to obey them. They also fired and pillaged the
villages of those who refused to comply.

tine, i, 1867, pp. 468-471 ; J. Gutmann, " Ben Stada," *Ency.
Jud.* iv, 1929, p. 73 ; and M. Goldstein, *Jesus in the Jewish
Tradition*, 1950, pp. 57-62.
   [b] This false prophet gained a following of 30,000, according to *B.J.* ii. 261. He is probably the Egyptian for whom
Paul was mistaken and who, according to Acts xxi. 38,
" recently stirred up a revolt and led the 4000 men of the
sicarii out into the wilderness."
   [c] *B.J.* ii. 262 adds that the impostor intended to establish
himself as a tyrant, with those who had joined him acting as
his bodyguard.
   [d] *B.J.* ii. 263, without giving actual numbers, says that
most of the Egyptian's followers were slain or captured.
   [e] According to *B.J.* ii. 264-265 the brigands and impostors
banded together in inciting the people to throw off the Roman
yoke. In particular they pillaged the houses of the wealthy
and murdered the owners.

JOSEPHUS

173   (7) Γίνεται δὲ καὶ τῶν Καισάρειαν οἰκούντων
Ἰουδαίων. στάσις πρὸς τοὺς ἐν αὐτῇ Σύρους περὶ
ἰσοπολιτείας· οἱ μὲν γὰρ Ἰουδαῖοι πρωτεύειν ἠξίουν
διὰ τὸ τὸν κτίστην τῆς Καισαρείας Ἡρώδην αὐτῶν
βασιλέα γεγονέναι τὸ γένος Ἰουδαῖον, Σύροι δὲ τὰ
μὲν περὶ τὸν Ἡρώδην ὡμολόγουν, ἔφασκον δὲ τὴν
Καισάρειαν Στράτωνος πύργον τὸ πρότερον καλεῖ-
σθαι καὶ τότε μηδένα γεγονέναι τῆς πόλεως αὐτῶν
174 Ἰουδαῖον οἰκήτορα. ταῦτα ἀκούσαντες οἱ τῆς χώρας ἔπαρχοι λαβόντες ἀμφοτέρωθεν τοὺς αἰτίους
τῆς στάσεως πληγαῖς ἠκίσαντο καὶ τὴν ταραχὴν
175 οὕτω κατέστειλαν πρὸς ὀλίγον. πάλιν γὰρ οἱ κατὰ
τὴν πόλιν Ἰουδαῖοι τῷ πλούτῳ θαρροῦντες καὶ διὰ
τοῦτο καταφρονοῦντες τῶν Σύρων ἐβλασφήμουν εἰς
176 αὐτοὺς ἐρεθίσειν προσδοκῶντες. οἱ δὲ χρήμασι
μὲν ἡττώμενοι, μέγα δὲ φρονοῦντες[1] ἐπὶ τῷ τοὺς
πλείστους τῶν ὑπὸ Ῥωμαίοις ἐκεῖ στρατευομένων
Καισαρεῖς εἶναι καὶ Σεβαστηνοὺς μέχρι μέν τινος
καὶ αὐτοὶ τοὺς Ἰουδαίους λόγῳ ὕβριζον, εἶτα λίθοις
ἀλλήλους ἔβαλλον, ἕως πολλοὺς παρ' ἀμφότερα
τρωθῆναί τε καὶ πεσεῖν συνέβη· νικῶσί γε μὴν
177 Ἰουδαῖοι. Φῆλιξ δ' ὡς ἐθεάσατο φιλονεικίαν ἐν
πολέμου τρόπῳ γενομένην προπηδήσας παύεσθαι
τοὺς Ἰουδαίους παρεκάλει, μὴ πειθομένοις δὲ τοὺς
στρατιώτας ὁπλίσας ἐπαφίησι καὶ πολλοὺς μὲν αὐ-

---

[1] μέγα δὲ φρονοῦντες] sed sapientia fortiores Lat.

---

[a] The story of Herod's rebuilding of Strato's Tower is told
in *Ant.* xv. 331-341. It is probably to be identified with the
tower of Shir (var. Shed, *i.e.* " demon ") mentioned in Bab.
Megillah 6 a as having been captured by the house of the
Hasmonaeans (so I. Epstein, in the Soncino edition of the
Talmud, p. 28 n. 7).

(7) There arose also a quarrel between the Jewish
and Syrian inhabitants of Caesarea on the subject of
equal civic rights. The Jews claimed that they had
the precedence because the founder of Caesarea,
their king Herod, had been of Jewish descent ; the
Syrians admitted what they said about Herod, but
asserted that Caesarea had before that been called
Strato's Tower,[a] and that before Herod's time there
had not been a single Jewish inhabitant in the city.[b]
When the magistrates of the district heard of this
quarrel they arrested those on both sides who were
responsible for it and gave them a sound beating.
Thus they calmed the disturbance for a time but not
for long. For the Jews in the city, drawing confidence
from their wealth [c] and consequently despising the
Syrians, again started reviling them, expecting thereby to provoke the Syrians against the Jews. The
Syrians, though inferior in wealth, yet taking great
pride in the fact that most of those in military service
there under the Romans were from Caesarea and
Sebaste,[d] for a while retaliated by using insulting
language to the Jews. Next the Jews and Syrians
took to casting stones at each other, until it came
about that many on both sides were wounded and
fell. Nevertheless, it was the Jews who carried the
day. When Felix saw that their rivalry had taken
on the shape of war, he rushed ahead and summoned
the Jews to desist. When they did not obey, he
armed his soldiers, let them loose upon them, and

The
quarrel be-
tween Jews
and Syrians
at Caesarea
over civic
rights.

[b] The Syrians offer a different argument in *B.J.* ii. 266,
namely, that the city was built for the Greeks, since, if it
were meant for the Jews, Herod would not have erected
statues and temples there.

[c] " And physical strength " (*B.J.* ii. 268).

[d] *Cf. Ant.* xix. 365 and xx. 122.

τῶν ἀνεῖλεν, πλείους δὲ ζῶντας ἔλαβεν, οἰκίας δέ
τινας τῶν ἐν τῇ πόλει πολλῶν πάνυ χρημάτων γε-
178 μούσας διαρπάζειν ἐφῆκεν. οἱ δὲ τῶν Ἰουδαίων
ἐπιεικέστεροι καὶ προύχοντες κατὰ τὴν ἀξίωσιν
δείσαντες περὶ ἑαυτῶν παρεκάλουν τὸν Φήλικα
τοὺς στρατιώτας ἀνακαλέσασθαι τῇ σάλπιγγι[1] καὶ
φείσασθαι τὸ λοιπὸν αὐτῶν δοῦναί τε μετάνοιαν ἐπὶ
τοῖς πεπραγμένοις. καὶ Φῆλιξ ἐπείσθη.[2]
179 (8) Κατὰ τοῦτον τὸν καιρὸν ὁ βασιλεὺς Ἀγρίππας δίδωσιν τὴν ἀρχιερωσύνην Ἰσμαήλῳ· Φαβεῖ[3]
180 παῖς οὗτος ἦν. ἐξάπτεται δὲ καὶ τοῖς ἀρχιερεῦσι
ἔχθρα τις εἰς ἀλλήλους καὶ στάσις καὶ[4] πρὸς τοὺς
ἱερεῖς καὶ τοὺς[5] πρώτους τοῦ πλήθους τῶν Ἱεροσολυμιτῶν,[6] ἕκαστός τε αὐτῶν στῖφος ἀνθρώπων
τῶν θρασυτάτων καὶ νεωτεριστῶν ἑαυτῷ ποιήσας
καὶ καθ᾽ ἑαυτὸν συναγείρας[7] ἡγεμὼν[8] ἦν, καὶ συρ-
ράσσοντες ἐκακολόγουν τε ἀλλήλους καὶ λίθοις

[1] τῇ σάλπιγγι] turba missa Lat.
[2] δοῦναί . . . ἐπείσθη] quod Felix facere eorum precibus
adquievit Lat.
[3] MW : Φιαβὶ A Lat. : Φαβίου Jos. Hypom. ap. Fabricium.
[4] ἀρχιερεῦσι . . . στάσις καὶ] A (litt. ερευσι . . . πλήθους ἰ.
ras. m. 2) : ἀρχιερεῦσι στάσις MW Lat. Eus.
[5] ἱερεῖς καὶ τοὺς] E : om. codd.
[6] ἀρχιερεῦσι . . . Ἱεροσολυμιτῶν] ἀρχιερεῦσι πρὸς τοὺς ἱερεῖς
καὶ τοὺς πρώτους τοῦ πλήθους τῶν Ἱεροσολυμιτῶν ἔχθρα τίς πρὸς
ἀλλήλους καὶ διάστασις E.
[7] καὶ καθ᾽ ἑαυτὸν συναγείρας] A : om. MWE.
. εμὼν] ἡγεμὼν καὶ ἔξαρχος στάσεως E.

thus slew many of the Jews and took more alive. He
also allowed his men to plunder certain houses of the
inhabitants that were laden with very large sums of
money. The more moderate [a] Jews and those who
were of eminent rank, alarmed for themselves, besought Felix to sound the trumpet so as to recall the
soldiers, and to show mercy from then on, thus giving
them a chance to repent for what they had done.
And Felix was prevailed upon to do so.[b]

(8) At this time King Agrippa conferred the high
priesthood upon Ishmael,[c] the son of Phabi. There
now was enkindled mutual enmity and class warfare
between the high priests, on the one hand, and the
priests and the leaders of the populace of Jerusalem,
on the other. Each of the factions formed and collected for itself a band of the most reckless revolutionaries and acted as their leader.[d] And when they
clashed, they used abusive language and pelted each

The high
priests
quarrel
with
ordinary
priests and
with popu-
lar leaders.

[a] Or " respectable," " decent."
[b] In *B.J.* ii. 270 Josephus records that the quarrel between
the Syrians and Jews continued and that Felix selected
leaders from both groups to argue their cases before Nero.
Josephus does say in the *Antiquities* (xx. 182-184) that the
leaders of the Jews and of the Syrians of Caesarea went to
Rome to accuse Felix ; but this, we are told, occurred after
the removal of Felix and his replacement by Porcius Festus.
[c] Appointed in A.D. 59. He served for ten years, according
to the Talmud, *Yoma* 9 a. Since Josephus does not give a
cross-reference, as he generally does in the case of someone
whom he has cited previously, this Ishmael is probably not
to be identified with the Ishmael ben Phabi who was high
priest in A.D. 15-16 (*Ant.* xviii. 34). The rabbis recognized
his zeal for God by calling him Phineas' disciple (Bab.
Pesaḥim 57 a). We also learn that his mother made him a
tunic worth one hundred minas which he used at a private
service and then donated to the community.
[d] The Epitome adds " and prime mover of strife."

97

ἔβαλλον. ὁ δ᾽ ἐπιπλήξων¹ ἦν οὐδὲ εἷς,² ἀλλ᾽ ὡς ἐν
ἀπροστατήτῳ πόλει ταῦτ᾽ ἐπράσσετο μετ᾽ ἐξουσίας.
181 τοσαύτη δὲ τοὺς ἀρχιερεῖς κατέλαβεν ἀναίδεια καὶ
τόλμα, ὥστε καὶ πέμπειν δούλους ἐτόλμων ἐπὶ τὰς
ἅλωνας τοὺς ληψομένους τὰς τοῖς ἱερεῦσιν ὀφειλο-
μένας δεκάτας, καὶ συνέβαινεν τοὺς ἀπορουμένους
τῶν ἱερέων ὑπ᾽ ἐνδείας τελευτᾶν. οὕτως ἐκράτει
τοῦ δικαίου παντὸς ἡ τῶν στασιαζόντων βία.
182 (9) Πορκίου δὲ Φήστου διαδόχου Φήλικι πεμφθέντος ὑπὸ Νέρωνος οἱ πρωτεύοντες τῶν τὴν
Καισάρειαν κατοικούντων Ἰουδαίων εἰς τὴν Ῥώμην ἀναβαίνουσιν Φήλικος κατηγοροῦντες, καὶ
πάντως ἂν ἐδεδώκει τιμωρίαν τῶν εἰς Ἰουδαίους
ἀδικημάτων, εἰ μὴ πολλὰ αὐτὸν ὁ Νέρων τἀδελφῷ
Πάλλαντι παρακαλέσαντι συνεχώρησεν μάλιστα δὴ
183 τότε διὰ τιμῆς ἄγων ἐκεῖνον. καὶ τῶν ἐν Καισαρείᾳ δὲ οἱ πρῶτοι Σύρων³ Βήρυλλον,⁴ παιδαγωγὸς

¹ ἐπιπλήξων] ἐπιπλήξων καὶ τὴν στάσιν κωλύσων E.
² οὐδὲ εἷς] A : οὐδείς MW : non Lat.
³ οἱ πρῶτοι Σύρων] A : οἱ πρῶτοι δύο Σύροι MW : Σύρων οἱ
πρῶτοι E.   ⁴ Βούρρον Hudson.

ᵃ The Talmud, *Pesaḥim* 57 a, also refers to the violence
used by the adherents of Ishmael. " Woe is me," laments
one of the rabbis, " because of the house of Ishmael the son
of Phabi, woe is me because of their fists ! "
ᵇ The Epitome adds " and put an end to the strife."
ᶜ *Cf.* Bab. *Pesaḥim* 57 a, which records that the servants
of the high priests Ḥanin (= Ananus), Ḳathros (= Cantheras),
and Ishmael " beat the people with staves." It was forbidden
for a priest even to assist in the threshing floors, since such
assistance might have been thought to induce the Israelite to
give him the tithe (Bab. *Kiddushin* 6 b).
ᵈ See S. Belkin, *Philo and the Oral Law*, 1940, pp. 72-78,
for a brief account of the history of the practice with respect
to the collection of the tithes. Because, as he notes, pp. 73-74,
the priests could secure the tithe before it was brought to the

other with stones.[a] And there was not even one
person to rebuke them.[b] No, it was as if there was
no one in charge of the city, so that they acted as
they did with full licence. Such was the shameless-
ness and effrontery which possessed the high priests
that they actually were so brazen as to send slaves [c]
to the threshing floors to receive the tithes [d] that were
due to the priests, with the result that the poorer
priests starved to death. Thus did the violence of
the contending factions suppress all justice.

(9) When Porcius Festus [e] was sent by Nero as
successor to Felix, the leaders of the Jewish community of Caesarea went up to Rome to accuse Felix.
He would undoubtedly have paid the penalty for his
misdeeds [f] against the Jews had not Nero yielded to
the urgent entreaty of Felix's brother Pallas,[g] whom
at that time he held in the highest honour. Moreover, the leaders of the Syrians in Caesarea, by offering a large bribe, prevailed on Beryllus,[h] who was

*Festus suc-
ceeds Felix
as procura-
tor. The
Jews accuse
Felix be-
fore Nero.*

*The
Syrians in
Caesarea
obtain a re-
script from
Nero can-
celling
Jewish
rights.*

temple and thus deprive the Levites of their share, John
Hyrcanus instituted centralized collection of the tithes. But,
as indicated in our passage, the high priests took unfair
advantage ; and thus the rabbis of the Mishnah once again
allowed individual collection of the tithes by priests and
Levites.

 [e] Procurator A.D. 60–62. It was Festus who sent Paul to
Rome after Felix had left him with the case (Acts xxiv. 27 ff.).

 [f] Even Tacitus, in a passage hardly marked by friendliness towards the Jews, admits (*Hist.* v. 9) that Felix, during
his term of office, indulged in every kind of barbarity and
" exercised the power of a king in the spirit of a slave." *Cf.
Ann.* xii. 54 : " Felix . . . , by ill-timed remedies, stimulated
disloyal acts."

 [g] *Cf.* § 137.

 [h] Naber, following Hudson, reads Βοῦρρον and thus identifies him with Afranius Burrus (§ 152), Nero's commander of
the praetorian guard ; and those who make this identification equate *rector imperatoriae iuventae* (Tac. *Ann.* xiii. 2)

δ᾽ ἦν οὗτος τοῦ Νέρωνος τάξιν τὴν ἐπὶ τῶν Ἑλληνικῶν ἐπιστολῶν πεπιστευμένος, πείθουσι πολλοῖς
χρήμασιν αἰτήσασθαι παρὰ τοῦ Νέρωνος αὐτοῖς
ἐπιστολὴν ἀκυροῦσαν τὴν Ἰουδαίων πρὸς αὐτοὺς
184 ἰσοπολιτείαν. καὶ Βήρυλλος[1] τὸν αὐτοκράτορα πα-
ρακαλέσας ἐπέτυχε γραφῆναι τὴν ἐπιστολήν. αὕτη
τῷ ἔθνει ἡμῶν τῶν μετὰ ταῦτα κακῶν τὰς αἰτίας
παρέσχεν· πυθόμενοι γὰρ οἱ κατὰ τὴν Καισάρειαν
Ἰουδαῖοι τὰ γραφέντα τῆς πρὸς τοὺς Σύρους στάσεως μᾶλλον εἴχοντο μέχρι δὴ τὸν πόλεμον ἐξῆψαν.
185 (10) Ἀφικομένου δὲ εἰς τὴν Ἰουδαίαν Φήστου[2]
συνέβαινεν τὴν Ἰουδαίαν[2] ὑπὸ τῶν λῃστῶν κακοῦ-
σθαι τῶν κωμῶν ἁπασῶν ἐμπιπραμένων τε καὶ
186 διαρπαζομένων. καὶ οἱ σικάριοι δὲ καλούμενοι,
λῃσταὶ δέ εἰσιν οὗτοι, τότε μάλιστα ἐπλήθυον χρώ-
μενοι ξιφιδίοις παραπλησίοις μὲν τὸ μέγεθος τοῖς
τῶν Περσῶν ἀκινάκαις, ἐπικαμπέσι δὲ καὶ ὁμοίαις
ταῖς ὑπὸ Ῥωμαίων σίκαις[3] καλουμέναις, ἀφ᾽ ὧν
καὶ τὴν προσηγορίαν οἱ λῃστεύοντες ἔλαβον πολλοὺς

---

[1] Βοῦρρος Hudson.   [2] Φήστου . . . Ἰουδαίαν] om. E.
[3] ἐπικαμπέσι . . . σίκαις] A : om. MW.

---

with the term παιδαγωγός here used by Josephus. But if
Beryllus were the same as Burrus the name would not, in all
probability, have been spelled differently in § 152 and in our
section so shortly afterwards; and we would be likely to get
a cross-reference, of which Josephus is so fond. See Heinze,
" Beryllos," Pauly-Wissowa, iii, 1897, p. 319 ; and E.
Katterfeld, " Beryllos-Burrus," *Berl. Philol. Woch.* xxxiii,
1913, p. 59.
   [a] The position of *ab epistulis Graecis*.
   [b] Cf. the parallel passage, *B.J.* ii. 271.
   [c] Cf. *B.J.* ii. 254-255. This term (*sikarin*) is found in
Talmudic literature in reference to the terrorists during the

Nero's tutor and who had been appointed secretary
of Greek correspondence,[a] to apply for a rescript from
Nero annulling the grant of equal civic rights to the
Jews. Beryllus exhorted the emperor and succeeded
in getting his authorization for the rescript. This
rescript provided the basis that led to the subsequent misfortunes that befell our nation. For the
Jewish inhabitants of Caesarea, when they learned of
Nero's rescript, carried their quarrel with the Syrians
further and further until at last they kindled the
flames of war.

(10) [b] When Festus arrived in Judaea, it happened Festus and
the *sicarii.*
that Judaea was being devastated by the brigands,
for the villages one and all were being set on fire and
plundered. The so-called *sicarii* [c]—these are brigands
—were particularly numerous at that time. They
employed daggers, in size resembling the scimitars [d]
of the Persians, but curved and more like the weapons
called by the Romans *sicae,*[e] from which these brigands
took their name because they slew so many in this

---

siege of Jerusalem (see M. Jastrow, *A Dictionary of the Tar-
gumim,* etc., 1903, p. 986).

[d] Greek ἀκινάκης, Latin *acinaces.* *Cf.* the story in Herodotus iii. 118 of the Persian Intaphernes, who, upon being
refused admission to the king by a gate-warden and a messenger, drew his scimitar (ἀκινάκης) and cut off their noses
and ears. Again, a golden ἀκινάκης is enumerated among the
gifts given by the Persian king Cyrus to Syennesis (Xen.
Anab. i. 2. 27). Evidently the *acinaces* was sometimes employed in quarrels that arose while drinking, especially at
nocturnal banquets, for Horace, *Odes* i. 27. 5-6, urging an
end of such strife, exclaims : " How utterly at variance with
wine and lamps is the Median *acinaces!* "

[e] The term *sicarii* is found in the sense of bandits in the
Lex Cornelia de Sicariis and in Cicero, *Rosc. Am.* 8, 39, 103,
cited by Hug, " Sica," Pauly-Wissowa, 2. Reihe; ii, 1923,
p. 2184.

187 ἀναιροῦντες. ἀναμιγνύμενοι γὰρ ἐν ταῖς ἑορταῖς,
καθὼς καὶ πρότερον εἴπομεν, τῷ πλήθει τῶν πανταχόθεν εἰς τὴν πόλιν ἐπὶ τὴν εὐσέβειαν συρρεόντων
οὓς βουληθεῖεν ῥᾳδίως ἀπέσφαττον, πολλάκις δὲ
καὶ μεθ' ὅπλων ἐπὶ τὰς κώμας τῶν ἐχθρῶν ἀφ-
188 ικόμενοι διήρπαζον καὶ ἐνεπίμπρασαν. πέμπει δὲ
Φῆστος δύναμιν[1] ἱππικήν τε καὶ πεζικὴν ἐπὶ τοὺς
ἀπατηθέντας ὑπό τινος ἀνθρώπου γόητος σωτηρίαν αὐτοῖς ἐπαγγελλομένου καὶ παῦλαν κακῶν, εἰ
βουληθεῖεν ἕπεσθαι μέχρι τῆς ἐρημίας αὐτῷ, καὶ
αὐτόν τε ἐκεῖνον τὸν ἀπατήσαντα καὶ τοὺς ἀκο-
λουθήσαντας διέφθειραν οἱ πεμφθέντες.

189 (11) Κατὰ δὲ τὸν καιρὸν τοῦτον ὁ βασιλεὺς
Ἀγρίππας ᾠκοδομήσατο μεγέθει διαφέρον οἴκημα
ἐν τῷ βασιλείῳ ἐν Ἱεροσολύμοις πλησίον τοῦ
190 ξυστοῦ. τὸ δὲ βασίλειον ἐγεγόνει πάλαι[2] ὑπὸ τῶν
Ἀσσαμωναίου[3] παίδων, ἐφ' ὑψηλοῦ δὲ τόπου κείμενον τοῖς κατοπτεύειν ἀπ' αὐτοῦ βουλομένοις τὴν
πόλιν ἐπιτερπεστάτην παρεῖχεν τὴν θέαν, ἧς ἐφ-
ιέμενος ὁ βασιλεὺς ἐκεῖθεν ἀφεώρα κατακείμενος τὰ
191 κατὰ τὸ ἱερὸν πρασσόμενα.[4] ταῦτα δὲ θεασάμενοι
τῶν Ἱεροσολυμιτῶν οἱ προὔχοντες δεινῶς ἐχαλέ-
παινον· οὐ γὰρ ἦν πάτριον[5] τὰ κατὰ τὸ ἱερὸν δρώ-
μενα κατοπτεύεσθαι καὶ μάλιστα τὰς ἱερουργίας.
τοῖχον οὖν ἐγείρουσιν ἐπὶ τῆς ἐξέδρας ὑψηλόν, ἥτις

---

[1] πέμπει . . . δύναμιν] interea diversis rebus turbata pro-
vincia Festus multitudinem destinavit Lat.
[2] A : om. MW.
[3] A : Ἀσσαμωναίου M : Ἀσσαμωναίου W.
[4] κατακείμενος . . . πρασσόμενα] AW : om. M : τὰ κατὰ τὸ
ἱερὸν πραττόμενα πάντα κατακείμενος E.
[5] πάτριον] MW : πάτριον οὐδὲν νόμιμον A : πάτριον οὐδὲ νόμιμον E : πάτριον οὐδὲ νόμιμον ἡμῖν ed. pr.

way. For, as we said previously,[a] they would mingle
at the festivals with the crowd of those who streamed
into the city from all directions to worship, and thus
easily assassinated any that they pleased. They
would also frequently appear with arms in the villages
of their foes and would plunder and set them on fire.
Festus also sent a force of cavalry and infantry against
the dupes of a certain impostor who had promised
them salvation and rest from troubles, if they chose
to follow him into the wilderness. The force which
Festus dispatched destroyed both the deceiver himself and those who had followed him.

(11) About this time King Agrippa built a chamber
of unusual size in his palace at Jerusalem adjoining
the colonnade. The palace had been erected long
before by the sons of Asamonaios[b] and, being situated
on a lofty site, afforded a most delightful view to any
who chose to survey the city from it. The king was
enamoured of this view and used to gaze, as he re-
clined at meals there, on everything that went on in
the temple. The eminent men of Jerusalem, seeing
this, were extremely angry ; for it was contrary to
tradition[c] for proceedings in the temple—and in
particular the sacrifices—to be spied on. They therefore erected a high wall upon the arcade that was

Agrippa's addition to his palace.

---

[a] § 165.

[b] The Hasmonaeans ; *cf. Ant.* xii. 265.

[c] The Ambrosian ms. and the Epitome add " and to the
law " ; but there does not appear to be anything contrary
to Jewish law in what Agrippa did, however distasteful the
Jews might have found it. The Mishnah, *Yoma* iii. 8, notes
that on the Day of Atonement the people stood in the court
of the temple and presumably saw the sacrifices. The only
prohibition was on being in the temple itself when the priestly
functions were performed.

JOSEPHUS

192 ἦν ἐν τῷ ἔσωθεν ἱερῷ τετραμμένη πρὸς δύσιν. οὐ
μόνον δὲ τοῦ βασιλικοῦ τρικλίνου τὴν ἄποψιν οὗτος
οἰκοδομηθεὶς ἀπετέμνετο, ἀλλὰ καὶ τῆς δυτικῆς
στοᾶς τῆς κατὰ τὸ ἔξωθεν ἱερὸν οὔσης, ἔνθα τὰς
φυλακὰς οἱ Ῥωμαῖοι ταῖς ἑορταῖς ἐποιοῦντο διὰ τὸ
193 ἱερόν. ἐπὶ τούτοις ἠγανάκτησεν ὅ τε βασιλεὺς
Ἀγρίππας, μάλιστα δὲ Φῆστος ὁ ἔπαρχος, καὶ
προσέταξεν αὐτοῖς καθελεῖν. οἱ δὲ παρεκάλεσαν
ἐξουσίαν αὐτοῖς δοῦναι πρεσβεῦσαι περὶ τούτου
πρὸς Νέρωνα· ζῆν γὰρ οὐχ ὑπομένειν καθαιρεθέντος
194 τινὸς μέρους τοῦ ἱεροῦ. συγχωρήσαντος δὲ τοῦ
Φήστου πέμπουσιν ἐξ αὐτῶν πρὸς Νέρωνα τοὺς
πρώτους δέκα καὶ Ἰσμάηλον τὸν ἀρχιερέα καὶ
195 Ἑλκίαν τὸν γαζοφύλακα. Νέρων δὲ διακούσας
αὐτῶν οὐ μόνον συνέγνω περὶ τοῦ πραχθέντος, ἀλλὰ
καὶ συνεχώρησεν ἐᾶν οὕτως τὴν οἰκοδομίαν, τῇ
γυναικὶ Ποππαίᾳ,[1] θεοσεβὴς γὰρ ἦν, ὑπὲρ τῶν
Ἰουδαίων δεηθείσῃ χαριζόμενος, ἣ τοῖς μὲν δέκα
προσέταξεν ἀπιέναι,[2] τὸν δ' Ἑλκίαν καὶ τὸν Ἰσ-
196 μάηλον ὁμηρεύσοντας παρ' ἑαυτῇ κατέσχεν. ὁ δὲ
βασιλεὺς ταῦθ' ὡς ἐπύθετο δίδωσιν τὴν ἀρχιερω-

---

[1] Niese : Πομπηία codd. : Πομπαία E : Pompeiae Lat. :
cf. Vita 16.
[2] ed. pr. : ἀπεῖναι codd. E : redire Lat.

[a] Or perhaps " because the temple itself was sacred," *i.e.*
no non-Jew could be admitted to the inner temple.
[b] See § 179.
[c] Mistress (A.D. 58) and later (62) wife of Nero. When
Josephus (*Vita* 16) came to Rome in 64 seeking the release
from captivity of certain priests, he accomplished his mission
through her intercession. Poppaea died in 65.
[d] Poppaea is usually identified (*e.g.* by R. H. Pfeiffer,

in the inner temple facing west. This when built
blocked not only the view from the royal dining room
but also that from the western portico of the outer
temple, where the Romans used to post their guards
at the festivals for the sake of supervising the temple.[a]
At this King Agrippa was indignant, and still more
Festus the procurator ; the latter ordered them to
pull it down. But they entreated him for permission
to send an embassy on this matter to Nero ; for, they
said, they could not endure to live any longer if any
portion of the temple was demolished. When Festus
granted their request, they sent to Nero the ten
foremost of their number with Ishmael [b] the high
priest and Helcias the keeper of the treasury. Nero,
after a full hearing, not only condoned what they
had done, but also consented to leave the building as
it was. In this he showed favour to his wife Poppaea,[c]
who was a worshipper of God [d] and who pleaded on
behalf of the Jews. She then bade the ten depart
but detained Helcias and Ishmael in her house as
hostages. The king, on hearing this, gave the high

The Jewish
embassy to
Nero about
the wall
built in the
temple ;
Poppaea's
interven-
tion.

History of New Testament Times, 1949, p. 195) as a " sympathizer " with Judaism, *i.e.* one who observed certain Jewish
practices and held certain Jewish beliefs without actually
becoming a proselyte to Judaism. But the term θεοσεβής
(" worshipper of God ") which is here used does not necessarily identify Poppaea as a sympathizer in the technical
sense. J. Klausner, *From Jesus to Paul*, 1943, p. 43, compares Poppaea with the Roman senator who was a " God-
fearing man " and who, according to the *Midrash Rabbah on
Deut.* ii. 24, committed suicide so as to nullify a decree against
the Jews. But the senator is called a God-fearing man even
before it is learned that he actually had been circumcised
shortly before his death ; and the term there used is a
technical term for " sympathizer." *Cf.* my " Jewish ' Sym-
pathizers ' in Classical Literature and Inscriptions," *Trans.
of the Am. Philol. Assoc.* lxxxi, 1950, pp. 200-208.

σύνην Ἰωσήπῳ τῷ Σίμωνος παιδὶ ἀρχιερέως ἐπι-
καλουμένῳ δὲ Καβί.¹

197 (ix. 1) Πέμπει δὲ Καῖσαρ Ἀλβῖνον εἰς τὴν Ἰουδαίαν ἔπαρχον Φήστου τὴν τελευτὴν πυθόμενος. ὁ
δὲ βασιλεὺς ἀφείλετο μὲν τὸν Ἰώσηπον τὴν ἱερωσύνην, τῷ δὲ Ἀνάνου παιδὶ καὶ αὐτῷ Ἀνάνῳ
198 λεγομένῳ τὴν διαδοχὴν τῆς ἀρχῆς ἔδωκεν. τοῦτον
δέ φασι τὸν πρεσβύτατον Ἄνανον εὐτυχέστατον
γενέσθαι· πέντε² γὰρ ἔσχε παῖδας καὶ τούτους πάντας συνέβη ἀρχιερατεῦσαι τῷ θεῷ, αὐτὸς πρότερος
τῆς τιμῆς ἐπὶ πλεῖστον ἀπολαύσας, ὅπερ οὐδενὶ
199 συνέβη τῶν παρ' ἡμῖν ἀρχιερέων. ὁ δὲ νεώτερος
Ἄνανος, ὃν τὴν ἀρχιερωσύνην ἔφαμεν εἰληφέναι,
θρασὺς ἦν τὸν τρόπον καὶ τολμητὴς διαφερόντως,
αἵρεσιν δὲ μετῄει τὴν Σαδδουκαίων, οἵπερ εἰσὶ
περὶ τὰς κρίσεις ὠμοὶ παρὰ πάντας τοὺς Ἰουδαίους,
200 καθὼς ἤδη δεδηλώκαμεν. ἅτε δὴ οὖν τοιοῦτος ὢν
ὁ Ἄνανος, νομίσας ἔχειν καιρὸν ἐπιτήδειον διὰ τὸ
τεθνάναι μὲν Φῆστον, Ἀλβῖνον δ' ἔτι κατὰ τὴν
ὁδὸν ὑπάρχειν, καθίζει συνέδριον κριτῶν καὶ παρ-

---

¹ A : Καβεῖ MW : Κάμης Jos. Hypom. ap. Fabricium :
Cadis Lat. : Καμὶ supra § 16, cf. § 103. ² πέντε] om. Lat.

ᵃ Perhaps to be identified with the Joseph son of Simon
who was sent to take command at Jericho at the beginning
of the war against the Romans in A.D. 66 (*B.J.* ii. 567).

ᵇ *Cf.* the parallel passage, *B.J.* ii. 272.

ᶜ Lucceius Albinus, appointed procurator *c.* A.D. 62. He
arrived from Alexandria (§ 202), where he had perhaps held
(see Stein, " Lucceius " no. 11, Pauly-Wissowa, xiii, 1913,
p. 1559) the position of prefect of the camp or prefect of the
army. He later served as procurator of Mauretania Caesari-
ensis, where he met his death (see Tac. *Hist.* ii. 58-59).

ᵈ In contrast with the very unfavourable picture of Ananus
which is here given, compare the encomium in *B.J.* iv. 319-

priesthood to Joseph,[a] who was surnamed Kabi, son
of the high priest Simon.

(ix. 1) [b] Upon learning of the death of Festus, Caesar sent Albinus [c] to Judaea as procurator. The king removed Joseph from the high priesthood, and bestowed the succession to this office upon the son of Ananus, who was likewise called Ananus.[d] It is said that the elder Ananus [e] was extremely fortunate. For he had five sons, all of whom, after he himself had previously enjoyed the office for a very long period, became high priests of God—a thing that had never happened to any other of our high priests. The younger Ananus, who, as we have said, had been appointed to the high priesthood, was rash in his temper and unusually daring. He followed the school of the Sadducees, who are indeed more heartless [f] than any of the other Jews, as I have already explained,[g] when they sit in judgement. Possessed of such a character, Ananus thought that he had a favourable opportunity because Festus was dead and Albinus was still on the way. And so he convened the judges of the Sanhedrin and brought before

Albinus is appointed procurator.

Ananus the high priest has James, the brother of Jesus, stoned.

321, which, as Thackeray says in his note *ad loc.*, makes him the veritable counterpart of Pericles. He is particularly praised for putting the public welfare above his private interests and for his skill both as a general and as an orator. His bravery in opposing the Zealots is described at length with obvious sympathy by Josephus in *B.J.* iv. 160 ff.

  [e] *Cf.* note on *Ant.* xviii. 26.   [f] Or " savage."
  [g] *Cf. Ant.* xiii. 294, where King Hyrcanus, who had forsaken the Pharisees for the Sadducees, asks the Pharisees what penalty they thought Eleazar deserved for saying that Hyrcanus was unfit to be high priest because his mother had been a captive. They reply that he deserves merely stripes and chains ; " for they do not think it right to sentence a man to death for calumny, and anyway the Pharisees are naturally lenient in the matter of punishments."

107

αγαγὼν εἰς αὐτὸ τὸν ἀδελφὸν Ἰησοῦ τοῦ λεγομένου
Χριστοῦ, Ἰάκωβος ὄνομα αὐτῷ, καί τινας ἑτέρους,
ὡς παρανομησάντων κατηγορίαν ποιησάμενος παρ-
201 έδωκε λευσθησομένους. ὅσοι δὲ ἐδόκουν ἐπιει-
κέστατοι τῶν κατὰ τὴν πόλιν εἶναι καὶ περὶ τοὺς
νόμους ἀκριβεῖς βαρέως ἤνεγκαν ἐπὶ τούτῳ καὶ
πέμπουσιν πρὸς τὸν βασιλέα κρύφα παρακαλοῦντες αὐτὸν ἐπιστεῖλαι τῷ Ἀνάνῳ μηκέτι τοιαῦτα
πράσσειν· μηδὲ γὰρ τὸ πρῶτον ὀρθῶς αὐτὸν πε-
202 ποιηκέναι. τινὲς δ' αὐτῶν καὶ τὸν Ἀλβῖνον ὑπαντι-
άζουσιν ἀπὸ τῆς Ἀλεξανδρείας ὁδοιποροῦντα καὶ
διδάσκουσιν, ὡς οὐκ ἐξὸν ἦν Ἀνάνῳ χωρὶς τῆς ἐκεί-
203 νου γνώμης καθίσαι συνέδριον. Ἀλβῖνος δὲ πεισθεὶς
τοῖς λεγομένοις γράφει μετ' ὀργῆς τῷ Ἀνάνῳ
λήψεσθαι παρ' αὐτοῦ δίκας ἀπειλῶν. καὶ ὁ βασιλεὺς
Ἀγρίππας διὰ τοῦτο τὴν ἀρχιερωσύνην ἀφελόμενος
αὐτὸν ἄρξαντα μῆνας τρεῖς Ἰησοῦν τὸν τοῦ Δα-
μναίου¹ κατέστησεν.
204 (2) Ἐπεὶ δ' ἧκεν ὁ Ἀλβῖνος εἰς τὴν τῶν Ἱεροσολυμιτῶν πόλιν, πᾶσαν εἰσηνέγκατο σπουδὴν καὶ
πρόνοιαν ὑπὲρ τοῦ τὴν χώραν εἰρηνεύεσθαι τοὺς

¹ A : Δαμνέου MW : Δαμμαίου Eus. : Μνασέα Zonaras :
Damnaei Lat.

---

[a] Unlike the passage on Jesus (*Ant.* xviii. 63-64), few have
doubted the genuineness of this passage on James (on which
see Schürer, i. 546). If it had been a Christian interpolation
it would, in all probability, have been more laudatory of
James. Hegesippus (quoted by Eusebius, *Hist. Eccl.* ii. 23.
11-18) says that James was thrown down from the " pinnacle "
of the temple, stoned, and finally killed by a fuller's club
(cited by Thackeray, *Selections from Josephus*, p. 95).

[b] *Cf. Ant.* xviii. 63, where the mss. omit " called."

[c] *i.e.*, as explained in § 202, in convening the Sanhedrin
without Albinus' consent. Another possible translation is :

them a man named James,[a] the brother of Jesus who was called the Christ,[b] and certain others. He accused them of having transgressed the law and delivered them up to be stoned. Those of the inhabitants of the city who were considered the most fair-minded and who were strict in observance of the law were offended at this. They therefore secretly sent to King Agrippa urging him, for Ananus had not even been correct in his first step,[c] to order him to desist from any further such actions. Certain of them even went to meet Albinus, who was on his way from Alexandria, and informed him that Ananus had no authority to convene the Sanhedrin without his consent.[d] Convinced by these words, Albinus angrily wrote to Ananus threatening to take vengeance upon him. King Agrippa, because of Ananus' action, deposed him from the high priesthood which he had held for three months and replaced him with Jesus the son of Damnaeus.[e]

(2) When Albinus reached the city of Jerusalem, he bent every effort and made every provision to ensure peace in the land by exterminating most of

" for this was not the first time that Ananus had acted unjustly."

[d] F. Büchel, " Noch einmal : Zur Blutgerichtsbarkeit des Synedrions," *Zeitschr. f. d. Neutest. Wiss.* xxxiii, 1934, p. 86, conjectures from Albinus' anger that the high priests did not have the power to impose the death penalty during the period of the procurators.

[e] The sufferings that the Jews endured during the war against the Romans are said by Origen (*Cels.* i. 47) and Eusebius (*Hist. Eccl.* ii. 23) to have been ascribed by Josephus to God's vengeance for the death of James, but there is no such passage extant in Josephus. Origen and Eusebius may be thinking of Josephus' statement about the divine vengeance for the murder of John the Baptist by Herod (*Ant.* xviii. 116).

JOSEPHUS

205 πολλοὺς[1] τῶν σικαρίων διαφθείρας. ὁ δὲ ἀρχιερεὺς
Ἀνανίας καθ' ἑκάστην ἡμέραν ἐπὶ μέγα προὔκοπτε
δόξης καὶ τῆς παρὰ τῶν πολιτῶν εὐνοίας τε καὶ
τιμῆς ἠξιοῦτο λαμπρῶς· ἦν γὰρ χρημάτων πορι-
στικός· καθ' ἡμέραν γοῦν τὸν Ἀλβῖνον καὶ τὸν
206 ἀρχιερέα δώροις ἐθεράπευεν. εἶχεν δ' οἰκέτας πάνυ
μοχθηρούς, οἳ συναναστρεφόμενοι τοῖς θρασυτάτοις
ἐπὶ τὰς ἅλωνας πορευόμενοι τὰς τῶν ἱερέων δεκάτας ἐλάμβανον βιαζόμενοι καὶ τοὺς μὴ διδόντας
207 οὐκ ἀπείχοντο τύπτειν, οἵ τε ἀρχιερεῖς[2] ὅμοια τοῖς
ἐκείνου δούλοις ἔπρασσον μηδενὸς κωλύειν δυνα-
μένου. καὶ τῶν ἱερέων τοὺς πάλαι ταῖς δεκάταις
τρεφομένους τότε συνέβαινε θνήσκειν τροφῆς ἀπο-
ρίᾳ.
208 (3) Πάλιν δ' οἱ σικάριοι κατὰ τὴν ἑορτήν, ἐνει-
στήκει γὰρ αὕτη, διὰ νυκτὸς εἰς τὴν πόλιν παρελ-
θόντες συλλαμβάνουσι ζῶντα τὸν γραμματέα τοῦ
στρατηγοῦντος Ἐλεαζάρου, παῖς δ' ἦν οὗτος
Ἀνανίου[3] τοῦ ἀρχιερέως, καὶ δήσαντες ἐξήγαγον.

---

[1] τοὺς πολλοὺς] A : πολλοὺς MWE : plurimos Lat.
[2] οἵ τε ἀρχιερεῖς] sed etiam alii pontifices Lat.
[3] A Lat. : Ἀνάνου MWE.

---

[a] The estimates that Josephus gives of Albinus' work in
B.J. ii. 272-276 and in the present passage disagree, chiefly
in the omission from the former of Albinus' zeal in putting
down the *sicarii*; but A. Momigliano, *Camb. Anc. Hist.* x,
1934, p. 855, concludes that Albinus initiated, in his brief
term of office, a policy of mildness that caused him to be
accused of corruption.

[b] *Cf.* §§ 103, 131.

[c] Or perhaps " had a flair for making money," a translation which leads S. Lieberman, *Greek in Jewish Palestine*,
1942, p. 182 n. 195, to suggest that he was perhaps nicknamed
" Ben Nadbai," *i.e.* " the generous one," in ironic allusion to
this avarice. But our passage indicates that Ananias had

the *sicarii*.[a] Now the high priest Ananias [b] daily The influ-
advanced greatly in reputation and was splendidly ence of the
rewarded by the goodwill and esteem of the citizens ; Ananias.
for he was able to supply them with money [c] : at any
rate he daily paid court with gifts to Albinus and the
high priest.[d] But Ananias had servants who were
utter rascals and who, combining operations with the
most reckless men, would go to the threshing floors
and take by force the tithes of the priests ; nor did
they refrain from beating those who refused to give.
The high priests were guilty of the same practices as
his slaves, and no one could stop them. So it happened at that time that those of the priests who in
olden days were maintained by the tithes now starved
to death.[e]

(3) Once more the *sicarii* at the festival, for it was *Sicarii* kid-
now going on, entered the city by night and kid- nap the
napped the secretary [f] of the captain [g] Eleazar [h]— the captain
he was the son of Ananias [i] the high priest—and led Eleazar.

won popularity among the people, and it is hardly likely that
greed would have done so. There is nothing, however, to
prevent our taking the nickname literally and as a compliment.
   [d] Jesus the son of Damnaeus.   [e] *Cf.* § 181.
   [f] Or " officer," in which sense the term is found in
Egyptian Greek, including the Septuagint (*cf.* G. A. Deiss-
mann, *Bible Studies*, 1901, p. 110, cited by H. A. Wolfson,
Philo, ii, 1947, p. 345).
   [g] Lit. " general," but presumably the reference is to the
office of captain of the temple (see note on § 131).
   [h] In *B.J.* ii. 409 he is described as a very daring youth
who laid the foundation of the war against the Romans by
persuading the priests to refuse the sacrifices that were offered
on behalf of the emperor and of the Roman nation. Derenbourg, *op. cit.* p. 248 n. 1, identifies him with the Eleazar
who was the high priest under the procurator Gratus (*Ant.*
xviii. 34), but this identification is doubtful.
   [i] Variant Ananus. *Cf.* Schürer, i. 584 n. 50.

209 εἶτα πέμψαντες πρὸς τὸν Ἀνανίαν ἀπολύσειν ἔφασαν τὸν γραμματέα πρὸς αὐτόν, εἰ πείσειεν τὸν
Ἀλβῖνον δέκα δεσμώτας τοὺς ἐξ αὐτῶν ληφθέντας
ἀπολῦσαι. καὶ ὁ Ἀνανίας διὰ τὴν ἀνάγκην πεί-
210 σας τὸν Ἀλβῖνον τῆς ἀξιώσεως ἐπέτυχεν. τοῦτο
μειζόνων κακῶν ἦρξεν· οἱ γὰρ λησταὶ παντοίως
ἐπεμηχανῶντο τῶν Ἀνανίου τινὰς συλλαμβάνειν
οἰκείων καὶ συνεχῶς ζωγροῦντες οὐκ ἀπέλυον πρὶν
ἤ τινας τῶν σικαρίων ἀπολάβοιεν γενόμενοί τε πάλιν ἀριθμὸς οὐκ ὀλίγος ἀναθαρρήσαντες τὴν χώραν
ἅπασαν ἐκάκουν.

211 (4) Κατὰ τοῦτον δὲ τὸν καιρὸν ὁ βασιλεὺς
Ἀγρίππας μείζονα τὴν Φιλίππου καλουμένην
Καισάρειαν κατασκευάσας εἰς τιμὴν τοῦ Νέρωνος
Νερωνιάδα προσηγόρευσεν, καὶ Βηρυτίοις δὲ θέα-
τρον ἀπὸ πολλῶν χρημάτων κατεσκευασμένον ταῖς
κατ᾽ ἔτος θέαις ἐδωρεῖτο πολλὰς εἰς τοῦτο μυριάδας
212 ἀναλίσκων· σῖτον γὰρ ἐδίδου τῷ δήμῳ καὶ ἔλαιον
διένεμεν[1] καὶ τὴν πᾶσαν δὲ πόλιν ἀνδριάντων ἀνα-
θέσεσιν καὶ ταῖς τῶν ἀρχαίων ἀποτύποις εἰκόσιν
ἐκόσμει καὶ μικροῦ δεῖν πάντα τὸν τῆς βασιλείας
κόσμον ἐκεῖ μετήνεγκεν. μῖσος οὖν αὐτῷ παρὰ
τῶν ὑπηκόων ηὔξετο διὰ τὸ περιαιρούμενον τὰ
213 ἐκείνων εἰς ξένην πόλιν κοσμεῖν. λαμβάνει δὲ καὶ
Ἰησοῦς ὁ τοῦ Γαμαλιήλου τὴν διαδοχὴν τῆς ἀρχιερωσύνης παρὰ τοῦ βασιλέως Ἰησοῦν ἀφελομένου

---

[1] σῖτον . . . διένεμεν] frumenta namque populo copiosa et
oleum opulenter exhibuit Lat.

---

[a] Or " household."   [b] Cf. Ant. xviii. 28 and B.J. ii. 168.
[c] The name appears also on coins ; cf. F. W. Madden,
History of Jewish Coinage, 1864, p. 116, and Coins of the Jews,
1881, pp. 145-146.

him off in bonds. They then sent to Ananias saying that they would release the secretary to him if he would induce Albinus to release ten of their number who had been taken prisoner. Ananias under this constraint persuaded Albinus and obtained this request. This was the beginning of greater troubles ; for the brigands contrived by one means or another to kidnap some of Ananias' staff [a] and would hold them in continuous confinement and refuse to release them until they had received in exchange some of the *sicarii*. When they had once more become not inconsiderable in number, they grew bold again and proceeded to harass every part of the land.

(4) At this time King Agrippa enlarged Caesarea Philippi,[b] as it is called, and renamed it Neronias [c] in honour of Nero. He furthermore built at great expense a theatre [d] for the people of Berytus and presented them with annual spectacles, spending many tens of thousands of drachmas upon this project. Moreover, he used to give the people grain and distribute olive oil. He also adorned the whole city by erecting statues, as well as replicas of ancient sculptures. He thus transferred to that place well-nigh all the ornaments of the kingdom. The hatred of his subjects for him consequently increased because he stripped them of their possessions to adorn a foreign city. And now the king deposed Jesus the son of Damnaeus from the high priesthood and appointed as his successor Jesus the son of Gamaliel. In conse-

Agrippa offends the Jews by his buildings and spectacles at Berytus.

---

[d] Cf. *Ant.* xix. 335-336, which describes the special favours that Agrippa's father had likewise conferred upon Berytus, including a theatre " surpassing many others in its costly beauty," an amphitheatre, baths, and porticoes. Herod had also provided porticoes, temples, and a market-place for Berytus (*B.J.* i. 422).

τὸν τοῦ Δαμναίου, καὶ διὰ τοῦτο στάσις αὐτῶν πρὸς
ἀλλήλους ἐγένετο· σύστημα γὰρ τῶν θρασυτάτων
ποιησάμενοι πολλάκις μέχρι λίθων βολῆς ἀπὸ τῶν
βλασφημιῶν ἐξέπιπτον. ὑπερεῖχεν δὲ Ἀνανίας τῷ
πλούτῳ προσαγόμενος τοὺς λαμβάνειν ἑτοίμους.

214 Κοστόβαρος[1] δὲ καὶ Σαοῦλος[2] αὐτοὶ καθ' αὑτοὺς
μοχθηρὰ πλήθη συνῆγον γένους μὲν ὄντες βασιλικοῦ καὶ διὰ τὴν πρὸς Ἀγρίππαν συγγένειαν εὐνοίας
τυγχάνοντες, βίαιοι δὲ καὶ ἁρπάζειν τὰ τῶν ἀσθε-
νεστέρων ἕτοιμοι. ἐξ ἐκείνου μάλιστα τοῦ καιροῦ
συνέβη τὴν πόλιν ἡμῶν νοσεῖν προκοπτόντων πάντων ἐπὶ τὸ χεῖρον.

215 (5) Ὡς δ' ἤκουσεν Ἀλβῖνος διάδοχον αὐτῷ Γέσ-
σιον Φλῶρον ἀφικνεῖσθαι, βουλόμενος δοκεῖν τι
τοῖς Ἱεροσολυμίταις παρεσχῆσθαι προαγαγὼν[3] τοὺς
δεσμώτας, ὅσοι ἦσαν αὐτῶν προδήλως θανεῖν ἄξιοι,
τούτους προσέταξεν ἀναιρεθῆναι, τοὺς δ' ἐκ μικρᾶς
καὶ τῆς τυχούσης αἰτίας εἰς τὴν εἱρκτὴν κατατεθέν-
τας χρήματα λαμβάνων αὐτὸς ἀπέλυεν. καὶ οὕτως
ἡ μὲν φυλακὴ τῶν δεσμωτῶν ἐκαθάρθη, ἡ χώρα δὲ
λῃστῶν ἐπληρώθη.

216 (6) Τῶν δὲ Λευιτῶν, φυλὴ[4] δ' ἐστὶν αὕτη, ὅσοιπερ
ἦσαν ὑμνῳδοὶ πείθουσι τὸν βασιλέα καθίσαντα

[1] Custobarus Lat.
[2] i. marg. A : Σαλοῦος AM Exc. Peiresc. : Σαλοῦλος W :
Σάλουος E : Saul Lat.
[3] Niese : producens Lat. : προσαγαγὼν codd. E Exc. Peiresc.

114

quence, a feud arose between the latter and his pre-
decessor. They each collected a band of the most
reckless sort and it frequently happened that after
exchanging insults they went further and hurled
stones. Ananias, however, kept the upper hand by
using his wealth to attract those who were willing to
receive bribes. Costobar and Saul [a] also on their own
part collected gangs of villains. They themselves
were of royal lineage and found favour because of
their kinship with Agrippa, but were lawless and
quick to plunder the property of those weaker than
themselves. From that moment particularly, sickness
fell upon our city, and everything went steadily from
bad to worse.

(5) [b] When Albinus heard that Gessius Florus [c]
was coming to succeed him, he sought to gain a name
as one who had done some service to the inhabitants
of Jerusalem. He therefore brought out those
prisoners who clearly deserved to be put to death
and sentenced them to execution, but released for a
personal consideration those who had been cast into
prison for a trifling and commonplace offence. Thus
the prison was cleared of inmates and the land was
infested with brigands.

(6) Those of the Levites—this is one of our tribes [d]
—who were singers of hymns urged the king to con-

*Albinus re-
leases
Jewish
prisoners,
thus filling
the country
with
brigands*

*Levite
singers ob-
tain per-
mission to
wear linen
like priests.*

[a] Costobar and Saul were brothers (*B.J.* ii. 556) who
formed part of a delegation sent by the leading citizens to
Agrippa in 66 (*B.J.* ii. 418) urging him to send troops to
crush the incipient revolt of the Jewish revolutionaries. After
the rout of Cestius, the Roman governor of Syria, they
abandoned the city and joined the Roman forces (*B.J.* ii. 556).

[b] *Cf.* the parallel passage, *B.J.* ii. 273.

[c] *Cf.* §§ 252-258.   [d] Variant " this is a watch."

4 MW : φυλακή A.

συνέδριον φορεῖν αὐτοῖς ἐπίσης τοῖς ἱερεῦσιν ἐπιτρέψαι λινῆν στολήν· πρέπειν γὰρ αὐτοῦ τοῖς τῆς
ἀρχῆς χρόνοις ἔφασκον ἀφ' ὧν μνημονευθήσεται
217 καινοποιεῖν. καὶ τῆς ἀξιώσεως οὐ διήμαρτον· ὁ
γὰρ βασιλεὺς μετὰ γνώμης τῶν εἰς τὸ συνέδριον
ἐποιχομένων συνεχώρησεν τοῖς ὑμνῳδοῖς ἀποθε-
μένους τὴν προτέραν ἐσθῆτα φορεῖν λινῆν οἵαν
218 ἠθέλησαν. μέρους δέ τινος τῆς φυλῆς λειτουργοῦν-
τος κατὰ τὸ ἱερὸν καὶ τούτοις ἐπέτρεψεν τοὺς
ὕμνους ἐκμαθεῖν, ὡς παρεκάλουν. πάντα δ' ἦν
ἐναντία ταῦτα τοῖς πατρίοις νόμοις,[1] ὧν παραβα-
θέντων οὐκ ἐνῆν μὴ οὐχὶ δίκας ὑποσχεῖν.
219   (7) Ἤδη δὲ τότε καὶ τὸ ἱερὸν ἐτετέλεστο. βλέπων οὖν ὁ δῆμος ἀργήσαντας τοὺς τεχνίτας ὑπὲρ
μυρίους καὶ ὀκτακισχιλίους ὄντας καὶ μισθοφορίας
ἐνδεεῖς ἐσομένους διὰ τὸ τὴν τροφὴν ἐκ τῆς κατὰ
220 τὸ ἱερὸν ἐργασίας κομίζεσθαι,[2] καὶ χρήματα μὲν
ἀπόθετα διὰ τὸν ἐκ Ῥωμαίων φόβον ἔχειν οὐ
θέλων, προνοούμενος δὲ τῶν τεχνιτῶν καὶ εἰς τούτους ἀναλοῦν τοὺς θησαυροὺς βουλόμενος, καὶ γὰρ
εἰ μίαν τις ὥραν τῆς ἡμέρας ἐργάσαιτο, τὸν μισθὸν

---

[1] A : om. MWE.
[2] A : πορίζεσθαι MW.

---

[a] See Wolfson, *op. cit.* ii. 346, who appositely notes that
the first judges and officers were appointed by Moses, who is
regarded in both the Jewish tradition and in Philo as a king,
and that it was he who thus fulfilled the Biblical commandment : " Judges and officers shalt thou make thee in all thy
gates " (Deut. xvi. 18). Thus Agrippa, in convening the
Sanhedrin, was simply exercising the Scriptural prerogative
to appoint judges.
[b] The Levites were divided into two groups, the " singers "

vene the Sanhedrin [a] and get them permission to
wear linen robes on equal terms with the priests,
maintaining that it was fitting that he should introduce, to mark his reign, some innovation by which he
would be remembered. Nor did they fail to obtain
their request ; for the king, with the consent of those
who attended the Sanhedrin, allowed the singers of
hymns to discard their former robes and to wear linen
ones such as they wished. A part of the tribe that
served in the temple were also permitted to learn the
hymns by heart,[b] as they had requested. All this was
contrary to the ancestral laws, and such transgres-
sion was bound to make us liable to punishment.

(7) Just now, too, the temple had been completed.
The people therefore saw that the workmen, number-
ing over eighteen thousand, were out of work and
would be deprived of pay, for they earned their living
by working on the temple. Moreover, owing to their
fear of the Romans, they did not want to have any
money that was kept on deposit. Hence, out of regard for the workmen and choosing to expend their
treasures upon them—for if anyone worked for but
one hour of the day, he at once received his pay for

*Completion
of the
temple;
work found
for the idle
workmen.*

and the " gate-keepers," as indicated in their separate enumeration in Ezra ii. 41-42 (see Rashi's comment *ad loc.*), vii.
7, x, 24, and in Nehemiah x. 28. Membership in each of these
groups was gained by birth. There was a sharp division
between them, the singers being regarded as lower in rank,
as is indicated by the Talmud, *'Arakin* 11 b, in which Abaye
says that according to tradition a singing Levite who did his
colleague's work at the gate actually incurs the penalty of
death. But in any case all the rabbis agree that a transgres-
sion is involved. On the background of the dispute see the
exhaustive study by H. Vogelstein, *Der Kampf zwischen
Priestern und Leviten*, 1889 ; and, more briefly, R. Meyer,
" Levitische Emanzipationsbestrebungen in nachexilischer
Zeit," *Orient. Literaturzeit.* xli, 1938, pp. 721-728, esp. 727.

ὑπὲρ ταύτης εὐθέως ἐλάμβανεν, ἔπειθον τὸν βασιλέα
221 τὴν ἀνατολικὴν στοὰν ἀνεγεῖραι. ἦν δὲ ἡ στοὰ τοῦ
μὲν ἔξωθεν ἱεροῦ, κειμένη δ' ἐν φάραγγι βαθείᾳ
τετρακοσίων πηχῶν τοὺς τοίχους ἔχουσα ἐκ λίθου
τετραγώνου κατεσκεύαστο καὶ λευκοῦ πάνυ, τὸ μὲν
μῆκος ἑκάστου λίθου πήχεις εἴκοσι, τὸ δὲ ὕψος ἕξ,
ἔργον Σολόμωνος τοῦ βασιλέως πρώτου δειμαμένου
222 τὸ σύμπαν ἱερόν. ὁ βασιλεὺς δ', ἐπεπίστευτο γὰρ
ὑπὸ Κλαυδίου Καίσαρος τὴν ἐπιμέλειαν τοῦ ἱεροῦ,
λογισάμενος παντὸς μὲν ἔργου τὴν καθαίρεσιν εἶναι
ῥᾳδίαν δυσχερῆ δὲ τὴν κατασκευήν, ἐπὶ δὲ τῆς
στοᾶς ταύτης καὶ μᾶλλον, χρόνου τε γὰρ καὶ πολλῶν χρημάτων εἰς τοὖργον δεήσειν, ἠρνήσατο μὲν
περὶ τούτου δεομένοις, καταστορέσαι δὲ λευκῷ
223 λίθῳ τὴν πόλιν οὐκ ἐκώλυσεν. Ἰησοῦν δὲ τὸν τοῦ
Γαμαλιήλου τὴν ἀρχιερωσύνην ἀφελόμενος ἔδωκεν
αὐτὴν Ματθίᾳ τῷ Θεοφίλου, καθ' ὃν καὶ ὁ πρὸς
Ῥωμαίους πόλεμος Ἰουδαίοις ἔλαβε τὴν ἀρχήν.[1]
224 (x. 1) Ἀναγκαῖον δ' εἶναι νομίζω καὶ τῇ ἱστορίᾳ
ταύτῃ προσῆκον διηγήσασθαι περὶ τῶν ἀρχιερέων,
πῶς ἀρξάμενοι καὶ τίσιν ἔξεστι τῆς τιμῆς ταύτης
μεταλαμβάνειν καὶ πόσοι γεγόνασιν μέχρι τῆς τοῦ
225 πολέμου τελευτῆς. πρῶτον μὲν οὖν πάντων λέγου-
σιν Ἀαρῶνα τὸν Μωυσέως ἀδελφὸν ἀρχιερατεῦσαι
τῷ θεῷ, τελευτήσαντος δὲ ἐκείνου διαδέξασθαι τοὺς
παῖδας εὐθὺς κἀπ' ἐκείνων τοῖς ἐγγόνοις αὐτῶν
226 διαμεῖναι τὴν τιμὴν ἅπασιν. ὅθεν καὶ πάτριόν ἐστι

[1] Ἰουδαίοις . . . ἀρχήν] ἔλαβε τὴν ἀρχὴν τοῖς Ἰουδαίοις καὶ ἐπὶ
μέγα προκεχωρήκει Ε.

[a] Cf. Deut. xxiv. 15 : " In the same day thou shalt give
him his hire, neither shall the sun go down upon it." See
also the Talmudic discussion in Baba Meẓia 111 a. Cf. Matt.

this *a*—, they urged the king to raise the height of the east portico. This portico was part of the outer temple, and was situated in a deep ravine. It had walls four hundred cubits *b* long and was constructed of square stones, completely white, each stone being twenty cubits long and six high.*c* This was the work of King Solomon, who was the first to build the whole temple. The king, who had been appointed by Claudius Caesar to be curator of the temple, reasoned that it is always easy to demolish a structure but hard to erect one, and still more so in the case of this portico, for the work would take time and a great deal of money. He therefore refused this request of theirs ; but he did not veto the paving of the city with white stone. He also deprived Jesus the son of Gamaliel of the high priesthood and gave it to Matthias the son of Theophilus, under whom the war of the Jews with the Romans began.

(x. 1) Now I think it necessary and befitting in this history to give a detailed account of the high priests—how they began, who may lawfully participate in this office, and how many there were up to the end of the war.*d* It is said that Aaron the brother of Moses was the first to act as high priest to God, that after his death his sons at once succeeded him, and that thereafter the office remained permanently with all their descendants. Wherefore it is also a tradition

Enumeration of the high priests until the first temple.

---

xx. 8, where, when evening comes, the owner of the vineyard says to his steward : " Call the labourers and pay them their wages."

b 586 feet.

c About 29 feet long and 8·8 feet high.

d That Josephus' account of the high priests here is not a mere summary of his previous accounts can be seen from divergencies and new facts added in the present listing.

μηδένα τοῦ θεοῦ τὴν ἀρχιερωσύνην λαμβάνειν ἢ τὸν
ἐξ αἵματος τοῦ ᾿Ααρῶνος, ἑτέρου δὲ γένους οὐδ᾽ ἂν
227 βασιλεὺς ὢν τύχῃ τεύξεται τῆς ἀρχιερωσύνης. ἐγέ-
νοντο οὖν πάντες τὸν ἀριθμὸν ἀπὸ ᾿Ααρῶνος, ὡς
ἔφαμεν, τοῦ πρώτου γενομένου μέχρι Φανάσου[1] τοῦ
κατὰ τὸν πόλεμον ὑπὸ τῶν στασιαστῶν ἀρχιερέως
228 ἀναδειχθέντος ὀγδοήκοντα τρεῖς. ἐκ τούτων κατὰ
τὴν ἔρημον ἐπὶ τῶν Μωυσέως χρόνων τῆς σκηνῆς
ἑστώσης, ἣν Μωυσῆς τῷ θεῷ κατεσκεύασεν, μέχρι
τῆς εἰς ᾿Ιουδαίαν ἀφίξεως, ἔνθα Σολόμων ὁ βασιλεὺς τῷ θεῷ τὸν ναὸν ἤγειρεν, ἀρχιεράτευσαν
229 δεκατρεῖς. τὸ γὰρ πρῶτον ἕως τοῦ βίου τελευτῆς
τὰς ἀρχιερωσύνας εἶχον, ὕστερον δὲ καὶ παρὰ ζών-
των διεδέχοντο. οἱ τοίνυν δεκατρεῖς οὗτοι τῶν δύο
παίδων ᾿Ααρῶνος ὄντες ἔγγονοι κατὰ διαδοχὴν τὴν
τιμὴν παρελάμβανον. ἐγένετο δὲ αὐτῶν[2] ἀριστο-
κρατικὴ μὲν ἡ πρώτη πολιτεία, μετὰ ταύτην δὲ
230 μοναρχία, βασιλέων δὲ τρίτη. γίνεται δὲ τῶν ἐτῶν

[1] γρ ἐν ἄλλοις Φηνάσου i. marg. A : Φινεέσου E : Finasum
Lat. : Φαννί aut Φαννίτης B.J. iv. 155.
[2] δὲ αὐτῶν] codd. E Phot. : autem Hebreorum Lat. : δ᾽ ἐπ᾽
αὐτῶν coni. Niese.

[a] Variants Phenasus, Phineesus, Finasus. In *B.J.* iv. 155
he is called Phanni (or Phannites) the son of Samuel. He
was chosen by lot by the Zealots and is said not only not to
have been descended from high priests but also to have been
such a clown as not to have any conception of what the high
priesthood meant.
[b] According to Bab. *Yoma* 9 a, there were more than three
hundred high priests during the period of the second temple
alone. The Palestinian *Yoma* i. 1 says that the number is
between eighty and eighty-five.
[c] In his narrative in the earlier books of the *Antiquities*,
Josephus likewise enumerates thirteen : Aaron, Eleazar,

that none should hold God's high priesthood save him who is of Aaron's blood, and that no one of another lineage, even if he happened to be a king, should attain to the high priesthood. The total number of the high priests beginning with Aaron, who, as I have said, was the first, up to Phanasus,[a] who during the war was appointed high priest by the revolutionary party, is eighty-three.[b] Of these, thirteen [c] served as high priests from the sojourn in the wilderness in the time of Moses, when the tabernacle was standing which Moses constructed for God, until the arrival in Judaea, when King Solomon erected the temple to God. At first they held the high priesthoods for life, but afterwards succeeded to it during the lifetime of their predecessors. These thirteen consequently, being descendants of Aaron's two sons, received the office in succession. Their [d] first constitution [e] was an aristocracy, then followed monarchy,[f] and thirdly came the rule of the kings.

Phinees, Abiezer, Bokki, Ozis, Eli (v. 361-362), Jesus (viii. 12), Achias (vi. 107), Achitob (vi. 122), Abimelech (vi. 242), Sadok (vii. 110), and Abiathar (vii. 110). Jesus (viii. 12), however, is perhaps to be identified with Abiezer (so Marcus, note *ad loc.*).

[d] The Jews'.

[e] Under Moses and Joshua (*Ant.* vi. 84). In his previous enumeration of the Jewish constitutions Josephus notes that after Joshua's death there was anarchy for eighteen years (*ibid.*).

[f] Presumably the rule of the Judges, who are represented as ruling one at a time. This is clear from *Ant.* xi. 112, where Josephus says that during this period the Jews were ruled by " men called judges and monarchs." *Cf. Ant.* vi. 85, where Josephus says that during this interval the nation returned to an aristocratic rule, " entrusting supreme judicial authority to him who in battle and in bravery had proved himself the best ; and that is why they called this period of their political life the age of Judges."

ἀριθμὸς ὧν ἦρξαν οἱ δεκατρεῖς ἀφ᾽ ἧς ἡμέρας οἱ
πατέρες ἡμῶν ἐξέλιπον Αἴγυπτον Μωυσέως ἄγοντος
μέχρι τῆς τοῦ ναοῦ κατασκευῆς, ὃν Σολόμων ὁ
βασιλεὺς ἐν Ἱεροσολύμοις ἀνήγειρεν, ἔτη δώδεκα
πρὸς τοῖς ἑξακοσίοις.

231 (2) Μετὰ δὲ τοὺς δεκατρεῖς ἀρχιερέας ἐκείνους οἱ
δέκα καὶ ὀκτὼ τὴν ἀρχιερωσύνην ἔσχον ἀπὸ Σολόμωνος βασιλέως ἐν Ἱεροσολύμοις αὐτὴν διαδεξά-
μενοι, μέχρι οὗ Ναβουχοδονόσορος ὁ τῶν Βαβυ-
λωνίων βασιλεὺς ἐπιστρατεύσας τῇ πόλει τὸν μὲν
ναὸν ἐνέπρησεν, τὸ δὲ ἔθνος ἡμῶν εἰς Βαβυλῶνα
μετήνεγκεν καὶ τὸν ἀρχιερέα Ἰωσαδάκην[1] αἰχ-
232 μάλωτον ἔλαβεν. τούτων χρόνος τῆς ἱερωσύνης τετρακοσίων[2] ἑξηκονταὲξ ἐτῶν ἐστι μηνῶν ἓξ ἡμε-
233 ρῶν δέκα ἤδη βασιλευομένων Ἰουδαίων. μετὰ δὲ
χρόνον ἐτῶν ἁλώσεως ἑβδομήκοντα τῆς ὑπὸ Βα-
βυλωνίων γενομένης Κῦρος ὁ Περσῶν βασιλεὺς
ἀπέλυσεν τοὺς ἐκ Βαβυλῶνος Ἰουδαίους ἐπὶ τὴν
οἰκείαν γῆν πάλιν καὶ συνεχώρησεν τὸν ναὸν ἀν-
234 εγεῖραι. τότε δὴ τῶν ὑποστρεψάντων αἰχμαλώτων
Ἰησοῦς ὁ τοῦ Ἰωσεδὲκ εἷς ὢν τὴν ἀρχιερωσύνην

---

[1] MW : Ἰωσεδέκην, ε utrumque ex a corr. A : Iosedec Lat. :
Ἰωσεδέκ Photius habuisse vid. nunc corruptus.
[2] W : τριακοσίων AM Phot.

---

[a] Cf. Ap. ii. 19, which also gives 612 years from the
Exodus to the building of Solomon's temple. In Ant. viii.
61 Josephus gives 592 years. The Bible (1 Kings vi. 1) has
480.
[b] According to Ant. x. 152-153, the number is seventeen ;
cf. Marcus' note ad loc. The Talmud, Yoma 9 a, agrees with

The number of years during which the thirteen held
office from the day when our fathers left Egypt under
the leadership of Moses down to the building of the
temple which King Solomon erected in Jerusalem
was six hundred and twelve.[a]

(2) After these thirteen high priests, eighteen[b] Enumeration of the others held the high priesthood in succession from high priests the time of Solomon, who was king in Jerusalem, from the until the time when Nebuchadnezzar, king of Baby- first temple lon, led his army against the city, set fire to the chus Eupa- temple and carried away our nation to Babylon, tor. taking prisoner the high priest Josadakes.[c] The
period covered by the high priesthood of these men
was four hundred and sixty-six years,[d] six months,
and ten days, during which time the Jews were now
governed by kings. After a period of seventy[e] years
of captivity under the Babylonians, Cyrus, king of
the Persians, freed the Jews from Babylon and permitted them to return to their own land and to re-
build the temple. At that time Jesus[f] son of Josedek,[g] who was one of the captives who returned,[h]

Josephus in stating that there were eighteen high priests
during the period of the first temple.

[a] Biblical Jehozadak (Jozadak, Josedech). *Cf. Ant.* x. 150
and 153, where the name is spelled Josadakos, and xi. 73,
where it is spelled Josedekos.

[d] *Cf.* note on *Ant.* x. 147 (470 years, six months, ten days).
Josephus carelessly subtracts four years from the duration of
the temple instead of adding ; the total should be 474 years,
six months, and ten days. The Talmud, *Yoma* 9 a, says that
the first temple stood for 410 years.

[e] So also *Ant.* xi. 1.

[f] *Cf. Ant.* xi. 73 ff.

[g] This is the Josadakes who is mentioned above (§ 231) as
having been taken prisoner by the Babylonians.

[h] The Epitome has " Jesus, son of Josedek, who had been
taken captive, being one of those who returned."

λαμβάνει.[1] λαμβάνει δ' οὗτος αὐτὸς καὶ οἱ ἔγγονοι
αὐτοῦ πεντεκαίδεκα συνάπαντες μέχρι βασιλέως
᾿Αντιόχου τοῦ Εὐπάτορος, ἐπολιτεύοντο δὲ δημο-
κρατικῶς ἔτη τετρακόσια[2] δεκατέσσαρα.

235   (3) Πρῶτος δ' ᾿Αντίοχος ὁ προειρημένος καὶ ὁ
στρατηγὸς αὐτοῦ Λυσίας τὸν ᾿Ονίαν, ᾧ Μενέλαος
ἐπίκλην, παύουσι τῆς ἀρχιερωσύνης ἀνελόντες
αὐτὸν ἐν Βεροίᾳ καὶ τὸν παῖδα τῆς διαδοχῆς ἀπελά-
σαντες[3] καθιστᾶσιν ᾿Ιάκιμον[4] ἀρχιερέα, γένους μὲν
236   τοῦ ᾿Ααρῶνος, οὐκ ὄντα δὲ τῆς οἰκίας ταύτης.   διὰ

---

[1] τότε δὴ . . . λαμβάνει] τότε τῶν ὑποστρεψάντων εἰς ὢν ὁ τοῦ
αἰχμαλωτισθέντος ᾿Ιωσαδάκου παῖς ᾿Ιησοῦς λαμβάνει τὴν ἀρχιερωσύνην Ε : εἰς οὖν τῶν ἀναχθέντων αἰχμαλώτων λαμβάνει τὴν
ἀρχιερωσύνην Phot. : captivis igitur remeantibus Sison ponti-
ficatum sumpsit Lat.
[2] τριακόσια Ε.
[3] τὸν παῖδα . . . ἀπελάσαντες] AE Phot. p. 52 : om. MW
Phot. p. 317.
[4] ᾿Ιωάκειμον Ε : Ioachim Lat.

---

[a] 164/163 B.C. Cf. Ant. xii. 360-361.
[b] If Josephus is counting from the return from Babylon
(537 B.C.) until Antiochus Eupator, the number should be
373, if from the beginning of the captivity it should be 443 ;
if he is reckoning from the end of the captivity and in accordance with the chronology implicit in B.J. i. 70, it should be
411, if in accordance with the chronology implicit in Ant.
xiii. 301 it should be 421. In Ant. xiii. 301 Josephus says
that Aristobulus I transformed the government into a kingdom ; if Josephus regards the democracy as having extended

assumed the office of high priest. He and his descendants, fifteen in all, held the office until the reign of Antiochus Eupator [a] ; and for four hundred and fourteen years [b] they lived under a democratic [c] form of government.

(3) The aforesaid Antiochus and his general Lysias were the first [d] to depose anyone from the high priesthood. This they did in the case of Onias,[e] surnamed Menelaus ; for they put him to death [f] at Beroea,[g] excluded his son from the succession, and appointed as high priest Jacimus,[h] who was of Aaron's line but not of the same family as Onias.[i] In consequence of

from the end of the captivity until the beginning of his reign (104 B.C.), the number should be 433 (Josephus there actually gives 481, and in *B.J.* i. 70 gives 471).

[c] Contrast *Ant.* xi. 111, where Josephus says that the form of government from the return until the Hasmonaean kings was a mixture of aristocracy and oligarchy, with the high priests at the head of the people.

[d] But according to *Ant.* xii. 237-241 and xv. 41, it was Antiochus Epiphanes, the father of Antiochus Eupator, who first deposed a high priest, for he removed Jesus (Jason) the son of Simon from this office and replaced him with Onias (Menelaus), who is the Onias here mentioned as having been murdered by order of Antiochus Eupator and Lysias.

[e] In *Ant.* xii. 384-385, however, Lysias advises Eupator to put Menelaus to death in order to keep the Jews quiet, since it was Menelaus, he says, who had caused all the trouble for Epiphanes by persuading him to force the Jews to give up their ancestral religion. The implication is, therefore, that his removal was justified.

[f] See *Ant.* xii. 383-385.

[g] Aleppo in Syria. *Cf. Ant.* xii. 385. It was so called by Seleucus Nicator in remembrance of the Macedonian city of the same name.

[h] The Hebrew equivalent (*i.e.* Joachim) of Alcimus (*Ant.* xii. 385, where the name is spelled Ἰάκιμος in some MSS., as in the Epitome here).

[i] So also *Ant.* xii. 387.

JOSEPHUS

τοῦτο καὶ Ὀνίας¹ ὁ τοῦ τετελευτηκότος Ὀνίου
ἐξάδελφος ὁμώνυμος τῷ πατρὶ παραγενόμενος εἰς
Αἴγυπτον καὶ διὰ φιλίας ἀφικόμενος Πτολεμαίῳ
τῷ Φιλομήτορι καὶ Κλεοπάτρᾳ τῇ γυναικὶ αὐτοῦ,
πείθει τούτους κατὰ τὸν Ἡλιοπολίτην² νομὸν³ δει-
μαμένους τῷ θεῷ ναὸν παραπλήσιον τῷ ἐν Ἱερο-
237 σολύμοις αὐτὸν ἀρχιερέα καταστῆσαι. ἀλλὰ περὶ
μὲν τοῦ ἱεροῦ τοῦ κατασκευασθέντος ἐν Αἰγύπτῳ
πολλάκις ἐδηλώσαμεν.⁴ ὁ δὲ Ἰάκιμος ἔτη τρία τὴν
ἀρχιερωσύνην κατασχὼν ἐτελεύτησεν. διεδέξατο
δ’ αὐτὸν οὐδείς, ἀλλὰ διετέλεσεν ἡ πόλις ἐνιαυ-
238 τοὺς ἑπτὰ χωρὶς ἀρχιερέως οὖσα. πάλιν δὲ οἱ τῶν
Ἀσαμωναίου παίδων ἔγγονοι τὴν προστασίαν τοῦ
ἔθνους πιστευθέντες καὶ πολεμηθέντες καὶ⁵ πολεμή-

¹ Niese : Ἀνανίας A Phot. : ὁ Ἀνανίας MW : νεανίας E :
Ananias Lat. : ὁ Ὀνίας Hudson.
² A : Ἡλιουπολίτην MWE Phot.
³ Niese : νόμον codd. E Lat.
⁴ ἀλλὰ περὶ . . . ἐδηλώσαμεν] om. E Phot.
⁵ πολεμηθέντες καὶ] A : om. MWE.

ᵃ V. Tcherikover, *Hellenistic Civilization and the Jews*,
1959, p. 277, remarks that since Onias fled to Egypt during
a period (c. 162–160 b.c.) when the temple was once again
functioning properly so that even the Hasidim recognized
Alcimus as high priest, his motive in leaving Palestine could
not have been to create a replacement for the desecrated
temple. But Tcherikover neglects what appears to be the
real reason, namely, the one given here, that Onias was dis-
contented with having the high priesthood pass out of the
hands of his family. Once he had arrived in Egypt, Onias
may have found other reasons for establishing a temple,
namely, a desire for personal glory (*Ant.* xiii. 63), a desire to
build a place where Egyptian Jews could gather and pray
for the welfare of the Egyptian rulers (xiii. 67), or a desire to

126

this,[a] Onias,[b] who was the nephew [c] of the deceased
Onias and who bore the same name as his father,[d]
made his way to Egypt, where he won the friendship
of Ptolemy Philometor [e] and Cleopatra his queen,
and persuaded them to build a temple to God in the
nome of Heliopolis,[f] similar to the one at Jerusalem,
and to appoint him high priest. I have, however,
frequently [g] told the story of the temple that was
constructed in Egypt. Now Jacimus died after holding the high priesthood for three years.[h] No one
succeeded him ; and the city continued for seven
years without a high priest.[i] Then the descendants
of the sons of Asamonaios, entrusted with the leadership of the nation, after war had been waged against

The Has-
monaean
high
priests.

build a shrine for the Jewish military colony at Leontopolis
(so Tcherikover, pp. 278-280).
 [b] Onias IV.   [c] So also *Ant.* xii. 387.
 [d] From this account, as from *Ant.* xii. 237-238, it would
appear that both Onias' father and the latter's brother were
named Onias. S. Krauss, " Onias III," *Jewish Ency.* ix,
1905, p. 403, suggests that this confusion may have arisen
from the Greek transcription of the related names, Johanan,
Honya, and Nehonya. From the account in *B.J.* vii. 423,
which mentions the name of Onias' father as Simon, it appears
that the temple was built by Onias III, the father of Onias
IV.
 [e] Reigned between 182 and 146 B.C.
 [f] At Leontopolis, probably to be identified with modern
Tell el-Yehudiyeh, at the southern end of the Nile Delta.
 [g] *Ant.* xii. 387-388, xiii. 62-73, 285 ; *B.J.* i. 33, vii. 422-
432.
 [h] Four years in *Ant.* xii. 413, where part of a year is
counted as a full year.
 [i] Contrast *Ant.* xii. 434, which records that after the death
of Jacimus, Judas the Maccabee served as high priest for
three years. But there was an interval of seven years (not
four, as stated in *Ant.* xiii. 46) between the death of Judas
in 159 B.C. and the assumption of the high priesthood by
Johathan in 152 B.C. (1 Macc. x. 21).

σαντες Μακεδόσιν Ἰωνάθην ἀρχιερέα καθιστᾶσιν, ὃς
239 ἦρξεν ἐνιαυτοὺς ἑπτά. τελευτήσαντος δὲ ἐξ ἐπιβουλῆς αὐτοῦ καὶ ἐνέδρας τῆς ὑπὸ Τρύφωνος μηχανη-
θείσης, ὡς ἀνωτέρω που προειρήκαμεν, λαμβάνει
240 τὴν ἀρχιερωσύνην Σίμων ἀδελφὸς αὐτοῦ. καὶ τοῦτον δὲ δόλῳ παρὰ συμπόσιον ὑπὸ τοῦ γαμβροῦ
διαφθαρέντα διεδέξατο παῖς Ὑρκανὸς ὄνομα ὃν
κατασχόντα τὴν ἱερωσύνην πλείονα τἀδελφοῦ χρόνον ἐνιαυτῷ, τριακονταὲν ἔτη τῆς τιμῆς Ὑρκανὸς
ἀπολαύσας τελευτᾷ γηραιὸς Ἰούδᾳ τῷ καὶ Ἀριστο-
241 βούλῳ κληθέντι τὴν διαδοχὴν καταλιπών. κληρο-
νομεῖ δὲ καὶ τοῦτον ἀδελφὸς[1] Ἀλέξανδρος, ὑπὸ
νόσου μὲν τελευτήσαντα, τὴν ἱερωσύνην δὲ κατασχόντα μετὰ βασιλείας, καὶ γὰρ διάδημα πρῶτος
περιέθετο ὁ Ἰούδας, ἐνιαυτὸν ἕνα.
242 (4) Βασιλεύσας δὲ ὁ Ἀλέξανδρος καὶ ἱερατεύσας
ἔτη εἰκοσιεπτὰ καταστρέφει τὸν βίον Ἀλεξάνδρᾳ
τῇ γυναικὶ καταστῆσαι τὸν ἀρχιερατευσόμενον ἐπι-
τρέψας. ἡ δὲ τὴν μὲν ἀρχιερωσύνην Ὑρκανῷ δίδωσιν, αὐτὴ δὲ τὴν βασιλείαν ἔτη ἐννέα κατασχοῦσα
τελευτᾷ τὸν βίον· τὸν ἴσον δὲ χρόνον τὴν ἀρχιερω-

---

[1] ἀδελφός] ἀδελφὸς βασιλεὺς E.

[a] According to *Ant.* xiii. 45-46, it is not the Hasmonaeans
but Alexander Balas, the son of Antiochus Epiphanes, who
named Jonathan as high priest.

[b] Four years according to *Ant.* xiii. 212. Both figures
are incorrect : Jonathan was high priest for ten years, from
152 to 143/142 B.C. See Marcus' note on *Ant.* xiii. 212.

[c] *Ant.* xiii. 187-212 ; the story is also told briefly in *B.J.*
i. 49.

[d] *Ant.* xiii. 213.   [e] *Ant.* xiii. 228.

[f] Named Ptolemy (*ibid.*).

[g] So also *Ant.* xiii. 228. Simon served from 142 to 135 B.C.

[h] *Ant.* xiii. 230.

them and they had taken the offensive against the
Macedonians, resumed the tradition, appointing as
high priest Jonathan,[a] who held office for seven years.[b]
When he was killed by a plot and ambush devised
by Tryphon, as I have already described somewhere
in the preceding narrative,[c] his brother Simon [d] obtained the high priesthood. Simon likewise was
killed [e] craftily by his son-in-law [f] at a banquet after
he had held the high priesthood one year longer than
his brother.[g] He was succeeded by his son named
Hyrcanus,[h] who, after enjoying the office for thirty-
one years, died in old age,[i] leaving the succession to
Judas,[j] also called Aristobulus. Judas died of illness
after having held the high priesthood for one year [k]
together with the kingship, for Judas also put the
diadem upon his head for a single year, being the
first [l] to hold both offices. His heir was his brother
Alexander.[m]

(4) Alexander departed this life after holding the
kingship and the high priesthood for twenty-seven
years,[n] entrusting his wife Alexandra [o] with the
appointment of a successor to the latter office. She
gave the high priesthood to Hyrcanus [p] and herself
occupied the throne for nine years,[q] after which she
died ; her son Hyrcanus held the high priesthood for

---

[f] The earlier account, *Ant.* xiii. 299, omits the fact that
Hyrcanus lived to an old age. His rule lasted from 135 to
105 B.C.
[j] The alternate name, Judas, is a new detail not found in
the earlier account, *Ant.* xiii. 301–319, where he is called
simply Aristobulus.
[k] 104–103 B.C. ; so also *Ant.* xiii. 318.
[l] So also *Ant.* xiii. 301.   [m] Jannaeus. *Ant.* xiii. 320.
[n] From 103 to 76 B.C. So also *Ant.* xiii 404.
[o] So also *Ant.* xiii 407.   [p] *Ant.* xiii. 408.
[q] 76 to 67 B.C. So also *Ant.* xiii. 430.

JOSEPHUS

243 σύνην ὁ παῖς αὐτῆς Ὑρκανὸς ἔσχεν· μετὰ γὰρ τὸν
θάνατον αὐτῆς πολεμήσας πρὸς αὐτὸν ὁ ἀδελφὸς
Ἀριστόβουλος καὶ νικήσας ἀφαιρεῖται μὲν ἐκεῖνον
τὴν ἀρχήν, αὐτὸς δ᾿ ἐβασίλευέ τε καὶ ἀρχιεράτευεν
244 τοῦ ἔθνους. ἔτει δὲ τρίτῳ τῆς βασιλείας καὶ πρὸς
μησὶν τοῖς ἴσοις Πομπήιος ἐλθὼν καὶ τὴν τῶν
Ἱεροσολυμιτῶν πόλιν κατὰ κράτος ἑλὼν αὐτὸν μὲν
εἰς Ῥώμην μετὰ τῶν τέκνων[1] δήσας ἔπεμψεν, τῷ
δ᾿ Ὑρκανῷ πάλιν τὴν ἀρχιερωσύνην ἀποδοὺς τὴν
μὲν τοῦ ἔθνους προστασίαν ἐπέτρεψεν, διάδημα δὲ
245 φορεῖν ἐκώλυσεν. ἦρξεν δὲ πρὸς τοῖς ἐννέα τοῖς
πρώτοις ὁ Ὑρκανὸς τέσσαρα καὶ εἴκοσιν.[2] Βαρ-
ζαβάνης[3] δὲ καὶ Πάκορος οἱ τῆς Παρθυηνῆς δυνά-
σται διαβάντες τὸν Εὐφράτην καὶ πολεμήσαντες
Ὑρκανῷ αὐτὸν μὲν ζωγρίᾳ συνέλαβον, τὸν Ἀριστοβούλου δὲ υἱὸν Ἀντίγονον κατέστησαν βασιλέα.
246 τρία δ᾿ ἔτη καὶ τρεῖς μῆνας ἄρξαντα τοῦτον Σόσ-
σιός τε καὶ Ἡρώδης ἐξεπολιόρκησαν, Ἀντώνιος δ᾿
ἀνεῖλεν εἰς τὴν Ἀντιόχειαν ἀναχθέντα.

[1] μετὰ τῶν τέκνων] om. E.
[2] τέσσαρα καὶ εἴκοσιν] viginti tres Lat.
[3] codd. E : γρ Βαρζαφράνης i. marg. A : Barzanes Lat. :
Βαζαφαρμανης Phot. p. 318 : Φαρναβαζου Phot. p. 53 : Βαζα-
φρανης Niese.

[a] According to *Ant.* xv. 180, he served for three months
after Alexandra's death.
[b] *Ant.* xiv. 4-7 ; *cf. B.J.* i. 120-122.
[c] So also *Ant.* xiv. 41, 97.
[d] 65–63 B.C. Lit. " In the third year of his reign and after
as many months.'' Marcus' note on *Ant.* xiv. 5 should be
corrected, since our passage is inconsistent with *Ant.* xiv. 97,
which he cites as being in accordance with ours, but which
states that Aristobulus served for three years and six months.
[e] 63 B.C. See *Ant.* xiv. 34-79 and *B.J.* i. 127-158.
[f] 63–40 B.C. Forty years, according to *Ant.* xv. 180.

an equal period.[a] For after her death, Hyrcanus'
brother Aristobulus made war upon him, defeated
him, deprived him of his office [b] and himself became
both king and high priest [c] of the nation. When he
had reigned two years and three months,[d] Pompey [e]
came and took the city of Jerusalem by storm and
sent him with his children to Rome in bonds. Pompey
also restored the high priesthood to Hyrcanus and
permitted him to have the leadership of the nation,
but forbade him to wear a diadem. Hyrcanus ruled
for twenty-four years,[f] in addition to the nine years
of his previous rule. Then Barzabanes [g] and Pacorus,[h]
the rulers of Parthia, crossing the Euphrates, made
war on Hyrcanus, captured him alive, and appointed
Antigonus, son of Aristobulus, king. The latter ruled
for three years and three months,[i] following which
he was captured after a siege by Sossius and Herod.[j]
When he had been taken to Antioch, he was slain by
Antony.

[g] Barzaphranes in *Ant.* xiv. 330, where he is called a
Parthian satrap.

[h] *Cf. Ant.* xiv. 340 ff.

[i] 40–37 B.C. The length of Antigonus' reign is not given
in Josephus' earlier account of his death, *Ant.* xiv. 487-491
and xv. 8-10. The total number of years during which the
Hasmonaeans, starting from Jonathan, ruled is, therefore,
112½ years. In *Ant.* xiv. 490 the total given is 126 years. In
Ant. xvii. 162, however, the total is 125 years, but these last two
totals presumably include Judas, who assumed his leadership
upon the death of Mattathias in 167/166 B.C. The Talmud,
'Abodah Zarah 8 b, gives the duration of the Hasmonaean
dynasty as 103 years, reckoning, it would appear (so J.
Lehmann, " Quelques Dates importantes de la chronologie
du 2e Temple," *Rev. d. Ét. juiv.* xxxvii, 1898, pp. 1-44), from
the official recognition of the dynasty by the Romans in
140 B.C. to the victory of the Roman general Sosius over the
Hasmonaean Antigonus in 37 B.C.

[j] *Cf. Ant.* xiv. 468 ff. and *B.J.* i. 345 ff.

247   (5) Τὴν δὲ βασιλείαν Ἡρώδης παρὰ Ῥωμαίων
ἐγχειρισθεὶς οὐκέτι τοὺς ἐκ τοῦ Ἀσαμωναίου γένους καθίστησιν ἀρχιερεῖς, ἀλλά τισιν ἀσήμοις καὶ
μόνον ἐξ ἱερέων οὖσιν πλὴν ἑνὸς Ἀριστοβούλου τὴν
248 τιμὴν ἀπένεμεν. τὸν δ' Ἀριστόβουλον Ὑρκανοῦ
τοῦ ὑπὸ Πάρθων ληφθέντος υἱωνὸν ὄντα καταστή-
σας ἀρχιερέα τῇ ἀδελφῇ αὐτοῦ συνῴκησεν Μαρι-
άμμῃ, τὴν τοῦ πλήθους πρὸς ἑαυτὸν θηρώμενος
εὔνοιαν διὰ τὴν Ὑρκανοῦ μνήμην. εἶτα φοβηθείς,
μὴ πρὸς τὸν Ἀριστόβουλον πάντες ἀποκλίνωσιν,
ἀνεῖλεν αὐτὸν ἐν Ἱεριχοῖ πνιγῆναι μηχανησάμενος
249 κολυμβῶντα, καθὼς ἤδη δεδηλώκαμεν. μετὰ τοῦτον οὐκέτι τοῖς ἐγγόνοις τῶν Ἀσαμωναίου παίδων
τὴν ἀρχιερωσύνην ἐπίστευσεν. ἔπραξεν δὲ ὅμοια
τῷ Ἡρώδῃ περὶ τῆς καταστάσεως τῶν ἱερέων Ἀρ-
χέλαός τε ὁ παῖς αὐτοῦ καὶ μετὰ τοῦτον τὴν ἀρχὴν
250 Ῥωμαῖοι τῶν Ἰουδαίων παραλαβόντες. εἰσὶν οὖν
οἱ ἀπὸ τῶν Ἡρώδου χρόνων ἀρχιερατεύσαντες
μέχρι τῆς ἡμέρας, ἧς τὸν ναὸν καὶ τὴν πόλιν Τίτος
ἑλὼν ἐπυρπόλησεν, οἱ πάντες εἴκοσι καὶ ὀκτώ,
251 χρόνος δὲ τούτων ἔτη πρὸς τοῖς ἑκατὸν ἑπτά. καὶ
τινὲς μὲν αὐτῶν ἐπολιτεύσαντο ἐπί τε Ἡρώδου
βασιλεύοντος καὶ ἐπὶ Ἀρχελάου τοῦ παιδὸς αὐτοῦ,

ᵃ Cf. *Ant.* xv. 22, where Herod appoints an obscure priest
from Babylon named Ananelus as high priest.
ᵇ Son of Alexander and Alexandra. Cf. *Ant.* xv. 39-41.
ᶜ *Ant.* xv. 51-56 ; cf. *B.J.* i. 437.
ᵈ For a convenient listing and a critical evaluation of the
worth of Josephus' list see G. Hölscher, *Die Hohenpriesterliste bei Josephus und die evangelische Chronologie*, 1940,
esp. pp. 9-19. The total number of high priests, according
to Josephus (§ 227), from Aaron to the destruction of the
second temple is eighty-three (or eighty-four if we include

(5) Herod, when the kingdom was committed to him by the Romans, abandoned the practice of appointing those of Asamonaean lineage as high priests, and, with the exception of Aristobulus alone, assigned the office to some insignificant persons who were merely of priestly descent.[a] Herod appointed as high priest Aristobulus,[b] the grandson of that Hyrcanus who was taken captive by the Parthians ; and Herod married Aristobulus' sister Mariamme, hoping to capture the goodwill of the people for himself, thanks to their recollection of Hyrcanus. Afterwards, fearing that everyone would incline to Aristobulus, he put him to death at Jericho by contriving to have him strangled while swimming, as I have reported.[c] After Aristobulus' death Herod ceased to entrust the high priesthood to the descendants of the sons of Asamonaios. Herod's son Archelaus also followed a similar policy in the appointment of high priests, as did the Romans after him when they took over the government of the Jews. Now those who held the high priesthood from the times of Herod up to the day on which Titus captured and set fire to the temple and the city numbered twenty-eight [d] in all, covering a period of one hundred and seven years.[e] Of these some held office during the reigns of Herod and

Alcimus). The Babylonian Talmud, *Yoma* 9 a, as noted above, says that there were more than 300 for the period of the second temple alone. The Palestinian Talmud, *Yoma* 1, gives a number in the 80's, but only for the high priests of the period of the second temple. H. Bloch, *Die Quellen des Flavius Josephus*, 1879, pp. 149-150, asserts his belief that Josephus had at his disposal official lists of the high priests and refers to *Ap.* i. 30 ff.

[e] 37 B.C.–A.D. 70. The Talmud, *'Abodah Zarah* 8 b, gives the number of years as 103, presumably reckoning from 37 B.C. to the beginning of the revolt in A.D. 66.

μετὰ δὲ τὴν τούτων τελευτὴν ἀριστοκρατία μὲν ἦν
ἡ πολιτεία, τὴν δὲ προστασίαν τοῦ ἔθνους οἱ ἀρχιερεῖς ἐπεπίστευντο. περὶ μὲν οὖν τῶν ἀρχιερέων
ἱκανὰ ταῦτα.

252   (xi. 1) Γέσσιος δὲ Φλῶρος ὁ πεμφθεὶς Ἀλβίνου
διάδοχος ὑπὸ Νέρωνος πολλῶν ἐνέπλησε κακῶν
Ἰουδαίους. Κλαζομένιος μὲν ἦν τὸ γένος οὗτος,
ἐπήγετο δὲ γυναῖκα Κλεοπάτραν, δι᾽ ἣν φίλην οὖ-
σαν Ποππαίας[1] τῆς Νέρωνος γυναικὸς καὶ πονη-
ρίᾳ μηδὲν αὐτοῦ διαφέρουσαν τῆς ἀρχῆς ἐπέτυχεν.
253 οὕτω δὲ περὶ τὴν ἐξουσίαν ἐγένετο κακὸς καὶ
βίαιος, ὥστε διὰ τὴν ὑπερβολὴν τῶν κακῶν Ἀλβῖ-
254 νον ἐπήνουν ὡς εὐεργέτην Ἰουδαῖοι· ἐκεῖνος μὲν
γὰρ ἐπεκρύπτετο τὴν πονηρίαν καὶ τοῦ μὴ παντάπασιν κατάφωρος εἶναι προύνόει, Γέσσιος δὲ
Φλῶρος καθάπερ εἰς ἐπίδειξιν πονηρίας πεμφθεὶς
τὰς εἰς τὸ ἔθνος ἡμῶν παρανομίας ἐπόμπευεν, μήτε
ἁρπαγῆς παραλιπὼν μηδένα τρόπον μήτε ἀδίκου
255 κολάσεως· ἦν γὰρ ἄτεγκτος μὲν πρὸς ἔλεον, παντὸς
δὲ κέρδους ἄπληστος, ᾧ γε μηδὲ τὰ πλεῖστα τῶν
ὀλίγων διέφερεν, ἀλλὰ καὶ λῃσταῖς ἐκοινώνησεν[2]·
ἀδεῶς γὰρ οἱ πολλοὶ τοῦτ᾽ ἔπραττον ἐχέγγυον παρ᾽
ἐκείνου τὴν σωτηρίαν ἐπὶ τοῖς μέρεσιν ἔχειν πεπι-
256 στευκότες.[3] καὶ τοῦτο μέτριον οὐκ ἦν. ἀλλ᾽ οἱ
δυστυχεῖς Ἰουδαῖοι μὴ δυνάμενοι τὰς ὑπὸ τῶν

---

[1] Niese : Πομπηίας codd. Lat. Exc. Peiresc. : Πομπαίας E ;
cf. § 195.

[2] παντὸς . . . ἐκοινώνησεν] et omnibus lucris avarus qui
etiam in latronum direptione communicabat Lat.

Archelaus his son. After the death of these kings,
the constitution became an aristocracy, and the high
priests were entrusted with the leadership of the
nation. This will suffice about the high priests.

(xi. 1) [a] Gessius Florus,[b] who had been sent by
Nero as successor to Albinus, filled the cup of the Jews
with many misfortunes. He was a native of Clazomenae [c] and brought with him a wife Cleopatra, who
was not a whit behind him in wickedness. It was
through her influence that he obtained the post, she
being a friend of Poppaea,[d] Nero's consort. So wicked
and lawless was Florus in the exercise of his authority
that the Jews, owing to the extremity of their misery,
praised Albinus as a benefactor. For the latter used
to conceal his villainy and took precautions not to be
altogether detected ; but Gessius Florus, as if he
had been sent to give an exhibition of wickedness,
ostentatiously paraded his lawless treatment of our
nation and omitted no form of pillage or unjust
punishment. Pity could not soften him, nor any
amount of gain sate him ; he was one who saw no
difference between the greatest gains and the smallest,
so that he even joined in partnership with brigands.
In fact, the majority of people practised this occupation with no inhibitions, since they had no doubt that
their lives would be insured by him in return for his
quota of the spoils. There was no limit in sight.[e]
The ill-fated Jews, unable to endure the devastation

Gessius
Florus'
outrageous
administra-
tion as pro-
curator.

---

[a] For §§ 252-256 *cf.* the parallel passage, *B.J.* ii. 277-279.
[b] Procurator A.D. 64. See § 215.
[c] On the central coast of Asia Minor.
[d] *Cf.* § 195.   [e] Or "And this was intolerable."

[3] ἐχέγγυον . . . πεπιστευκότες] cum illius promissione de
sua salute minime cogitarent Lat.

λῃστῶν γινομένας πορθήσεις ὑπομένειν ἠναγκάζοντο
τῶν ἰδίων ἠθῶν[1] ἐξανιστάμενοι φεύγειν ἅπαντες,
ὡς κρεῖττον ὁπουδήποτε παρὰ τοῖς ἀλλοφύλοις
257 κατοικήσοντες. καὶ τί δεῖ πλείω λέγειν;[2] τὸν γὰρ
πρὸς Ῥωμαίους πόλεμον ὁ καταναγκάσας ἡμᾶς
ἄρασθαι Φλῶρος ἦν κρεῖττον ἡγουμένους ἀθρόως ἢ
κατ' ὀλίγον ἀπολέσθαι. καὶ δὴ τὴν ἀρχὴν ἔλαβεν
ὁ πόλεμος δευτέρῳ μὲν ἔτει τῆς ἐπιτροπῆς Φλώρου,
258 δωδεκάτῳ δὲ τῆς Νέρωνος ἀρχῆς. ἀλλ' ὅσα μὲν
δρᾶν ἠναγκάσθημεν ἢ παθεῖν ὑπεμείναμεν, ἀκριβῶς
γνῶναι πάρεστιν τοῖς βουλομένοις ἐντυχεῖν ταῖς ὑπ'
ἐμοῦ περὶ τοῦ Ἰουδαϊκοῦ πολέμου βίβλοις γεγραμ-
μέναις.

259 (xii. 1) Παύσεται δ' ἐνταῦθά μοι τὰ τῆς ἀρχαιο-
λογίας μεθ' ἣν καὶ τὸν πόλεμον ἠρξάμην γράφειν.
περιέχει δ' αὕτη τὴν ἀπὸ πρώτης γενέσεως ἀνθρώπου παράδοσιν μέχρι ἔτους δωδεκάτου τῆς Νέρωνος
ἡγεμονίας τῶν ἡμῖν συμβεβηκότων τοῖς Ἰουδαίοις
κατά τε τὴν Αἴγυπτον καὶ Συρίαν καὶ Παλαιστίνην,
260 ὅσα τε πεπόνθαμεν ὑπὸ Ἀσσυρίων τε καὶ Βαβυ-
λωνίων, τίνα τε Πέρσαι καὶ Μακεδόνες δεινὰ[3] δια-
τεθείκασιν ἡμᾶς, καὶ μετ' ἐκείνους Ῥωμαῖοι· πάντα

---

[1] MW : ἐθῶν A : sollemnitatibus Lat.
[2] καὶ τί δεῖ πλείω λέγειν] om. Lat.
[3] AE : om. MW.

---

[a] So also Tacitus, *Hist.* v. 10 : " Yet the endurance of the
Jews lasted till Gessius Florus was procurator."
[b] A.D. 66. The same dating is found in *B.J.* ii. 284.
[c] R. Laqueur, *Der jüdische Historiker Flavius Josephus*,
1920, p. 5, presents the theory that there were two different
editions of the *Antiquities*, the first omitting both §§ 259-266
and the *Vita*, and the second omitting § 258 and §§ 267-268.

by brigands that went on were one and all forced to
abandon their own country and flee, for they thought
that it would be better to settle among gentiles, no
matter where. What more need be said ? It was
Florus who constrained us to take up war with the
Romans,[a] for we preferred to perish together rather
than by degrees. The war in fact began in the second
year of the procuratorship of Florus and in the twelfth
of Nero's reign.[b] But all the things that we were
forced to do or sufferings that we endured may be
learnt with accuracy by any who choose to read the
books that I have written on the Jewish war.

(xii. 1) Here will be the end of my *Antiquities*,[c]
following which begins my account of the war.[d] The
present work contains the recorded history,[e] from
man's original creation up to the twelfth year of the
reign of Nero, of the events that befell us Jews in
Egypt, in Syria, and in Palestine.[f] It also comprises
all that we suffered at the hands of Assyrians and
Babylonians, and the harsh treatment that we received from the Persians and Macedonians and after

Conclusion of the Antiquities. Josephus speaks of himself and of his future writings.

The second edition, he suggests, was due to the publication
of a rival account of the Jewish war by Justus of Tiberias,
who had attacked Josephus for the rôle which he had played
in that revolt. Hence Josephus decided to append an apologia, namely his *Vita*, to the *Antiquities*, while introducing
§§ 259-266 to provide the transition.

[d] Lit. " after which I began to write an account of the
war." But since the *Bellum Judaicum* was written before
the *Antiquities*, what Josephus means is that the *Antiquities*
ends at the point at which the *Bellum Judaicum* begins.

[e] Lit. " the tradition."

[f] *Cf.* G. Hölscher, " Josephus," Pauly-Wissowa, ix, 1916,
pp. 1956-1957, who says that the term " Palestine " is not
found before A.D. 70 except here in Josephus. Elsewhere
Josephus uses the older expression, the land of the Philistines
(*cf.* also *B.J.* v. 384).

γὰρ οἶμαι μετ' ἀκριβείάς ἀπάσης[1] συντεταχέναι.
261 τηρῆσαι δὲ πεπείραμαι καὶ τὴν τῶν ἀρχιερέων ἀνα-
γραφὴν τῶν ἐν δισχιλίοις ἔτεσι γενομένων. ἀπλανῆ
δὲ πεποίημαι καὶ τὴν περὶ τοὺς βασιλεῖς διαδοχήν
τε καὶ ἀγωγὴν[2] τὰς πράξεις αὐτῶν καὶ τὰς[3] πολιτείας
ἀπαγγέλλων μοναρχῶν τε δυναστείας, ὡς αἱ ἱεραὶ
βίβλοι περὶ πάντων ἔχουσι τὴν ἀναγραφήν· τοῦτο
γὰρ ποιήσειν ἐν ἀρχῇ τῆς ἱστορίας ἐπηγγειλάμην.
262 λέγω δὴ θαρσήσας ἤδη διὰ τὴν τῶν προτεθέντων
συντέλειαν,[4] ὅτι μηδεὶς ἂν ἕτερος ἠδυνήθη θελήσας
μήτε Ἰουδαῖος μήτε ἀλλόφυλος τὴν πραγματείαν
263 ταύτην οὕτως ἀκριβῶς εἰς Ἕλληνας ἐξενεγκεῖν· ἔχω
γὰρ ὁμολογούμενον παρὰ τῶν ὁμοεθνῶν πλεῖστον
αὐτῶν κατὰ τὴν ἐπιχώριον καὶ παρ' ἡμῖν[5] παιδείαν
διαφέρειν καὶ τῶν Ἑλληνικῶν δὲ γραμμάτων καὶ
ποιητικῶν μαθημάτων πολλὰ[6] ἐσπούδασα μετα-
σχεῖν τὴν γραμματικὴν ἐμπειρίαν ἀναλαβών, τὴν
δὲ περὶ τὴν προφορὰν ἀκρίβειαν πάτριος ἐκώλυσεν
264 συνήθεια. παρ' ἡμῖν γὰρ οὐκ ἐκείνους ἀποδέχονται
τοὺς πολλῶν ἐθνῶν διάλεκτον ἐκμαθόντας καὶ γλα-

---

[1] A : om. MWE.
[2] τε καὶ ἀγωγὴν] A : om. MWE.
[3] τε καὶ ἀγωγὴν τὰς πράξεις αὐτῶν καὶ τὰς] i. ras. m. 2 A.
[4] συντέλειαν] ὑποθέσεων ἀνακεφαλέωσιν καὶ i. ras. m. 2 A :
ἀνακεφαλαίωσιν καὶ συντέλειαν E.
[5] καὶ παρ' ἡμῖν A : om. MWE.
[6] καὶ ποιητικῶν μαθημάτων πολλὰ] A : καὶ ποιητικῶν μαθημάτων E : om. MW.

---

[a] Ant. i. 5 ff.
[b] Epitome : " the summary and consummation."
[c] Cf. Vita 9, where Josephus asserts that when he was
only fourteen, the high priests and the leaders of Jerusalem

them the Romans. For I think that I have drawn up
the whole story in full and accurate detail. I have
also endeavoured to preserve the record of the line of
the high priests who have served during a space of
two thousand years. I have further noted without
error the succession and conduct of the kings, report-
ing their achievements and policies, as well as the
period of rule by the Judges—all as recorded by the
Holy Scriptures. For this was what I promised to
do at the beginning of my history.[a] And now I take
heart from the consummation [b] of my proposed work
to assert that no one else, either Jew or gentile, would
have been equal to the task, however willing to under-
take it, of issuing so accurate a treatise as this for
the Greek world. For my compatriots admit that in
our Jewish learning I far excel them.[c] I have also
laboured strenuously to partake of the realm of Greek
prose [d] and poetry, after having gained a knowledge
of Greek grammar,[e] although the habitual use of my
native tongue has prevented [f] my attaining precision
in the pronunciation.[g] For our people do not favour
those persons who have mastered the speech of many

constantly used to consult him on particular points of Jewish
law.
   [d] Or " learning."
   [e] Or perhaps " after acquiring practice in writing." G. C.
Richards, " The Composition of Josephus' Antiquities,"
Class. Quart. xxxiii, 1939, p. 36, says that the meaning is " I
learned by rote the scholarship of the language."
   [f] Or " the usages of our nation have prevented."
   [g] Josephus, *Ap.* i. 50, says that in writing the *Bellum
Judaicum* he employed " some assistants for the sake of the
Greek." On Josephus' knowledge of Greek and on his use
of assistants see H. St. J. Thackeray, *Josephus the Man and
the Historian*, 1929, pp. 100-124. That there were many
Jews, including rabbis, who knew the Greek language and
literature well has been amply illustrated by S. Lieberman,

φυρότητι λέξεων τὸν λόγον ἐπικομψεύοντας¹ διὰ τὸ
κοινὸν εἶναι νομίζειν τὸ ἐπιτήδευμα τοῦτο μόνον
οὐκ ἐλευθέροις² τοῖς τυχοῦσιν ἀλλὰ καὶ τῶν οἰκετῶν
τοῖς θέλουσι, μόνοις δὲ σοφίαν μαρτυροῦσιν τοῖς
τὰ νόμιμα σαφῶς ἐπισταμένοις καὶ τὴν τῶν ἱερῶν
265 γραμμάτων δύναμιν ἑρμηνεῦσαι δυναμένοις. διὰ
τοῦτο πολλῶν πονησάντων περὶ τὴν ἄσκησιν ταύτην μόλις δύο τινὲς ἢ τρεῖς κατώρθωσαν καὶ τῶν
266 πόνων τὴν ἐπικαρπίαν εὐθὺς ἔλαβον. ἴσως δ' οὐκ
ἂν ἐπίφθονον γένοιτο οὐδὲ σκαιὸν τοῖς πολλοῖς
φανήσεται³ καὶ περὶ γένους τοὐμοῦ καὶ περὶ τῶν
κατὰ τὸν βίον πράξεων βραχέα διεξελθεῖν ἕως ἔχω
ζῶντας ἢ τοὺς ἐλέγχοντας ἢ τοὺς μαρτυρήσοντας.
267 Ἐπὶ τούτοις δὲ καταπαύσω τὴν ἀρχαιολογίαν
βιβλίοις μὲν εἴκοσι περιειλημμένην, ἓξ δὲ μυριάσι

---

¹ καὶ γλαφυρότητι λέξεων τὸν λόγον ἐπικομψεύοντας] A : om.
MWE.

² τοῦτο μόνον οὐκ ἐλευθέροις] οὐκ ἐλευθέρων τοῦτο μόνον E :
τοῦτο οὐκ ἐλευθέροις μόνον Hudson.

³ οὐδὲ σκαιὸν τοῖς πολλοῖς φανήσεται] A : om. MWE.

Greek in Jewish Palestine, 1942, esp. pp. 1-67. Especially
impressive is the statement of Rabbi Simeon the son of Rab-
ban Gamaliel (*Soṭah* 49 b, cited by Lieberman, p. 20) that
his father, at the beginning of the second century, had a
thousand students, five hundred of whom studied Torah,
while five hundred studied Greek wisdom. The large number
of Greek loan-words, perhaps as many as 1500, in the Talmudic literature and the prevalence of Greek inscriptions on
Jewish tombstones in Palestine are other indications that
Greek was well known. See M. Hadas, *Hellenistic Culture*,
1959, pp. 35-39 and 48-49.

ᵃ But *cf.* Mishnah, *Sheḳalim* v. 1, where Mordecai is said,
in an obvious tone of approbation, to have known seventy
languages.

nations,^a or who adorn their style with smoothness of
diction, because they consider that not only is such
skill common to ordinary freemen but that even slaves
who so choose may acquire it.   But they give credit
for wisdom to those alone who have an exact knowledge of the law and who are capable of interpreting
the meaning of the Holy Scriptures.   Consequently,
though many have laboriously undertaken this training, scarcely two or three have succeeded, and have
forthwith reaped the fruit of their labours.   Perhaps it will not seem to the public invidious or awk-
ward for me to recount briefly my lineage and the
events of my life ^b while there are still persons living
who can either disprove or corroborate my state-
ments.

With this I shall conclude my *Antiquities*, contained
in twenty books ^c with sixty thousand lines.^d   God

^b The reference is to Josephus' *Vita*, which seems to be
attached to the *Antiquities*, though Schürer, i. 87, asserts that
the two works are not connected.

^c The division into twenty books was most probably
prompted, as Thackeray, *Josephus*, p. 56, suggests, by the
similar division into twenty books of a work by Dionysius of
Halicarnassus which bore a like title, ʽΡωμαϊκὴ Ἀρχαιολογία
(*Roman Antiquities*).

^d Since the *Antiquities* consists, in Niese's division, of
7375 subsections, this would make an average subsection
consist of a little over eight lines.   There were, therefore,
somewhat fewer letters per line in Josephus' original edition
than is the case in the present edition.   Among other purposes
served by such a count of lines was to indicate how much was
to be paid the one who copied the manuscript, the scribe being
paid by the hundred lines (see Thackeray, *Josephus*, p. 73,
who cites R. Harris, *Stichometry*, p. 26).   Usually, however,
this count was not included in the text but was appended
separately at the end of the manuscript.   See Weinberger,
"Stichometrie," Pauly-Wissowa, 2. Reihe, iii, 1929, pp.
2487-2489.

στίχων, κἂν τὸ θεῖον ἐπιτρέπῃ κατὰ περιδρομὴν
ὑπομνήσω πάλιν τοῦ τε πολέμου καὶ τῶν συμβεβηκότων ἡμῖν μέχρι τῆς νῦν ἐνεστώσης ἡμέρας, ἥτις
ἐστὶν τρισκαιδεκάτου μὲν ἔτους τῆς Δομετιανοῦ
Καίσαρος ἀρχῆς, ἐμοὶ δ' ἀπὸ γενέσεως πεντηκοστοῦ
268 τε καὶ ἕκτου. προῄρημαι δὲ συγγράψαι κατὰ τὰς

---

^a Or " I shall once more."

^b Petersen, *op. cit.* p. 260, says (he had been anticipated
on this point by H. Clementz in his German translation of
the *Antiquities*) that the reference here is to Josephus' autobiography, and that " our " is really, as so commonly in
Josephus, used in place of " my." He cites as an indication
of this the fact that Josephus gives not only the year of
Domitian's reign, but also his own age, the latter being
appropriate in an autobiography but not in a history. But
in § 266, where the reference is clearly to Josephus' autobiography, the first person singular is used ; and at the end
of § 267, in speaking of his own age, Josephus likewise uses
the first person singular. When, therefore, he uses the first
person plural here, he probably refers not to his own autobiography but to the history of the Jewish people, just as the
running account of the war, with which it is coupled, refers
to the events that befell the Jewish people in the war. The
statement of his own age seems to be, like the statement of the
year of Domitian's reign, merely a way of dating the completion of the *Antiquities* ; since Josephus has just spoken
of his personal qualifications for writing history it is not inappropriate to continue in this vein by citing his age at the
time of the completion of the work. Petersen finds it difficult
to believe that Josephus would have intended to write another
account of the Jewish war, since he had already described it
in a lost work in Aramaic and in the extant work in Greek,
the latter of which he recommends to his readers in § 258.
But Josephus is here proposing a running account of the war,
which will presumably be considerably briefer than the extant work : such a work would surely find a much wider
audience than the existing, rather detailed work, even as the
epitomes of such bulky works as Livy's history achieved
considerable popularity in Rome during Josephus' time (*cf.*

willing, I shall at some future time [a] compose a running account of the war and of the later events of our history up to the present day,[b] which belongs to the thirteenth year of the reign of Domitian Caesar and to the fifty-sixth of my life.[c] It is also my intention to compose a work in four books [d] on the opinions

Martial xiv. 190). The autobiography, however, is too personal, too brief, and too spotty to be called a running account of the war.

[c] A.D. 93/94.

[d] Cf. *Ant.* i. 25. Petersen, *op. cit.* pp. 263-265, proposes the identification of this work with the so-called *Contra Apionem*. That the *Contra Apionem* is in and was intended to comprise two books is not an insurmountable obstacle, he states ; Josephus' prophecy here simply did not turn out to be correct. But the real objection to Petersen's identification is that, while the *Contra Apionem* does contain a discussion of the nature of God (ii. 180, 188-192, 197) and of the Jewish code of laws (ii. 145-187, etc.), this discussion is brief and is surely not the central theme of that work, whereas we are told here that the work is to be about these subjects. H. R. Moehring, in his doctoral dissertation *Novelistic Elements in the Writings of Flavius Josephus*, 1957, pp. 11-12, presents the following conspectus of the contents of this work, basing his reconstruction on the many references to it in Josephus and assuming, as is probably the case, that the references are to the same work : the bulk of the Law (*Ant.* iii. 94) ; the law concerning " mutual relations " distinguished from laws concerning the political constitution (iv. 198, 302) ; ritual of the sacrifices (iii. 205) ; details in the laws of Moses, in particular the reasons why some things are forbidden and others allowed (xx. 268) ; clean and unclean food (iii. 259) ; reason for circumcision of Jews (i. 192) ; table of shewbread (iii. 143, 257) ; two daily sacrifices of the priests (iii. 257) ; sin offerings (iii. 230) ; cessation of shining of breastplate (iii. 218) ; comparison of Essenes with Pythagoreans (xv. 371) ; Israelites in Egypt (*Ap.* i. 92) (Moehring has omitted Josephus' statement here that he intends to discuss God and His essence, probably at the beginning of his work.) From this, Moehring, p. 12, plausibly suggests that Josephus had at least drawn up an outline of this work.

ἡμετέρας δόξας τῶν Ἰουδαίων ἐν τέσσαρσι βίβλοις περὶ θεοῦ καὶ τῆς οὐσίας αὐτοῦ καὶ περὶ τῶν νόμων, διὰ τί κατ᾽ αὐτοὺς τὰ μὲν ἔξεστιν ἡμῖν ποιεῖν, τὰ δὲ κεκώλυται.

that we Jews hold concerning God and His essence, as well as concerning the laws, that is, why according to them we are permitted to do some things while we are forbidden to do others.

APPENDIX A

AN ANCIENT TABLE OF CONTENTS

BIBΛION K

α'.[1] Ὡς Κλαύδιος Καῖσαρ μετὰ τὴν Ἀγρίππου τελευτὴν Φᾶδον ἔπεμψεν εἰς Ἰουδαίαν ἐπίτροπον.

β'. Στάσις[2] Φιλαδελφηνῶν πρὸς τοὺς ἐν τῇ Περαίᾳ κατοικοῦντας Ἰουδαίους περὶ ὅρων κώμης μιᾶς, καὶ ὡς ὑπὸ τούτων πολλῶν ἀναιρεθέντων Φιλαδελφηνῶν[3] Φᾶδος ἀγανακτήσας τῶν Περαϊτῶν[4] Ἰουδαίων τοὺς πρώτους τρεῖς ἄνδρας λαβὼν ἀπέκτεινεν.

γ'. Ὡς Θολομαῖος[5] ὁ ἀρχιληστὴς τοὺς Ἄραβας ληστεύων ληφθεὶς καὶ ἐπὶ Φᾶδον ἀχθεὶς ἀνηρέθη.[6]

δ'. Ὡς Φᾶδος καὶ Κάσσιος Λογγῖνος ὁ τῆς Συρίας ἡγεμὼν ἀναβάντες εἰς Ἱεροσόλυμα τοῖς πρώτοις τῶν Ἰουδαίων ἐκέλευσαν τὸν ποδήρη καὶ τὴν ἱερὰν στολὴν ἐν τῇ Ἀντωνίᾳ καταθέσθαι ὑπὸ τῇ Ῥωμαίων ἐξουσίᾳ, καθὰ καὶ πρότερον ἦν.

ε'. Παράκλησις[7] ἐπὶ τούτῳ τῶν Ἰουδαίων πρὸς Φᾶδον καὶ Λογγῖνον ἀξιούντων αὐτοὺς ἐπιτρέψαι

---

[1] numeros hab. (α'-κε' W, I-XX Lat.) W Lat.
[2] στάσις] et seditio Lat. cap. I continuans.
[3] A : Φιλαδελφέων MW : Filadelphinorum Lat.
[4] A : Περαιατῶν MW.
[5] coni. (cf. supra, p. 392) : Θολεμαῖος codd. : Tholomeus Lat.
[6] ὡς Θολομαῖος . . . ἀνηρέθη] A : om. MW.
[7] A : παρακλήσεις MW.

APPENDIX A

AN ANCIENT TABLE OF CONTENTS

BOOK XX

---

[a] MSS. Tholemaeus. But *cf.* § 5, where the spelling is Tholomaeus.

πέμψαι πρεσβείαν πρὸς Καίσαρα Κλαύδιον περὶ
τούτου.

ϛʹ. Ὡς Φᾶδος λαβὼν ὁμήρους ἐπέτρεψεν.[1]

ζʹ. Ὡς Κλαύδιος Καῖσαρ παρακληθεὶς ὑπ' Ἀ-
γρίππα τοῦ νεωτέρου συνεχώρησεν τοῖς Ἰουδαίοις
τὰ αἰτήματα καὶ πρὸς Φᾶδον ἔγραψε περὶ τούτων.

ηʹ. Ὃν τρόπον Ἑλένη ἡ τῶν Ἀδιαβηνῶν βασιλὶς
καὶ οἱ παῖδες αὐτῆς Μονόβαζος καὶ Ἰζάτης[2] καὶ τὸ
πᾶν γένος αὐτῶν ἐζήλωσαν τὰ Ἰουδαίων ἔθη.

θʹ. Ὡς Ἡρώδου τελευτήσαντος τοῦ τῆς Χαλκίδος βασιλέως Ἀγρίππας ὁ νεώτερος τὴν ἀρχὴν
ἔλαβεν δόντος αὐτῷ Κλαυδίου Καίσαρος.[3]

ιʹ. Ὡς Τιβέριος Ἀλέξανδρος ἐπίτροπος εἰς Ἰουδαίαν ἐλθὼν τοὺς υἱοὺς Ἰούδα τοῦ Γαλιλαίου τὸν
ὄχλον ἀπατῶντας ἐκόλασεν.

ιαʹ. Περὶ τοῦ λιμοῦ τοῦ γενομένου κατὰ τὴν χώραν.[4]

ιβʹ. Κουμάνου ἄφιξις εἰς τὴν Ἰουδαίαν ἐπιτρόπου
πεμφθέντος ὑπὸ Καίσαρος.

---

[1] παράκλησις . . . ἐπέτρεψεν] et quia rogantes Iudaei Fa-
dum et Longinum eis concedentibus datis obsidibus lega-
tionem ad Caesarem Claudium destinarunt Lat.

[2] Iazatis cod. Ambr. Lat.

[3] ὡς Ἡρώδου . . . Καίσαρος] infra post cap. XII exhibent
MW (ιαʹ in W), post cap. X Lat. (VIII in Lat.), ut capitum
ordo in MW hic sit : VIII, X, XI, XII, IX, XIII ; in Lat.
vero hic : VIII, XI, X, IX, (XII + XIII).

[4] περὶ . . . χώραν] post cap. VIII exhibet numero VI
ascripto Lat.

---

[a] The table omits special mention of how Artabanus was

ANCIENT TABLE OF CONTENTS

restored to the Parthian throne through Izates' intervention (§§ 54-68), how Artabanus' son Vardanes was frustrated in his attempt to wage war against Izates (§§ 69-74), and how Izates, despite being betrayed by his own nobles, was delivered from the Arabs and later from the Parthians (§§ 75-91). It also omits mention of the impostor Theudas (§§ 97-99).

b This section, as well as sections xi and xii, belongs before section ix.

ιγ΄. Ὡς ἐπὶ τούτου πολλοὶ τῶν Ἰουδαίων[1] κατὰ
τὸ ἱερὸν ἀπώλοντο.[2]

ιδ΄. Στάσις Ἰουδαίων πρὸς Σαμαρεῖς καὶ ὡς
πολλοὶ διεφθάρησαν τῶν Σαμαρειτῶν.

ιε΄. Ὡς Μόδιος[3] Κουαδρᾶτος ὁ τῆς Συρίας ἡγεμὼν ἀκούσας ταῦτα καὶ ἀναβὰς εἰς Ἰουδαίαν τοὺς
πρώτους τῶν Ἰουδαίων καὶ Σαμαρειτῶν ἐκέλευσεν
εἰς Ῥώμην ἀναβῆναι, ὁμοίως[4] καὶ Κούμανον τὸν
ἐπίτροπον καὶ Κέλερα τὸν χιλίαρχον λόγον ὑφέξοντας Κλαυδίῳ Καίσαρι περὶ τῶν πεπραγμένων,
τινὰς δὲ καὶ Ἰουδαίων αὐτὸς ἐκόλασεν.

ιϛ΄. Ὡς Κλαύδιος ἀκούσας αὐτῶν τοὺς μὲν Ἰουδαίους τῆς αἰτίας ἀπέλυσεν παρακληθεὶς ὑπὸ βασιλέως Ἀγρίππα, Κούμανον δὲ ἐξώρισε, Κέλερα δὲ
τὸν χιλίαρχον καὶ τοὺς πρώτους τῶν Σαμαρειτῶν
ἐκόλασεν.

ιζ΄. Ὡς Φῆλιξ ἐπίτροπος πεμφθεὶς καὶ καταλαβὼν τὴν χώραν κεκακωμένην ὑπὸ τῶν λῃστῶν
προὐνοήσατο διαφθείρας αὐτοὺς εἰρήνην ἐν τῇ χώρᾳ
καταστῆσαι, τὸν δὲ πρῶτον τῶν λῃστῶν Ἐλεάζαρον ὄνομα δήσας εἰς Ῥώμην[5] ἀνέπεμψεν.

ιη΄. Ὡς ἐπιδημήσαντος Αἰγυπτίου τινὸς γόητος

---

[1] τῶν Ἰουδαίων] sacerdotum Lat.

[2] ὡς ἐπὶ τούτου . . . ἀπώλοντο] in Lat. antecedentibus con-
tinuo adiuncta sunt (cap. VIII).

[3] codd. Lat. : Νουμίδιος i. marg. A, idem ed. pr. et Latinae
editiones ex § 125 : Οὐμμίδιος Norisius.

[4] ὁμοίως] novum cap. incip. A.

[5] εἰς Ῥώμην] ad Caesarem Lat.

---

[a] The Latin version has " many of the priests," but in § 111
it is the Jewish masses who are said to have perished.

[b] So according to § 125 (Hudson's emendation, based on
B.J. ii. 239); mss. : Modius.

ANCIENT TABLE OF CONTENTS

^c The table omits special mention of the marriages contracted by Agrippa's sisters (§§ 139-147).

καὶ πολλῶν Ἰουδαίων ὑπ' αὐτοῦ πλανηθέντων
Φῆλιξ ἐπεξελθὼν αὐτοῖς πολλοὺς ἀπέκτεινεν.

ιθ'. Ὡς στασιάζοντας Ἰουδαίων τοὺς πρώτους
ἐν Καισαρείᾳ πρὸς τοὺς Σύρους Φῆλιξ ὁ ἐπίτροπος
ἔπαυσεν.

κ'. Ὃν τρόπον Κλαυδίου τελευτήσαντος Νέρων
τὴν ἀρχὴν διεδέξατο.[1]

κα'. Ὡς Πορκίου Φήστου πεμφθέντος εἰς Ἰουδαίαν ἐπιτρόπου συνέβη κακωθῆναι τὴν χώραν ὑπὸ
τῶν σικαρίων.

κβ'. Περὶ τῆς στοᾶς τοῦ ἔσωθεν ἱεροῦ καὶ ὃν
τρόπον ὕψωσαν αὐτὴν οἱ Ἰουδαῖοι.[2]

κγ'. Ὡς Φῆστος ἀγανακτήσας ἐπὶ τούτῳ τοὺς
πρώτους τῶν Ἰουδαίων εἰς Ῥώμην ἔπεμψεν πρὸς
Νέρωνα πείσοντας αὐτὸν περὶ τῶν πεπραγμένων.

κδ'. Ὡς τελευτήσαντος Φήστου ἐν τῇ Ἰουδαίᾳ
Ἀλβῖνος ἦλθεν διάδοχος.[3]

κε'. Ὡς ἐπὶ τούτου ἐπαύσαντο οἱ σικάριοι τὴν
χώραν κακοποιεῖν.

κϛ'. Ὡς Φλῶρος ἐλθὼν Ἀλβίνῳ διάδοχος τοσ-
αῦτα διέθηκε τοὺς Ἰουδαίους κακά, ὡς ἀναγκάσαι
αὐτοὺς ἐφ' ὅπλα χωρῆσαι.

---

[1] ὃν τρόπον . . . διεδέξατο] post cap. XVI tr. MW, post
cap. XVII tr. Lat., Niesio superadditum vid.
[2] περὶ τῆς στοᾶς . . . οἱ Ἰουδαῖοι] priori capiti (κ' in W)
adiungunt MW.
[3] ὡς Φῆστος . . . διάδοχος] Lat. priori capiti (XVIII) ad-
iungens.

---

[a] This section belongs before section xviii.
[b] The table omits special mention of how James, the
brother of Jesus, was sentenced to death (§§ 199-203).
[c] The table omits special mention of the attempt of the

ANCIENT TABLE OF CONTENTS

Levites to gain certain privileges reserved for the priests (§§ 216-218), the completion of the building of the temple (§§ 219-222), and Josephus' catalogue of the high priests (§§ 224-251).

κζ'. Περὶ Ἰωσήπου καὶ γένους αὐτοῦ καὶ πολιτείας.[1]

Περιέχει ἡ βίβλος χρόνον ἐτῶν κβ'.[2]

[1] περὶ Ἰωσήπου . . . πολιτείας] A : om. Lat. : περὶ γένους Ἰωσήπου καὶ πολιτείας MW.
[2] W : κϛ' AME Lat.

---

[a] This is to be found not in the *Antiquities* but in the autobiography, which forms a sequel to it.

[b] A.D. 44–66. This is the reading of one of the mss. ; the others have twenty-six years, *i.e.* from 44 to 70, the year of

ANCIENT TABLE OF CONTENTS

This book covers a period of twenty-two years.[b]

the destruction of the temple. But in § 257 Josephus says that he is closing his narrative with the start of the Jewish revolt against the Romans, which, he says, occurred in the second year of Florus' procuratorship and the twelfth of Nero's reign, *i.e.* A.D. 66. Similarly in § 259 Josephus says that the *Antiquities* covers the period from creation to the twelfth year of Nero's reign.

APPENDIX B

Selected Literature on the Conversion of King
Izates and the Adiabenians to Judaism
(*Ant.* xx. 17-96)

Bamberger, B. J., *Proselytism in the Talmudic Period*,
esp. pp. 45-52, 225-228. 1939.

Braude, W. G., *Jewish Proselytizing in the First Five
Centuries of the Common Era : The Age of the
Tannaim and Amoraim.* 1940.

**Brüll, N., " Adiabene," *Jahrb. f. Jüd. Gesch. u. Lit.*
1 (1874), 58-86.

Brüll, N., " Mischnahlehrer von heidnischer Abkunft,"
Jahrb. f. Jüd. Gesch. u. Lit. 2 (1876), 154 ff.

Derenbourg, J., *Essai*, 224-227.

Grätz, H., " Zeit der Anwesenheit der adiabenischen
Königin in Jerusalem und der Apostel Paulus,"
Monatsschr. f. d. Gesch. u. Wiss. d. Jud. 26 (1877),
241-255, 289-306 (esp. 303-306).

Kahle, P. E., *The Cairo Geniza*², pp. 270-272. 1960.

Marquart (Markwart), J., *Osteuropäische und ostasiatische Streitzüge : ethnologische und historisch-topo-
graphische Studien zur Geschichte des 9. und 10.
Jahrhunderts (ca. 840–940)*, pp. 288-292. 1903.

Rowley, H. H., " Jewish Proselyte Baptism and the
Baptism of John," *Heb. Union Coll. Ann.* 15
(1940), 313-334.

Schürer, E., *Geschichte* iii⁴, 1909, 169-172.

APPENDIX C

SELECTED LITERATURE ON THE HIGH PRIESTS DURING
THE FIRST CENTURY OF THE CHRISTIAN ERA
(*Ant.* xviii. 26 ff. and esp. xx. 224-251)

Allon, G., " On the History of the High-Priesthood
at the Close of the Second Temple," *Tarbiz* 13
(1941–2), 1-24 [in Hebrew].

Derenbourg, J., *Essai*, 194-197, 232-236.

*Grätz, H., " Die Wahl- oder absetzbaren Hohen-
priester in der herodianischen und nachherodia-
nischen Zeit," in *Geschichte* iii. 2⁵, 1906, note 19,
esp. pp. 723-754.

Grätz, H., " Zur Geschichte der nachexilischen
Hohenpriesten," *Monatssch. f. Gesch. u. Wiss. d.
Jud.* 30 (1881), 49-64, 97-112.

*Hölscher, G., " Die Hohenpriesterliste bei Josephus
und die evangelische Chronologie," *Sitzungsber.
d. Heidelberger Akad. d. Wiss.*, Phil.-hist. Klasse,
1940.

Schürer, E., " Die ἀρχιερεῖς im Neuen Testamente,"
Stud. u. Krit., pp. 593-657.   1872.

Schürer, E., *Geschichte* ii⁴, 1907, 267-277.

BIBLIOGRAPHICAL NOTE (1980)

UNDER the direction of K. H. Rengstorf a *Concordance to Josephus* in four volumes has been planned (Leiden, Brill), of which the following have appeared : Vol. I, A-Δ, 1973 ; Vol. II, E-K, 1975. A supplement, *Namenworterbuch zu Flavius Josephus*, by A. Schalit, preceded the above in 1968.

Note also H. Schreckenberg, *Bibliographie zu Flavius Josephus*, Leiden 1968.

GENERAL INDEX

This is primarily an index of names. References are to books and to the sections shown in the left margin of the Greek text and in the headline of the English text (Arabic figures). References are cited in the order in which Josephus composed his works: *B.* (=*Bellum Judaicum*), *A.* (=*Antiquities*), *V.* (=*Vita*), *Ap.* (=*Contra Apionem*). A number in parentheses indicates that the reference is not by name.

AARON, brother of Moses, *A.* ii. 279; his age at the Exodus, ii. 319; supports Moses in fight against Amalekites, iii. 54; iii. 64; appointed high priest, iii. 188-192; his four sons, iii. 192; iii. 205; two of his sons burnt to death, iii. 208-211; abused by Hebrews, iii. 307; iii. 310; his authority as high priest challenged by Korah, iv. 15, 18, 21, 23; iv. 26, 29, 33, 46, 54, 56-58; budding of his rod quells rebels, iv. 64-66; his death, iv. 83; v. 361; vi. 86, 89; viii. 228; ix. 224; x. 65; first high priest (in genealogy of high priests), xx. 225-227, 229, 235

Ab. See Abba

Abaiz (var. Baiz; Bibl. Boaz), name of one of the columns in the temple in Jerusalem, *A.* viii. 78

abanêth (Bibl. 'abnêt; see *hemian*), tunic of Jewish priests, *A.* iii. 156

Abarim. See Abaris

Abaris (Bibl. Abarim), mountain opposite Jericho where Moses disappeared, *A.* iv. 325

Abar(os) (Bibl. Heber), son of Asher, *A.* ii. 183

Abassaros. See Sanabasaros

Abba (var. Saba; Hebrew Ab; Athenian Hecatombaeon, Macedonian Lous), Hebrew month, *A.* iv. 84

Abbar, high priest and judge of Tyre, *Ap.* i. 157

Abdaeus, father of Chelbes (judge of Tyre), *Ap.* i. 157

Abdagases, military chief of staff of Parthian King Artabanus, *A.* xviii. 333-334

Abdastratus, King of Tyre, son of Balbazer, slain by conspiracy, *Ap.* i. 122

Abdeel (Bibl. Adbeel), son of Ishmael, *A.* i. 220

Abdelimus, father of Gerastratus (judge of Tyre), *Ap.* i. 157

Abdemon(os) (Abdemun), Tyrian youth wiser than Solomon, *A.* viii. 146, 149; (Abdemun) *Ap.* i. 115, 120

Abdemun. See Abdemon(os)

Abdenago (Bibl. Abed-nego), name given to Azariah by King Nebuchadnezzar, *A.* x. 189

Abdera, native city of Hecataeus, *A.* xii. 38; *Ap.* i. 183

Abdon, Hebrew judge, son of Hillel, *A.* v. 273

Abed-nego. See Abdenago

Abel, etymology, *A.* i. 52; slain by Cain, i. 53-55, 67

Abela. See Abila (1), (2) and (4)

Abel-beth-maachah. See Abellane

Abele. See Abila (1)

Abelios (Bibl. Abiel), father of Kish, *A.* vi. 130

Abellane (Abelochea; Bibl. Abel-beth-maachah), city in northern Palestine, (Abelochea) *A.* vii. 288; viii. 305

GENERAL INDEX

Abel-meholah. See Abila (2)

Abelochea. See Abellane

Abel-shittim. See Abila (1)

Abenar (Abener, Abenner ; Bibl. Abner), son of Ner, kinsman of Saul, *A.* vi. 58 ; commander of Saul's army, vi. 129 ; (Abener) vi. 235, 312, 314 ; (Abenner) proclaims Ish-bosheth king, is defeated by Joab, vii. 9-19 ; (Abenner) transfers allegiance to David, vii. 22-30 ; (Abenner) killed by Joab, vii. 31-36 ; (Abenner) mourned by David, vii. 39-44 ; (Abenner) vii. 46, 52, 285, 386

Abener. See Abenar

Abenner. See Abenar

Abennerigus, king of Charax Spasini, *A.* xx. 22-23

Abes(s)alomos. See Absalom (1)

Abi. See Abia

Abi. See Abia (Bibl. Abi), mother of King Hezekiah, *A.* ix. 260

Abias (1) (Bibl. Abijah), son of Rehoboam, *A.* vii. 190, 244 ; succeeds to kingship of Judah, viii. 249-250, 264 ; defeats Jeroboam, viii. 274-284 ; his death, viii. 285, 287, 393

Abias (2), king of Arabs, declares war on Izates and is defeated, *A.* xx. 77, 80

Abias (3). See Abira

Abiathar (Heb. Ebyathar), son of Abimelech the high priest, *A.* vi. 261, 269-270, 359 ; chosen high priest by David, vii. 110, 200, 201, 222, 260, 293 ; joins Adonijah's plot, vii. 346-347, 350, 359, 366 ; deposed from high priesthood by Solomon, viii. 9-11, 16

Abibalos (Abibalus), king of Tyre, father of Hiram, *A.* viii. 144, 147 ; *Ap.* i. 113, 117

Abibalus. See Abibalos

Abida (1) (Bibl. Azubah), wife of Asa, mother of Jehoshaphat, *A.* viii. 315

Abida (2). See Ebidas

Abiel. See Abelios

Abiezer (Jesus ; Bibl. Abishua), high priest, son of Phinehas, *A.* v. 362 ; (Jesus) viii. 12

Abigaia (1) (Bibl. Abigail), wife of Nabal, appeases David by presents, *A.* vi. 300-306 ; marries David, vi. 308, 320 ; vii. 21

Abigaia (2), wife of Ithra, mother of Amasa, *A.* vii. 232

Abigail. See Abigaia (1)

Abihu, son of Aaron, *A.* iii. 192 ; burnt to death, iii. 209

Abijah (1). See Abias (1)

Abijah (2). See Abira ; Obime

Abila (1) (Abile, Abela, Abele ; Bibl. Abel-shittim), city near the Jordan, place of assembly held by Moses, *A.* iv. 176 ; (Abele) v. 4

Abila (2), city in Peraea, *B.* ii. 252 ; iv. 438 (probably identical with [1])

Abila (3) (Abela ; Bibl. Abel-meholah), native city of Elisha, *A.* viii. 352

Abila (4), city near Gadara, *A.* xii. 136

Abila (5) (Abela), district in Lebanon, added to Agrippa I's kingdom by Claudius, *A.* xix. 275 ; xx. 138

Abile. See Abila (1)

Abilmathadachos (Evilmaraduch ; Bibl. Evilmerodach), king of Babylonia, son of Nebuchadnezzar, *A.* x. 229, 231 ; *Ap.* i. 146

Abimael, son of Joktan, *A.* i. 147

Abimelech (1), king of Gerar, makes pact with Abraham, *A.* i. 207-212 ; his friendship and controversies with Isaac, i. 259-264

Abimelech (2), bastard son of Gideon, *A.* v. 233 ; slays all but one of Gideon's sons, v. 234 ; v. 239 ; expelled from Shechem, v. 240 ; terrorizes Shechem, v. 242-249 ; death of, v. 251-253 ; vii. 142

Abimelech (3) (Bibl. Elimelech), father-in-law of Ruth, *A.* v. 318 ; death of, v. 319 ; v. 323, 333

Abimelech (4), high priest, *A.* vi. 242, 254 ; slain on Saul's orders, vi. 260 ; vi. 261, 268-269, 378

160

GENERAL INDEX

Abimelech (5), the Hittite, *A.* vi. 311

Abinadab (1). See Aminadab (1), (2), (3)

Abinadab (2), governor of Dor, *A.* viii. 35

Abira (var. Abias, Ebias; Bibl. Abijah), son of Samuel, *A.* vi. 32

Abiram, elder of tribe of Reuben, *A.* iv. 19 ; rebels against Moses, iv. 37-39 ; iv. 47

Abisai (Bibl. Abishai), son of Zeruiah, nephew of David, *A.* vi. 311-312 ; vii. 11 ; pursues Abner, vii. 16 ; buries Asahel, vii. 19 ; helps Joab kill Abner, vii. 35 ; vii. 45 ; conquers Idumaea, vii. 109 ; vii. 124, 126, 208 ; fights against Absalom, vii. 233 ; vii. 265, 282, 286 ; rescues David from a Philistine giant, vii. 299 ; his exploits summarized, vii. 314-315

Abisake (Bibl. Abishag), comforts David's old age, *A.* vii. 344 ; sought in marriage by Adonijah, viii. 5, 8-9

Abisar (Bibl. Jezreel), city in Palestine, *A.* vi. 309

Abishag. See Abisake

Abishai. See Abisai

Abishua. See Abiezer

Abital. See Abitale

Abitale (Bibl. Abital), wife of David, mother of Shephetaiah, *A.* vii. 21

Abner. See Abenar

'abnēt. See *abanēth*

abortion, prohibited by Jewish law, *Ap.* ii. 202

Abraham (Abram[es]), *B.* iv. 531, v. 380 ; son of Terah, marries Sarah, *A.* i. 148-151 ; goes to Canaan, i. 154 ; mentioned by Berosus, i. 158 ; (Abram[es]) mentioned by Nicolas of Damascus, i. 159-160 ; teaches Egyptians arithmetic and astronomy, i. 161-168 ; divides land with Lot, i. 169 ; rescues Lot from Assyrians, i. 176-179 ; meets Melchizedek, i. 181-182 ; promised a son, i. 184 ; lives

near oak called Ogyges, i. 186 ; has a son Ishmael by Hagar, i. 187-190 ; has son Isaac by Sarah, i. 191 ; circumcision of Abraham and his family, i. 192-193 ; visited by three angels, i. 196-198 ; begs God to spare Sodom, i. 199 ; migrates to Gerar and meets Abimelech, i. 207-212 ; birth and circumcision of Isaac, i. 213-214 ; agrees to send Hagar and Ishmael away, i. 216-217 ; prepares to sacrifice Isaac, i. 222-236 ; buys burial ground for Sarah, i. 237 ; marries Keturah and begets sons, i. 238-240 ; seeks wife for Isaac, i. 242-255 ; death of, i. 256 ; i. 259, 281, 289, 346 ; ll. 213, 229 (*bis*), 257, 269, 318 ; iii. 87 ; iv. 4 ; v. 97, 113 ; vii. 67, 333 ; dating of temple from, viii. 61 ; viii. 155 ; xi. 169 ; xii. 226 ; xiv. 255

Abram(es). See Abraham

Abram's abode, village near Damascus, *A.* i. 160

Absalom (1) (var. Abes[s]alomos), son of David and Maacah, *A.* vii. 21, 70, 162, 172 ; slays his brother Amnon, vii. 173-176 ; vii. 178, 180-181, 186-188, 191 ; David reconciled to him, vii. 193 ; plots to secure kingdom, vii. 194-198, 202, 204, 211, 213-216, 221, 223, 225, 227-229 ; leads army against David, is killed by Joab, vii. 232-242 ; vii. 243-244, 247, 250-252, 255, 258, 261, 279, 281, 348 ; viii. 249

Absalom (2), father of Matthias, *A.* xiii. 161

Absalom (3), father of Jonathan (may be same as father of Matthias), *A.* xiii. 202

Absalom (4), uncle and father-in-law of Aristobulus, *A.* xiv. 71

Absalom (5), most eminent supporter of Menahem, *B.* ii. 448

Absalom's Hand, monument erected by Absalom the son of David, *A.* vii. 244

Abuma (Bibl. Rumah), city in Judaea, *A.* x. 83

161

GENERAL INDEX

Acatelas. See Cathlas

Acchabaron, rock in Galilee, fortified by Josephus, *B.* ii. 573

Accho. See Ptolemais

Acedasa, village in Galilee, *B.* i. 47

Achab (Bibl. Ahab), king of Israel, *A.* vii. 103 ; succeeds Omri, viii. 313, 316 ; marries Jezebel, viii. 317 ; drought in his reign, viii. 319, 324 ; seeks Elijah, viii. 328, 334-335 ; summons people to Mt. Carmel, viii. 337 ; viii. 344-345, 347 ; takes possession of Naboth's vineyard, viii. 358-360 ; repents of his sin against Naboth, viii. 362 ; attacked by and defeats Ben-hadad, viii. 363-388 ; rebuked for releasing Ben-hadad, viii. 391-393 ; allies with Jehoshaphat, viii. 398-400 ; death of, viii. 401-420 ; ix. i, 17-19, 27, 29, 45, 47, 96, 99 ; his line destroyed by Jehu, ix. 108-109, 119-120, 125-132, 134-135 ; ix. 138, 140, 154

Achaea (Achaia), *B.* i. 531 ; ii. 558 ; iii. 8, 64 ; iv. 499

Achaeans, in quotation from Homer, *A.* xix. 92

Achaia. See Achaea

Achamon (Bibl. Amon), governor of Samaria, *A.* viii. 410

Achan. See Achar

Achar (Bibl. Achan), son of Zabdi, appropriates booty, *A.* v. 33 ; his crime discovered, v. 43-44

Acharabe, village in Upper Galilee, fortified by Josephus, *V.* 188

Acharampsaris, Babylonian commander assigned to sack of Jerusalem, *A.* x. 135

Achaz (Bibl. Ahaz), son and successor to Jotham, king of Judah, *A.* ix. 243, 247-249 ; bribes Assyrians to attack Syria and Israel, ix. 252-255 ; idolatry of, ix. 256 ; death of, ix. 257, 260

Achemaios (Bibl. Tachmonite), father of Jashobeam, *A.* vii. 308

Achia (Bibl. Jecholiah), mother of Uzziah, *A.* ix. 216

Achiab(us), cousin of Herod, prevents Herod from committing suicide, *B.* i. 662 ; ii. 55, 77 ; *A.* xv. 250 ; prevents Herod from committing suicide, xvii. 184 ; leads revolt against Jewish " royalists," xvii. 270 ; counsels Jews to surrender to Varus, xvii. 297

Achias (1) (Bibl. Ahijah), prophet, foretells split of Jewish kingdom, *A.* viii. 206-208 ; viii. 209, 218, 266-267

Achias (2) (Bibl. Ahiah), high priest, *A.* vi. 107

Achiba. See Epsiba

Achilos (1) (Bibl. Ahilud), father of Jehoshaphat, *A.* vii. 110, 293

Achilos (2) (Bibl. Ahilud), father of Baana, *A.* viii. 36 (perhaps identical with father of Jehoshaphat)

Achima. See Achina

Achimanos (Bibl. Chimham), son of Barzillai, *A.* vii. 274

Achimas (Bibl. Ahimaaz), son of Zadok, *A.* vii. 201 ; tells David of Joab's victory, vii. 245-250 ; succeeds his father as high priest, x. 152

Achina (Achima ; Bibl. Ahinoam), wife of David, *A.* (vi. 309) ; (Achima) vi. 320 ; vii. 21

Achinadab (Bibl. Ahinadab), governor of Galilee, *A.* viii. 36

Achish. See Anchus

Achitob (Bibl. Ahitub), high priest, son of Amariah, *A.* vi. 122 ; father of Zadok the high priest, viii. 12

Achitophel (Bibl. Ahithophel), counsellor to David, *A.* vii. 197 ; joins Absalom's party, vii. 202, 204, 211-222 ; his suicide, vii. 228-229

Achonios (Bibl. Shechaniah), head of people of Jerusalem, *A.* xi. 145 ; his advice accepted by Ezra, xi. 146

Achratheos (Bibl. Hatach), eunuch of Esther, *A.* xi. 223

Achzib. See Ekdippa

Acme, Jewess, slave of Julia (Livia) the wife of Augustus,

162

GENERAL INDEX

B. i. 641-643, 645; condemned to death, i. 661; plots with Antipater against Salome, xvii. 134-145; put to death by Augustus, xvii. 182-183

Acra (Akra), citadel of Jerusalem, *B.* i. 39, 50; v. 137-139, 253; vi. 354, 355, 392; (Akra) built by Antiochus Epiphanes, *A.* xii. 251-252; (Akra) xii. 318; (Akra) besieged by Judas the Maccabee, xii. 362-364; (Akra) xii. 369, 405, 406

Acrabatene (= Acrabet[t]a), toparchy south-east of Shechem, *B.* ii. 235; (Acrabet[t]a) ii. 568; ii. 652; iii. 48; (Acrabet[t]a) iii. 55; iv. 504, 511; (Acrabet[t]a) iv. 551

Acrabet(t)a. See Acrabatene

Acropolis of Athens, burning of, *Ap.* ii. 131

Actian era (28–24 B.C.), *B.* i. 398

Actium, site of battle, *B.* i. 364, 370, 386, 388; *A.* xv. 109, 121, 161-162, 190; xvi. 147; xviii. 26; (*Ap.* ii. 59)

Acusilaus of Argos, Greek historian, *A.* i. 108; his date, *Ap.* i. 13; discrepancies between him and Hellanicus on genealogies, his correction of Hesiod, i. 16

Ada (1) (Bibl. Adah), wife of Lamech, *A.* i. 63-64

Ada (2) (Bibl. Adah), wife of Esau, *A.* i. 265

Adados (1) I (Bibl. Ben-hadad), king of Damascus, defeated by David, *A.* vii. 100-101, 104

Adados (2) III (var. Ader, Aderos, Adder; Bibl. Ben-hadad), sacks Samaritis, *A.* vii. 103; is defeated but spared by Ahab, viii. 363-388, 392; attacked by Ahab, viii. 401; kills Ahab, viii. 411-415; alliance of Ahab and Jehoshaphat against him, ix. 1; attempts to capture Elisha, ix. 52-54; besieges Jehoram, ix. 59-61; flees before four lepers, ix. 77-78; his death foretold by Elisha, he is killed by Hazael, ix. 87-94, 105

Adados (3) IV (Bibl. Ben-hadad), son and successor to Hazael, *A.* ix. 184

Adah (1). See Ada (1)

Adah (2). See Ada (2)

Adah (3). See Adasa

Adam, creation of, *A.* i. 34-51, 66-67, 70, 79, 82-83; iii. 87; dating of temple from, viii. 62; x. 148

Adamah, village in Galilee, where Josephus conceals his troops, *V.* 321

Adar, Hebrew month, *A.* iv. 327; xi. 107; Esther and Ahasuerus married in, xi. 202; thirteenth of, xi. 281, 286; Nicanor killed by Judas in, xii. 412

Adasa, village near Bethoron in Palestine, *A.* xii. 408

Adasa (Bibl. Adah), wife of Esau, *A.* ii. 4

Adbeel. See Abdeel

Addaios (= Asaph?), eparch of Syria, Phoenicia, and Samaria, *A.* xi. 167; Nehemiah delivers letters to, xi. 168

Adder. See Adados III

Addida (Adida, Haditheh), city near Lydda, *B.* iv. 486; *A.* xiii. 203, 392

Ader. See Adados III.

Aderos (1) (Bibl. Hadad), Edomite, rebels against Solomon, *A.* viii. 199-204

Aderos (2). See Adados III

Adiabene, district in northern Mesopotamia, *B.* i. 6; ii. 388, 520; iv. 567; v. 147, 252, 474; *A.* xx. 17-18; Izates becomes king of, xx. 35-36; xx. 80; nobles of object to Monobazus' conversion, xx. 81; xx. 86, 94

Adida. See Addida

Adnah. See Ednaios

Adom (Edom), nickname of Esau, *A.* ii. 1, 3

adoma, Hebrew word for " red," *A.* ii. 3

adōni, Hebrew word for " lord," *A.* v. 121

Adonias (Bibl. Adonijah), son of David and Haggith, *A.* vii. 21; plots to secure the kingdom for

163

GENERAL INDEX

GENERAL INDEX

Agrippias (Agrippium), name
given to Anthedon by King
Herod, *B.* i. 87, 118, 416 ; *A.*
xiii. 357

Agrippina, wife of Emperor
Claudius, *B.* ii. 249 ; *A.* xx.
135 ; rumoured to have poisoned Claudius, xx. 148 ; kills
Claudius, xx. 151

Agrippinus, son of Mariamme
and Demetrius, *A.* xx. 147

Agrippium. See Agrippias

Ahab. See Achab

Ahasuerus. See Artaxerxes (1) I

Ahaz. See Achaz

Ahaziah I. See Ochozias (1) I

Ahaziah II. See Ochozias (2) II

Ahenobarbus, Domitius. See
Domitius (1) Ahenobarbus

Ahiah. See Achias (2)

Ahijah (1). See Achias (1)

Ahijah (2). See Seidos

Ahikam. See Aikamos

Ahilud. See Achilos (1) and (2)

Ahimaaz. See Achimas

Ahinadab. See Achinadab

Ahinoam. See Achina

Ahisamach. See Isamach

Ahithophel. See Achitophel

Ahitub. See Achitob

Ai. See Naia

Aia. See Naia

Aiah. See Sibatos

Aichiba. See Epsiba

Aigla (Aethe ; Bibl. Eglah), wife
of David, mother of Ithream,
A. vii. 21

Aijalom. See Elom

Aïkamos (Bibl. Ahikam), father
of Gedaliah, *A.* x. 155

Ailane (Elathus ; Bibl. Eloth,
Elath), city near Gulf of
Akabah, later called Berenike,
A. viii. 163 ; (Elathus) ix.
245

Aïn. See Nain

Aion (Joannu ; Bibl. Ijon), city
in Palestine, sacked by Ben-
hadad, *A.* viii. 305

Aithalidean deme, in Athens, *A.*
xiv. 150

Akairos. See Demetrius (5)
Akairos

Ake (Bibl. Asher, Aloth), city
near Tyre, *A.* viii. 37

Akenchêres, Egyptian queen,
daughter of Orus, *Ap.* i. 96

Akenchêres I, Egyptian king,
son of Rathotis, *Ap.* i. 97

Akenchêres II, Egyptian king,
son of Akenchêres I, *Ap.* i. 97

Akkaron (Bibl. Ekron), city
belonging to Dan, *A.* v. 87;
withstands capture, v. 128 ;
v. 177 ; Philistine city, vi. 8 ;
vi. 30 ; god of, ix. 26 ; xiii.
102

Akmon (Bibl. Ishbi-benob), Philistine giant, *A.* vii. 298

Akra. See Acra

Akrabatene. See Acrabatene

Alani, Scythian tribe, invade
Media, *B.* vii. 244-251; attack
Parthian king Artabanus, *A.*
xviii. 97

Albanians, tribe of Caucasus,
urged by Tiberius to make war
on Parthian king Artabanus,
A. xviii. 97

Albinus, procurator of Judaea,
summary of his misdeeds, *B.*
ii. 272-277 ; vi. 305 ; succeeds
Festus as procurator, *A.* xx.
197, 200 ; his anger with
Ananus for stoning James, xx.
202-203 ; wipes out *sicarii*,
xx. 204 ; courted by Ananias,
xx. 205 ; his trouble with
sicarii, xx. 209 ; releases
Jewish prisoners, thus filling
country with brigands, xx.
215 ; succeeded by Gessius
Florus, xx. 252-253

Alcimus (Jakelmos, Jacimus),
appointed high priest by
Antiochus V Eupator, *A.* xii.
385, 387 ; enemy of Judas,
xii. 391-401 ; death of, xii.
413 ; (Jacimus) succeeds Onias
as high priest, xx. 235 ;
(Jacimus) death of, xx. 235

Alcyon, physician in Rome, *A.*
xix. 157

Alexander (1) of Macedon, the
Great, *B.* ii. 360 ; grants Jews
of Alexandria equality with
Greeks, ii. 487-488 ; fortune
of, v. 465 ; closes " Caspian
Gates," vii. 245 ; *A.* i. 138 ;
ii. 348 ; his victory at the

167

GENERAL INDEX

Granicus, xi. 305 ; captures
Tyre and besieges Gaza, xi.
313-320 ; sanctions building
of a Samaritan temple, xi. 321-
324 ; prostrates himself before
Jewish high priest and sacrifices in the temple at Jerusalem, xi. 329-339 ; is courted
by Samaritans, xi. 340-345 ;
death of, xi. 346, xii. 1 ; xii. 8 ;
length of his reign, xii. 11 ;
xii. 354 ; xiii. 74, 256 ; *Ap.* i.
183 ; death of in 114th
Olympiad, i. 184-185 ; exempts
Jews from helping to restore
temple of Bel in Babylon, i.
192 ; i. 194 ; participation of
Jews in his campaigns, i. 200 ;
presents residential quarter
and privileges to Jews in
Alexandria, ii. 35 ; his letters
bestow rights on Jews of
Alexandria, ii. 37 ; rewards
Jewish valour and fidelity by
settling them in Alexandria, ii.
42-44 ; his testimonials to
Jews, ii. 62 ; gives privileges
to Alexandrian Jews, ii. 72

Alexander (2) Balas, son of
Antiochus Epiphanes, invades
Syria, *A.* xiii. 35, 37 ; bids for
Jonathan's support, xiii. 43,
45, 47 ; defeats Demetrius,
xiii. 58 ; becomes king of Syria
and marries daughter of Ptolemy Philometor, xiii. 80-82 ;
honours Jonathan, xiii. 83-85 ;
opposed by Demetrius II, xiii.
87 ; rewards Jonathan, xiii.
102 ; aided by Ptolemy Philometor, xiii. 103-104 ; his plot
against Ptolemy Philometor
discovered, xiii. 106-112 ; death
of, xiii. 116-119 ; xiii. 131, 218

Alexander (3) Zebinas, seizes
throne of Syria from Demetrius II, *A.* xiii. 268-269 ; his
friendship with Hyrcanus, xiii.
273

Alexander (4) Jannaeus, son of
Hyrcanus I, King of Judaea,
brother of Aristobulus, placed
on throne by Aristobulus'
widow, *B.* i. 85 ; early wars of,
i. 86-87 ; revolt of Jews

against, i. 88 ; attacks Arabia,
i. 89 ; defeated by Obedas, i.
90 ; his long wars with his
subjects, i. 91-98 ; defeated
by Demetrius, i. 94-95 ; massacres Jews, i. 97 ; tries to
check Antiochus Dionysus, i.
99 ; defeated by Aretas, i. 103 ;
his last expeditions, i. 104-105 ;
his death, i. 106 ; i. 109, 113 ;
his tomb, v. 304 ; vii. 171 ;
succeeds Aristobulus as king of
Judaea, *A.* xiii. 320 ; hated by
his father, xiii. 322 ; attacks
cities on coast of Syria, xiii.
324-329 ; is defeated by Ptolemy Lathyrus, xiii. 330-341 ;
makes treaty with Cleopatra,
xiii. 353, 355 ; destroys Gaza,
xiii. 356-364 ; oppresses his
Jewish adversaries, xiii. 372-
383 ; is nicknamed Thrakidas
(the " Cossack "), xiii. 383 ;
xiii. 390 ; is defeated by
Aretas, xiii. 393 ; his victories
in Transjordan, xiii. 393-394 ;
extent of his territory, xiii.
395-397 ; death of, xiii. 398-
404 ; his splendid burial, xiii.
405-406 ; his sons, xiii. 407 ;
xiii. 410, 415-416 ; xiv. 10, 18,
36, 44, 151, 191-200, 206, 211,
226 ; xx. 241-242

Alexander (5), son of Aristobulus
II, escapes from Pompey, *B.*
i. 158 ; revolts, i. 160 ; prepares to meet Gabinius, i. 161 ;
fights with Gabinius and is
defeated, i. 162-167 ; i. 168,
176-177, 182 ; death of, i. 185 ;
i. 241, 344, 432, 551 ; *A.* xiv. 79 ;
is twice defeated by Gabinius,
xiv. 82-85, 89-90, 100-102 ;
executed by Scipio, xiv. 125,
140 ; father-in-law of Herod,
xiv. 300, 353, 467 ; xv. 23

Alexander (6) (=Ptolemy IX),
son of Cleopatra, king of Egypt,
A. xiii. 350

Alexander (7) (var.), son of
Alexander (son of Aristobulus
II), *A.* xiv. 387

Alexander (8), son of Mariamme
and Herod, his hostility toward
his father, *B.* i. 445-447 ; is

168

GENERAL INDEX

tried before Augustus, i. 452-454 ; i. 456, 467, 469-479 ; denounced by Herod's eunuchs, i. 488-491 ; arrested, i. 496 ; his written statement, i. 498, 501-502, 504, 508 ; denounced to Herod by Eurycles, i. 513-533 ; i. 535 ; implicated in alleged plot of Tiro against Herod, i. 538-551 ; i. 552-553, 557, 559, 561, 563, 581, 586, 588, 599, 603, 627, 644 ; impersonated by false Alexander, ii. 101-110 ; ii. 114, 116, 222 ; sent to Rome, *A*. xv. 342 ; married to Glaphyra, Archelaus' daughter, xvi. 11, 97 ; defends himself and his brother before Augustus, xvi. 104-122 ; xvi. 131 ; named by Herod as successor after Antipater, xvi. 133 ; his wife incurs hatred of Salome, xvi. 193 ; incited by Pheroras against his father, xvi. 206-208 ; accused by Herod's eunuchs of plotting against him, xvi. 231-234 ; his friends tortured by Herod, xvi. 243-253 ; further exasperates his father, xvi. 255 ; Archelaus reconciles Herod to him, xvi. 263, 265-269 ; Herod brings charges against him before Augustus, xvi. 273 ; betrayed by Eurycles, xvi. 302-309 ; imprisoned by his father, xvi. 311-321 ; denies having plotted with Archelaus against Herod, xvi. 325-331 ; implicated in alleged plot of Tiro against Herod, xvi. 375, 387-391 ; killed by strangling at command of Herod, xvi. 394 ; xvi. 401 ; xvii. 11 ; his children, xvii. 12, 14 ; his sisters given in marriage, xvii. 22 ; his death, xvii. 80 ; impersonated by false Alexander, xvii. 324-338 ; his widow married to his brother, Archelaus, xvii. 341, 349, 351 ; xviii. 134 ; his children, xviii. 139-141

Alexander (9), son of Alexander (son of Herod) and Glaphyra, *B*. i. 552 ; *A*. xviii. 139 ; his son Tigranes, xviii. 140

Alexander (10), son of Tigranes, *A*. xviii. 140 ; his children, xviii. 141

Alexander (11), son of Phasael and Salampsio, *A*. xviii. 131, 138

Alexander (12), son of Jason, Jewish envoy to the Roman Senate, *A*. xiv. 146

Alexander (13), son of Dorotheus, Jewish envoy to the Roman Senate, *A*. xiv. 146

Alexander (14), father of Apollonius the Jewish envoy, *A*. xiii. 260 ; xiv. 248

Alexander (15), son of Theodorus, envoy from Hyrcanus to the Roman Senate, *A*. xiv. 222, 226 ; envoy of Jews to Antony, xiv. 307

Alexander (16), Marcus, of Halicarnassus (probably a Roman official), *A*. xiv. 256

Alexander (17), father of Tiberius Alexander, *B*. v. 205 ; alabarch, lends money to Cypros, Agrippa I's wife, *A*. xviii. 159-160 ; brother of Philo the philosopher, xviii. 259 ; liberated by Claudius, xix. 276 ; his son marries Berenice, daughter of Agrippa I, xix. 277 ; xx. 100

Alexander (18), Marcus, prob. Roman official, *A*. xiv. 256

Alexander (19), Marcus Julius, son of Alexander the alabarch, marries Berenice, *A*. xix. 276-277

Alexander (20), leader of brigands, *B*. ii. 235

Alexander (21), a Jew of Libya, *B*. vii. 445

Alexander (22), Polyhistor, Greek writer, quoted, *A*. i. 240

Alexander (23) (var.). See Alexas (1)

Alexander (24), Tiberius, procurator in Judaea, *B*. ii. 220, 223 ; governor of Egypt, ii. 309 ; ii. 492-493, 497 ; secures Alexandria, iv. 616-618 ; v. 45, 205, 510 ; vi. 237, 242 ; *A*. xx. 100, 102-103

Alexandra (1) (Salina, Salome), wife of Aristobulus and of

GENERAL INDEX

Alexander Jannaeus, Queen of Jews, (Salina) concerts for murder of Antigonus, *B.* i. 76 ; (Salina) appoints Alexander Jannaeus as king, i. 85 ; is bequeathed the kingdom by Alexander Jannaeus, i. 107 ; her piety, i. 108 ; her two sons, i. 109 ; Pharisees' influence on her, i. 110-114 ; her foreign policy, i. 115-116 ; her illness, i. 117 ; imprisons wife and children of Aristobulus, i. 118 ; her death, i. 119 ; (Salina) appoints Alexander Jannaeus as king, *A.* xiii. 320 ; succeeds to throne after death of Alexander Jannaeus and appeases Pharisees, xiii. 405-417 ; wages war against Ptolemy, son of Mennaeus, xiii. 418 ; bribes Tigranes to leave Judaea, xiii. 419 ; her illness and death, xiii. 422-432, xiv. 1 ; xv. 179 ; xx. 242 ; *V.* 5

Alexandra (2), daughter of Hyrcanus II, charges to Cleopatra that Herod slighted her son, *A.* xv. 23-27 ; temporarily reconciled with Herod, xv. 31-38 ; appeals to Cleopatra against Herod again, xv. 42 ; plans to flee to Egypt, xv. 46-47 ; xv. 53 ; her grief at death of Aristobulus, xv. 58 ; informs Cleopatra that Herod murdered her son, xv. 62-63 ; discovers Herod's secret instructions concerning Mariamme, xv. 69 ; plans to flee with Joseph and Mariamme, xv. 72, 80 ; put in chains by Herod, xv. 87 ; urges Hyrcanus to seek aid of Malchus against Herod, xv. 166, 169 ; held in suspicion by Herod, xv. 183 ; placed in Alexandrion by Herod, xv. 185 ; angry at Herod, xv. 202 ; betrays Mariamme, xv. 232-236 ; executed by Herod, xv. 247-252

Alexandra (3), daughter of Aristobulus II, *B.* i. 186 ; wife of Philippion and of Ptolemy Mennaeus, *A.* xiv. 126

Alexandra (4), daughter of Phasael and Salampsio, *A.* xviii. 131

Alexandr(e)ion, fortress in Judaea, *B.* i. 134 ; fortified by Alexander, son of Aristobulus, i. 161 ; besieged by Gabinius, i. 163-168 ; i. 171, 308, 528, 551 ; *A.* xiii. 417 ; xiv. 49, 83, 86, 89 (*bis*), 92 ; fortified by Herod, xiv. 419 ; xv. 185 ; place where Herod entertains Agrippa, xvi. 13 ; xvi. 317 ; place where Alexander and Aristobulus are buried, xvi. 394

Alexandria, Alexandrian(s), in Egypt, *B.* i. 278, 598 ; ii. 309, 335, 385 ; riots at, ii. 487-499 ; iii. 8, 64 ; iv. 605-606 ; description of its port, iv. 612-615 ; iv. 616, 631 ; second to Rome in magnitude, iv. 656 ; iv. 658-659 ; v. 2, 44, 169, 287 ; vi. 238 ; vii. 21, 75, 116, 409, 420, 423, 433, 447 ; site of translation of Torah into Greek, *A.* i. 12 ; viii. 156 ; its Jews given equal civic rights by Ptolemy, xii. 8 ; arrival there of Jewish elders, xii. 86 ; attempt to get citizenship rights of its Jews revoked, xii. 121, 123 ; visited by Joseph the Tobiad, xii. 168, 170, 174 ; xii. 180 ; place where Joseph the Tobiad begets Hyrcanus, xii. 187 ; place where birth of Ptolemy Epiphanes' son is celebrated, xii. 196, 199-203 ; Antiochus Epiphanes defeated there, xii. 243-244 ; xiii. 62 ; its Jews quarrel with Samaritans, xiii. 74, 77, 79 ; xiii. 120 ; its Jewish community flourishes under Cleopatra, xiii. 284 ; xiv. 113 ; its Jewish population, xiv. 117 ; Jews declared citizens of, xiv. '188 ; xiv. 193, 236, 250 ; Herod reaches it, xiv. 375 ; xv. 320 ; Agrippa I's attempt to raise money there, xviii. 159-160 ; strife between Jews and Greeks there and appointment of rival dele-

GENERAL INDEX

gations, xviii. 257; Gaius
Caligula prepares to sail there,
xix. 81; strife between Jews
and Greeks there, xix. 278-279;
edict of Claudius on behalf of
its Jews, xix. 280-286, 288, 292;
edicts favourable to its Jews,
xix. 310; xx. 51, 100, 147,
202; Vespasian goes there,
accompanied by Josephus, V.
415; Josephus is sent from
there with Titus to siege of
Jerusalem, 416, *Ap.* i. 48;
Apion on its Jews, ii. 7; falsely
claimed by Apion to be his
birthplace, ii. 29; bestows
citizenship upon Apion, ii. 32;
hatred of its inhabitants for
Jews, ii. 32; its Jews originally
from Syria, according to Apion,
ii. 33; its Jewish quarter near
seaboard, ii. 33-36; slab there
records rights bestowed upon
Jews by Julius Caesar, ii. 37;
citizenship of its Jews, ii. 38-
42; falsely claimed by Apion as
his birthplace, ii. 41-42; honoured by Alexander, Ptolemy
son of Lagus, and Ptolemy
Philadelphus, ii. 42-47; saved
by Jewish generals Onias and
Dositheus, ii. 49-50; its Jews
keep feast commemorating deliverance from Ptolemy Physcon's elephants, ii. 55; Cleopatra, its last queen, ii. 56;
captured by Octavius, ii. 60;
its inhabitants receive corn
distributed by Germanicus, ii.
63; high opinion of its Jews
held by Roman emperors, ii.
63; administration of corn
supplies taken from its inhabitants, ii. 64; Jews emigrate
there, ii. 67; its Jews accused
of causing sedition, ii. 68-70;
extension of citizenship there,
ii. 69; Egyptians there hold
citizenship under no regular
title, ii. 71-72; its Jewish
citizens called "aliens" by
Egyptians, ii. 71; ii. 78;
felicitated by Apion on posses-
sing such a citizen as himself, ii.
135-136

Alexandria, lake of (= Lake Ma-
reotis), *B.* iii. 520
Alexandrion. See Alexandreion
Alexas (1), friend of Antony, *B.* i.
393; *A.* xv. 197
Alexas (2), friend of Herod and
husband of Salome, *B.* i. 566,
660, 666; Salome forced by
Herod into marriage with him,
A. xvii. 9-10; Herod's final
instructions to him, xvii. 175;
refuses to carry out Herod's
funeral plans, xvii. 193-194
Alexas (3), father of Alexas
Helcias (perhaps identical with
Alexas [2] the husband of
Salome), *A.* xviii. 138
Alexas (4), surnamed Helcias,
son of Alexas, marries Cypros,
daughter of Cypros and Anti-
pater, *A.* xviii. 138
Alexas (5), soldier in army of
John of Gischala, *B.* vi, 92, 148
Allbame (Bibl. Oholibamah), wife
of Esau, *A.* i. 265; ii. 4
aliens, attitude to, according to
Jewish law, *Ap.* ii. 209
Alienus, A. Caecinna. See Cae-
cinna
Aliphaz(es) (Bibl. Eliphaz), son of
Esau, *A.* ii. 4-5
Alisphragmouthosis. See Mis-
phragmouthosis
Aliturus, Jewish actor, special
favourite of Nero, befriends
Josephus, *V.* 16
Alkanes (Bibl. Elkanah), the
Levite, father of Samuel, *A.* v.
342-343, 347
allegorists, Greek, *Ap.* ii. 255
Almodad. See Elmodad
Aloth. See Ake
alphabet, lateness of Greeks in
learning it, *Ap.* i. 10-11; its
late acquisition by Arcadians,
i. 22
Alps, *B.* ii. 371
Alurus, village in Idumaea, *B.* iv.
522
Alusa (var. Lus[s]a), Arabian city,
A. xiv. 18
Amadathos (Bibl. Hammedatha),
father of Haman, *A.* xi. 209,
270, 277
Amalek. See 'Amalek(os)

171

GENERAL INDEX

Amalekites, make war on Hebrews, *A.* iii. 40-42 ; defeated by Hebrews, iii. 53-54 ; iii. 60 ; iv. 304 ; attack Israelites, v. 210 ; vi. 129 ; defeated by Saul, vi. 132, 134-142 ; vi. 146, 155, 323, 336 ; sack Ziklag, vi. 356 ; pursued and slain by David, vi. 359, 362, 364, 367 ; vi. 371, 378 ; vii. 1, 6 ; defeated by Amaziah, ix. 188 ; their gods worshipped by Amaziah, ix. 193 ; ix. 198 ; descent of Haman from them, xi. 209 ; xi. 211, 277

Amalekitis, region in Idumaea, *A.* ii. 6

Amalek(os), son of Esau, *A.* ii. 5-6 ; vi. 133

Amanos, page of King Ben-hadad, wounds Ahab, *A.* viii. 414

Amanus, mountain-range inhabited by sons of Japheth, *A.* i. 122 ; occupied by descendants of Ham, i. 130

Amaraios (Bibl. Jambri), his sons slay John son of Mattathias, *A.* xiii. 11 ; his sons killed by Jonathan and Simon, sons of Mattathias, xiii. 18-21

Amaram(es) (Bibl. Amram), father of Moses, is promised that his son will deliver Hebrews from bondage, *A.* ii. 210 ; ii. 217 ; hides Moses in basket, ii. 219-221 ; ii. 229 ; iii. 86

Amaramus, Jewish leader of Peraeans against Philadelphians, *A.* xx. 4

Amarapsides (Bibl. Amraphel), Assyrian commander, *A.* i. 173

Amariah (1). See Amasias (1)

Amariah (2). See Arophaios

Amarinos (Bibl. Omri), succeeds Zimri as king of Israel, *A.* viii. 310-312 ; his death, viii. 313

Amasa (var. Amessa), son of Ithra, commander of Absalom's army, *A.* vii. 232, 261-262 ; appointed commander of David's army, vii. 280-281 ; slain by Joab, vii. 283-296 ; vii. 386

Amase, son of David, *A.* vii. 70

Amases. See Nemesaios

Amasias (1) (Bibl. Amariah), priest, appointed officer over judges by King Jehoshaphat, *A.* ix. 6

Amasias (2) (Bibl. Amaziah), King of Judah, son of and successor to Joash, *A.* ix. 172, 186 ; defeats Amalekites, ix. 188-192 ; rebuked by a prophet, ix. 193 ; captured by Joash, ix. 196-203 ; his death, ix. 204 ; ix. 205, 216, 218

Amasias (3) (Bibl. Maaseiah), son of Ahaz, *A.* ix. 247

Amasias (4) (Bibl. Maaseiah), governor of Jerusalem, *A.* x. 55

Amatha. See Amathe

Amathaeans (Hamathites), their land unassigned by Joshua, *A.* v. 89

Amathe (Amatha, Amathos, Amathus; Bibl. Riblah, Hamath), city in Syria founded by Amathus, renamed Epiphaneia by Macedonians, *A.* i. 138 ; iii. 303 ; vii. 107-108 ; viii. 160 ; (Amathos) ix. 206 ; x. 82 ; xiii. 174

Amathitis. See Hamath

Amathos. See Amathe

Amathus (1) (Bibl. " the Hamathite "), founder of Amathe (Amathus) in Syria, *A.* i. 138

Amathus (2), fortress in Transjordan, *B.* i. 86, 89, 170 ; captured by Alexander Jannaeus, *A.* xiii. 356 ; demolished by him, xiii. 374 ; xiv. 91

Amathus (3). See Amathe

Amathus (4). See Emmaus (1)

Amaziah. See Amasias (2)

Ambibulus, Marcus. See Ambivulus, Marcus

Ambivius, Marcus. See Ambivulus, Marcus

Ambivulus (var. Ambibulus, Ambivius), Marcus, procurator of Judaea, *A.* xviii. 31

Ambronas. See Asprenas

Amenophis (1) I, Egyptian king, son of Chebron, *Ap.* i. 95

Amenophis (2) II, Egyptian king, son of Thmosis, *Ap.* i. 96

Amenophis (3) III, Egyptian king, son of Harmesses Miamoun, *Ap.* i. 97

GENERAL INDEX

Amenophis (4) (IV or III),
Egyptian king invented by
Manetho, according to Josephus, *Ap.* i. 230 ff. ; Manetho's
account of him criticized by
Josephus, i. 254 ff. ; Chaeremon's account of him, i. 288 ff. ;
Isis appears to him, i. 289 ;
leaves 380,000 persons at
Pelusium, i. 291 ; flees to
Ethiopia but is brought back
by his son Ramesses, i. 292 ;
i. 295 ; leaves 380,000 persons
at Pelusium and flees to
Ethiopia, i. 297 ; i. 300

Amenophis (5), son of Paapis,
advises King Amenophis to
purge Egypt of lepers so as to
see the gods, *Ap.* i. 232-235 ;
commits suicide, i. 236 ; his
prediction recalled, i. 243 ;
criticism by Josephus of Manetho's account of him, i. 256-
259 ; i. 267 ; called Phrito-
boutes in Chaeremon's account,
i. 295

Ameroth. See Meroth

Amessa. See Amasa

Amesses, Egyptian queen, sister
and successor of Amenophis I,
Ap. i. 95

Aminadab (1) (Bibl. Abinadab),
Levite, ark stored in his house,
A. vi. 18 ; vii. 79

Aminadab (2) (Bibl. Abinadab),
son of Jesse, *A.* vi. 161

Aminadab (3) (Bibl. Abinadab),
son of Saul, *A.* vi. 369

Aminadabos (Bibl. Henadad),
father of Judas, *A.* xi. 79

Amitale (Bibl. Hamutal), mother
of Jehoahaz, *A.* x. 81

Ammah. See Ammata

Amman (1) (Bibl. Ben-ammi),
son of Lot and his daughter,
A. i. 205-206

Amman (2). See Ammanitis

Ammanites, tribe of Palestine,
descended from Amman, *A.* i.
206 ; attack Hebrews, v. 255 ;
v. 257, 261, 267 ; defeated by
Saul, vi. 68 ; harass the Jews,
vi. 71 ; defeated by Saul, vi.
77, 79-80 ; vi. 90, 129 ; war
with David, vii. 117-128 ; vii.

139 ; defeated at Rabatha by
David, vii. 159, 161 ; Solomon
marries one of their women, viii.
191, 212 ; attack Jehoshaphat,
ix. 7 ; defeated by Jehoshaphat,
ix. 13 ; subdued by Uzziah, ix.
218 ; defeated by King Jotham,
ix. 238 ; x. 160 ; send Ishmael
to slay Gedaliah, x. 164, 172 ;
x. 174 ; defeated by Nebuchadnezzar, x. 181 ; xi. 174 ;
subdued by Judas Maccabaeus,
xii. 329

Ammanitis (Amman), region of
Ammanites with capital Rabatha, *A.* iv. 98 ; v. 262-263 ;
vii. 230 ; its people send letter
to Cambyses, xi. 21

Ammata (var. Ommaton ; Bibl.
Ammah), place near Gibeon,
A. vii. 16

Ammatha. See Betharamphtha

Ammathus (Emmaus), village
near Tiberias containing hot
spring, *B.* iv. 11 ; *A.* xviii. 36

Ammaus. See Emmaus

Ammon (1), oracle of, consulted
by Egyptian king Bocchoris
about failure of crops, *Ap.* i.
306 ; its oracle concerning
victims of leprosy, i. 312

Ammon (2) (Bibl. Amon), king of
Judah, son of Manasseh, *A.*
x. 46 ; his death, x. 48

Ammonius, friend of Alexander
Balas, plots against Ptolemy
Philometor, *A.* xiii. 106-108 ;
xiii. 112

Amnon (1), son of David and
Ahinoam, *A.* vii. 21 ; ravishes
his sister Tamar, vii. 163-170 ;
killed by Absalom, vii. 173,
175, 178

Amnon (2). See Amnu

Amnu (apparently identical with
Amnon), son of David, *A.* vii.
70

Amon (1). See Achamon

Amon (2). See Ammon (2)

Amoraea (Amoria, Amoritis,
Amorite country), district be-
yond the Jordan, *A.* iv. 85 ;
(Amorite country) awarded
to Hebrew tribes, iv. 166, 171 ;
(Amorite country) comprises

173

GENERAL INDEX

Ananus (3), son of Ananias, sent to Rome in chains, *B.* ii. 243 ; captain of the temple, *A.* xx. 131

Ananus (4), high priest, son of Ananus, elected to supreme control of Jerusalem, *B.* ii. 563 ; ii. 648 ; favours moderation, ii. 651 ; ii. 653 ; iv. 151, 160 ; his speech against Zealots, iv. 162-192 ; attacks the Zealots, iv. 193-207 ; betrayed by John of Gischala, iv. 208-223 ; iv. 224-229 ; shuts the gates against the Idumaeans, iv. 236-238 ; iv. 288, 296-297, 301 ; murdered by the Idumaeans, iv. 314-318 ; encomium on him, iv. 319-322 ; iv. 325, 349, 504, 508 ; appointed high priest, *A.* xx. 197, 199 ; has James, brother of Jesus, stoned, xx. 200-202 ; deposed as high priest, xx. 203 ; seeks to remove Josephus from command in Galilee, *V.* 193-204 ; 216 ; popular indignation at Jerusalem against him for seeking to expel Josephus from Galilee, 309

Ananus (5), son of Jonathan, urges surrender to Cestius, *B.* ii. 533-534

Ananus (6), son of Bagadates of Emmaus, satellite of Simon the son of Giorias, *B.* v. 531 ; deserts to Romans, vi. 229-231

anarabaches, Hellenized form of Aramaic term (=*kahana rabba*) for high priest, *A.* iii. 151

Anath, father of Hebrew judge Shamgar, *A.* v. 197

Anathoth, native city of Jeremiah, *A.* x. 114

Anaxagoras, similar to Moses in his view of God's nature, *Ap.* ii. 168 ; native of Clazomenae, almost condemned by Athenians, ii. 265

Anchus (Bibl. Achish), king of Gath (Philistine city), expels David, *A.* vi. 245-247 ; vi. 319 ; allows David to live in Ziklag, vi. 322-324 ; enlists David in his army, vi. 325-326 ; vi. 351

" Ancient," " the most " (of God), *Ap.* ii. 206

Ancyra, city in Galatia, *A.* xvi. 165

Andreas, seconds efforts of Aristaeus, *A.* xii. 18, 24 ; xii. 50, 53, 86 ; bodyguard of Ptolemy Philadelphus, appointed his commissioner, *Ap.* ii. 46

Andromachos (Bibl. Adrammelech), son of King Sennacherib of Assyria, *A.* x. 23

Andromachus, friend of Herod, dismissed by him, *A.* xvi. 242, 245

Andromeda, legendary figure, impressions of her chains at Joppa, *B.* iii. 420

Andronicus, son of Messalamus, speaks for Jews against Samaritans before Ptolemy Philometor, *A.* xiii. 75, 78-79

Aner. See Enner

angaroi, messengers sent out by Ahasuerus, *A.* xi. 203

Anilaeus, with his brother Asinaeus organizes outlaw band, *A.* xviii. 314 ff. ; xviii. 327, 329, 332 ; his affair with a Parthian general's wife creates a scandal, xviii. 342-352 ; captures Mithridates but releases him, xviii. 353-360 ; defeated and killed by Mithridates, xviii. 363-371

animals (1) in Egyptian religion : worship of as gods by Egyptians, *Ap.* i. 225, 239, 244 ; though sacred to Egypt, roasted by Solymites, i. 249, 254 ; worshipped by Egyptians, ii. 66, 81, 86, 128-129, 139

animals (2) in Jewish religion : rights of, according to Jewish law, *A.* iv. 233 ; Jewish law on assistance to them in distress, iv. 275-276 ; representation of them forbidden to Jews, *V.* 65 ; humane use of them prescribed by Jewish law, *Ap.* ii. 213

Anna (1) (Bibl. Hannah), wife of Elkanah and mother of Samuel, *A.* v. 342-347

An(n)a (2). See Naia

175

GENERAL INDEX

Anna (3). See Cana (1)

Annaeus (Jannaeus), son of Levi, most important citizen of Tarichaeae, *B.* ii. 597; special friend of Agrippa II, secretly sent by Josephus to return stolen goods to Agrippa, *V.* 131

Annibas (1). See Hannibal

Annibas (2), Jew, executed by Fadus, *A.* xx. 4

Annius (1), Lucius, sent by Vespasian to capture Gerasa, *B.* iv. 487-488

Annius (2) Rufus. See Rufus, Annius

Annius (3) Vinicianus, leader of a conspiracy against Gaius Caligula, *A.* xix. 18, 20; joins Chaerea in conspiracy against Gaius, xix. 49-59; xix. 96; released by Clemens, xix. 153-154; restrains Asiaticus from attempting to secure the empire after death of Gaius, xix. 252

Annon (Bibl. Hanun), son of Nahash, mistreats David's envoys, *A.* vii. 117, 119

Anoch (1) (Bibl. Enoch), son of Cain, *A.* i. 62-63

Anoch (2) (Bibl. Enoch), son of Jared, *A.* i. 79, 85-86; becomes invisible at death, ix. 28

Anoch (3). See Anoch(os)

Anocha (Bibl. Enoch), city built by Cain, *A.* i. 62

Anoch(es) (Bibl. Hanoch), eldest son of Reuben, *A.* ii. 178

Anoch(os), son of Medan, *A.* i. 238

Anos (Bibl. Enosh), son of Seth, *A.* i. 79, 83

Antaeus, opponent of Heracles, *A.* i. 241

Anteius (1), father of Anteius the senator, exiled and put to death by Gaius Caligula, *A.* xix. 125

Anteius (2), Roman senator, son of Anteius, killed by Gaius Caligula's German bodyguard, *A.* xix. 125-126

Anthedon, maritime city in Palestine, named Agrippias by King Herod, *B.* i. 87; rebuilt by

Gabinius, i. 166; annexed to Herod's kingdom, i. 396; i. 416; razed by Jews, ii. 460; captured by Alexander Jannaeus, *A.* xiii. 357; xiii. 395; rebuilt by Gabinius, xiv. 88; added to Herod's realm, xv. 217; xviii. 158

Anthesterion, Halicarnassian month, *A.* xiv. 256

Antigone, name given mockingly to Antigonus (son of Aristobulus II) by Sosius, *B.* i. 353, *A.* xiv. 481

Antigonus (1) the One-Eyed, becomes master of Asia, *A.* xii. 2; father of Demetrius Poliorcetes, *Ap.* i. 185; Hieronymus friendly to him, i. 213

Antigonus (2) Gonatas (?), defeated by Ptolemy Philadelphus in naval battle, *A.* xii. 93

Antigonus (3), son of John Hyrcanus, besieges Sebaste, *B.* i. 64-65; honours conferred upon him by his brother, i. 71; murdered by his brother Aristobulus, i. 72-80; i. 82; besieges Samaria with his brother Aristobulus, *A.* xiii. 276-281; killed by Aristobulus, xiii. 302-314; xiii. 322

Antigonus (4), son of Aristobulus, conducted to Rome, *B.* i. 158; i. 173, 186; accuses Antipater, i. 195-198; returns from exile, i. 239; banished by Herod, i. 240; i. 248-250, 254, 257, 259, 269-270, 273, 282, 284; besieges Masada, i. 286-287; i. 289-291, 294, 296-297, 300, 302-303, 314, 317-319, 323; outrages Joseph's corpse, i. 325; i. 327, 333, 335, 339; throws himself at Sossius' feet, i. 353; his death, i. 357; i. 358, 364, 665; v. 398; carried to Rome as captive by Pompey, *A.* xiv. 79; xiv. 96, 126; appeals to Caesar against usurpation of Hyrcanus, xiv. 140-142; defeated by Herod, xiv. 297-298; secures support from Parthians against Herod, xiv. 330-346; mutilates Hyrcanus and kills Phasael, xiv.

176

GENERAL INDEX

365, 368 ; set up as king, xiv.
379 ; hated by Antony, xiv.
382 ; considered enemy by
Romans, xiv. 384 ; besieges
Masada, xiv. 390-391 ; victim
of Romans' extortion, xiv. 392-
393 ; attacked by Herod, xiv.
394 ; bribes Silo, xiv. 395 ;
besieged in Jerusalem by
Herod, xiv. 399-412 ; his army
defeated in Galilee by Herod,
xiv. 413-414 ; xiv. 418 ; sought
by Herod in Galilee, xiv. 431 ;
bribes Machaeras, xiv. 435 ;
xiv. 437-438 ; cuts off Joseph's
head, xiv. 450 ; defeated by
Herod at Jericho, xiv. 457-461 ;
besieged in Jerusalem by
Herod, xiv. 469-478 ; surren-
ders to Sossius, xiv. 481 ; taken
to Rome, xiv. 488 ; killed by
Antony, xiv. 489-490 ; taken
captive, xv. 1 ; executed by
Mark Antony, xv. 6-9 ; mutilates Hyrcanus, xv. 17 ; deprives Hyrcanus of high priesthood and mutilates him, xv.
181 ; Sons of Baba loyal to
him, xv. 262-263 ; xv. 323 ;
xvii. 92 ; put to death by
Herod, xvii. 191 ; xx. 245
Antimachus. See Antiochus (18)
Antioch (1), city in Syria, B. i.
185, 243, 328, 425, 512 ; ii. 18,
41, 79, 186, 201, 244, 281, 479,
481, 500 ; iii. 29 ; iv. 630 ;
danger to its Jews, vii. 41-62 ;
Titus refuses local petition to
expel its Jews, vii. 100-111 ;
capital of Lower Syria, its Jews
given citizenship rights, A. xii.
119-120 ; its inhabitants try
to get citizenship rights of Jews
revoked, xii. 121, 123 ; xii. 247,
315, 367, 383, 394, 397, 401,
421 ; xiii. 33, 36, 42, 87 ; its
inhabitants offended by Alexander Balas, xiii. 108 ; its
inhabitants accept Demetrius
as king, xiii. 111-115 ; its territory plundered by Alexander
Balas, xiii. 116 ; xiii. 123 ;
subdued by Demetrius II with
help of Jews, xiii. 135-141 ;
xiii. 144, 188, 209, 385-386 ;

xiv. 125 ; Jews' rights there
protected by Antony, xiv. 323 ;
xiv. 440, 451 ; scene of Antigonus' execution, xv. 8-9 ; xv.
218, 359 ; its inhabitants bene-
fited by Herod, xvi. 148 ; xvi.
270 ; xvii. 24, 132, 222, 251,
299 ; xviii. 95, 104, 126 ; xx.
133, 246 ; revolution aroused
there by Stratonice against
Macedonian King Demetrius
II, Ap. i. 206-207 ; its Jews
given citizenship, ii. 39
Antioch (2), in Mesopotamia,
founded by Macedonians, surnamed Epimygdonia, A. xx. 68
Antiochenes, Jews of Antioch (1)
called, Ap. ii. 39
Antiochus (1) I (Soter), Syrian
king, B. vii. 43 (apparently)
Antiochus (2) II (Theos), grandson of Seleucus, grants citizenship to Syrian Jews, A. xii.
125
Antiochus (3) III (the Great),
takes Judaea away from
Ptolemies, A. xii. 129-133 ;
sends letter to his governor
Ptolemy favourable to Jews,
xii. 134-144 ; publishes decree
concerning the temple of the
Jews, xii. 145-146 ; orders
transportation of Babylonian
Jews to Phrygia, xii. 147-153 ;
makes treaty of friendship with
Ptolemy Epiphanes, gives his
daughter Cleopatra to him in
marriage, xii. 154 ; father of
Seleucus, xii. 223 ; defeated by
Rome, xii. 414
Antiochus (4) IV (Epiphanes),
captures Jerusalem, B. i. 19,
31-38 ; his death, i. 40 ; v.
394 ; vi. 436 ; vii. 44 ; his
treatment of Jews foretold by
Daniel, A. x. 276 ; ascends the
throne, xii. 234 ; seizes Hyrcanus' property, xii. 236 ;
appoints high priest, xii. 237 ;
petitioned by Hellenizers, xii.
240 ; marches against Egypt,
xii. 242 ; captures Jerusalem,
xii. 246 ; petitioned by Samaritans, xii. 257-264 ; his edicts
defied by Mattathias, xii. 268-

177

to Agrippa I's daughter, xix. 355 ; xx. 139

Antiochus (16) Epiphanes, son of Antiochus IV of Commagene, vainly attempts to mount wall of Jerusalem, *B.* v. 460-465 ; allegedly in league with Parthians against Rome, vii. 221 ; 232, 236, 241 ; betrothed to Agrippa's daughter, *A.* xix. 355 ; rejects this marriage because of unwillingness to convert to Judaism, xx. 139

Antiochus (17) Callinicus. See Callinicus

Antiochus (18) (var. Antimachus), father of Numenius the Jewish envoy to the Romans, *A.* xiii. 169 ; xiv. 146

Antiochus (19), Syrian Jew, renegade, accuses Antiochene Jews of incendiarism, *B.* vii. 47-60

Antiochus (20) of Syracuse, writer on Sicilian history, contradicted by Timaeus, *Ap.* i. 17

Antiochus (21), Ravine (Valley) of (apparently in Gaulanitis), captured by Alexander Jannaeus, *B.* i. 105 ; *A.* xiii. 394

Antiochus (22), Valley of. See Antiochus, Ravine of

Antipas (1), father of Antipas (Antipater), governor of Idumaea, *A.* xiv. 10

Antipas (2), previous name of Antipater (3), *A.* xiv. 10

Antipas (3), Herod (Herod the tetrarch), son of Herod the Great and Malthace, *B.* i. 562, 646, 664, 668 ; contends for throne of Judaea, ii. 20-22 ; made tetrarch, ii. 94-95 ; ii. 167-168 ; accused by Agrippa, ii. 178 ; his banishment to Spain by Gaius and death, ii. 181-183 ; son of Herod by his Samaritan wife, *A.* xvii. 20 ; designated tetrarch of Galilee and Peraea, xvii. 188 ; sails for Rome to claim throne, xvii. 224-227, 238 ; receives a portion of Herod's kingdom from Augustus, xvii. 318 ; builds cities, xviii. 27 ; builds

Tiberias, xviii. 36-38 ; gives feast for Vitellius and Artabanus, xviii. 102 ; anticipates Vitellius in sending news of treaty with Parthians to Tiberius, xviii. 104-105 ; xviii. 106 ; divorces daughter of Aretas and marries Herodias, xviii. 109-112 ; defeated by Aretas, xviii. 113-115 ; his defeat attributed to his murder of John the Baptist, xviii. 116-119 ; welcome Vitellius in Jerusalem, xviii. 122 ; xviii. 136 ; dissuades Agrippa from committing suicide, xviii. 148, 150 ; urged by Herodias to improve his fortunes, xviii. 240-243 ; accused of conspiracy by Agrippa, xviii. 247-251 ; his tetrarchy given to Agrippa, xviii. 252, 255 ; xix. 351 ; founder of Tiberias, intends that Sepphoris be subordinate to it, according to Justus, *V.* 37 ; builder of palace at Tiberias containing representations of animals, 65

Antipas (4), relative of Agrippa II, in deputation to Agrippa, *B.* ii. 418, 557 ; murdered by brigands, iv. 140-146

Antipater (1), son of Jason, envoy sent to Romans by Jonathan, *A.* xiii. 169

Antipater (2), father of Aeneas the Jewish envoy to Romans, *A.* xiv. 248

Antipater (3) the Idumaean (earlier called Antipas), procurator of Judaea, *B.* i. 19 ; seeks to reinstate Hyrcanus, i. 123-124 ; i. 130 ; takes refuge with Pompey, i. 131 ; negotiates surrender of Aretas to Scaurus, i. 159 ; aids Gabinius, i. 162 ; i. 175, 177, 178, 180 ; his family and rise, i. 181 ; helps Caesar in Egypt, i. 187-188 ; prevails on Egyptian Jews, i. 190 ; rescues Mithridates, i. 191 ; praised by Mithridates, i. 192 ; i. 193 ; becomes Roman citizen, i. 194 ; i. 195, 197 ; appointed

179

GENERAL INDEX

314; orders Tyrians to return possessions of Jews, xiv. 319-320; meets Cleopatra, xiv. 324; favours Herod, xiv. 325-327, 329; makes Herod king, xiv. 379-389; urges support for Herod, xiv. 394; promises aid to Herod, xiv. 407; his favour sought by Antigonus, xiv. 412; in Athens, xiv. 420; urges Machaeras to aid Herod, xiv. 434; sends Machaeras to Herod, xiv. 437; his troops rescued by Herod from Parthian ambush, xiv. 439-441; welcomes Herod with honours, xiv. 445-447; xiv. 448; aids Herod, xiv. 453; sends Sossius to aid Herod, xiv. 469; kills Antigonus, xiv. 488-490; executes Antigonus, xv. 5-10; Alexandra's children commended to him by Dellius, xv. 24-31; xv. 32; questions Herod about Aristobulus' death, xv. 63-65; his desire for Mariamme, xv. 67; rumoured to have killed Herod, xv. 71; his desire for Mariamme, xv. 73; refuses to condemn Herod for Aristobulus' death, xv. 74-75, 77-80; xv. 85; gives Cleopatra part of Syria, xv. 88-93; escorted by Herod, xv. 96; Herod's desire to benefit him by murdering Cleopatra, xv. 99, 101-102; in Armenia, xv. 104; gives territories to Cleopatra, xv. 106; at battle of Actium, xv. 109; orders Herod to attack the Arabs, xv. 110-111; at battle of Actium, xv. 121; protects Judaea and Arabia from Cleopatra's annexation, xv. 131; defeated at Actium, xv. 161-162; murders enemies at Tyre, xv. 169; Herod's friendship with him, xv. 183; Herod recounts his friendship and loyalty for him to Octavia, xv. 189-190, 193, 195; xv. 197; defeated by Octavius, xv. 215; refuses to give Idumaea to Cleopatra, xv.

256, 258; Herod names Antonia for him, xv. 409; his defeat at Actium, xviii. 26; shares his rule with Augustus Caesar, xviii. 32; Herod names Antonia in his honour, xviii. 92; slays Antigonus, xx. 246; corrupted by Cleopatra, who deserts him at Actium, *Ap.* ii. 58-59

Antyllus, father of Capella (Jewish leader in Tiberias), *V.* 69

Anuath Borcaeus, village in Judaea, *B.* iii. 51

Anubis, Egyptian god in whose guise Mundus has intimate relations with Paulina, *A.* xviii. 72-73, 75, 77

Apachnas, third Hycsos king of Egypt, *Ap.* i. 80

Apame, concubine of King Darius, *A.* xi. 54

Apamea, city in Syria, site of fighting between Pompeians and Caesarians, *B.* i. 216; i. 218-219, 362; ii. 479; *A.* xiii. 131; besieged by Antiochus Sidetes, xiii. 224; xiv. 38, 268, 271; xv. 96

Apate (Deceit), deified by Greeks, *Ap.* ii. 248

Apellaeus (Apellaios), Macedonian name for ninth month, *B.* iv. 654; *A.* xi. 148; xii. 248, 319, 321

Apellaios. See Apellaeus

Apelles, officer of Antiochus Epiphanes slain by Mattathias, *A.* xii. 270

Aphairema, district given to Jewish nation by Demetrius II, *A.* xiii. 127

Aphek (1). See Amphekas

Aphek (2). See Apheka

Apheka (Bibl. Aphek), city in Palestine (identity uncertain), *A.* viii. 381, 383

Apheku, tower near Antipatris in Palestine, *B.* ii. 513

Apheras, son of Abraham, *A.* i. 241

Aphra (var. Ephra), city in Libya, *A.* i. 241

Aphranes, son of Abraham, *A.* i. 241

182

GENERAL INDEX

Aphthia, village in Judaea, *B.* iv. 155

Apion, Alexandrian delegate to Emperor Gaius Caligula, *A.* xviii. 257, 259 ; grammarian, references to Jews in his *History of Egypt* refuted by Josephus, *Ap.* ii. 2-144 ; his lies, ii. 295

Apis, Egyptian sacred animal picked up by King Amenophis in Memphis, *Ap.* i. 246 ; entrusted by King Amenophis to priests, i. 263

Apollo, temple of on Palatine Hill in Rome, *B.* ii. 81 ; temple of at Gaza, *A.* xiii. 364 ; temple of on Palatine Hill in Rome, xvii. 301 ; worshipped by Idumaeans from Dorii, *Ap.* ii. 112 ; walks upon the earth, ii. 117 ; as lawgiver, ii. 162 ; depicted as beardless, (ii. 242) ; lute-player, devoted to archery, (ii. 243) ; hired as builder and as shepherd to men, (ii. 247)

Apollodorus, historian, cited on Antiochus Epiphanes' motive in plundering temple in Jerusalem, *Ap.* ii. 84

Apollodotus, Gazaean general, *A.* xiii. 359-361

Apollonia, city in Palestine, rebuilt by Gabinius, *B.* i. 166 ; *A.* xiii. 395

Apollonius (1), governor of Samaria under Antiochus Epiphanes, *A.* xii. 261, 264 ; defeated by Judas Maccabaeus, xii. 287

Apollonius (2) Taos (var. Daos), governor of Syria, defeated by Jonathan, *A.* xiii. 88-102

Apollonius (3), son of Alexander, Jewish envoy sent to Rome by Hyrcanus I, *A.* xiii. 260, xiv. 248

Apollonius (4) Molon. See Molon, Apollonius

Aponius, Roman senator wounded by Claudius' soldiers, *A.* xix. 264

Apophis, fourth Hycsos king of Egypt, *Ap.* i. 80

Apphus, surname of Jonathan, son of Mattathias, *A.* xii. 266

Appius Menas, Roman mentioned in decree of Lentulus, *A.* xiv. 239

April, Ides of, *A.* xiv. 219

Apsanes (Bibl. Ibzan), judge, rules Israel, *A.* v. 271-272

Apulius (1), Lucius, father of Lucius Apulius, of Sergian tribe, *A.* xiv. 220

Apulius (2), Lucius, Roman senator, *A.* xiv. 220

Aquila (1), delivers death wound to Gaius Caligula, *A.* xix. 110

Aquila (2), prefect of Egypt under Augustus, *A.* xix. 283

Aquileia, city in Italy, *A.* xvi. 91

Aquilius. See Gellius (1) and (2)

Arabatha (1). See Arablatha

Arabatha (2) (var. Rabatha, Barbatha, Tharabatha ; Bibl. Rabbath Moab), *A.* xiv. 18

Arabia (1) (see also Arab[s]), *B.* i. 6, 89-90, 124-125, 159, 181, 267, 274, 276, 286, 360, 365, 385, 419, 487, 583 ; iii. 47, 51 ; iv. 454, 482 ; v. 160 ; vii. 172 ; bequeathed to Ishmael, *A.* ii. 213 ; iv. 82, 85, 173 ; v. 82 ; its kings send gifts to Solomon, viii. 179 ; ix. 191 ; xii. 233 ; xiii. 116, 144, 179, 389 ; invaded by Antiochus Dionysus, xiii. 391 ; xiv. 15, 80, 83, 128, 362 ; coveted by Cleopatra, xv. 92 ; parts of it leased by Herod from Cleopatra, xv. 96 ; invaded by Herod, xv. 111 ; xvi. 220, 224, 275, 280 ; invaded by Herod, xvi. 283, 287 ; xvi. 297, 340 ; invaded by Herod, xvi. 341 ; becomes base of operations for brigands of Trachonitis, xvi. 347 ; given to Aretas, xvi. 353 ; xvii. 62-63 ; xviii. 112 ; conquered by Nebuchadnezzar, king of Babylon, *Ap.* i. 133 ; ii. 25

Arabia (2) Felix, *B.* ii. 385 ; *A.* i. 239

Arabian Gulf, *A.* iii. 25

Arabians. See Arab(s)

Arablatha (var. Arabatha, Aramatha, Salabatha, Salamatha, Sabolatha ; Bibl. Riblah), city in Syria, *A.* x. 135, 149, 150

Arab(s) (Arabians ; see also

183

GENERAL INDEX

Arabia), *B.* i. 99, 128, 131, 159, 161, 181, 363-385, 388, 440, 534, 566, 574-577 ; ii. 68-70, 76, 362 ; iii. 51, 68 ; archers at Jotapata, iii. 168 ; iii. 211, 262 ; v. 290, 551, 556 ; circumcise at age of thirteen, *A.* i. 214 ; origin of names of their tribes, i. 221 ; Joseph sold to them, ii. 32-33 ; iv. 82, 161 ; attack Israelites, v. 210 ; defeated by Gideon, v. 229 ; pay tribute to Jehoshaphat, viii. 396 ; join Ammanites against Jehoshaphat, ix. 7 ; attack Jehoram, ix. 102 ; subdued by Uzziah, ix. 217 ; Herodotus' erroneous account of Sennacherib's invasion of them, x. 18-19 ; warred on by Hyrcanus, xii. 229, 236 ; aid Timotheus, xii. 341 ; xiii. 10, 18, 118, 131, 360 ; subdued by Alexander Jannaeus, xiii. 374-375 ; xiii. 382, 384 ; slay Antiochus Dionysus, xiii. 387, 391 ; xiii. 414 ; xiv. 10, 14-15, 18, 20-21, 121-122, 227 ; refuse to aid Herod, xiv. 370-372 ; xiv. 390 ; attacked by and defeat Herod, xv. 107-120 ; attack Jews after earthquake, xv. 123, 130 ; cheat Jews, xv. 131-133 ; xv. 142 ; defeated by Jews, xv. 147-160 ; xv. 167, 172 ; distract Herod from aiding Antony, xv. 189 ; invade Herod's territory, xv. 351 ; spoils taken from them adorn Herod's temple, xv. 402 ; xvi. 225-226 ; war with Herod, xvi. 271-285 ; xvi. 284 ; Syllaeus appeals to Augustus on their behalf, xvi. 288, 291-292 ; ruled by Aeneas, xvi. 294 ; xvi. 296 ; war with Herod, xvi. 337-351 ; provide evidence against Syllaeus, xvi. 337, 339 ; xvii. 10 ; plot against Herod, xvii. 54-57 ; their hatred for Herod, xvii. 290 ; terrorized by brigand Tholomaeus, xx. 5 ; war with Izates and are defeated, xx. 77-79 ; Hycsos identified with them, *Ap.* i. 82

Aracharis (Bibl. Rab-saris), Assyrian commanding officer at siege of Jerusalem, *A.* x. 4

Aradus, city in Syria, *A.* i. 138 ; xiii. 367 ; Jewish rights there protected by Antony, xiv. 323

Aram. See Aramus

Aramaeans, termed Syrians by Greeks, *A.* i. 144

Aramaic, *A.* x. 8

Aramatha (1) (Aramathe, Ariman ; Bibl. Ramoth), city of refuge in Galadene, (Ariman) *A.* iv. 173 ; (Aramathe) viii. 398, 411 ; (Aramathe) Ahab dies there, viii. 417 ; (Aramathe) ix. 105-106, 112

Aramatha (2). See Arablatha ; Armatha

Aramathe. See Aramatha (1)

Aramathon. See Armatha

Aram Beth-Rehob. See Syros (2)

Aram Naharaim. See Syros (2)

Aramus (Bibl. Aram), son of Shem, *A.* i. 144-145

Aran (Arran ; Bibl. Haran), brother of Abraham, *A.* i. 151-152, 154, 289

Araos (Bibl. Rehob), father of Hadadezer, *A.* vii. 99

Araphos (Bibl. Raphah), Philistine, father of Ishbi-benob, *A.* vii. 298

Arasamos. See Erasamos

Arases (Bibl. Rezin), king of Syria and Damascus, *A.* ix. 244-245 ; killed by Assyrians, ix. 253

Araske (Bibl. Nisroch), temple of Sennacherib, *A.* x. 23

Arauna. See Oronnas

Arbela (1), village in Galilee, *B.* i. 305 ; *A.* xii. 421 ; xiv. 415 ; village where Josephus convenes meeting of Galilaeans to inform them of the confirmation of his appointment as commander in Galilee, *V.* 311

Arbela (2), Cave of, village in Lower Galilee, fortified by Josephus, *V.* 188

Arcadians, vaunted antiquity of, *Ap.* i. 22

Arce (1) (Arcea, Arke), town in

GENERAL INDEX

GENERAL INDEX

Aregetes, father of Syphas, *B.* iv. 141

Areios (1) (Areius ; var. Areus), Lacedaemonian king, sends letter to Onias, *A.* xii. 225-228 ; xiii. 167

Areios (2). See Arius

Areius. See Areios (1)

Areli. See Arieles

Aremantos, Babylonian commander assigned to sack of Jerusalem, *A.* x. 135

Ares, Greek god, fights among men (*Ap.* ii. 242)

Aretas (1), Arab king, *B.* i. 103, 124-131, 159 ; *A.* xiii. 360 ; reigns over Syria, xiii. 392 ; xiii. 414 ; persuaded by Antipater to help Hyrcanus against Aristobulus, xiv. 14-17 ; besieges Aristobulus in temple during Passover, xiv. 19, 21 ; forced by Pompey to leave siege of Jerusalem, xiv. 32 ; defeated by Aristobulus, xiv. 33 ; xiv. 81

Aretas (2), Arab king of Petra, previously called Aeneas, *B.* i. 574 ; ii. 68 ; succeeds Obadas, *A.* xvi. 294 ; battles for power with Syllaeus, xvi. 295-296 ; accuses Syllaeus, xvi. 339 ; confirmed as ruler of Arabia, xvi. 353, 355 ; accuses Syllaeus, xvii. 54 ; helps Varus subdue brigands in Judaea, xvii. 287 ; his army dismissed by Varus, xvii. 296 ; quarrels with Herod the tetrarch, xviii. 109-115 ; expedition of Vitellius against him halted by death of Tiberius, xviii. 120, 125

Arethusa, city in Palestine, freed by Pompey, *B.* i. 156 ; *A.* xiv. 75

Areus. See Areios (1)

Argarizin (Garizein), town in Palestine captured by John Hyrcanus, *B.* i. 63 ; (Garizein) *A.* xiii. 255

Argos, city in Greece, site of statue of Hera, *B.* i. 414 ; Acusilaus of, *Ap.* i. 13 ; discrepancies among its historians, i. 17 ; Danaus comes to it, i.

103 ; flight of Danaus to it, ii. 16

Ari (Arinus), father of Simon and Judes, (Arinus) *B.* v. 250 ; vi. 92, 148 ; vii. 215

Aridaeans (Arvadites), their land unassigned by Joshua, *A.* v. 89

Arieles (Bibl. Areli), son of Gad, *A.* ii. 182

Aries, sun is there during Nisan, *A.* iii. 248

Arinus. See Ari

Arioch (1), Assyrian commander, *A.* i. 173

Arioch (2). See Arioches

Arioches (Bibl. Arioch), commander of bodyguard of King Nebuchadnezzar, *A.* x. 197-199, 202

Arion, steward of Joseph the Tobiad, *A.* xii. 200-204

Aristaeus. See Aristeas

Aristeas (Aristaeus), persuades Ptolemy Philadelphus to free Jewish captives, *A.* xii. 17, 19, 24, 26 ; arranges to have Jewish law translated into Greek, xii. 50, 53, 86 ; xii. 100 ; bodyguard of Ptolemy Philadelphus, appointed his commissioner, *Ap.* ii. 46

Aristeus, secretary of Sanhedrin, slain by Simon, *B.* v. 532

Aristides, father of Memnon of Halicarnassus, *A.* xiv. 255

Aristobulus (1), son of Amyntas, envoy from Jews to Rome, *A.* xiv. 248

Aristobulus (2), eldest son of John Hyrcanus, besieges Sebaste, *B.* i. 64-65 ; establishes monarchy, i. 70 ; kills brother Antigonus, i. 72-77 ; his death, i. 81-85 ; *A.* xiii. 276 ; defeats Antiochus Cyzicenus, xiii. 277 ; becomes king upon death of Hyrcanus, xiii. 301 ; has Antigonus murdered, xiii. 304, 306, 307, 309 ; his remorse at killing of Antigonus, xiii. 314-315 ; his death, xiii. 320 ; xiii. 322-323 ; also called Judas, succeeds Hyrcanus as high priest, xx. 240-241

186

GENERAL INDEX

Aristobulus (3), son of Alexander Jannaeus and Alexandra, *B.* i. 109, 114 ; proclaims himself king, i. 117 ; i. 118-119 ; defeats Hyrcanus, i. 120-124 ; defeated by forces of Aretas, i. 126 ; i. 128, 130, 132 ; his war with Pompey, i. 133-154 ; taken to Rome by Pompey, i. 157 ; i. 160 ; escapes from Rome, i. 171 ; defeated by Romans, retreats to Machaerus, i. 172 ; captured by Gabinius and sent to Rome, i. 173 ; i. 174, 176, 180-181 ; freed by Caesar, i. 183 ; his death, i. 184 ; his widow, i. 186 ; i. 195, 241, 344, 482 ; v. 396, 398 ; vii. 171 ; *A.* xiii. 407 ; denounces his mother for supporting the Pharisees, xiii. 411, 416 ; xiii. 418 ; plots to seize power from Alexandra, xiii. 422-425, 429, 433 ; receives kingship from his brother Hyrcanus, xiv. 4-7 ; slandered by Antipater, xiv. 8-14 ; besieged by Aretas in temple during Passover, xiv. 19-26 ; gains support of Pompey, xiv. 30-32 ; defeats Hyrcanus, xiv. 33 ; sends gift to Pompey, xiv. 34, 36 ; brings quarrel with Hyrcanus to Pompey, xiv. 37, 41-42 44 ; condemned by Pompey, xiv. 46 ; resists Pompey, xiv. 47 ; forced to yield, xiv. 48-50 ; arrested by Pompey, xiv. 55-57 ; his partisans resist Pompey, xiv. 58 ; xiv. 71, 73 ; with Hyrcanus responsible for national misfortunes, xiv. 77 ; taken as captive to Rome, xiv. 79 ; xiv. 82 ; escapes from Rome, xiv. 92 ; defeated by Gabinius, xiv. 93-94 ; taken captive to Rome again, xiv. 96-97 ; xiv. 100, 120, 122 ; released from prison, xiv. 123-124 ; xiv. 125-126 ; xiv. 140, 142, 297, 300, 330, 353, 387 ; Herod marries his granddaughter, xiv. 467 ; xv. 23 ; removes brother Hyrcanus from high priesthood, xv. 41 ; his deeds recalled by the Jews, xv. 52 ; deprives Hyrcanus of high priesthood, xv. 180, xx. 243 ; xx. 245

Aristobulus (4) (Jonathan), son of Alexander and Alexandra, *B.* i. 437 ; *A.* xv. 23 ; his beauty attracts Antony, xv. 25, 29 ; appointed high priest by Herod, xv. 31, 34, 41 ; murdered by Herod, xv. 51-56 ; xv. 64 ; appointed high priest, xx. 247-248

Aristobulus (5), son of Herod and Mariamme, *B.* i. 445-446, 467, 478, 479, 496, 516, 519, 520, 528, 531, 534, 551, 552, 553, 557, 563, 565, 581, 586, 588, 599, 603 ; ii. 102, 108, 178, 222 ; brought up in Rome, *A.* xv. 342 ; marries Berenice, daughter of Salome, xvi. 11 ; named by Herod successor after his brothers, xvi. 133 ; xvi. 193 ; Salome's hatred for him, xvi. 201 ; plotted against by Antipater, xvi. 249 ; hated by his father, xvi. 311 ; imprisoned by Herod his father, xvi. 322 ; killed by strangling at command of Herod, xvi. 394 ; his widow married to Antipater, xvii. 9 ; his children, xvii. 12, 14, 18 ; xvii. 22 ; his death, xvii. 80 ; impersonated by pretender, xvii. 326 ; xvii. 334-335 ; father of Herodias and brother of Herod the tetrarch, xviii. 110 ; father of Agrippa I, xviii. 126, 131 ; his children, xviii. 134 ; xviii. 242

Aristobulus (6), son of Aristobulus and Berenice, and brother of Agrippa I, *B.* i. 552 ; ii. 221 ; *A.* (xvii. 12-13) ; xviii. 133 ; marries Jotape, xviii. 135 ; involves Agrippa in quarrel with Flaccus, xviii. 151-154 ; joins appeal to Petronius not to set up statue in temple, xviii. 273, 276

Aristobulus (7) the Younger, son of Herod king of Chalcis, *B.* ii. 221,

187

GENERAL INDEX

GENERAL INDEX

Ptolemy II Philadelphus, *A.* xii. 51

Arsinoe (2), sister of Cleopatra, killed by Antony, *A.* xv. 89; slain on Cleopatra's orders, *Ap.* ii. 57

Artabanus, Parthian king, wages civil war with Vonones, *A.* xviii. 48-52; Vitellius negotiates treaty of friendship with him, xviii. 96-104; xviii. 250; hears of outlaw band of Anilaeus and Asinaeus, xviii. 317; enlists services of Anilaeus and Asinaeus, xviii. 325-332; xviii. 353; receives brothers of Izates as hostages, xx. 37; seeks help from Izates, xx. 54-60; restored to his throne through Izates' help, xx. 62-66; his death, xx. 69

Artabazes, son of Tigranes, Armenian king, taken prisoner by Antony, *B.* i. 363, *A.* xv. 104-105

Artaxerxes (1) (Bibl. Ahasuerus), Persian king, *A.* xi. 184; extent of his kingdom, xi. 186; xi. 190-194; marries Esther, xi. 202; crucifies plotters, xi. 208; orders Haman honoured, xi. 209; presents Haman with men and money, xi. 215; his decree against Jews, xi. 216; embraces Esther, xi. 237; inquires after Mordecai's reward, xi. 250; asks Haman's advice, xi. 252; orders Haman to honour Mordecai, xi. 255; accuses Haman, xi. 265; decides to hang Haman, xi. 267; presents Haman's property to Esther, xi. 269; permits Esther to send letter throughout the kingdom, xi. 271; orders scribes to write on Jews' behalf, xi. 272; his letter to governors, xi. 273; xi. 290, 296; his reign as final terminus of prophetic books, *Ap.* i. 40-41

Artaxerxes (2) II, Persian King (perhaps Artaxerxes III Ochus) Bagoses his general, *A.* xi. 297; xi. 300

Artaxias, son of Artabazes, becomes king of Armenia, *A.* xv. 105

Artemis, Greek goddess, her temple in Elymais in Persia, *A.* xii. 354, 358; her temple at Ephesus, xv. 89; devoted to archery (*Ap.* ii. 243)

Artemision. See Artemisius

Artemisios. See Artemisius

Artemisius (Artemisios, Artemision), Macedonian month (= Hebrew Iyar), *B.* ii. 284, 315; iii. 142; *v.* 302, 466; vi. 296; *A.* viii. 61; (Artemision) xiv. 262

Artemon, president of Ephesians, *A.* xiv. 225

Artorius, Roman soldier, *B.* vi. 188-189

Arucaeans (Arkites), their land unassigned by Joshua, *A.* v. 89

Arucaeus (Bibl. the Arkite), son of Canaan, *A.* i. 138

Arudaeus (Bibl. the Arvadite), son of Canaan, *A.* i. 138

Aruntius. See Arruntius (2)

Arura (Aroura; "Plowland"), place in Judaea, *A.* vi. 251; (Aroura) vi. 377

Arvadite. See Arudaeus

Arvadites. See Aridaeans

Arydda (var. Sarydda, Rydda, Marisa), Arab city, *A.* xiv. 18

Arza. See Osa

Asa. See Asanos

Asabel(os) (Bibl. Ashbel), son of Benjamin, *A.* ii. 180

Asael (Bibl. Asahel), son of Zeruiah and Suri, brother of Joab, *A.* vii. 11, 14; killed by Abner, vii. 16-17; vii. 19, 36, 285

Asahel. See Asael

Asam (Bibl. Ozem), son of Jesse, brother of David, *A.* vi. 161

Asamon, mountain in Galilee, *B.* ii. 511

Asamonaeus (Asamonaios), priest, father of Mattathias, ancestor of Hasmonaeans, *B.* i. 16, 36; his descendants, *A.* xi. 111; father of Symeon, xii. 265; rule of his family ended by Herod, xiv. 490-491; his

189

GENERAL INDEX

family builds citadel around the temple, xv. 403 ; Josephus descended from his relatives, xvi. 187 ; his descendants, xvii. 162 ; xx. 190 ; enumeration of high priests descended from him, xx. 238 ; xx. 247, 249 ; ancestor of Josephus, *V.* 2, 4

Asamonaios. See Asamonaeus

Asamonean family. See Asamonaeus

Asanos (Bibl. Asa), son and successor of Abijah, *A.* viii. 286-287 ; his death, viii. 288 ; his victory over Ethiopians, viii. 290, 292, 294, 295, 298 ; allies with Syrians, viii. 303-304 ; defeats Baasha, viii. 306-307 ; viii. 312 ; his long reign, viii. 314-315

Asaph (1), sons of, sing in the temple, *A.* xi. 80

Asaph (?) (2). See Addaios

Asaphon. See Asophon

Asarachoddas (Bibl. Esarhaddon), Assyrian king, successor to Sennacherib, *A.* x. 23

Asartha, Hebrew month when Pentecost takes place, *A.* iii. 252

Ascalon, Ascalonites, city in Palestine, *B.* i. 185, 187, 422 ; ii. 98, 460, 477 ; iii. 9, 12, 23 ; iv. 663 ; city allotted to Judah, *A.* v. 81 ; captured by Judah and Simeon, v. 128 ; v. 177 ; people of, v. 294 ; vi. 4, 5, 8, 191 ; Joseph the Tobiad collects taxes there, xii. 181-182 ; xiii. 101, 149, 180 ; xiv. 10, 126, 128, 139 ; Caesar's decrees about Jews inscribed there, xiv. 197 ; xvi. 253 ; royal palace there given to Salome by Augustus, xvii. 321

Aschanaxes (Bibl. Ashkenaz), son of Gomer, *A.* i. 126

Aschanaxians, called Reginians by the Greeks, *A.* i. 126

Aschanes (Bibl. Ashpenaz), eunuch of Nebuchadnezzar, *A.* x. 190-193

Asclepiades, an Athenian, *A.* xiv. 149

Asellius. See Gellius (1) and (2)

Asenath. See Asennethis

Asennethis (Bibl. Asenath), daughter of Pentephres, wife of Joseph, *A.* ii. 91

Aser (1) (Bibl. Asher), son of Jacob, *A.* i. 306 ; his children, ii. 182-183

Aser (2) (Bibl. Asher), tribe of, its territory, *A.* v. 85 ; pays homage to David, vii. 59

Ashbel. See Asabel(os)

Ashdod. See Azotus

Asher (1). See Ake

Asher (2). See Aser (1) and (2)

Ashkenaz. See Aschanaxes

Ashpenaz. See Aschanes

Ashtoreth. See Astarte

Asia (1), Asiatic, *B.* i. 242, 358-359, 366 ; v. 387 ; *A.* i. 122, 131 ; inhabited by Shem's sons, i. 143 ; controlled by Assyrians, i. 171 ; v. 220 ; ix. 214 ; x. 20, 74 ; xi. 3 ; its Jews subject to Romans, xi. 133 ; xi. 313, 315, 334 ; ruled by Antigonus, xii. 2 ; xii. 119 ; governed by Antiochus the Great, xii. 129 ; ruled by Seleucus, xii. 223-224 ; xiii. 78 ; ruled by Ptolemy Philometor, xiii. 113 ; ruled by Alexander Balas, xiii. 119 ; xiii. 165 ; xiv. 104, 110, 113, 186 ; its Jews granted privileges by Dolabella, xiv. 223-224 ; its Jews exempted from military service, xiv. 230 ; campaign of Antony there, xiv. 301, 309, 311-312 ; xvi. 12, 63 ; governed by Agrippa, xvi. 86 ; xvi. 160, 165, 167 ; its Jews, xvi. 172 ; xix. 104 ; dominion of Medes and Persians there, *Ap.* i. 64 ; dominated by Assyrians, i. 90 ; Cyrus its king, i. 145 ; Aristotle meets learned Jew there, i. 181 ; its conquerors enslave Egyptians, ii. 128 ; Macedonians succeed Persians as its rulers, ii. 133 ; changes in its rulers, ii. 228

Asia (2), Lower, boundary of Antiochus Epiphanes' realm, *A.* xii. 295

GENERAL INDEX

Asiaticus, Valerius. See Valerius (1), Asiaticus

Asinaeus, Jew, with his brother Anilaeus organizes outlaw band in Babylonia, *A.* xviii. 314; fights on Sabbath and routs Parthians, xviii. 320, 323; makes pledge with Artabanus xviii. 327, 331, 333, 338; his downfall, xviii. 342-343, 346, 348, 352

Asinius Pollio, C., cited by Strabo, *A.* xiv. 138; Roman consul, xiv. 389; Herod's sons Alexander and Aristobulus stay at his home xv. 343

Asochis, town in Galilee, captured by Ptolemy Lathyrus, *B.* i. 86; *A.* xiii. 337; place where delegation from Jerusalem is met by popular demonstration in favour of Josephus, *V.* 233 town where large throng condemns citizens of Tiberias as traitors, *V.* 384

Asochis, plain of. See Plain, the Great (1) of Asochis

Asophon (var. Asaphon; prob Bibl. Saphon), place near Jordan River, *A.* xiii. 338

Asor (Asora; Bibl. Hazor), city in Galilee, *A.* v. 199, 209; city built by Solomon, viii. 151; (Asora) captured by Tiglath-Pileser, ix. 235; xiii. 158

asosra, Hebrew name for trumpet, *A.* iii. 291

Aspendius. See Antiochus (8)

Asphaltitis (Asphaltophorus), Lake (Bituminous Lake) (= Dead Sea), *B.* i. 657; iii. 515; iv. 437-438, 453, 455-456, 474; description of, iv. 476-477; vii. 168, 281; *A.* i. 174, 203; iv. 85; (Asphaltis: read Asphaltitis) iv. 7; ix. 206; xv. 168; (Asphaltophorus) xvii. 171; (Bituminous Lake) identified by Josephus with Choerilus' " broad lake," *Ap.* i. 174

Asphaltophorus, Lake. See Asphaltitis, Lake

Asphar, Pool of, near Jerusalem, *A.* xiii. 8

Asprenas (var. Ambronas, Am-

pronas), Roman senator, *A.* xix. 87; one of plotters against Gaius Caligula, xix. 98; killed by German bodyguard, xix. 123; his head fixed upon an altar, xix. 142, 216

asps, imputation by Egyptians of virtue to, *Ap.* ii. 86

ass, place of collapse of, avoided by Pythagoras, *Ap.* i. 164; its head worshipped by Jews in the temple according to Apion, ii. 80-88; fable of Jewish cult of, ii. 114, 120

assaron (Bibl. *omer*), Hebrew measure, *A.* iii. 29-30, 142, 252, 255, 257, 270, 320; viii. 92

Asshur. See Assyras

Asshurim. See Assuris

Assis, sixth and last Hycsos king of Egypt, *Ap.* i. 81

assistants, aid Josephus in Greek, *Ap.* i. 50; not needed by God in creation, ii. 192

Assuris (Bibl. Asshurim), son of Dedan, *A.* i. 238

Assyras (Bibl. Asshur), son of Shem, eponymous ancestor of Assyrians, *A.* i. 143

Assyria. See Assyrians

Assyrians (1), (Assyria), Greek histories of, *B.* i. 13; v. 387, 388, 404, 407-408; their descent from Assyras, *A.* i. 143; their war against Sodomites, i. 171-175; defeated by Abraham, i. 176-179, 182; origin of their name, i. 241; attack Israelites, v. 180; routed by Keniaz, v. 183; vi. 90; receive tribute from Menahem, ix. 232; exile Israelites, ix. 235; their downfall prophesied by Nahum, ix. 239; bribed by Ahaz to attack Israel, ix. 252-253; settle in Damascus, ix. 253; paid off by Ahaz, ix. 254; their gods worshipped by Ahaz, ix. 256; threaten war against Hezekiah, ix. 275; defeat and exile Israelites, ix. 277; invade Syria, ix. 283; ix. 284-285, 287; send priests to Cuthaeans, ix. 289; exact tribute from

GENERAL INDEX

192

GENERAL INDEX

Attica, discrepancies among its historians, *Ap.* i. 17

Auaran. See Auran

Auaris, city in Egyptian nome of Sethroite, rebuilt by Hycsos king Salitis, *Ap.* i. 78; place where Hycsos were confined after defeat by Misphragmouthosis, i. 86; abandoned city of Hycsos, assigned to lepers by King Amenophis of Egypt, i. 237-238; Osariph undertakes to escort Hycsos there, i. 242; Hycsos arrive there, i. 243; city given to lepers and cripples by King Amenophis of Egypt, i. 260-262, 296

Augustus (1) (Octavian, Octavius, Young Caesar), *B.* i. 20, 118, 225, 242, 283, 285, 298, 386-388, 391, 393-395, 398-400, 403-404, 412, 414-415, 447, 451-452, 454, 457-459, 465, 474, 483, 510, 523, 531, 535, 538, 554, 566, 573, 575, 607, 613, 620, 623, 625, 633, 640, 645-646, 661, 669; ii. 2, 17, 19, 24-26, 28, 32, 34-35, 37, 39, 78-80, 82-83; divides Herod's kingdom, ii. 93-100; ii. 106, 109-111, 117, 167; his death, ii. 168; ii. 215; v. 562; his war with Cassius, *A.* xiv. 280; defeats Cassius at Philippi, xiv. 301; promises aid to Herod, xiv. 383; honours Herod, xiv. 388; promises aid to Herod, xiv. 407; at battle of Actium, xv. 109, 121; victor at Actium, xv. 161; his enmity to Herod, xv. 164, 167; his meeting with Herod, xv. 183, 187, 189; honours Herod, xv. 194; puts Alexas to death, xv. 197; visits Judaea, xv. 198-201; xv. 208; defeats Antony, xv. 215; meets Herod in Egypt, xv. 217; escorted by Herod, xv. 218; xv. 221; Herod establishes athletic contests in his honour, xv. 268, 272; appoints Petronius prefect of Egypt, xv. 307; receives soldiers from Herod, xv. 317;

his couch in Herod's palace in Jerusalem, xv. 318; receives flattering attention from Herod, xv. 328, 330; xv. 336; temple to him built at Caesarea, xv. 339; welcomes Herod's sons, xv. 343; gives Herod additional territory, xv. 344-348; xv. 350, 352; acquits Herod of charges of cruelty against Gadarenes, xv. 354-358; gives Herod Zenodorus' territory, xv. 360-363; Herod consecrates a temple to him, xv. 364; met by Herod in Italy, xvi. 6; xvi. 26, 74; gets good report of Antipater from Herod, xvi. 85-86; consulted by Herod about his sons, xvi. 90-100; hears Herod's sons' defence, xvi. 103-104, 106, 116, 118, 121; reconciles Herod with his sons, xvi. 121-127; exchanges gifts with Herod, xvi. 128; gives Herod the right to choose his successor, xvi. 129; xvi. 132; honoured by Herod at games at Caesarea, xvi. 138-139, 141; founder of Nicopolis, xvi. 147; honoured by Herod, xvi. 157; his decrees in favour of the Jews of Asia, xvi. 161-166; reaffirms right of Jews to send money to the temple, xvi. 171; Pontifex Maximus, xvi. 162; protects rights of Jews in Cyrene, xvi. 169; affirms right of Jews of Ephesus to send money to the temple, xvi. 172-173; xvi. 253; visited by Herod, xvi. 270; adds to Herod's territory, xvi. 271; visited by Herod, xvi. 273; xvi. 275, 277; receives appeal from Syllaeus on behalf of Arabs, xvi. 287, 289-291; becomes angry with Herod, xvi. 293-294; courted by both Syllaeus and Aretas in their struggle for power, xvi. 295-297; becomes angry with Herod, xvi. 298-299; xvi. 323; Herod appeals to him against his sons, xvi.

193

GENERAL INDEX

333-334; reconciled with Herod, xvi. 335, 338, 340-351; condemns Syllaeus to death, xvi. 352; confirms Aretas as ruler of Arabia, xvi. 353-355; advises Herod to convene a council concerning his sons, xvi. 356-358, 365; xvii. 10, 42; hears Antipater's charges against Syllaeus, xvii. 52, 54; xvii. 87, 93; his friendship invoked by Antipater when tried before Herod, xvii. 103; informed by Herod of Antipater's villainy, xvii. 133; xvii. 141, 142, 144; beneficiary of Herod's will, xvii. 146; his letter to Herod, xvii. 182; Herod's bequest to him, xvii. 190; xvii. 195; his confirmation of Archelaus as king awaited, xvii. 202, 208-209, 222-223; hears charges against Archelaus, xvii. 228-239; hears Nicolas' defense of Archelaus, xvii. 241-247; postpones his decision about Archelaus, xvii. 248-249; xvii. 252; punishes leaders of Jewish revolt, xvii. 297-298; receives petition from Jews to end rule of Herodians, xvii. 301-302, 312; divides Herod's kingdom among his sons, xvii. 317-320; gives royal palace at Ascalon to Salome, xvii. 321; gives gifts to Herod's unmarried daughters, xvii. 322, 324; unmasks false Alexander, xvii. 332-333, 336-337; banishes Archelaus to Gaul, xvii. 342-344, 348; sends Quirinius to Syria, xvii. 355; dispatches Quirinius to govern Judaea, xviii. 1; defeats Mark Antony, xviii. 26; xviii. 28; his death xviii. 32-33; Palatine games held in his honour, xix. 75; games at Palatine instituted by him, xix. 87; confirms rights of Jews in Alexandria, xix. 282-283; upholds rights of Jews in Alexandria, xix. 289; xix. 307, 310; Cleopatra revolts against him, *Ap.* ii. 58;

captures Alexandria, ii. 60; his letters attest services of Jews against Egyptians, ii. 61

Augustus (2), Port of. See Sebastos

Auletes. See Ptolemy (9)

Aulus Furius. See Furius (2), Aulus

Auran (Auaran), surname of Eleazar, son of Mattathias, *A.* xii. 266, 373

Auranitis, region in Transjordan, added to Herod's realm, *B.* i. 398; given to Philip, ii. 95; given to Agrippa, ii. 215; ii. 421; given to Herod by Augustus, *A.* xv. 343, 352; given to Herod's son Philip by Augustus, xvii. 319

auspices, taking of, interrupted by Jew Mosollamus, *Ap.* i. 202-204

Autocratoris, name later given to Sepphoris, *A.* xviii. 27

Auza, city in Libya, founded by Ethbaal, *A.* viii. 324

Avitus. See Jabin

Axioramos, Jewish high priest, *A.* x. 152

Aza (Var. Eza, Gazara), Mount, mountain in Judaea, *A.* xii. 429

Azaelos (Bibl. Hazael), king of Syria, *A.* viii. 352; servant of Ben-hadad, consults Elisha, ix. 88-89, 91; becomes king of Syria, ix. 92-93; ix. 159; marches on Jerusalem, ix. 170; becomes king in accordance with prophecy of Elisha, ix. 175; his death, ix. 184

Azaraiah. See Azaros

Azariah. See Azarias (1), (2), (3), and (4)

Azarias (1) (Bibl. Azariah), Hebrew prophet, *A.* viii. 295

Azarias (2) (Bibl. Azariah), high priest in reign of Uzziah, *A.* ix. 224

Azarias (3) (Bibl. Azariah), high priest, successor to Ahimaaz, *A.* x. 152

Azarias (4) (Bibl. Azariah), called Abdenago, *A.* x. 188-189

Azarias (5), commander under

194

GENERAL INDEX

GENERAL INDEX

by Antiochus Epiphanes, slain by Mattathias, *B.* i. 35-36 ; sent by Demetrius against Judas, *A.* xii. 393-396, 420, 422-423 ; defeats Judas at Berzetho, xii. 426, 428 ; oppresses Jews after Judas' death, xiii. 4 ; seeks to slay Jonathan, xiii. 7, 9-10 ; attacks Jews on the Sabbath, xiii. 12, 14 ; fortifies cities of Judaea, xiii. 15 ; returns to Syria, xiii. 22 ; besieges Jonathan, xiii. 23-28, 30 ; makes peace with Jonathan, xiii. 33 ; xiii. 38, 43

Bachor. See Choranos

Bactria, *A.* xx. 87

Bactrians, founded by Gether, *A.* i. 145

Badakos (Bibl. Bidkar), commander in King Jehu's army, *A.* ix. 119

Bagadates (var. Magadates), father of Ananus, *B.* v. 531

Bagathoos (var. Gabathoos, Gabataios ; Bibl. Bigthan, Bigthana), eunuch, plots against Ahasuerus, *A.* xi. 207 ; mentioned in records of King Ahasuerus, xi. 249

Bagoas (1), eunuch, put to death by Herod, *A.* xvii. 44-45

Bagoas (2). See Bagoses

Bagoses (var. Bagoas), general of Artaxerxes II, defiles Jewish sanctuary, *A.* xi. 297 ; promises to obtain high priesthood for Jeshua, xi. 298 ; persecutes Jews for seven years, xi. 300-301 ; tries to enter temple, xi. 301

Bahurim. See Choranos

Baiae, city in Campania in Italy, *A.* xviii. 248

Baithoron. See Bethhoron

Baiz. See Abaiz

Bala (Bibl. Bezek), city in Palestine, *A.* vi. 78

Balaam, non-Jewish diviner, *A.* iv. 104 ; asked to curse Israelites, iv. 105, 107 ; angel appears to him, iv. 108-111 ; angrily dismissed by Balak, iv. 126 ; iv. 157 ; his prophecies recorded by Moses, iv. 158

Baladas (Bibl. Berodach-baladan, Merodach-baladan), king of Babylonia, sends gifts to Hezekiah, *A.* x. 30-31, 34

Balaias (Bibl. Birsha), king of Sodom, *A.* i. 171

Balak, king of Moabites, *A.* iv. 102 ; entreats Balaam to curse Israelites, iv. 104, 107 ; escorts Balaam to Israelite camp, iv. 112 ; furious with Balaam, iv. 118-119 ; iv. 124 ; dismisses Balaam, iv. 126

Balanea, city in Syria, favoured by Herod, *B.* i. 428

Balas (1) (Bibl. Bera), king of Sodom, *A.* i. 171

Balas (2). See Alexander (2) Balas

Balator, king of Tyre after period of Judges, *Ap.* i. 157

Balbazer (var. Baleazer), king of Tyre, son of Hiram, *Ap.* i. 121

Balbus, Titus Ampius. See Ampius

Baleazer. See Balbazer

Baleni, (Bibl. Bela), division of Sodomites, *A.* i. 171

Baleth (var. Beleth ; Bibl. Baalath), city built by Solomon, *A.* viii. 152

Balezor, king of Tyre, son of Ithobal, *Ap.* i. 124

Balla (Bibl. Bilhah), handmaid of Rachel, *A.* i. 303 ; bears two sons to Jacob, i. 305 ; her children by Jacob, ii. 181

balsam, of Jericho, *B.* i. 138, 361 ; iv. 469 ; opobalsamon given by Queen of Sheba to Solomon, *A.* viii. 174 ; balsam of Engedi, ix. 7 ; balsam of Jericho, xiv. 54, xv. 96

Baltasares (Baltasaros ; Bibl. Belshazzar), king of Babylonia, called Naboandelos, *A.* x. 231 ; handwriting on his wall, x. 233, 239, 242, 245 ; captured by Persians, x. 247

Baltasaros (1), name given Daniel by King Nebuchadnezzar, *A.* x. 189

Baltasaros (2). See Baltasares

Bana (Bibl. Baanah), son of Rimmon, slayer of Ishbosheth,

197

GENERAL INDEX

Bassus, Caecilius, supporter of Pompey, kills Sextus Caesar, *B.* i. 216, 219 ; kills Sextus Caesar, occupies Apamea, is defeated, *A.* xiv. 268-272

Bassus, Lucilius, Roman legate, sent to Judaea as successor to Cerealius Vetilianus, marches on Machaerus, *B.* vii. 163-164 ; successfully besieges Machaerus vii. 190-209 ; massacres Jews in battle of forest of Jardes, vii. 210-215 ; vii. 216 ; dies, vii. 252

Batanaea (Batanaia ; Batanaeans ; Bibl. Bashan), district south-west of Trachonitis, added to Herod's realm, *B,* i. 398 ; ii. 95, 247, 421, 482 ; iii. 56 ; *A.* iv. 173 ; ravaged by Syrians, ix. 159 ; taken by Antiochus the Great, xii. 136 ; given to Herod by Augustus, xv. 343 ; settled by Babylonian Jews at urging of Herod, xvii. 25 ; bequeathed by Herod as tetrarchy to Philip, xvii. 189 ; given to Philip by Augustus, xvii. 319 ; ruled by Philip the tetrarch, xviii. 106 ; granted to Agrippa II by Emperor Claudius, xx. 138 ; joins Varus, viceroy of Agrippa, in attack on "Babylonian Jews" in Ecbatana, *V.* 54 ; site of colony of Babylonian Jews, reinstatement of whom is ordered by Agrippa II, 183

Batanaia. See **Batanaea**

bath, Hebraic measure, *A.* viii. 57

Bath-sheba. See **Beethsabe**

Bathuel (Bibl. Bethuel), son of Nahor, *A.* i. 153 ; father of Rebecca, i. 248 ; i. 289

Bathybius, Roman praetor with senatorial rank, *A.* xix. 91

Bathyllus, freedman of Antipater, *B.* i. 601 ; *A.* xvii. 79

Bathyra (var. Barthyra), village in Batanaea, *A.* xvii. 26

Battaia (Bibl. Betah), city in Syria, *A.* vii. 105

Baux (Bibl. Buz), son of Nahor, *A.* i. 153

Bazaeus, surname of Monobazus

(1), king of **Adiabene,** *A.* xx. 18

Bazaphranes. See **Barzapharnes**

bdellium, spicy herb, *manna* resembles it, *A.* iii. 28

Becher. See **Bacchar(is)**

Bedriacum, town in Cisalpine Gaul between Verona and Cremona, *B.* iv. 547

Beelsephon (Bibl. Baal-zephon), place in Egypt near the Red Sea (site unknown), *A.* ii. 315

Beelzemos, a Syrian, *A.* xi. 26

Beersabe. See **Beethsabe**

Beer-sheba. See **Bersubai (1)**

Beersubae. See **Bersabe (2)**

Beersubee. See **Bersubai (1)**

Beerzelos (Berzelaios, Berzelos ; Bibl. Barzillai), a Galadite, (Berzelaios) welcomes David at "The Camps," *A.* vii. 230 ; declines David's invitation to dwell with him, vii. 272-273, 275 ; (Berzelos) vii. 387

Beethsabe (Bersabe ; var. Beersabe ; Bibl. Bath-sheba), wife of Uriah, *A.* vii. 130, 146 ; bears Solomon, vii. 158 ; warned by Nathan of Adonijah's plot and tells David, vii. 348-349, 353 ; intercedes for Adonijah in his request for Abishag, viii. 3, 6, 7

Bel, Babylonian deity, *A.* x. 224 ; temple of in Babylon, decorated by Nebuchadnezzar, *Ap.* i. 139 ; temple of in Babylon, restored by Alexander the Great, i. 192

Bela (1). See **Baleni**

Bela (2). See **Bol(os)**

Beleth. See **Baleth**

Beleus, small river in Phoenicia, *B.* ii. 189

Belgas, father of Meirus, *B.* vi. 280

Belias. See **Baal (1)**

Bellum Judaicum. See **Josephus** (1), works : *Bellum Judaicum*

Belsephon (Bibl. Baal-hazor), city in territory of Ephraim, *A.* vii. 174

Belshazzar. See **Baltasares**

Belzedek, village near Ascalon, *B.* iii. 25

199

GENERAL INDEX

GENERAL INDEX

Berosus, Hellenized Chaldaean priest, author of history of Babylon in three books, *A.* i. 93, 107; mentions Abraham (not by name), i. 158; x. 20; mentions Baladas, x. 34; x. 219; author of works for Greek readers on Chaldaean astronomy and philosophy, cited by Josephus for antiquity of the Jews, *Ap.* i. 129-153

Berothe. See Meroth

Bersabe (1). See Beethsabe

Bersabe (2). See Bersubai (2)

Bersabee. See Bersubai (1)

Bersubai (1) (Bersabee, Bersubee, Bersubel, Well of Oath; Bibl. Beersheba), well over which Abraham and Abimelech swear friendship, *A.* i. 212; (Well of Oath) location of Jacob's vision, ii. 170; (Bersubei), vi. 32; (Bersubee) city to which Elijah flees, viii. 348; (Bersabee) birthplace of Sabia, ix. 157

Bersubai (2) (Beersubae, Bersabe), town in Lower Galilee, *B.* ii. 573; iii. 39

Bersubee. See Bersubai (1)

Bersubel. See Bersubai (1)

Beryllus, Nero's tutor, *A.* xx. 183-184

Berytus, Phoenician city, Roman colony, *B.* i. 422, 538; ii. 67, 504, 506; iv. 620; vii. 39, 96; *A.* xvi. 344; place where Herod convenes council to accuse his sons, xvi. 357, 361, 370; its people help Varus put down brigands in Judaea, xvii. 287; Agrippa I's buildings there, xix. 335, 338; adorned by Agrippa II, xx. 211; place where Agrippa II and his sister go to wait upon Cestius, *V.* 49; place where Agrippa II receives letter from Philip, son of Jacimus, 181; place where Justus is with King Agrippa II, 357

Berzelaios (Berzelos, Beerzelos; Bibl. Barzillai), a Galadite, friend of David, *A.* vii. 230, 272, 275; (Berzelos) his sons

commended to Solomon by David, vii. 387

Berzelos. See Berzelaios

Berzetho (var. Bethzetho, Barzetho, Birzetho, Zetho), city in Judaea, *A.* xii. 397, 422

Besalel. See Basael

Besara, town twenty miles from Gaba, on borders of Ptolemais, outside which Josephus posts his troops while removing corn, *V.* 118; storage place of large quantity of corn belonging to Queen Berenice, 119

Besebel. See Basael

Beseleel. See Basael

Besera (Bibl. Bor-sirah), place near Hebron in Judaea (site unknown), *A.* vii. 34

Besimoth, village in Peraea, *B.* iv. 438

Besor. See Baselos

Betabris, town in Idumaea (site unknown), *B.* iv. 447

Betah. See Battaia

Betchora (Bibl. Beth-horon, city near Jerusalem built by Solomon, *A.* viii. 152

Bethalaga, village in Judaea (site unknown), *A.* xiii. 26

Betharamatha. See Betharamphtha

Betharamphtha (Betharamatha, Ammatha, Julias; Bibl. Betharam), city in Peraea east of the Jordan, *B.* ii. 59; (Julias) ii. 168, 252; (Julias) iv. 438; (Ammatha) royal palace there burned by Simon, *A.* xvii. 277; city called Julias, xviii. 27; given to Agrippa II by Nero, xx. 159

Beth-car. See Korraea.

Beth Diblathaim. See Dabaloth

Bethega. See Bethel(os)

Bethela. See Bethel(os)

Bethel(os) (Bethela; var. Bethega), city in Palestine, captured by Vespasian, *B.* iv. 551; consecrated by Jacob, *A.* i. 284; i. 342; on border of territory of Benjamin, v. 82; on border of Ephraim, v. 83; captured by Ephraim, v. 130; v. 159; vi. 32, 55, 95; city where

201

GENERAL INDEX

" Bitumen pits," area in Sodom, *A.* i. 174

Bituminous Lake. See Asphaltitis, Lake

" Black Norther," wind, *B.* iii. 422

Black Sea (Euxine Sea), *B.* ii. 366 ; *A.* ix. 213 ; Scythians known to Greeks through its navigators, *Ap.* i. 64

blasphemy, Jewish law on, *Ap.* iv. 202

" Blessing, Valley of," site in Palestine where Jews thank God for victory over Ammonites, *A.* ix. 15

blind, respect for, according to Jewish law, *A.* iv. 276

Blood-libel, alleged annual murder of Greek by Jews, *Ap.* ii. 91-102

Blue Nile. See Astapus

Bnon (Banon), second Hycsos king of Egypt, *Ap.* i. 80

Boaz (1). See Abaiz

Boaz (2), husband of Ruth, *A.* v. 323 ; Ruth gleans in his fields, v. 324-327 ; v. 328-329 ; marries Ruth, v. 332-335

Bocchores. See Choranos

Bocchoris, King of Egypt, exodus during reign of, *Ap.* i. 305 ff., ii. 16

Bochorios (Bibl. Bichri), father of Sheba, *A.* vii. 278, 280, 290

Boeotus, archon of Delos, *A.* xiv. 231

Boethus (1), Alexandrian Jewish priest, father of Simon, Joazar, and Eleazar, *A.* xv. 320 ; xvii. 78, 339 ; xviii. 3

Boethus (2), father of Simon and Matthias, *B.* v. 527 ; *A.* xix. 297

Bokki (Bibl. Bukki), son of Abishua, high priest, *A.* v. 362

Bokkias (Bibl. Bukki), son of high priest Abishua, father of Uzzi, *A.* viii. 12

Bologeses (Vologeses I=Arsaces XXIII), King of Parthia, *B.* vii. 105, 237, 242 ; (Vologeses) *A.* xx. 74, 81-91

Bol(os) (Bibl. Bela), son of Benjamin, *A.* ii. 180

" Booths " (Bibl. Succoth), place east of the Jordan (site unknown), where Jacob pauses, *A.* i. 337

Borcius, friend of Agrippa II, *B.* ii. 524, 526

Borsippa, town in Babylonia whither Nabonnedus flees after defeat by Cyrus, *Ap.* i. 151-152 ; captured by Cyrus, i. 152

Bor-sirah. See Besera

Boscath. See Bosketh

Bosketh (Bibl. Boscath), town of Judaea, *A.* x. 48

Bosor, city of Galaaditis, *A.* xii. 340

Bosora (Bibl. Bezer), city of refuge bordering Arabia, *A.* iv. 173 ; xii. 336

Bosphorus, kingdom, *B.* ii. 366

Bosporus, strait, *A.* xvi. 16

Botrys, city in Phoenicia founded by Ithobalos, *A.* viii. 324

Bracchus, Gaius Servilius. See Servilius

Breach of Ozas (Bibl. Perez-Uzzah), place where Uzzah dies, *A.* vii. 82

bribery of judges, punishment of, in Jewish law, *Ap.* ii. 207

brigands, *V.* 21, 28, 46, 77-78, 105-106, 145-148, 175, 206

Britain, subdued by Vespasian, *B.* iii. 4 ; vii. 82

Britannicus, son of Claudius and Messalina, *B.* ii. 249 ; *A.* xx. 149 ; poisoned by Nero, xx. 151, 153

Britons, *B.* ii. 363, 378 ; vi. 331

Brixellum, town in Italy, *B.* iv. 548

Broad Place, embankment of, laid by Hiram, King of Tyre, *Ap.* i. 118

Brocchus, envoy from Senate to Claudius, *A.* xix. 234

Brundisium, Italian city, *B.* i. 281 ; *A.* xiv. 378

Brutus, M. Junius, *B.* i. 218, 225 ; proconsul, *A.* xiv. 263 ; kills Caesar, xiv. 270 ; is defeated, xiv. 311 ; slayer of Caesar, xix. 184

Bubastis (1), arm of Egyptian river, *Ap.* i. 78

203

GENERAL INDEX

Bubastis (2) of the Fields, Egyptian deity, *A*. xiii. 66; xiii. 70
" bubo," owl, its ominous role in Agrippa I's life, *A*. xviii. 195
Buedon (var. Buelon, Butelon; part of corrupt division of Bibl. Shethar-boznai), prefect of Samaria, written to by Darius, *A*. xi. 118
Buelon. See Buedon
Bukki. See Bokki; Bokkias
Burrus, praetorian prefect under Nero, *A*. xx. 152
Butelon. See Buedon
Buz. See Baux
Byblus, city of Phoenicia, provided for by generosity of Herod, *B*. i. 422
Byzantium, city on Bosporus, *A*. xvi. 20

CAATH. See Kaath(os)
Caathas. See Cathlas
Cabharsaba. See Capharsaba
Cabul. See Chabalo(n)
Cadiz. See Gadeira
Cadmus (1) of Phoenicia, teaches Greeks the alphabet, *Ap*. i. 10
Cadmus (2) of Miletus, among first Greek historians; his date, *Ap*. i. 13
Caecilius Bassus. See Bassus Caecilius
Caecinna Alienus, general of Vitellius, *B*. iv. 547; goes over to Antonius, bound as a traitor, finally liberated with honour, iv. 634-644
Caesar (1), Gaius Julius, frees Aristobulus, *B*. i. 183; i. 184, 187; is told of Antipater's prowess, i. 192; i. 193-197, 199-202, 205, 216-217; death of, i. 218; ii. 488; releases Aristobulus from prison, *A*. xiv. 123-124; assisted by Antipater and Hyrcanus in Egypt, xiv. 127, 129, 131-132; commends Antipater for his prowess in battle in Egypt, xiv. 136-137; honours Antipater and Hyrcanus despite Antigonus' protests, xiv. 140, 143; xiv. 156, 157, 160; issues

decrees favourable to the Jews, xiv. 185; declares Jews citizens of Alexandria, xiv. 188; confers benefits on Jews, xiv. 190, 192, 196; confers high priesthood on Hyrcanus and his descendants, xiv. 199; confers benefits on Jews, xiv. 200, 202; commends loyalty of the Jews, xiv. 211; confers privileges on Jews of Parium, xiv. 213, 215; his policy toward Jews continued after his death, xiv. 217, 221; death of, xiv. 270-271, 309; aided by Antipater, xvi. 52-54; emperor, xvi. 162; sends Thesmusa to Phraates as a gift, viii. 40; destroyed Roman democracy, xix. 173; his death recalled by Sentius Saturninus, xix. 184; bestows rights on Jews of Alexandria, *Ap*. ii. 37; Cleopatra owes throne to him, ii. 58; loyalty of Jews to him against the Egyptians, ii. 61
Caesar (2), Sextus, plot against, *A*. xiv. 268; supported by Antipater, xiv. 269-270
Caesar (3), Augustus. See Augustus (1)
Caesar (4), Young. See Augustus (1)
Caesar (5), Gaius, son of M. Vipsanius Agrippa, *B*. ii. 25; *A*. xvii. 229
Caesar (6). See Augustus; Tiberius; Gaius; Claudius; Nero; Vespasian; Titus; Domitian
Caesarea (1), also called Sebaste, a coastal town, once Straton's Tower and refounded by Herod, *B*. i. 80, 156, 414, 543, 551, 613; ii. 16, 17, 171, 219, 230, 236, 241, 266, 282, 284; incident at synagogue there, ii. 285-292; ii. 296, 318, 332, 407; slaughter of Jews there, ii. 457-458; ii. 459, 507, 509, 513; iii. 66, 409, 412, 443, 446, 510; iv. 88, 130, 419, 443, 491, 501, 550, 588, 620, 663; v. 1, 40; vii. 20, 23, 36, 37, 361, 362, 363, 407; *A*. xiii. 313; xiv. 76; name given Straton's

204

GENERAL INDEX

Tower by Herod, xv. 293, 339 ; Herod entertains Agrippa there, xvi. 13 ; xvi. 62, 136, 373 ; xvii. 221, 222 ; xviii. 55, 57, 59 ; xix. 332 ; Agrippa hailed as god in theatre there, xix. 343 ; included in Agrippa's kingdom, xix. 351 ; celebrates death of Agrippa, xix. 356, 361 ; rebuked by Fadus, xix. 365 ; xx. 116 ; quarrel between Jews and Syrians there, xx. 173, 176, 182-184 ; woman taken captive there is married by Josephus, *V.* 414

Caesarea (2) Philippi, once Paneion (Paneas), founded by Philip, *B.* ii. 168 ; iii. 443, 510 ; vii. 23 ; *A.* xviii. 28 ; xx. 211 ; its Syrian inhabitants lead Varus to hope for the throne of the Jews, *V.* 52 ; twelve of its Jews sent by Varus, Agrippa's viceroy, to "Babylonian Jews" at Ecbatana, 55 ; envoys slain there, 57 ; Philip son of Jacimus urged to lead Jews of Ecbatana against its Syrian inhabitants, 59 ; its Jewish inhabitants are shut up by Modius, Agrippa II's viceroy, 74 ; price of oil there, 75

Caesareum, Herod's royal palace, *B.* i. 402

Caesars, names of Roman emperors, *A.* viii. 157

Caesennius Gallus. See Gallus (1)

Caesius (1) (var. Casius, Cassius, Rasius, Raesius, Raecius), Quintus, father of Caesius (2), *A.* xiv. 229, 238

Caesius (2) (var. Casius, Cassius, Rasius, Raesius, Raecius), Quintus, son of Quintus, legate, present at promulgation of Lentulus' decree exempting Jewish citizens of Ephesus from military service, *A.* xiv. 229, 238

Caesonia, wife of Gaius, killed by Julius Lupus, *A.* xix. 195, 198

Caiaphas, Joseph, son-in-law of Ananus, removed from high priesthood, *A.* xviii. 35, 95

Cain, son of Adam, etymology of, *A.* i. 52 ; kills his brother Abel, i. 53-59 ; his character and achievements, i. 60-62 ; his posterity, i. 63-67

Cainas (Bibl. Kenan), son of Enosh, *A.* i. 79 ; in genealogy of patriarchs from Adam to Noah, i. 83

Caius. See Gaius

Calani, name of philosophers in India, *Ap.* i. 179

Caligula. See Gaius Caligula

Calleas. See Alexas (2)

Callias, writer on Sicilian history, contradicted by Timaeus, *Ap.* i. 17

Callimandrus, general of Antiochus Cyzicenus who directs war against the Jews, *A.* xiii. 279-280

Callinicus, son of Antiochus king of Commagene, *B.* vii. 232, (241)

Calliphon, disciple of Pythagoras, native of Crotona, his soul accompanies Pythagoras, *Ap.* i. 164

Callirrhoe, warm springs northeast of Dead Sea, visited by Herod, *B.* i. 657, *A.* xvii. 171

Callistus, freedman of Gaius, joins conspiracy against him, *A.* xix. 64, 68, 69

Calvarius, Sextus, Roman tribune, *B.* iii. 325

Calvinus, Gnaeus Domitius, consul when Herod assumes royal power, *A.* xiv. 389

Cambyses, Persian king, *A.* ii. 249 ; founder of Babylon in Egypt, ii. 315 ; son of Cyrus, xi. 21 ; forbids building of temple, xi. 26 ; his death, xi. 30-31 ; xi. 88 ; his letter cited by Samaritans, xi. 97

Camel, father of Joseph the high priest, *A.* xx. 16, 103

Camith, father of Simon the high priest, *A.* xviii. 34

Camp of the Assyrians. See Assyrians, Camp of the

GENERAL INDEX

Camp of the Jews. See Jews' Camp

Campania, district in Italy, *A.* xviii. 249 ; xix. 5

" Camps " (The Camps ; Bibl. Mahanaim), unidentified city near Jordan valley, meaning of *Parembolai, A.* vii. 10, 18 ; vii. 230, 232, 235, 272, 388

Cana (1) (var. Ana, Anna), village in Arabia, troops of Antiochus Dionysus take refuge there, *B.* i. 102

Cana (2) (var. Isana), village north of Jerusalem, *B.* i. 334

Cana (3), village in Galilee, head-quarters of Josephus, *V.* 86

Cana (4). See Kana (1)

Canaan (1) (Chananaea), another name for Judaea, (Chananaea) *A.* i. 134 ; Abraham moves there, i. 154, 157 ; i. 160 ; in grip of famine, i. 161 ; Abraham returns there, i. 169 ; i. 186, 191, 278, 325 ; stricken by famine, ii. 95 ; ii. 111, 118, 170 ; destined to be land of the Jews, ii. 194 ; ii. 195, 200 (*bis*), 213 (*bis*), 318, 323 ; iii. 87 ; traversed by Hebrew scouts, iii. 303-305 ; iii. 313 ; iv. 67, 102, 116, 173, 189, 199-200, 305 ; v. 3, 62 ; nature of the land, v. 77 ; its land divided among Hebrew tribes, v. 88 ; v. 126, 128 ; viii. 61 ; its boundaries, ix. 207

Canaan (2). See Chananaeus

Canaanites, *B.* iv. 459 ; vi. 438, 439 ; prediction that they would be vanquished by Jews, *A.* i. 185 ; offer burial ground for Sarah, i. 237 ; i. 265, 277, 299, 337, 345 ; iii. 308 ; attacked by Hebrews, iv. 1-6 ; iv. 9-10, 167 ; necessity for their extermination, iv. 300 ; iv. 315, 325 ; v. 5, 12, 21-22, 49, 52, 54-56, 59, 63 ; almost completely destroyed, v. 68 ; v. 71-72, 107-108, 120 ; defeated by Judah and Simeon, v. 121 ; allowed to live in peace, v. 129 ; spared by Hebrews, v. 133 ; v. 140, 155 ; attack

Danites, v. 176 ; v. 179 ; subdue Israelites, v. 198 ; v. 201, 205 ; remnant of them at peace with the Jews, vi. 30 ; vii. 61, 68 (*bis*) ; reduced to slavery by Solomon, viii. 160, 162 ; their customs followed by Ahaz king of Judah, ix. 243

Canata. See Canatha

Canatha (Canata, Kanata ; var. Cana, Kana), place in Coele-Syria, *B.* i. 366-367 ; (Kanata ; var. Kana), *A.* xv. 112

Canenius. See Rebilus

Caninius. See Gallus (5), Caninius

Cantabrians, warlike Spanish people, *B.* ii. 374

Cantheras (var. Cithaerus), surname of Simon the high priest, *A.* xix. 297 ; deposed as high priest by Agrippa I, xix. 313 ; his son appointed high priest, xix. 342 ; removed from high priesthood, xx. 16

Capella. See Capellus

Capellus (Capella), Julius, head of pro-Roman Jewish faction at Tiberius, *V.* 32 ; (Capella) finally agrees to demolition of palace erected by Herod the tetrarch in Tiberias, 66 ; (Capella) his conference with Josephus, 67 ; (Capella) son of Antyllus, 69 ; (Capella) is declared by Josephus to have spoils from confiscated royal palace at Tiberias, 296

Capernaum. See Capharnaum (1)

Capharabis, town in upper Idumaea besieged by Cerealius, *B.* iv. 552

Caphareccho, village in Lower Galilee, *B.* ii. 573

Capharnaum (1) (Capernaum), spring and village in region of Gennesareth, *B.* iii. 519 ; *V.* 403 (probably identical with Cepharnocus)

Capharnaum (2). See Cepharnocus

Capharsaba (Cabharsaba), town in Judaea in plain of Sharon, *A.* xiii. 390 ; xvi. 142

Caphartoba, village in Idumaea, *B.* iv. 447

GENERAL INDEX

GENERAL INDEX

enslaved by him freed, xiv. 313 ; possessions he seized from Jews returned by Antony, xiv. 317, 320 ; damages Rhodes, xiv. 378 ; slayer of Caesar, xix. 184

Cassius (3) Longinus, governor of Syria, orders Jews to deposit priestly robes in Antonia, *A*. xv. 406 ; appointed governor of Syria, xx. 1 ; petitioned by Jews in connexion with Roman custody of priestly vestments, xx. 7

Cassius (4). See Caesius (1) and (2)

Castor (1), Jewish impostor, *B*. v. 317-330

Castor (2), dates battle of Gaza as eleven years after death of Alexander the Great, *Ap*. i. 184 ; chronicler, cited on Antiochus Epiphanes' motive in plundering the temple in Jerusalem, ii. 84

castration, practised by Persians, *Ap*. ii. 270

Cathlas (Thaceas, Caathas, Catthaias, Cattheas, Clathas, Acatelas), father of Simon the Idumaean chief, (Thaceas ; var. Cathlas, Clathas) *B*. iv. 235 ; (Caathas ; var. Cathlas, Clathas) iv. 271 ; (var. Cattheas) v. 249 ; (Acatelas ; var. Nacatelas, Catthaias, Cathlas) vi. 148

Cato, Caesar's opponent, *A*. xiv. 185

Catthaias. See Cathlas

Cattheas. See Cathlas

Catullus, governor of Libyan Pentapolis, *B*. vii. 439-441, 449, 451

Cave of Arbela. See Arbela (2), Cave of

caves, in Galilee, west of Sea of Galilee and northwest of Tiberias, near Arbela, captured by Herod, *B*. i. 304 ; remnants of Galilaeans, pursued by Herod, lurk there, i. 307-308 ; open into mountain precipices, thus being inaccessible, i. 310 ; king lowers his men in cradles

with ropes to possess cavern mouths, i. 311 ; Josephus fortifies those in Lower Galilee in area of Lake of Gennesareth with walls, ii. 573 ; those near village of Arbela conquered by Herod, *A*. xiv. 415 ; Herod unable to crush the Galilaeans who live there, xiv. 417 ; Herod's method of destroying Galilaean brigands living there, xiv. 420-430 ; Josephus fortifies the villages of the Cave of Arbela, *V*. 188

Ceagiras (i.e. " lame ") (Agiras), nickname of Nabataeus of Adiabene, *B*. v. 474

Celadus, close friend of Alexander son of Herod, *B*. ii. 106 ; freedman of Augustus, *A*. xvii. 332

Celenderis, town in Cilicia, *B*. i. 610 ; *A*. xvii. 86

Celer, Roman tribune, *B*. ii. 244, 246 ; *A*. xx. 132, 136

Celtic, *A*. xix. 119

Celts, Germanic tribes, *B*. i. 5

Cendebaeus, general of Antiochus VII Sidetes, *B*. i. 51 ; *A*. xiii. 225

Cenedaeus, brave Jew, kinsman of Monobazus the king of Adiabene, *B*. ii. 520

Censorinus, Gaius Marcius, Roman consul, *A*. xvi. 165

Cepharnocus (probably identical with Capharnaum), village in region of Gennesareth, where Josephus is carried after his fall from a horse, *V*. 403

Cephthomus (Bibl. Caphtorim), son of Mizraim, *A*. i. 137

Cerealius (1) Vettulenus (Vetilianus), Sextus, head of fifth legion, attacks Samaritans, *B*. iii. 310-315 ; iv. 552-555 ; vi. 131, 237, 242 ; vii. 163 ; is sent with Josephus to consider suitability of Tekoa as camp for Titus' forces, *V*. 420

Cerealius (2) Petilius, sent by Vespasian to Germany, *B*. vii. 82-83

Ceron, father of Cornelius the

GENERAL INDEX

bearer of Claudius' letter to the Jews, *A.* xx. 14

Cestius Gallus, Roman governor of Syria, *B.* i. 20-21 ; Jews complain to him, ii. 280-283 ; ii. 333-334, 341, 481 ; takes to the field, ii. 499-555 ; ii. 556-558, 562, 564 ; iii. 9, 31, 133, 414 ; v. 41, 267, 302 ; vi. 338, 422 ; vii. 18 ; looked to by Josephus to quell Jewish revolution in Palestine, *V.* 23 ; is defeated by Jewish revolutionaries in Palestine, 24 ; events after his defeat, 28 ; is given allegiance by Jewish inhabitants of Sepphoris, 30 ; holds Jews of Sepphoris as hostages, 31 ; waited upon by Agrippa and his sister, 49 ; sends Placidus to burn Galilaean villages, 214 ; commander-in-chief of Roman legions in Syria, garrison provided by him is admitted into Sepphoris, 347 ; Sepphoris requests him to take over the city, 373-374 ; sends large forces to aid Sepphoris, 394

Cetis, place in Cilicia, *A.* xviii. 140

Chaalis, town in Idumaea, *B.* iii. 20

chaanasae, Hellenized form of Aramaic name (*kahanya*) for Jewish priests, *A.* iii. 151

Chabalon (= " Not Pleasing " ; Chabulon ; Bibl. Cabul, Kabul) Land of, region in Galilee presented by Solomon to Hiram, *A.* viii. 142 ; (Chabulon) *Ap.* i. 110

Chabarsaba. See Antipatris

Chabolo. See Chabulon (1)

Chabulon (1) (Chabolo), city in Galilee, *B.* ii. 503 ; iii. 38 ; (Chabolo) village on frontiers of Ptolemais whither Josephus marches with his troops, *V.* 213-214 ; (Chabolo) Josephus keeps watch from there on Placidus, 227 ; (Chabolo) Josephus sets out from there with his army to Jotapata, 234

Chabulon (2). See Chabalon

Chaerea, Cassius, leader of a conspiracy against Gaius Caligula, *A.* xix. 18, 21, 23, 27 ; insulted by Gaius, xix. 28-31 ; tortures Quintilia at Gaius' orders, xix. 34-35 ; plots with Clemens and Papinius against Gaius, xix. 37, 40, 44-46 ; enlists Cornelius Sabinus in the conspiracy, xix. 46 ; enlists Vinicianus in the conspiracy, xix. 48, 53, 60-61 ; postpones attempt to assassinate Gaius, xix. 70-71, 73 ; resolves to assassinate Gaius at Palatine Games, xix. 78-84 ; his role in assassination of Gaius, xix. 91, 96, 99-100, 105-107, 111, 113; flees scene of assassination, xix. 115 ; xix. 153; receives watch-word " liberty," xix. 186-187, 189; orders wife and daughter of Gaius slain, xix. 190, 200; opposes Claudius, xix. 254, 256, 258, 261-262; executed by Claudius, xix. 267-270; honoured by Roman people, xix. 272

Chaeremon, author of history of Egypt, disagrees with Manetho, *Ap.* i. 288-303 ; challenged by Josephus, ii. 1

Chaireas, Jewish envoy from Hyrcanus to Rome, *A.* xlv. 222

Chalamas (Josephus' error for Biblical Helam [Helama]), king of Syria, *A.* vii. 127-128

Chalcidice, region in either the Lebanon range or further north in Syria, *B.* vii. 226

Chalcis, city in the Lebanon valley, *B.* i. 185 ; ii. 217, 221, 223, 247 ; *A.* xiv. 40, 126 ; kingdom requested by Agrippa I for his son-in-law, xix. 277 ; ruled by Herod, brother of Agrippa I, xix. 338 ; xix. 353; xx. 15, 103 ; taken away from Agrippa II, xx. 138 ; xx. 158

Chalcol. See Chalkeos

Chaldaeans (Chaldees, Chaldaea), Babylonian people, *B.* ii. 112 ; modern name for Arphaxadaeans, *A.* i. 144 ; (Chaldaea) place where Haran dies, i. 151-152; (Chaldaea) Abraham leaves from there, i. 154 ; rise up

209

GENERAL INDEX

against Abraham, i. 157; mentioned by Berosus, i. 158; (Chaldees) mentioned by Nicolas of Damascus, i. 159; arithmetic and astronomy travel from them to Egypt, i. 168; (Chaldaea) captures Manasseh, x. 40; (Chaldaea) x. 183; x. 187; their wisdom mastered by Daniel, x. 194; fail to tell Nebuchadnezzar his dream, x. 195, 198-199, 203; x. 223; unable to interpret handwriting on wall, x. 234; x. 235; (Chaldaea) xi. 91; admitted even by Greeks to possess a very ancient record of the past, Ap. i. 8-9; teachers of first Greek philosophers, i. 14; chronicles kept by them, i. 28; original ancestors of Jews, are adduced by Josephus as witnesses of Jews' antiquity, i. 71; their evidence for antiquity of the Jews, i. 128-160, 215; their writings demonstrate antiquity of the Jews, ii. 1

Chaldees, Ur of, A. i. 151

Chalkeos (Bibl. Chalcol), Jew known for his wisdom, son of Mahol, A. viii. 43

Chananaea. See Canaan (1)

Chananaeus (Bibl. Canaan), son of Ham, A. i. 134, 138, 142; v. 88-89

Chapsaios, father of Judas (a commander of Jonathan's army), A. xiii. 161

Charada. See Garada

Charax Spasini. See Spasini Charax

Chares, leader of Gamala, B. iv. 18, 68; kinsman of Philip, V. 177; slain by followers of Josephus, the midwife's son, 186

Chariots, Cities of, cities where Solomon kept his chariots, A. viii. 188

Charmis(os) (Bibl. Carmi), son of Reuben, A. ii. 178

Charon, ferryman over River Styx in Hades, A. xix. 358

Charran (var. Karran), city in Mesopotamia, A. i. 152; (var. Karran) Rebecca's residence

there, i. 244; Jacob arrives there, i. 285

Chasleu. See Chasleus

Chasleus (Chasleu; var. Xelios, Xenios; Heb. Kislew), ninth month in Hebrew calendar, approximately December, gathering in Jerusalem on twentieth day thereof, A. xi. 148; (Chasleu) xii. 248; (Chasleu) month when the temple is rededicated, xii. 319

Chasphomake (var. Chasthomaki, Chasphomakei), city in Galaaditis in Palestine, A. xii. 340

Chasphomakei. See Chasphomake

Chasthomaki. See Chasphomake

Chazam, son of Nahor, A. i. 153

Chebron (1), Egyptian king, son of Tethmosis (Thoummosis), Ap. i. 94

Chebron (2). See Ibron

Chedorlaomer. See Chodolamor

Cheesemakers, Valley of (Tyropoeon), between two hills on which Jerusalem is built, B. i. 140; (v. 136)

Cheidon (Bibl. Chidon, Nachon), threshing-floor of, place in Palestine where Uzzah met his death, A. vii. 81

Cheiromos (Bibl. Hiram), Tyrian craftsman who helped build the temple, A. viii. 76-77, 88

Chelbes, son of Abdaeus, judge of Tyre, Ap. i. 157

Chelcias (1). See Helcias (1)

Chelcias (2) (var. Chelicas), father of Judes (member of Eleazar's faction), B. v. 6

Chelicas. See Chelcias (2)

Chelkias, son of Onias, general of Cleopatra, A. xiii. 285, 287, 349; his death, xiii. 351

Chellion (Bibl. Chilion), son of Elimelech and Naomi, marries Orpah, A. v. 318-319

Chephirah. See Kepherites

Cherubim (Cherubs), angels placed upon the ark as a covering, A. iii. 137; vii. 378; viii. 72-73, 103

Chesloimus (Bibl. Casluhim), son of Mizraim, A. i. 137

decree honouring Antipater and Hyrcanus, *A.* xiv. 145

Coptus, city on Nile River, *B.* iv. 608

coracin, a fish, *B.* iii. 520

Corban, a Jewish sacrificial offering, *B.* iv. 73; Jewish oath, meaning "God's gift," *Ap.* i. 167

Corbonas, Jewish sacred treasure, used for construction of an aqueduct by Pontius Pilate, *B.* ii. 175

Corcyra, island off western coast of Greece, *B.* vii. 22

Cordova, city in Spain, *A.* xix. 17

Cordyaeans, their mountain in Armenia is said to have portion of Noah's ark, *A.* i. 93

Corea. See Coreae

Coreae (Corea), city on border of Judaea, *B.* i. 134; iv. 449; *A.* xiv. 49, 83

Corinthian gate of temple, made of bronze, *B.* v. 201, 204; style of architecture in Solomon's palace, *A.* viii. 133; columns of the temple ornamented in this style, xv. 414; candelabra in palace of Herod the tetrarch at Tiberias, *V.* 68

Corinthus, one of Augustus' bodyguard, *B.* i. 576-577; bodyguard of Herod, *A.* xvii. 55-57

Cornelian, Roman tribe, *A.* xiv. 238

Cornelius (1) Sabinus, conspirator against Emperor Gaius Caligula, joins Chaerea's plot, *A.* xix. 46, 48; aids in assassination of Gaius, xix. 110; opposes Claudius, xix. 261; xix. 267; released by Claudius, xix. 273

Cornelius (2) Lentulus, L. See Lentulus, Cornelius

Cornelius (3), brother of Longus, Roman hero, *B.* vi. 187

Cornelius (4), Quintus, Roman quaestor, *A.* xiv. 219

Cornelius (5), son of Ceron, bearer of Claudius' letter to the Jews, *A.* xx. 14

Cornelius (6), Faustus. See Faustus, Cornelius

corn-stores in Galilee, *V.* 71 ff., 118-119

cors, Hebrew measure of grain, *A.* iii. 321; xiv. 201; xv. 314

Corvinus. See Messala

Cos, Greek island in Aegean Sea, *B.* i. 423, 532; *A.* xiii. 349; xiv. 112-113; affords privileges to Jews, xlv. 233; xvi. 17, 312

Costobar (1), brother of Saul, with whom he is sent to Agrippa to seek military reinforcements, *B.* ii. 418, 556; *A.* xx. 214

Costobar (2). See Costobar(us)

Costobar(us), second husband of Salome, *B.* i. 486; killed by Herod, *A.* xv. 252; governor of Idumaea, marries Salome, xv. 253-255; offers his services to Cleopatra but is pardoned by Herod, xv. 256-258; divorced by Salome, xv. 259-266; xvi. 227; xviii. 133

Cotardes, King of Parthians, brother of Vardanes, succeeds him, *A.* xx. 73

Cotulas. See Zeno (2)

cotylae, Attic measure, *A.* iii. 142

Cotylas. See Zeno (2)

Cotys, king of Armenia Minor, entertained by Agrippa at Tiberias, *A.* xix. 338

Council. See Sanhedrin

Counsel. See Hebel

Cozbi. See Chosbia

Crassus, Licinius, governor of Syria, *B.* i. 179-180; succeeds Gabinius as governor of Judaea, *A.* xiv. 104; plunders the temple, xiv. 105, 107, 109; killed in Parthia, xiv. 119; occupies the temple in Jerusalem, *Ap.* ii. 82

Cratippus, a prytanis in Pergamum, *A.* xiv. 247

creation of the world, *A.* i. 27-33

Cremona, town in northern Italy, *B.* iv. 634, 642

Crete (Cretans), island south of Greece, *B.* ii. 103; *A.* xiii. 86, 129; its Jews welcome false Alexander, xvii. 327; Josephus' wife from there, *V.* 427;

GENERAL INDEX

and Salampsio, *A.* xviii. 131;
married to Agrippa, xviii. 131;
her children by Agrippa, xviii.
132; deters Agrippa from committing suicide, xviii. 148;
aids her husband, xviii. 159-160
Cypros (3), daughter of Cypros
and Antipater, married to
Alexas, *A.* xviii. 138
Cypros (4), daughter of Cypros
and Alexas, *A.* xviii. 138
Cypros (5), daughter of Herod
and Mariamme, spurned by
Pheroras, becomes wife of
Antipater, *A.* xvi. 196; xviii.
130; mother of Cypros, xviii.
138
Cypros (6), fortress built by
Herod, *B.* i. 407; i. 417; ii.
484; built by Herod, *A.* xvi. 143
Cyprus (1). See Cypros (1)
Cyprus (2), island in Eastern
Mediterranean, *B.* ii. 108; *A.*
i. 128; Jewish community
there flourishes under Cleopatra, xiii. 284; xiii. 287;
ruled by Ptolemy Lathyrus,
xiii. 328; xiii. 331; Ptolemy
Lathyrus withdraws to it,
xiii. 359; revenue from its
copper mines given to Herod
by Augustus, xvi. 128; xvii.
335; xviii. 131; xx. 51, 142;
successful campaign against it
by Egyptian king Sethosis
(Ramesses II), *Ap.* i. 99
Cyrenaean Libya. See Cyrene
Cyrene (Cyrenaean Libya, Cyren-
ians), city on northern coast of
Africa, *B.* ii. 381; vi. 114;
vii. 437, 439; its Jewish
population, *A.* xiv. 114-116,
118; (Cyrenaean Libya) xvi.
160; ordered to respect rights
of Jews, xvi. 169; ship from
there rescues Josephus after
shipwreck in *c.* 61, *V.* 15;
insurrection of Jews there,
424; Jews settled there by
Ptolemy Lagus, *Ap.* ii. 44;
left by Ptolemy Physcon,
intending to usurp Egyptian
throne, ii. 51
Cyrus (1), Persian king, *B.* v.
389; vi. 270; marches against

Babylonia, *A.* x. 232, 247
x. 248; allows Jews to return
to Judaea, xi. 1, 3, 5-6, 8, 10,
12; his death, xi. 20-21; xi.
63, 78, 86, 88, 92-93; orders
building of the temple, xi. 99;
archives of, xi. 104; consents
to building of the temple, xi.
106; xi. 113; prescribes dimensions of the Second Temple, xv. 386; permits Jews to
return to their land, xx. 233;
ends Babylonian captivity of
the Jews, *Ap.* i. 132; re-erection
of the temple begins under him,
i. 145; captures Babylon, i. 150-
152; treats Nabonnedus humanely, i. 153; foundations of
the temple laid in second year
of his reign, i. 154; becomes
monarch of Persia in reign of
Hiram, king of Tyre, i. 158-159
Cyrus (2). See Asueros
Cyzicenus. See Antiochus (9)
Cyzicus, city in northwestern
Asia Minor, *A.* xiii. 270-271

DABALOTH (var. Nabaloth, Naballo; prob. Bibl. Beth Diblathaim), Arab city near Libba,
A. xiv. 18
Dabaritta. See Dabarittha
Dabarittha (Dabaritta; Bibl.
Daberath), village under western slopes of Mt. Tabor, *B.*
ii. 595; (Dabaritta), its highwaymen plunder baggage of
wife of Ptolemy, Agrippa II's
overseer, *V.* 126 ff.; reached
by Jonathan's party on way
from Tiberias to Jerusalem, 318
Daberath. See Dabarittha
Dabora (Bibl. Deborah), prophe-
tess, *A.* v. 200; leads Hebrews
to battle against Sisera, v.
202, 204; v. 209; her death,
v. 210
Dacians, inhabitants of modern
Rumania, *B.* ii. 369; *A.* xviii.
22
Dacles (Bibl. Diklah), son of
Joktan, *A.* i. 147
Dadan(es) (Bibl. Dedan), son of
Shuah, *A.* i. 238
Daesius (Daisios), Jewish month

217

GENERAL INDEX

219

GENERAL INDEX

wiped out by Athaliah, ix.
140; his line continued in
Joash, ix. 145; ix. 148, 155,
166, 196, 269, 280, 282; x.
49, 67; end of his royal line,
x. 143; xi. 73, 80, 112; xiii.
249; his tomb opened by
Herod, xvi. 179, 181, 188;
subjugates many nations, *Ap.*
ii. 132

Day of Fast. See Fast, Day of

Dead Sea. See Asphaltitis, Lake

Deborah. See Dabora

Decalogue (ten commandments),
A. iii. 91-92

Decapolis, district in Syria, *B.*
iii. 446; fought against by
Justus of Tiberias, its inhabitants press Emperor Vespasian
to punish Justus, *V.* 341-342;
its leaders present remon-
strances against Justus to
Vespasian at Ptolemais for
setting fire to their village, 410

December, Ides of, *A.* xiv. 145

Decius Mundus. See Mundus

Dedan (1). See Dadan(es)

Dedan (2). See Judadas

Deilum. See Dium

Deimos (Terror), deified by
Greeks, *Ap.* ii. 248

Deinaeus (Dinaeus), father of
Eleazar (leader of brigands),
B. ii. 235; *A.* xx. 121, 161

Deity, *passim*

Deizus. See Azizus (1)

Deleastartus, father of Methusastartus the king of Tyre,
Ap. i. 122

Delians. See Delos

Delilah. See Dalala

Dellius, Antony's emissary, *B.* i.
290; *A.* xiv. 394; commends
Alexandra's children to Antony,
xv. 25-27

Delos (Delians), island in Aegean
Sea, its Jews granted special
privileges, *A.* xiv. 213; (Delians) exempt Jews from military
service, xiv. 231

Delphi, site of oracle in Greece,
its table compared with that of
tabernacle, *A.* iii. 139; burning of its temple, *Ap.* ii. 131;
its oracle as lawgiver, ii. 162

Delta (1) of Nile River, *B.* i. 190;
A. xiv. 133

Delta (2) quarter in Alexandria,
B. ii. 495

Demaenetus, influences people of
Ptolemais to risk a contest
with Jews, *A.* xiii. 330

Demetrius (1) of Phalerum, li-
brarian of Ptolemy Philadelphus, *A.* xii. 12, 16; presents a
memorial of the proposed translation of the Jewish Laws, xii.
34, 36; x^ii. 103, 107-108; explains why Jewish Law is unknown to Greeks, xii. 110-111,
113-114; praised for accuracy,
Ap. i. 218; "the most learned
man of his time," appointed
commissioner by Ptolemy Philadelphus, ii. 46

Demetrius (2) I Poliorcetes, king
of Macedonia, son of Antigonus,
defeated by Ptolemy son of
Lagus, *Ap.* i. 184-185, 200;
is deserted by his wife Stratonice, who starts unsuccessful
revolution against him, i.
206-207

Demetrius (3) I, son of Seleucus,
becomes king of Syria, *A.* xii.
389; kills King Antiochus V
Eupator, xii. 390; sends
Bacchides against Judas, xii.
393; xii. 397; appealed to by
Alcimus, xii. 400; sends Nicanor against Judas, xii. 402-403;
xii. 415; sends Bacchides
against Judas, xii. 420; sends
Bacchides to capture Jonathan,
xiii. 23; seeks alliance with
Jonathan, xiii. 35, 37, 39; tries
to win support of Jonathan, xiii.
43-44, 47-48; his death, xiii.
58-61; xiii. 80; father of
Demetrius II, xiii. 86

Demetrius (4) II (Nicator), son
of Demetrius (3) I, father of
Antiochus the Pious, *A.* vii.
393; opposes Alexander Balas,
xiii. 86-87; allies himself with
Ptolemy Philometor, xiii. 109-
115; aids Ptolemy Philometor
against Alexander Balas. xiii.
116; son-in-law of Ptolemy
Philometor, ascends to power,

221

GENERAL INDEX

225

GENERAL INDEX

against Assyrians, x. 17; spared attack of Sennacherib, x. 18, 20-21; makes war on Medes and Babylonians, x. 74; one of them slays Josiah, x. 76; enslaves Jehoahaz, x. 82-83; defeated by Nebuchadnezzar, x. 84; trusted by Jehoiakim, x. 88-89; x. 103-104; their alliance with Zedekiah and defeat by Babylonia, x. 108, 110, 112; x. 147, 175; Jeremiah taken there, x. 177; conquered by Babylonia, x. 180 (*bis*); conquered by Nebuchadnezzar, x. 182; x. 195, 220, 222; conquered by Cambyses, xi. 30; xi. 345; falls to Ptolemy after Alexander the Great's death, xii. 2; Jews brought there by Ptolemy, xii. 7, 9; ruled by Ptolemy Philadelphus, xii. 11; xii. 29, 45 (*bis*); defeated by Antiochus the Great, xii. 138; visited by Joseph the Tobiad, xii. 166-167; xii. 179, 235; attacked by Antiochus Epiphanes, xii. 242-243; repels Antiochus, xii. 244, 246; boundary of Antiochus' realm, xii. 295; xii. 387; temple built there by Onias, xiii. 63-64; xiii. 66; temple built there, xiii. 67-68; xiii. 81; ruled by Ptolemy Philometor, xiii. 113, 115; xiii. 146, 274, 278; Jewish community flourishes there under Cleopatra, xiii. 284; xiii. 328, 330, 348, 351-352, 358; xiv. 21, 34-35, 79, 98-100; its Jewish community, xiv. 116-118; xiv. 127, 134, 138; Herod flees there, xiv. 374; xiv. 383, 447; Alexandra plans to flee there, xv. 45-46; xv. 95; Artabazes sent there as prisoner, xv. 104; xv. 196; invaded by Octavian, xv. 198, 201; secured by Octavian, xv. 215, 217; Herod buys provisions from there, xv. 307; xv. 333; xvi. 52, 141; xvii. 70, 73, 134; exodus therefrom commemorated by Passover, xvii. 213;

Emperor Gaius Caligula plans to inspect it, xix. 81; xix. 82, 205, 279; xx. 101, 169; false prophet from there, xx. 171-172; xx. 230; Onias founds temple there at Heliopolis, xx. 236-237; xx. 259; admitted even by Greeks to possess a very ancient record of the past, *Ap.* i. 8-9; teachers of first Greek philosophers, i. 14; care exercised by them in chronicles, i. 28; priests of, i. 28; care in marriages of Jewish priests of, i. 33; contact with Greeks by commerce, i. 61; became known to Greeks through transportation of their merchandise by Phoenicians, i. 63; bitterest enemies of Jews, adduced by Josephus as witnesses of Jews' antiquity, i. 70, 73-105; Jews not originally from there, according to Manetho, i. 75, 104, 252, 278; language of, i. 83; treaty whereby Hycsos are to leave, i. 88-89; sacred books of, describe Hycsos as captives, i. 91; king of, permits Joseph to bring brethren into Egypt, i. 92; conquered by Nebuchadnezzar, king of Babylon, i. 133; satrap of, rebels against Nabopalassar, king of Babylon, i. 135; taken prisoner by Nebuchadnezzar and conducted to Babylonia, i. 137; practice of circumcision by them mentioned by Herodotus, i. 169-170; taught circumcision to Phoenicians and Syrians of Palestine, i. 169-170; Syrians accompany Ptolemy son of Lagus there, i. 186; Jews migrate there after Alexander the Great's death, i. 194; records of establish antiquity of Jews, i. 215; circumstances of entry of Jews there and departure therefrom falsified by Egyptian writers, i. 223; originators of libels against Jews, i. 223 ff.; reasons for their hatred of Jews, i. 224-

226

GENERAL INDEX

birthplace of Menander the historian, *Ap.* i. 116; Jews there given citizenship by Alexander's successors, ii. 39; burning of its temple, ii. 131

ephod, vestment of Jewish high priest, resembling the Greek *epômis*, *A.* iii. 162, 164

Ephorus, Greek historian, *A.* i. 108; exposes mendacity of Hellanicus, his own mendacity exposed by Timaeus, *Ap.* i. 16; reputed to be among the most exact of historians; his ignorance of Iberians, i. 67

Ephra (1). See Aphra

Ephra (2) (Bibl. Ophrah), home of Gideon, *A.* v. 229; Gideon buried there, v. 232

Ephraim (1), small town northeast of Bethel, *B.* iv. 551

Ephraim (2) (Bibl. Ephron), sells burial ground for Sarah to Abraham, *A.* i. 237

Ephraim (3), son of Joseph, *A.* ii. 92, 180, 195

Ephraim (4), tribe of, Joshua stems from it, *A.* iii. 49; iii. 288, 308; territory of tribe, v. 83; Shechem belongs to it, v. 91; where Timnath-serah is, v. 119; captures Bethel, v. 130; v. 136, 141-142; aggrieved at Gideon's success, v. 230; wars with Jephthah, v. 267; tribe of Abdon, v. 273; Elkanah's tribe, v. 342; vi. 118; pays homage to David, vii. 57; vii. 174; its governor under Solomon, viii. 35; garrisons established there by Jehoshaphat, viii. 393; xi. 341

Ephratene (Bibl. Ephrath), site of Rachel's death, *A.* i. 343

Ephrath. See Ephratene

Ephron. See Ephraim (2)

Epicrates, left by Antiochus Cyzicenus to fight Hyrcanus, *A.* xiii. 279-280

Epicurean(s), *A.* x. 277; xix. 32

Epimygdonia, surname of Antioch, *A.* xx. 68

Epiphaneia, Macedonian name

for Amathe, Syrian city, *A.* i. 138

Epiphanes (1). See Antiochus (4), (11), and (16)

Epiphanes (2). See Ptolemy (5)

epômis, Greek word for the upper part of a woman's tunic (see *ephod*), *A.* iii. 162, 165

Epsiba (var. Aichiba, Achiba; Bibl. Hephzibah), mother of Manasseh, *A.* x. 37

Erasamos (Arasamos; Bibl. Pasdammim or Ephes-dammim), place where David kills Goliath, *A.* vii. 308

Erchian deme, in Athens, *A.* xiv. 150

Eremmon (Bibl. Rimmon), father of Baanah and Rechab, *A.* vii. 46

Eri. See Irenes

Erikam (Bibl. Azrikam), governor of Judah, *A.* ix. 247

Eroge (Bibl. possibly En-rogel), place southeast of Jerusalem, *A.* ix. 225

Eroides (Bibl Arodi), son of Gad, *A.* ii. 182

erôn, Hebrew name for the sacred ark, *A.* iii. 134

Erucius (1), Lucius, father of Lucius Erucius of Steletinian tribe, *A.* xiv. 220

Erucius (2), Lucius, Roman of Steletinian tribe, present at promulgation of senate's decree confirming Julius Caesar's decisions regarding the Jews, *A.* xiv. 220

Erythraean Sea. See Red Sea

Esaias. See Isaiah

Esarhaddon. See Asarachoddas

Esau, son of Isaac and Rebecca, origin of name, *A.* i. 258; marries, i. 265; receives father's blessing, i. 267-275; takes third wife, i. 277; i. 295; encounters Jacob on return from Canaan, i. 326-336; sells birthright to Jacob, ii. 1-3; his sons, ii. 4-5; forefather of Idumaeans, xii. 328

êsauron, Hebrew word for shaggy hair (see Esau), *A.* i. 258

Esbonitis. See Heshbon (1)

231

GENERAL INDEX

Eschon (Bibl. Eshcol), comrade in arms of Abraham, *A.* i. 182
Esdraelon. See Plain (2), the Great
Esdras. See Ezra
Esebonitis. See Heshbon
Esek. See Eskos
Esermoth (Bibl. Hazeroth), place where Hebrews revolt again, *A.* iii. 295
Eshcol. See Eschon
Eskos (Bibl. Esek), well dug by Isaac, *A.* i. 262
Esron (1), father of Simon (who joins the new faction of Eleazar the son of Simon), *B.* v. 6
Esron (2) (Bibl. Hezron), son of Perez, *A.* ii. 178
Essa (1). See Gerasa
essa (2), Hebrew word for " woman " (=*isshah*), *A.* i. 36
Essaron (Bibl. Hezron), son of Reuben, *A.* ii. 178
Essebon. See Heshbon
Essebonites. See Heshbon
essēn, part of the *ephod*, means *logion* (" oracle ") in Greek, *A.* iii. 163, 166, 170-171, 185, 217-218
Essenes, *B.* i. 78; ii. 119; description of, ii. 120-161; John the Essene, ii. 567; iii. 11; v. 145; one of the three Jewish schools of thought, *A.* xiii. 171; their attitude towards Fate, xiii. 171; xiii. 298; Judas the Essene, xiii. 311; follow way of life taught by Pythagoras, xv. 371; honoured by Herod, xv. 372; Manaemus the Essene, xv 373; honoured by Herod, xv. 378; Simon the Essene, xvii. 346; xviii. 11; their doctrines, xviii. 18-22; *V.* 10; Josephus submits to hard training for this sect (11)
Esther, beauty of, *A.* xi. 199; Persian king Ahasuerus marries her, xi. 202; enters palace, is crowned, xi. 203; aids in exposing plotters, xi. 208; sends men to dress Mordecai, xi. 222; inquires after Mordecai's dress, xi. 223; copy of decree sent to her, xi. 225; sends answer to Mordecai, xi. 226; instructs Mordecai to lead fasting, xi. 228; prays to God, xi. 231; goes to king, xi. 234; requests attendance of king and Haman at banquet, xi. 242, 244; her eunuchs, xi. 261; accuses Haman, xi. 264; receives Haman's property, xi. 269; reveals to Ahasuerus her relation to Mordecai, xi. 269; gives Mordecai Haman's possessions, xi. 270; xi. 278; informed of number of their enemies killed by Jews of Susa, xi. 289; begs king to permit Jews to slay their remaining enemies, xi. 289

Etam (1). See Aeta
Etam (2). See Etame
Etame (probably same as Aeta, Etan), city in Judah fortified by Rehoboam, *A.* viii. 246
Etan, city in Judah (probably same as Etame), *A.* viii. 186
Ethaios. See Ethis
Ethan. See Athanos
Ethbaal. See Ithobalos (1)
Ethiopians (Ethiopia, Aethiopians, Aethiopia), *B.* ii. 382, 385, iv. 608; called Chusaeans, *A.* i. 131; i. 135; Ethiopian war, i. 137; invade Egypt, ii. 239-240; defeated by Egyptian army with Moses as general, ii. 248-249; ii. 252, 253, 282; viii. 159; their queen visits Solomon, viii. 165; their queen departs from Solomon, viii. 175; brought to Solomon, viii. 181; mercenaries of Shishak, viii. 254; viii. 262; attacks Asa, viii. 292; defeated by Asa, viii. 293-294; ix. 102; attacked by Sennacherib, x. 4; aids Egypt against Assyria, x. 17; rescues Jeremiah, x. 122-123; xi. 33; ruled by Ahasuerus, xi. 186, 216; xi. 272; practice of circumcision among them mentioned by Herodotus, *Ap.* i. 169; their originality in practice of circumcision dis-

GENERAL INDEX

cussed by Herodotus, i. 170 ;
King Amenophis of Egypt
welcomed there, i. 246-248 ;
King Amenophis of Egypt
advances from there with
army and defeats Hycsos, i.
251 ; Amenophis, king of
Egypt, flees thither upon
attack by Jerusalemites, i.
263 ; King Amenophis advances from there and defeats
Hycsos and lepers, i. 266 ;
passes between it and Egypt
not fortified by Jerusalemites,
i. 277 ; Amenophis flees to it
upon attack by afflicted Egyptians, is brought home by his
son Ramesses, i. 292 ; i. 297 ;
Ramesses flees to it with his
father King Amenophis of
Egypt, i. 300

Ethis (Ethaios ; Bibl. Ittai), the
Gittite, comrade of David, *A.*
vii. 201 ; (Ethaios) vii. 233

Euaeus (Bibl. Hiv[v]ite), son of
Canaan, *A.* i. 139

Euaratus. See Euarestus (1)

Euarestus (1) (Euaratus) of Cos,
friend of Herod, *B.* i. 532 ; (Euaratus) *A.* xvi. 312

Euarestus (2), Arruntius. See
Arruntius (1), Euarestus

Eucles, son of Xenander,
Athenian scribe, *A.* xiv. 150

Euergetes. See Ptolemy (3)

Euhemerus, Greek writer, testifies to antiquity of Jews, *Ap.* i.
216

eunuchs, Jewish law on, *A.* iv.
290-291

Euonymus (var. Menollus),
priest of Halicarnassus, *A.* xiv.
256

Eupator (1). See Antiochus (5)

Eupator (2). See Mithridates
(3)

Euphemus, father of Nicanor of
Ephesus, *A.* xiv. 262 (omitted
in translation)

Euphrates, river in Mesopotamia,
B. i. 5, 6, 157, 175, 179, 182,
321, 362, 433-434 ; ii. 363,
388 ; iii. 107 ; v. 44, 252 ;
vi. 343 ; vii. 17, 105, 224, 236 ;
origin of name, *A.* i. 39 ;

boundary of land occupied by
Shem's sons, i. 143 ; i. 221 ;
iii. 318 ; iv. 104, 126 ; v. 183 ;
vii. 99-100 ; David defeats
king of Damascus there, vii.
101, 127 ; border of Solomon's
kingdom, viii. 39 ; viii. 153,
189, 271, 363 ; x. 74, 75, 84,
86, 183 ; ten tribes dwell
beyond it, xi. 133 ; Ezra
tarries beyond it for three
days, xi. 134 ; Jews set out
from it, xi. 135 ; xi. 314 ;
boundary of Antiochus Epiphanes' realm, xii. 295, 297 ;
xiv. 79, 98, 122, 439 ; xv. 15,
39, 96, 178, xvii. 24 ; treaty
made there between Vitellius
and Artabanus, xviii. 101 ;
protects Nearda, xviii. 311 ;
boundary of Parthia, xx. 87 ;
xx. 245

Eupolemus (1), son of Joannes,
A. xii. 415 ; signs treaty with
Rome, xii. 415

Eupolemus (2), Greek writer,
praised for accuracy, *Ap.* i. 218

Europe, *B.* ii. 358 ; iv. 598 ; *A.*
i. 122 ; its Jews subject to
Romans, xi. 133 ; xiii. 165 ;
xiv. 110, 186 ; its inland
nations for the most part
unknown to historians, *Ap.* i.
66 ; its conquerors have enslaved Egyptians, ii. 128

Eurychoros (Broad Place), embankment set up by Hiram,
king of Tyre, *A.* viii. 145

Eurycles the Lacedaemonian, *B.*
i. 513-532 ; assists Antipater
in his intrigues against Alexander, *A.* xvi. 301, 306,
308-310

Eusebeon (Bibl. Zibeon), a
Canaanite chieftain, father of
Oholibamah, *A.* i. 265

Eusebes. See Antiochus (7) and
(10)

Eutychus (1), freedman of Agrippa, *A.* xviii. 168, 179 ; accuses
Agrippa to Tiberius, xviii.
183-186

Eutychus (2), charioteer, Chaerea
awaits password from him,
A. xix. 257

233

GENERAL INDEX

Falernian tribe, in Rome, *A.* xiii. 260

false prophet. See prophet, false

Fannius (1), Marcus, father of Fannius the praetor, *A.* xiii. 260

Fannius (2), Roman praetor, son of Marcus, *A.* xiii. 260; xiii. 265-266

Fannius (3), Roman propraetor, *A.* xiv. 230

Fannius (4), Gaius, father of Gaius Fannius (5)

Fannius (5), Gaius, Roman proconsular praetor, writes letter to people of Cos, *A.* xiv. 233 (perhaps to be identified with Fannius [3])

Fast Day (Day of the Fast), Jerusalem captured thereon by Pompey, *A.* xiv. 66; Jerusalem captured thereon by Herod, xiv. 487

fasts, Jewish, announcement of, *V.* 290; adoption of by non-Jews, *Ap.* ii. 282

Fate, attitudes of the three Jewish schools of thought toward, *A.* xiii. 172-173; Zeus at mercy of, *Ap.* ii. 245

Faustus Cornelius, son of Sulla, fights bravely under Pompey at siege of Jerusalem, *B.* i. 149, 154; *A.* xiv. 69, 73

Faves. See Phabes

Fear. See Phobos

Feast of Alexandrian Jews, commemorating deliverance from Ptolemy Physcon's elephants, *Ap.* ii. 55

Feast of Wood-carrying. See Wood-carrying, Feast of

feasts. See also festivals

February, month of, *A.* xiii. 260; xiv. 222; xvi. 172

Felix (1), brother of Pallas, Roman procurator of Judaea, *B.* ii. 247, 252-253, 260, 263, 270; appointed procurator, *A.* xx. 137; induces Drusilla to marry him, xx. 142-143; puts down brigands and impostors in Judaea, xx. 161, 168, 171; has high priest Jonathan murdered, xx. 162-

163; puts down quarrel between Jews and Syrians in Caesarea, xx. 177-178; accused before Nero by Jews of Caesarea, xx. 181; sends Jewish priests in bonds to Nero, *V.* 13; 37

Felix (2), Claudius. See Claudius Felix

Festival of Dionysus. See Dionysian Festival

Festival of Lights (Hanukkah), Jewish holiday celebrating the restoration of sacrifices in the temple, observed since the time of Judas the Maccabee, *A.* xii. 325

Festival of Unleavened Bread. See Passover

Festivals (pilgrimages), Jewish law on, *A.* iv. 203-204

Festus, Porcius, Roman procurator in Judaea, *B.* ii. 271-272; succeeds Felix as procurator, *A.* xx. 182; attempts to put down *sicarii*, xx. 185, 188; xx. 193-194; his death, xx. 1?7, 200

Finasus. See Phanasus

Flaccus (1), Gaius Norbanus, Roman consul, *A.* xvi. 166; orders people of Sardis to stop interfering with collection of holy monies for the temple, xvi. 171

Flaccus (2), Roman proconsul, governor of Syria, his quarrel with Agrippa I, *A.* xviii. 150-154

Flavius (1) Sabinus. See Sabinus (2)

Flavius (2), praetor of Libya, *A.* xvi. 169

Flavius (3), Lucius, father of Flavius, of Lemonian tribe in Rome, *A.* xiv. 220

Flavius (4), son of Lucius, Roman senator, *A.* xiv. 220

Flavius (5) Silva. See Silva

fleet, a sham, used by Josephus as a ruse to quell revolt, *V.* 165 ff.

flies, fable of, told by Emperor Tiberius, *A.* xviii. 174-175

Flood, description of, by Berosus,

235

GENERAL INDEX

birthplace of Saul, vi. 67 ; vi. 156

Gabaa (Gabaon ; Bibl. Geba [of Benjamin]), city in Benjamin, *A.* viii. 306

Gabadan. See Nabatha

Gabaenians. See Gaba (2)

Gabalis. See Gobolitis

Gabalites. See Gobolitis

Gabao. See Gabaon (1)

Gabaon (1) (Gabao ; Bibl. Gibeon)(Gabaonites; Bibl. Gibeonites), place near Jerusalem, (Gabao) *B.* ii. 516, 544 ; *A.* vii. 11, 283; (Gabaonites) make pact with Joshua by trickery, v. 49, 51, 54, 56 ; appeal to Joshua for aid against league of kings, v. 58 ; v. 62 ; avenged by David, vii. 294-297; viii. 22 (Gibron is a corruption for Bibl. Gibeon)

Gabaon (2). See Gabaa

Gabara (Gabaroth), city in Galilee, *B.* ii. 629 ; its destruction, iii. 132-133 ; its Jews capture Gischala in 66, are then defeated by John of Gischala, *V.* 44-45 ; captured by Josephus, 82 ; one of three chief cities of Galilee, joins John of Gischala, 123-125 ; orders issued to it by deputies to send assistance to John of Gischala, 203 ; (Gabaroth) village where Josephus is charged by delegation from Jerusalem to meet them for hearing of his charges against John of Gischala, 229 ; place where John of Gischala meets deputation from Jerusalem, 233 ; in league with John of Gischala, Josephus refuses to meet deputation from Jerusalem there, 235 ; routes from there into Galilee guarded by Josephus' men, 240 ; demonstrations there in favour of Josephus, 242 ff. ; distance of Sogane therefrom, 265 ; its leading men summoned to meeting by embassy from Jerusalem, 313

Gabares (1) (Bibl. Ben-geber), governor under Solomon, *A.* viii. 36

Gabares (2) (Bibl. Geber), governor under Solomon, *A.* viii. 37

Gabaroth. See Gabara

Gabath Saul. See Gaba (2)

Gabatha. See Gaba (2)

Gabathaios. See Bagathoos

Gabathon (Bibl. Gibbethon), Philistine city, *A.* viii. 288, 308, 310

Gabathoos. See Bagathoos

Gabinius, governor of Syria, *B.* i. 140 ; succeeds Scaurus as governor of Syria and marches against Alexander the son of Aristobulus, i. 160 ; defeats Alexander, i. 162-167; demolishes Alexandreion, i. 168 ; reinstates Hyrcanus, i. 169 ; divides Jewish nation into five unions, i. 170 ; defeats Aristobulus, i. 171-174 ; i. 175-178, 244 ; vii. 171 ; *A.* xiv. 37, 55, 56 ; defeats Alexander the son of Aristobulus, xiv. 82, 84-85 ; rebuilds ruined cities in Judaea, xiv. 86-88 ; demolishes Alexandreion, xiv. 89 ; defeats Aristobulus again, xiv. 92, 96 ; releases Aristobulus' children from captivity, xiv. 97 ; assisted by Hyrcanus and Antipater in his Egyptian campaign, xiv. 98-100 ; defeats Alexander son of Aristobulus a second time, xiv. 101-102 ; returns to Rome, xiv. 103-104 ; xiv. 326

Gad (1) (Gad[as]), son of Jacob and Zilpah, his birth, *A.* i. 306 ; his children, ii. 182

Gad (2) (Gadites), tribe of, awarded its land, *A.* v. 3 ; erects altar, v. 100 ; as territory, vi. 99 ; (viii. 58-59) ; their land ravaged by Syria, ix. 159

Gad (3) prophet, *A.* vii. 321, 329

Gadalias (Bibl. Gedaliah), governor of Judaea, son of Ahikam, *A.* x. 155, 157 ; reassures those who remain in Judaea, x. 159, 161 ; is murdered, x. 163-173, 175

GENERAL INDEX

Gadam (Bibl. Gaham), son of Nahor, *A.* i. 153

Gadara (Gadarenes), city of Decapolis annexed to Herod's kingdom, *B.* i. 86, 155, 170, 396; ii. 97, 459, 478; iii. 37, 542; iv. 413-419, 428; taken by Antiochus the Great, *A.* xii. 136; captured by Alexander Jannaeus, xiii. 356; xiii. 396; rebuilt by Pompey, xiv. 75, 91; added to Herod's realm, xv. 217; (Gadarenes) bring charges against Herod, xv. 351, 354; (Gadarenes) accuse Herod of cruelty, xv. 356, 358; detached from Archelaus' kingdom and added to Syria, xvii. 320; set on fire by Justus of Tiberias and his followers, *V.* 42; its Jews capture Gischala in 66, are then defeated by John of Gischala, 44-45; sixty furlongs from Tiberias, 349

Gad(as). See Gad (1)

Gaddes. See John (1)

Gaddis. See John (1)

Gadeira (Gades), city in Spain, *B.* ii. 363; furthest point in Europe where sons of Japheth settled, *A.* i. 122

Gades. See Gadeira

Gadia. See Antipater (7)

Gaetulians, formerly called Evilaeans, founded by Havilah, *A.* i. 134

Gaham. See Gadam

Gaius Caligula (Caesar), Emperor, son of Germanicus, *B.* ii. 178-179; ascends throne and makes Agrippa I king over Philip's tetrarchy, ii. 181-183; ii. 184, 199; his death, ii. 203; ii. 208; his accession, *A.* xviii. 105; successor to Tiberius, xviii. 124; courted by Agrippa, xviii. 166-168, 187-188; xviii. 192, 194, 206; the gods' choice to succeed Tiberius, xviii. 214; appointed successor to Tiberius, xviii. 219, 223-224; assumes office of emperor upon death of Tiberius, xviii. 234, 236;

releases Agrippa from prison, xviii. 236-237; xviii. 238; Agrippa accuses Herod the tetrarch to him, xviii. 247-248, 250; banishes Herod and gives his tetrarchy to Agrippa, xviii. 252-256; receives delegations of Greeks and Jews of Alexandria, xviii. 257; hears Apion revile Jews, xviii. 258-259; refuses to hear Philo, xviii. 260; (Caesar) xviii. 265, 271; orders his statue set up in the temple, xviii. 261-262, 266, 268-269, 274-275; appealed to by Petronius to rescind his order, xviii. 277-278, 281-282, 287; offers to grant Agrippa any request, xviii. 289-291, 294-295; grants Agrippa's request that he desist from setting up his statue, xviii. 296, 298-299, 302; his death, xviii. 305-306, 308; his insolence and madness, xix. 1, 10-11, 13; the conspiracies against him, xix. 17-18, 20-23; his savagery to petitioners at the chariot races, xix. 25, 27; insults Chaerea, xix. 28-31; has Quintilia tortured, xix. 33-36; plotted against by Chaerea, Clemens, Papinius, and others, xix. 37, 40-43, 49-51, 57, 62, 64-66, 68-69; plot against him postponed by Chaerea, xix. 71-74; assassinated at Palatine games, xix. 78-83, 86-88, 91, 93, 96-98, 100-101, 105-107, 109, 113; his death, xix. 114-117; avenged by German bodyguard, xix. 119, 121-122, 125; news of his death reaches populace, xix. 127-128, 130, 133-137, 144, 146-149, 152; reactions to his death, xix. 156, 158, 160-161; assailed by Sentius Saturninus, xix. 175; xix. 185; his wife and daughter murdered, xix. 190, 192-193, 195, 197-198; his character and achievements, xix. 201-211; confusion after his death, xix. 212, 214, 218-219, 221, 230, 232; his corpse attended

GENERAL INDEX

to by Agrippa, xix. 237 ; xix.
251-252, 255 ; his charioteers,
xix. 257 ; xix. 261 ; his
assassins killed by Claudius,
xix. 267 ; xix. 270 ; presents
kingdom to Agrippa, xix. 274 ;
imprisons Alexander the alabarch, xix. 276 ; xix. 278 ; his
humiliation of Alexandrian
Jews, xix. 284-285 ; gives
golden chain to Agrippa, xix.
294 ; xix. 351 ; emperor when
Josephus is born, *V.* 5
Gaius (2), friend of Varus, *B.* ii. 68
Gaius (3), Julius. See Julius (7)
Gaius
Galaad. See Galaaditis
Galaadenians. See Samenians
Galaadetis. See Gaulanis
Galaaditis (Galadene, Galaad,
Galaad, Galaditis ; Bibl. Gilead) (Galadite, Galadenians),
district in Judaea, (Galaad)
B. i. 89 ; (Galadene) *A.* i. 324,
ii. 32, iv. 96, 173 ; (Gilead)
v. 164 ; (Gileadite) Jair the,
v. 254 ; (Gilead) v. 254 ;
(Gilead) invaded by Amma-
nites, v. 257 ; v. 260 ; (Gilead)
v. 269, 270 ; (Galadenians)
attacked by Ammanites, vi.
71-73 ; vi. 375 ; vii. 8, 230 ;
(Galadite) Barzillai the, vii.
230 ; vii. 232 ; (Galadite)
Barzillai the, vii. 272, 387 ;
its governor under Solomon,
viii. 36 ; viii. 319 ; (Galadene)
viii. 398 ; viii. 411 ; ix. 105 ;
ravaged by Syria, ix. 159 ;
(Galadene) subdued by Tiglath-
Pileser, ix. 235 ; xii. 330, 333,
336, 340, 345 ; scene of
Maccabaean struggle, xii. 350 ;
invaded by Tryphon, xiii. 209 ;
subdued by Alexander Jan-
naeus, xiii. 374 ; xiii. 382
Galadene. See Galaaditis
Galadenians. See Galaaditis
Galades (Bibl. Galeed), hill where
Jacob and Laban swear a pact
of friendship, *A.* i. 324
Galadite. See Galaaditis
Galaditis. See Galaaditis
Galatia, either territory of Gauls
in Asia Minor or Cisalpine

Gaul, subdued by Romans, *A.*
xii. 414
Galatians, formerly Gomarites
(probably the Cimmerians), *A.*
i. 123
Galba, Roman Emperor, *B.* iv.
494, 498-499 ; his death, iv.
546 ; *A.* xviii. 216
Galbouath (Bibl. Naioth), place
in Palestine, *A.* vi. 221
Galeed. See Galades
Galestes. See Palaestes
Galgala (Bibl. Gilgal), place
where Joshua establishes a
camp, *A.* v. 34 ; v. 48, 62,
68 ; vi. 57, 83, 98, 103, 134,
145, 155 ; David at, vii.
275-276
Galieni. See Samenians
Galilaeans. See Samenians
Galilee (1) (Upper, Lower) (Galilaeans), region in northern
Palestine, *B.* i. 21-22, 76, 170,
203, 210, 221, 238, 256, 290-291,
302-303, 307, 315, 326, 329,
400 ; ii. 43, 56, 68, 95, 118, 168,
188, 193, 232-244, 247, 252, 503,
510-511, 513, 568 ; fortified by
Josephus, ii. 569-576 ; ii. 585,
589, 592-593, 622, 629, 647 ; iii.
30, 34 ; description of, iii. 35-43 ;
iii. 44, 48, 61, 63, 110, 115, 127,
199, 229, 233, 293, 301, 306, 344 ;
iv. 1, 84, 96, 105, 120, 127, 249,
558 ; v. 408, 474 ; vi. 339 ; *A.* v.
63 ; upper part allotted to
Naphtali, v. 86 ; where Kedesh
is, v. 91 ; its governor under
Solomon, viii. 36-37 ; portions
of it presented by Solomon to
Hiram, viii. 142 ; captured by
Tiglath-Pileser, ix. 235 ; xii.
331 ; invaded by Simon, xii.
332, 334 ; scene of Maccabaean
struggle, xii. 350 ; xii. 421 ;
xiii. 50, 125, 154 ; Demetrius II
defeated there by Jonathan,
xiii. 158 ; xiii. 191-192, 322,
337 ; xiv. 91 ; governed by
Herod, xiv. 158, 169 ; xiv.
274 ; invaded by Marion, xiv.
298 ; site of battle between
Phasael and Parthians, xiv.
342 ; goes over to side of
Herod, xiv. 394-395 ; joins

239

GENERAL INDEX

Herod against Antigonus, xiv.
411 ; Herod's conquests there,
xiv. 413-417 ; further victories
of Herod there, xiv. 433 ;
(Galilaeans) rebel against Herod, xiv. 450 ; xiv. 452 ;
fortified by Herod, xv. 294 ;
on border of Zenodorus' territory, xv. 360 ; bequeathed by
Herod as tetrarchy to Antipas,
xvii. 188 ; (Galilaeans) join
revolt of Jews against Romans,
xvii. 254 ; terrorized by Judas
son of Ezekiel, xvii. 271 ;
(Galilaeans) defeated by Varus,
xvii. 288 ; given to Antipas by
Augustus, xvii. 318 ; xviii. 23,
27 ; site of Tiberias, xviii. 36 ;
(Galilaean) inhabitants of Tiberias, xviii. 37 ; xviii. 136 ;
tetrarchy of Herod, xviii. 240 ;
xix. 338 ; xx. 43 ; (Galilaeans)
slain by Samarians on way to
Jerusalem, xx. 118-120 ; portion of it given to Agrippa II,
xx. 159 ; (Galilaeans) passim
in V. as supporters of Josephus;
(Galilaeans) Josephus in command of them during Jewish
War, Ap. i. 48, 110

Galilee (2), Sea of. See Gennesar,
Lake of

Gallicanus, Roman tribune, B.
iii. 344

Gallim. See Gethla

Gallus (1), Caesennius, commander of twelfth legion, sent
to Galilee by Cestius, governor
of Syria, B. ii. 510-512 ; ii.
513 ; iii. 31

Gallus (2), Roman centurion,
B. iv. 37

Gallus (3), Aelius, leader of an
unsuccessful expedition against
the Sabaeans of Arabia Felix,
A. xv. 317

Gallus (4), Publius Clusius. See
Clusius (2) Gallus, Publius

Gallus (5), Caninius, Roman
consul, A. xiv. 487

Gamala, city east of Sea of
Galilee, B. i. 105 ; rebuilt by
Gabinius, i. 166 ; ii. 568, 574 ;
iii. 56 ; iv. 2 ; description of,
iv. 4-8 ; besieged by Vespasian,

iv. 11-54 ; captured by Romans, iv. 62-83 ; A. xiii. 394,
396 ; xviii. 4 ; loyal to Rome
in 66, V. 46 ; fortress whither
Philip son of Jacimus escapes,
47 ; Jews of Ecbatana with-
draw there awaiting Varus,
Agrippa's viceroy, 58 ; held
by Philip son of Jacimus, 61 ;
destruction of its fortress
ordered by Agrippa II, 114 ;
its people slay Chares, Philip's
kinsman, and murder his
brother Jesus in insurrection
against the Babylonians, 177 ;
its fortress left by Philip son
of Jacimus, 179 ; Agrippa II
orders Philip son of Jacimus
to return thither, 183 ; its
magistrates assaulted by Josephus, the midwife's son, and
his followers, 185 ; roads
leading to it are patrolled by
pickets posted by Sulla, Agrippa II's commander, 398

Gamalas, father of Jesus the
high priest (a friend of Josephus), B. iv. 160 ; V. 193, 204

Gamaliel, father of Symeon
(Simon), who is instructed to
remove Josephus from com-
mand of Galilee, and Jesus
the high priest, B. iv. 159 ; A.
xx. 213, 223 ; V. 190, 390

Gamalus, father of Herod, leader
of pro-Roman Jewish faction
at Tiberias in 66, V. 33

Gamini. See Samenians

Ganges, Greek name for river
Pishon in India, A. i. 38

Garada (var. Charada ; perhaps
identical with Gadara), village
east of Sea of Galilee, A. xiii.
376

Garden, Hanging, of Babylon, A.
x. 226 ; Ap. i. 141

Garis, village near Sepphoris, B.
iii. 129 ; v. 474 ; (var., viii.
330) ; Josephus entrenches
himself there, V. 395 ; Josephus first engages Vespasian
in battle there, 412

Garizaean, Mt. See Gerizim, Mt.
Garizein (1). See Argarizin
Garizein (2), Mt. See Gerizim, Mt.

GENERAL INDEX

Garizim, Mt. See Gerizim, Mt.
Garizin, Mt. See Gerizim, Mt.
Gasiongabel (Bibl. Ezion-geber), place on Red Sea near Eloth, *A.* viii. 163
Gatam. See Jotham(os) (5)
Gath (1). See Eipan
Gath (2). See Gitta
Gaul (Gauls), *B.* i. 5, 397, 437, 672; ii. 111, 364, 371-373; iv. 440, 494, 547, 634; vii. 76, 88; presented to Herod by Octavian, *A.* xv. 217; at Herod's funeral, xvii. 198; Archelaus banished thither by Augustus, xvii. 344; Herod the tetrarch banished thither by Gaius Caligula, xviii. 252; ignorance of even the most exact historians concerning them, *Ap.* i. 67-68
Gaulan, Upper and Lower, parts of Gaulanitis, *B.* iv. 2
Gaulana (Gaulane; Bibl. Golan), city in Batanaea in Palestine, (Gaulane) *B.* i. 90, 105; city of refuge, *A.* iv. 173; xiii. 393
Gaulane. See Gaulana
Gaulanis (var. Iudanis, Galaadetis), village east of Sea of Galilee, *A.* xiii. 375
Gaulanite, Judas the, *A.* xviii. 4
Gaulanitis (Gaulonitis), district east of Sea of Galilee, *B.* ii. 168, 247, 459, 574; iii. 37, 56, 542; iv. 2; *A.* iv. 96; its governor under Solomon, viii. 36; xiii. 396; (Gaulonitis) bequeathed by Herod as tetrarchy to Philip, xvii. 189; ruled by Philip the tetrarch, xviii. 106; revolts against Agrippa II, *V.* 187
Gaulonitis. See Gaulanitis
Gaza (Gazites, Gazaeans), city in southern Palestine near Mediterranean, *B.* i. 87; freed by Pompey, i. 156; annexed to Herod's kingdom, i. 396; ii. 97, 460; iv. 662; boundary of Mizraim's descendants, *A.* i. 136; allotted to Judah, v. 81; withstands capture, v. 128; v. 304; (Gazites) v. 304; Philistine city, vi. 8; ix. 275;

xi. 320, 325; overrun by Jonathan, xiii. 150-151; xiii. 324, 329, 334; held by Ptolemy Lathyrus, xiii. 348; xiii. 351; destroyed by Alexander Jannaeus, xiii. 358; (Gazaeans) their city destroyed by Alexander Jannaeus, xiii. 359-360, 362; xiii. 395; (Gazaeans) xiv. 10; xiv. 76, 88; added to Herod's realm, xv. 217; governed by Costobarus, xv. 254; detached from Archelaus' kingdom and added to Syria, *A.* xvii. 320; near site of battle in which Ptolemy defeats Demetrius Poliorcetes eleven years after Alexander the Great's death, *Ap.* i. 184-186; Idumaea in latitude of, ii. 116
Gazaeans. See Gaza
Gazaga. See Zarasa
Gazara (1). See Aza
Gazara (2) (Bibl. Gezer), town in central Palestine, captured by Simon, *B.* i. 50; on border of territory of Benjamin, *A.* v. 83; on border of Philistine country, vii. 77; vii. 301; built up by Solomon, viii. 151; xii. 308; fortified by Bacchides, xiii. 15; subdued by Simon, xiii. 215; restored to Jews by Rome, xiii. 261
Gazasa. See Zarasa
Gazites. See Gaza
Geba. See Gabaa
Gebala (Gabaon; Bibl. Gibeath Benjamin), city in Palestine, location uncertain, *A.* vi. 95 (perhaps to be identified with Gaba [2]); (Gabaon) vi. 105
Gebelos. See Hebel
Geber. See Gabares
Gedaliah. See Gadalias
Gedeon (Bibl. Gideon), son of Joash, Jewish leader, *A.* v. 213; gathers his army, v. 215, 217; gains courage, v. 218-219, 221-222; leads army against Midianites, v. 223, 225, 227-228; returns home, v. 229; pacifies Ephraim, v. 230; as judge, v. 232; v. 239-240; vi. 90; vii. 142

241

GENERAL INDEX

Geion (Bibl. Gihon), fountain in Jerusalem, *A*. vii. 355

geision, Hebrew word for parapet (see *thrinkos*), *A*. viii. 95

Gelas (Bibl. Gera), son of Benjamin, *A*. ii. 180

Gelboue (Bibl. Gilboa), mountain in Samaria near Scythopolis, *A*. vi. 328, 372

Gellius (1) (var. Sellius, Asellius, Sasellius, Aquilius), Marcus, father of Marcus Gellius the Roman senator, *A*. xiv. 220

Gellius (2) (var. Sellius, Asellius, Sasellius, Aquilius), Marcus, Roman senator, *A*. xiv. 220

Gelmon (Bibl. Giloh), city in Palestine, perhaps near Hebron, *A*. vii. 228

Gelmonite, Ahithophel the, *A*. vii. 197

Gema. See Ginaea

Gemellus (1), friend of Herod, dismissed by him, *A*. xvi. 242-243

Gemellus (2). See Tiberius (4), Gemellus

genealogies, in histories of Hellanicus and Acusilaus, *Ap*. i. 16

general, Moses' excellence as, *Ap*. ii. 158

Genesar. See Gennesar

Gennath, gate in first wall of Jerusalem, *B*. v. 146

Gennesar (Genesar, Gennesaret, Gennesaritis, Tiberias), Lake of, *B*. ii. 573; (Tiberias) iii. 57; iii. 463; description of, iii. 506-521; (Tiberias) iv. 456; boundary of Zebulun's territory, *A*. v. 84; xiii. 158; (Gennesaritis) xviii. 28; (Gennesaritis) site of Tiberias, xviii. 36; (Gennesaret) *V*. 96, 153, 165 ff., 304, 327, 349

Gennesaret. See Gennesar

Gennesaritis. See Gennesar

Geon (Bibl. Gihon), Biblical name for Nile River, *A*. i. 39

Gephthaeus (Gyphthaeus; var. Tephthaeus), soldier in John's army, *B*. v. 474; (Gyphthaeus) vi. 92; vi. 148

Gera (1). See Gelas

Gera (2), father of Ehud, *A*. v. 188

Gera (3), father of Shimei, *A*. vii. 207, 263, 388

Gerar. See Gerara

Gerara (Bibl. Gerar), city in Philistia, *A*. i. 207, 259-260; viii. 294

Gerasa (Essa), city in Galaaditis, *B*. i. 104; ii. 458, 480; iii. 47; iv. 487, 503; (Essa) *A*. xiii. 393

Gerasenes, people of Gerasa, *A*. xiii. 398

Gerastratus, son of Abdelimus, judge of Tyre, *Ap*. i. 157

Gergesaeus (Bibl. Girgashite), son of Canaan, *A*. i. 139

Gerizim (Garizaean, Garizein, Garizim, Garizin), Mt., mountain in central Palestine, *B*. iii. 307, 311; (Garizaean Mountain) *A*. iv. 305; (Garizin) iv. 306, v. 69, 235; (Garizein) xi. 310, 340, 346; (Garizein) Jews taken from there by Ptolemy and brought to Egypt, xii. 7; (Garizein) Samaritans send their sacrifices there, xii. 10; (Garizein) xii. 257, 259; xiii. 74, 78, 255; xiv. 100; xviii. 85

Germanicus (1), father of Gaius Caligula, *B*. ii. 178; his death, *A*. xviii. 54; son of Antonia, xviii. 164; his popularity, xviii. 206; xix. 117; brother of Claudius, his popularity, xix. 223; father of Agrippina, xx. 148; distributes corn to inhabitants of Alexandria, *Ap*. ii. 63

Germanicus (2), family name of Claudius, *A*. xix. 217, 280, 287; xx. 11

Germans, Herod's guards, *B*. i. 672; ii. 364, 376-377; iii. 4; vi. 331; vii. 75-89; at Herod's funeral, *A*. xvii. 198; one of them prophesies Agrippa I's future greatness, xviii. 196-202; bodyguard of Emperor Gaius Caligula, avenge his death, xix. 119-126; spare the Roman populace, xix. 138, 148-149, 152; avenge Gaius, xix. 153, 215

242

GENERAL INDEX

GENERAL INDEX

i. 326 ; fortified by Machaerus, *A.* xiv. 450

Gizrite. See Serrites

Glaphyra, wife of Alexander son of Herod, *B.* i. 476-478, (500), (508), 552-553 ; history of, ii. 114-116 ; daughter of Archelaus, married to Alexander son of Herod, *A.* xvi. 11 ; incurs Salome's wrath, xvi. 193 ; xvi. 206, 303 ; involved in charge of conspiracy against Herod, xvi. 329-332 ; her children, xvii. 12 ; married to Archelaus, xvii. 341 ; her dr am, xvii. 349-353

glosses in text of Josephus, *Ap.* i. 83, 92, 98, 134 ; ii. 195, 198, 253-254

Gobolis. See Gobolitis

Gobolitis (Gabalis, Gobolis) (Gabalites), region in Idumaea, former name of Amalekitis, *A.* ii. 6 ; land of the Amalekites iii. 40 ; (Gabalites) defeated by Amaziah. ix. 188 ; (Gobolis) xiv. 18 ; (Gabalis) xviii. 113

God, *passim*

"God's camp," name given to Canaan by Jacob on his return there, *A.* i. 325

god(s) of Egyptians, displeasure of, breaks upon Egyptians, according to Manetho, *Ap.* i. 75 ; King Amenophis did not desire to see them, according to Josephus, i. 254-255 ; Jewish refusal to worship them, ii. 65-67 ; ridiculed by Josephus, ii. 128-129 ; slaughtered by Persian invaders, ii. 129

gods of Greeks, Antiochus' respect for them appealed to by Greek in the temple, *Ap.* ii. 96 ; Jews do not deride or blaspheme them, ii. 237 ; criticism of by Josephus, ii. 238-249 ; Protagoras' views of, ii. 266

Golan. See Gaulana

gold, coins of swallowed by Jews in desertion to Titus, *B.* v. 422 ; Syrian picks gold coins from his excrements, v. 550 ; standard of, depreciated throughout Syria, vi. 317

Gold, Land of, in or near India, formerly called Sopheir (Bibl. Ophir), Solomon sends expedition there, *A.* viii. 164 ; precious stones and pine wood brought from there to Solomon, viii. 176

Golgom(es) (Bibl. Gershon), son of Levi, *A.* ii. 178

Goliath, Philistine giant, challenges Israelites to battle, *A.* vi. 171-177 ; slain by David, vi. 185-191 ; sword of, d dicated to God by David, vi. 192 ; sword of, vi. 244, 254

Gomar (Bibl. Gomer), son of Japheth, father of Gomarites (later called Galatians), *A.* i. 123, 126

Gomarites, people founded by Gomar the son of Japheth, called Galatians by Greeks, *A.* i. 123

Gomer. See Gomar

Gophna, sub-district of Judaea, *B.* i. 45, 222 ; ii. 568 ; iii. 55 ; iv. 551 ; v. 50 ; vi. 115, 118 ; *A.* xiv. 275

Gorgias, Syrian Greek general, sent against Judas the Maccabee, *A.* xii. 298 ; defeated by Judas, xii. 305-312 ; defeats Jewish home guard at Jamneia, xii. 351

Gorion (1), son of Nicomedes, envoy of Jews besieging Romans in Herod's palace, *B.* ii. 451

Gorion (2), Joseph son of, Jewish general against Romans, *B.* ii. 563 ; iv. 159 (probably identical with Gurion, iv. 358)

Gorpiaeus, month of, *B.* ii. 440 ; iii. 542 ; iv. 83 ; vi. 392, 407, 435

Gotholia(h). See Othlia

Gounis (Bibl. Guni), son of Naphtali, *A.* ii. 181

Governor(ship) of a district. See Meridarch(es)

Graces, temple of the, *A.* xiv. 153

Granicus, river in Phrygia, *A.* xi. 305, 313

Grapte, relative of Izas (Izates), king of Adiabene, *B.* iv. 567

Gratus (1), Roman infantry com-

244

GENERAL INDEX

his possessions given to Mordecai, xi. 270; letter sent by him throughout the land, xi. 270; an alien among the Persians, enjoys their hospitality, xi. 277; letter sent by him, xi. 279; his ten sons crucified, xi. 289; Jews marked for destruction by him, xi. 294

Hamath. See Amathe

Hamathite. See Amathus

Hamathites. See Amathaeans

Hammedatha. See Amadathos

Hamor. See Emmor

Hamul. See Amour(os)

Hamutal. See Amitale

Hananel. See Ananel

Hananiah. See Ananias (1) and (2)

hands, severing of, as punishment, V. 147, 171 ff.

Hanging Garden. See Garden, Hanging

Hanna(h). See Anna (1)

Hannibal (Annibas), Carthaginian general, pride of the Carthaginians in him, B. ii. 380

Hanoch. See Anoch(es)

Hanukkah. See Festival of Lights

Hanun. See Annon

Haran. See Aran

Harbonah. See Sabuchadas

Harmais (1), Egyptian king, son of Akencheres II, Ap. i. 97

Harmais (2) (Hermaeus), brother of Sethosis (Sethos) (Ramesses II), made viceroy of Egypt, revolts against his brother, Ap. i. 98-102; (Hermaeus) known as Danaus, expelled by his brother, i. 231

Harmesses Miamoun, Egyptian king, son of Ramesses I, Ap. i. 97

harmony, Jewish, Ap. ii. 179 ff.

Hasmonaeans (see also Asamonaeus, Asamonean), alternate appellation for the Maccabees, "the sons of Asamonaeus," expel Antiochus Epiphanes, B. i. 19; their dynasty, i. 19; their palace, ii. 344; level Acra, v. 139; denounced by Herod, A. xvii. 162

Hatach. See Achratheos

Haterius. See Fronto (1)

Havila. See Evilas

Havilah (1). See Cophen

Havilah (2). See Evilas

Havvah. See Eve

Hazael. See Azaelos

Hazarmaveth. See Azermoth

Hazeroth. See Esermoth

Hazo. See Azau

Hazor. See Asor

Hebel (Gebelos, Gibalu; Bibl. Ebal), mountain called "Counsel," near Shechem in Palestine, altar erected near it, A. iv. 305; v. 69

Heber (1), son of Asher. See Abar(os)

Heber (2) (Bibl, Eber), son of Shelah, A. i. 146-148, 150

Hebrew(s) (Hebraic; see also Israelites), Jesus their general, B. iv. 459; their territory, v. 160; Pharaoh bestows silver and gold upon them, v. 381; Sennacherib flees from them, v. 388; Simon and John disparage their race, v. 443; Josephus translates the Antiquities from their records, A. i. 5; Sabbath means "rest" in their language, i. 33; Adam means "red" in it, i. 34; essa is "woman" in it, i. 36; i. 80-81; confusion called "Babel" by them, i. 117; the name Chethim given to all islands by them, i. 128; destroy seven cities, i. 139; origin of their name, i. 146; their origin, i. 148; zoor means "little" in their language, i. 204; call shaggy hair ésauron, i. 258; Israel denotes the opponent of an angel of God in their language, i. 333; ii. 3, 78, 102; their women, ii. 226; take Joseph's bones with them back to Canaan, ii. 200; enslaved by Egyptians, ii. 201-204; their deliverance from Egypt will be remembered not just by them, ii. 216; Moses was the noblest of them, ii. 229; ii. 235; rest their

GENERAL INDEX

years and six months, vii. 389 ;
built by Rehoboam, Solomon's
son, viii. 246 ; captured by
Judas the Maccabee, xii. 353
Hebron (2). See Gibron
Hecataeus of Abdera, philosopher
and man of affairs, one of
Josephus' sources in *Antiquities*,
A. i. 108 ; composes book
about Abraham, i. 159 ; cited,
xii. 38 ; his book on the Jews
quoted, *Ap.* i. 183-205 ; con-
temporary of Hieronymus of
Cardia, i. 213 ; contrasted
with Hieronymus, i. 214 ;
Alexander's honouring of the
Jews noted by him, ii. 43
Hecatombaeon (Hekatombaion
Hyrkanios), Athenian month
called Abba by the Hebrews, *A.*
iv. 84 ; (Hekatombaion Hyrkanios) month in which Antiochus Epiphanes writes to
district-governor Apollonius,
xii. 264
Heimarmene. See Destiny
Hekatombaion Hyrkanios. See
Hecatombaeon
Helam. See Chalamas
Helama. See Chalamas
Helcias (1) the Elder (var.
Chelcias), surname of Alexas,
marries Cypros, the daughter
of Antipater and Cypros, *A.*
xviii. 138 ; appeals to Pé-
tronius, xviii. 273 ; conspires
with Herod to slay Silas, xix.
353 ; father of Julius Archelaus, xix. 355, xx. 140
Helcias (2), keeper of the Jewish
treasury, sent as ambassador
to Nero, *A.* xx. 194 ; kept
as hostage by Poppaea, xx.
195
Helena, queen of Adiabene and a
convert to Judaism, her monuments, *B.* v. 55, 119, 147 ; her
palace, v. 253, vi. 355 ; birth
of her son Izates, *A.* xx. 17-18,
20 ; urges that Izates be
named king to succeed Monobazus, xx. 26, 30, 32 ; her
conversion to Judaism, xx. 35 ;
her visit to Jerusalem and her
gifts for relief of the famine

there, xx. 49, 51 ; her death,
xx. 94 ; aids Jews in time of
famine, xx. 101
Heliopolis, nome (district) in
Egypt, Onias obtains land
from Ptolemy there to build
town, *B.* i. 33 ; vii. 426 ;
Joseph marries the daughter
of Pentephres, a priest there,
A. ii. 91 ; land given there to
Jacob's family in Egypt, ii.
188 ; Onias builds temple
there, xii. 388, xiii. 65, 70,
285 ; xiv. 40 ; founding of
temple there, xx. 236 ; Osariph,
one of the priests there, *Ap.* i.
238 ; Osariph (Moses) born
there, i. 250 ; Moses, priest of,
chosen as leader by lepers, i.
261 ; Osariph (Moses), a native
thereof, i. 265 ; Moses, priest
thereof, according to Manetho,
i. 279 ; Moses, native thereof,
according to Apion, ii. 10
Helix, leader of revolt, attacks
Phasael at Jerusalem and is defeated, *B.* i. 236-237 ; marches
against Phasael, *A.* xiv. 294 ;
shut up in a tower by Phasael,
xiv. 295
Hellanicus, Greek historian, discrepancies between him and
Acusilaus on genealogies, his
mendacity exposed by Ephorus,
Ap. i. 16 ; one of Josephus'
sources in *Antiquities*, *A.* i. 108
Hellas. See Greeks
Hellenic. See Greeks
Hellespont, strait connecting Ae-
gean Sea with Sea of Mar-
mara, crossed by Vespasian,
B. iii. 8 ; crossed by Alexander
the Great, *A.* xi. 305, 313 ;
ruled by Lysimachus after
Alexander, xii. 2
Helon (Bibl. Elon), father of
Adah, *A.* i. 265
Heman. See Haimanos
Hemaon (Bibl. Mahol), father of
Ethan, Heman, Chalcol, and
Darda, *A.* viii. 43
hemian, Aramaic word denoting
the tunic of Jewish priests (see
abanéth), *A.* iii. 156
Henadad. See Aminadabos

252

GENERAL INDEX

508; gives presents to Archelaus, i. 511-512; flattered and befriended by Eurycles, i. 513-515; Eurycles denounces Alexander to him, i. 516-531; is very receptive to slander, i. 533; Salome denounces his sons to him, i. 534-535; imprisons his sons and reports the case to Augustus, i. 535-536; Augustus gives him a free hand in trial of his sons, i. 537; holds trial at Berytus, i. 538-539; his sons condemned to death, i. 542; drags his sons to Tyre, i. 543; puts Tiro and Trypho under the torture, i. 548-549; has his sons executed, i. 550-551; his domestic settlements, i. 553-555; his care for his grandchildren, i. 556-558; his wives and children, i. 562-563; forces Salome to marry Alexas, i. 566; Salome reports proceedings of trouble-making women to him, i. 569-570; indignant at Pheroras' wife, i. 571-573; intrigues of Syllaeus the Arab against him, i. 575-577; banishes Pheroras and his wife, i. 578-579; tends the dying Pheroras, i. 580; reported to have poisoned Pheroras, i. 581; discovers that Pheroras has been poisoned, i. 582-583; subjects women to torture, i. 584-589; dismisses Doris, Antipater's mother, from court, i. 590-591; discovery of Antipater's and Pheroras' plot to poison him, i. 592-619; his trial of Antipater, i. 620-640; stricken by serious illness, i. 645; modifies his will, i. 646; his illness grows worse, i. 647; represses sedition, i. 648-655; his last illness, i. 656-660; attempts suicide, i. 662; orders Antipater executed, i. 663-664; his last will in favour of Archelaus, i. 664; his death, i. 665; his will is read by Ptolemy, i. 667-669; his funeral, i. 670-673; punishes those who defaced the gate of the temple, ii. 5; his favourites are punished, ii. 7; Sabinus on his way to Judaea to take charge of his estate, ii. 16; his confidence in Ptolemy, ii. 21; the number of his children, ii. 25; Antipater assumes kingship after his death, ii. 27; his brother Phasael, ii. 46; revolt of his veterans in Idumaea, ii. 55; his subjugation of Ezechias, the brigand-chief, ii. 56; Aretas' hatred for him, ii. 68; Arabs infuriated even against his friends, ii. 69; Arabs' hatred toward him, ii. 76; Augustus punishes his relatives, ii. 78; Augustus distributes his estate, ii. 83; speeches of Jewish deputies against him, ii. 84-92; Augustus divides his kingdom among his three sons, ii. 94; further division of Herod's estate by Augustus, ii. 99-100; his execution of Alexander, ii. 101; Alexander arraigned by him, ii. 106; his son Alexander, ii. 114; his execution of Aristobulus, ii. 178; Augustus gives districts of Trachonitis and Auranitis to him, ii. 215; Aristobulus and Alexander put to death by him, ii. 222; founder of Caesarea, ii. 266; his armoury, ii. 434; his cavalry, iii. 36; his monuments, v. 108, 507; his three towers, v. 161; tower of Antonia built by him, v. 238; his palace, v. 246; captures Jerusalem with Sossius, v. 398, vi. 436; his buildings, vii. 172-177; a huge plant grows within the palace during his time, vii. 179; builds fortress upon rock of Masada, vii. 285-303; takes money out of David's tomb, vii. 394; founder of Sebaste (Samaria), *A.* xiii. 275; changes name of Anthedon to Agrippias, xiii. 357; xiv. 9; refounds Straton's Tower, xiv. 76; xiv. 121;

255

GENERAL INDEX

his memoirs, xv. 174 ; unjustly punishes Hyrcanus, xv. 181-182 ; hastens to meet Octavian, xv. 183 ; admits to Octavian that he has been an ally of Antony, xv. 187-193 ; honoured by Octavian, xv. 194-198 ; welcomes Octavian in Judaea, xv. 199-201 ; Mariamme doubts his love for her, xv. 202-208 ; learns of Mariamme's dislike for him, xv. 209-214 ; meets Octavian in Egypt, xv. 215-217 ; his increasing distrust of Mariamme, xv. 218-231 ; puts Mariamme to death, xv. 232-236 ; his remorse and illness, xv. 240-246 ; executes Alexandra, xv. 247-252 ; pardons Costobarus though he had offered his services to Cleopatra, xv. 254-258 ; his enmity toward the Sons of Baba, xv. 260-266 ; offends the Jews by introducing pagan games, xv. 267-276 ; removes pagan ornaments to pacify Jews, xv. 277-279 ; conspiracy to assassinate him, xv. 280-283 ; puts conspirators to death, xv. 284-291 ; builds fortresses throughout the country, xv. 292-298 ; drought and plague afflict his people, xv. 299-304 ; relieves distress of the starving people, xv. 305-316 ; builds palace in Jerusalem, xv. 318 ; marries daughter of the priest Simon, xv. 319-322 ; builds fortress (Herodion), xv. 323-325 ; his gifts to pagan cities, xv. 326-330 ; rebuilds Strato's Tower in Caesarea, xv. 331-341 ; sends his sons to Rome, xv. 342-343 ; receives additional territory from Augustus, xv. 344-348 ; his newly acquired territory invaded by Arabs, xv. 349-353 ; acquitted by Augustus of charges of cruelty against Gadarenes, xv. 354-359 ; receives Zenodorus' territory from Augustus, xv. 360-364 ; builds temple to

Augustus, xv. 364 ; takes steps to prevent his subjects from revolting, xv. 365-372 ; predictions of Manaëmus about him, xv. 373-379 ; rebuilds the temple in Jerusalem, xv. 380-425 ; his strict laws about theft, xvi. 1-5 ; goes to Italy to see his sons, xvi. 6 ; his suspicion aroused about his sons, xvi. 10 ; provides his sons with wives, xvi. 11 ; entertains Marcus Agrippa, xvi. 12-15 ; meets Agrippa in Asia Minor, xvi. 162-6 ; secures Agrippa's aid for Jews, xvi. 60-61 ; dissension in his household, xvi. 66-72 ; distrusts his sons, xvi. 73-77 ; Antipater acquires influence with him, xvi. 78-86 ; aroused against Mariamme's sons by Antipater, xvi. 87-90 ; consults Augustus about his sons, xvi. 90-99 ; Mariamme's sons disturbed at his accusations, xvi. 100-103 ; Alexander's reply to him, xvi. 104-120 ; reconciled with his sons by Augustus, xvi. 121-126 ; exchanges gifts with Augustus, xvi. 128 ; given right to choose his successor by Augustus, xvi. 129 ; visits Archelaus, xvi. 130-132 ; names his successors, xvi. 133-135 ; celebrates completion of work in Caesarea, xvi. 136-141 ; his other buildings in Palestine, xvi. 142-145 ; his benefactions to the Greek cities, xvi. 146-149 ; his love of fame, xvi. 150-159 ; opens David's tomb, xvi. 179-187 ; partiality of the historian Nicolas of Damascus to him, xvi. 184 ; Antipater's hold over him, xvi. 188-193 ; quarrels with Pheroras, xvi. 194-200 ; incited against his sons by Salome, xvi. 203-205 ; Pheroras incites Alexander against him, xvi. 206-212 ; distrusts Salome and Pheroras, xvi. 213-219 ; Syllaeus asks him for the hand of Salome in marriage, xvi. 221-225 ; marries

GENERAL INDEX

xix. 354; Claudius' high regard for him, xx. 13; obtains further concessions from Claudius, obtains right to select high priests, xx. 15-16; king of Chalcis, appoints Ananias high priest, xx. 103; his death, xx. 104, 145; Aristobulus, his son, xx. 158

Herod (6), Agrippa II. See Agrippa (3) II

Herod (7), Antipas (Herod the Tetrarch), son of Herod the Great. See Antipas (3), Herod

Herod (8), son of Phasael and Salampsio, *A.* xviii. 131; brother of Antipater, xviii. 138

Herod (9), son of Aristobulus and Salome, *A.* xviii. 137

Herod (10) (" the most venerable ," unidentified), Josephus sells him copy of his *Jewish War*, vouches for Josephus' accuracy, *Ap.* i. 51

Herod (11), son of Miarus, leader of pro-Roman Jewish faction at Tiberias in 66, *V.* 33

Herod (12), son of Gamalus, leader of pro-Roman Jewish faction at Tiberias in 66, *V.* 33

Herod (13), of Tiberias (perhaps identical with one of the two foregoing), aids Josephus to escape from Tiberias to Tarichaeae, *V.* 96

Herodeion. See Herodion (2)

Herodia. See Herodion (2)

Herodias, daughter of Aristobulus and Berenice, *B.* i. 552; instigates her husband, Herod the Tetrarch, to aspire to throne, ii. 182; Herod the Tetrarch marries her, *A.* xviii. 110-111, 136; sister of Agrippa, wife of Herod the Tetrarch, dissuades Agrippa from suicide, xviii. 148; urges Herod the Tetrarch to seek his fortune in Rome, xviii. 240; Herod the Tetrarch sets sail for Rome with her, xviii. 246; banished by Gaius, xviii. 253-255

Herodion (1) (Herodium), fortress on Arabian frontier erected by Herod and named after himself,

name of two fortresses built by Herod, *B.* i. 419

Herodion (2) (Herodium, Herodeion, Herodia), fortress built by Herod sixty furlongs from Jerusalem, *B.* i. 265, 419; Herod's burial there, i. 673; one of the eleven districts of Judaea, iii. 55; its garrison, iv. 518; held by brigands, iv. 555; taken over by Lucilius Bassus, vii. 163; *A.* xiv. 360; (xv. 323-325); Herod entertains Agrippa there, xvi. 13; Herod buried there, xvii. 199

Herodium. See Herodion (1) and (2)

Herodotus of Halicarnassus, Greek historian, mentions that there were 330 kings of Egypt after Menes, *A.* viii. 157; in error concerning King Shishak, viii. 253; mentions expedition of King Shishak, viii. 260; says that Ethiopians learned the practice of circumcision from Egyptians, viii. 262; his account of Sennacherib's invasion of Egypt, x. 18-20; his mendacity exposed by everyone, *Ap.* i. 16; does not mention Rome, i. 66; accused by Manetho of being misled through ignorance on many points of Egyptian history, i. 73; his mention of circumcision by Palestinian Syrians quoted by Josephus, i. 168-171; says that Egyptians have taught others to adopt circumcision, ii. 142

Heroopolis, place in Egypt where Joseph meets Jacob, *A.* ii. 184

Heshbon (Esebonitis, Essebonitis, Heshbonitis), city on the east bank of the Jordan River, sacked by Jews, *B.* ii. 458; iii. 47; (Essebonitis) *A.* xii. 233; (Essebon) xii. 397; (Esebonitis) rebuilt by Herod, xv. 294

Heshbonitis. See Heshbon

Hesiod, Greek poet, reports that the ancients lived for a thousand years, *A.* i. 108; corrected by Acusilaus, *Ap.* i. 16

260

GENERAL INDEX

Hesitaeus, author of a Phoenician history, *A.* i. 107 ; quoted, i. 119

Heth. See Chettaeus

Hezekiah ((Grk. Ezekias), king of Judah, son of Ahaz, *A.* ix. 257, 260 ; his religious reforms, ix. 272-274 ; his war with the Philistines, ix. 275-276 ; ix. 278 ; pays tribute to Sennacherib, x. 1-4 ; threatened by Sennacherib, x. 5-15 ; defies Sennacherib, x. 16 ; his illness and miraculous cure, x. 24-29 ; receives gifts from king of Babylon, x. 30-34 ; his death, x. 36

Hezron (1). See Esron (2)

Hezron (2). See Essaron

Hiddekel. See Tigris

Hieronymus (1), author of history of Alexander's successors, his malicious silence concerning the Jews, *Ap.* i. 213-214

Hieronymus (2), the Egyptian, author of Phoenician history, *A.* i. 94, 107

Hierosolyma. See Jerusalem

Hierosolymites. See Jerusalem

Hierosyla. See Jerusalem

Hierusaleme. See Jerusalem

high priest(s), as keepers of records, *Ap.* i. 29 ; records containing their names, *Ap.* i. 36 ; alone admitted to sanctuary of the temple, ii. 104 ; direct other priests, ii. 185, 193-194 ; enumeration of, *A.* xx. 224-251

Hilkiah. See Elikias (2)

Hillel. See Elon (3)

hin, Hebrew measure, *A.* iii. 234 ; viii. 92

Hippicus, tower on city wall of Jerusalem, built by Herod the Great, *B.* ii. 439 ; v. 134, 144, 147, 161 ; description of, v. 163-165 ; v. 284, 304 ; preserved by Titus, vii. 1

Hippodrome at Tarichaeae, *V.* 132, 138

Hippos (Hippus), Greek town of Decapolis, freed by Pompey, *B.* i. 156 ; annexed to Herod's kingdom, i. 396 ; annexed to

Syria, ii. 97 ; destroyed by Jews, ii. 459 ; rising against the Jews there, ii. 478 ; iii. 37 ; its rebels, iii. 542 ; Pompey restores its inhabitants, *A.* xiv. 75 ; added to Herod's realm, xv. 217 ; detached from Archelaus' kingdom and added to Syria, xvii. 320 ; set on fire by Justus of Tiberias and his followers, *V.* 42 ; town beyond frontier of Agrippa II's territory, reached as refuge by Agrippa's noble vassals, 153 ; in Galilee, thirty furlongs from Tiberias, 349

Hippus. See Hippos

Hiram (1). See Hirom

Hiram (2). See Cheiromos

Hirom (1) (Eiromos ; Bibl. Hiram), king of Tyre, (Eiromos) writes to David proposing friendship, *A.* vii. 66 ; (Eiromos) sends greetings to Solomon, viii. 50-52 ; (Eiromos) helps Solomon build the temple, viii. 53-60 ; (Eiromos) viii. 62 ; (Eiromos) sends craftsmen to build temple, viii. 76 ; (Eiromos) receives gifts from Solomon, viii. 141-143 ; (Eiromos) mentioned by Menander the historian, viii. 144 ; (Eiromos) his achievements as related by Dios, viii. 147 ; (Eiromos) receives riddles from and sends them to Solomon, viii. 148-149 ; (Eiromos) helps Solomon build the fleet, viii. 163 ; his friendship with King Solomon inherited from his father, *Ap.* i. 109-111 ; son of Abibalus, fails to solve Solomon's riddles, i. 113-116 ; evidence of Menander of Ephesus concerning his achievements, i. 117-120 ; his death, succession of his son Balbazer, i. 121 ; temple in Jerusalem built in twelfth year of his reign, i. 126 ; lived more than 150 years before foundation of Carthage, contributed toward construction of Solomon's temple, ii. 18-19

Hirom (2), king of Tyre, brother

261

GENERAL INDEX

contemporary of Strabo, *A.*
xiv. 139

Hyrcania, Jewish fortress, adjacent to Arabian mountains, fortified by Alexander son of Aristobulus, *B.* i. 161; surrendered by Alexander to Gabinius, i. 167; captured by Herod, i. 364; Antipater buried there, i. 664; *A.* xiii. 417; surrendered by Alexander, xiv. 89; xv. 366; Herod entertains Agrippa there, xvi. 13; burial place of Antipater, xvii. 187

Hyrcanians, people living south of the Caspian Sea, *B.* vii. 245

Hyrcanium. See Hyrcania

Hyrcanus (1), son of Joseph the Tobiad, *A.* xii. 186; his remarkable character as a youth, xii. 189-195; sets out for Alexandria to celebrate the birth of son to Ptolemy Epiphanes, xii. 197-202; punishes his father's steward, xii. 203-207; mocked by his rivals, xii. 208-212; wins the favour of Ptolemy Epiphanes and Cleopatra, xii. 213-220; his struggle with his brothers, xii. 221-222; death of his father, xii. 224; withdraws to his fortress in Transjordan, xii. 228-234; commits suicide, xii. 236

Hyrcanus (2) I, John, high priest, son of Simon Psellus, also called John, *B.* i. 54; opposes his brother-in-law Ptolemy, i. 55-60; his war with Antiochus, i. 61; his victories, i. 62-66; his prosperous reign, his gift of prophecy, i. 67-69; his successor, i. 70-71; his tomb, v. 259, 304, 356; vi. 169; takes money from David's tomb, *A.* vii. 393; protected in Jerusalem from Ptolemy, xiii. 228-229; succeeds his father Simon, xiii. 230-235; besieged by Antiochus, xiii. 236-244; comes to terms with Antiochus Sidetes, xiii. 245-248; assists Antiochus Sidetes in his Par-

thian campaign, xiii. 249-253; destroys the Samaritan temple on Mt. Gerizim and Judaizes Idumaea, xiii. 254-258; renews the treaty with Rome, xiii. 259-266; his friendship with Alexander Zebinas, xiii. 269; makes himself independent of the Seleucids, xiii. 272-274; besieges Samaria, xiii. 275-279; destroys Samaria, xiii. 280-283; asked by Pharisees to give up high priesthood, xiii. 288-292; forsakes the Pharisees for the Sadducees, xiii. 293-298; his providential gifts, xiii. 299-300; xiii. 302, 322; mentioned in the decree of Pergamum, xiv. 247-255; makes Idumaeans adopt customs of the Jews, xv. 254; opens David's tomb, xvi. 179, 181; stores priestly vestments in Antonia, xviii. 91; succeeds Simon as high priest, xx. 240; *V.* 3-4

Hyrcanus (3), high priest, son of Alexander Jannaeus, appointed high priest, *B.* i. 109; complains about his brother Aristobulus, i. 118; abdicates in favour of Aristobulus, i. 120-122; his alliance with Antipater, i. 123-130; takes refuge with Pompey, i. 131; Pompey yields to his entreaties, i. 133; his partisans, i. 142; Piso assisted by his friends, i. 144; reinstated as high priest, i. 153; relieves Scaurus, i. 159; troubled by Alexander, i. 160; reinstated by Gabinius, i. 169; puts his services at disposal of Gabinius, i. 175; confirmed as high priest by Julius Caesar, i. 194; accused by Antigonus, i. 195; Caesar pronounces him more deserving of high priesthood than Antigonus, i. 199; i. 201-203, 207; instigated against Herod, i. 208-214; Antipater preserves kingdom for him, i. 226; i. 229; Malichus has dreams of deposing him, i. 232; invited by

263

invades it, iv. 515 ; its chieftains, iv. 516 ; Simon marches
into it, iv. 529 ; Simon
devastates it, iv. 534-537 ; its
upper region, iv. 552 ; harassed
by Simon, iv. 556 ; ruled by
Esau, *A.* ii. 1 ; how it got its
name, ii. 3 ; ii. 6 ; Moses
comes to its frontier, iv. 76 ;
part of it allotted to tribe of
Judah, v. 81 ; part of it
allotted to tribe of Simeon, v.
82 ; David sends Abishai with
a force into it, vii. 109 ; subdued by Joab, viii. 200 ;
entered by Hadad, viii. 203 ;
ix. 31, 37 ; invaded by
Jehoram, ix. 97 ; xii. 308,
367 ; xiii. 207, 395-396 ; xiv.
10 ; Herod escapes to it, xiv.
353 ; Herod flees to it, xiv.
361-362 ; xiv. 364 ; joins with
Herod's side in fight with
Antigonus, xiv. 411 ; occupied
by Herod's brother Joseph and
his troops, xiv. 413 ; ruled by
Costobarus, xv. 254, 256 ;
given to Archelaus by Augustus
xvii. 319 ; Agrippa withdraws
into a tower there, xviii. 147 ;
harassed by Thomaeus the
brigand, xx. 5 ; its location in
latitude of Gaza, *Ap.* ii. 116

Idumaean(s), Antipater one of
them by race, *B.* i. 123 ; their
aid invoked by the Zealots, iv.
228-232 ; iv. 236 ; addressed
by Jesus the chief priest next
to Ananus, iv. 238-269 ; their
chief Simon replies to Jesus,
iv. 270-282 ; encamp before
the walls of Jerusalem, iv.
283-287 ; concern of the
Zealots for them, iv. 288-299 ;
Zealots open the city gates to
them, iv. 300-304 ; slaughter
guards of Ananus, iv. 305-313 ;
murder Ananus and Jesus, iv.
314-317 ; torture and kill the
nobility, iv. 326-333 ; a Zealot
denounces the crimes of his
party to them, iv. 345-353 ;
iv. 517, 520, 522, 526 ; mutiny
among them in John's army,
iv. 566-572 ; v. 248-249 ; their

chieftain John dies, v. 290 ;
v. 358 ; vi. 92, 148 ; their
overtures to Titus frustrated by
Simon, vi. 378-381 ; vii. 267 ;
Moses sends envoys to them,
A. iv. 76 ; vi. 129 ; defeated
by Abishai, vii. 109 ; Solomon
marries their women, viii. 191 ;
Hadad's descent from them,
viii. 200 ; on boundary with
Judah, viii. 348 ; compelled to
aid Jehoshaphat, ix. 30 ; their
revolt against Jehoram, ix. 97 ;
xi. 61 ; defeated by Judas
Maccabaeus, xii. 328, 353 ;
their cities captured by Hyrcanus, xiii. 257 ; Antipater
one of them, xiv. 8 ; Antipater
held in great esteem by them,
xiv. 121 ; Herod called one of
them, xiv. 403 ; Costobarus
one of them, xv. 253 ; customs
of Jews forced upon them, xv.
255 ; governed by Costobarus,
xv. 257 ; settled in Trachonitis
by Herod, xvi. 285 ; overcome
by the Trachonites, xvi. 292 ;
join revolt of Jews against
Romans, xvii. 254 ; their war
with Jews, *Ap.* ii. 112

Idum(as) (Bibl. Dumah), son of
Ishmael, *A.* i. 220

Ies (Bibl. Ehi), son of Benjamin,
A. ii. 180

Ietheglaeus (Bibl. Jethro), surname of Reuel, *A.* ii. 264

Iglisaros. See Neriglisar

Ijon. See Aion

Ilium, Herod reconciles Agrippa
with its inhabitants, *A.* xvi. 26

illuminations at Jewish festivals,
Ap. ii. 118, 282

Illyrians, neighbours of the
Thracians, kept in check by
two legions, *B.* ii. 369

images, excluded from tabernacle
by Moses and from the temple
by Solomon, *Ap.* ii. 12 ;
making of them forbidden by
Moses, ii. 75 ; those of God
forbidden, ii. 191 ; see also
animals, statues

imitation of Jewish customs by
Gentiles, *Ap.* i. 166 ; ii. 281 ff.

Imlah. See Jemblaios

266

GENERAL INDEX

Imnah. See Jomnes
Imperator(s), Caesar's title, *A.* xiv. 190, 192, 196, 199, 202, 211; (Imperators) pass resolutions concerning Jews, xiv. 265
Indates, Parthian general, *A.* xiii. 251
India (Indians), *B.* ii. 385; (Indians) their example of self-immolation, *B.* vii. 351-357; *A.* i. 38; inhabited by descendants of Shem, i. 147; Ophir belongs to it, viii. 164; Megasthenes' history of it, x. 227; Philostratos' history of it, x. 228; xi. 33, 186, 216, 272; Megasthenes' history of it, *Ap.* i. 144; Jews descended from its philosophers, according to Aristotle, i. 170
Indian Ocean, boundary of land inhabited by Shem's sons, *A.* i. 143
inheritance, Jewish law of, *A.* iv. 174-175
inspiration of Jewish prophets, *Ap.* i. 37
interest, prohibited by Jewish law, *Ap.* ii. 208
inventiveness, alleged lack of it by Jews, *Ap.* ii. 135, 148, 182
Iob. See Job(os)
Iolam(os) (Bibl. Jalam), son of Esau, *A.* ii. 4
Ionia, *B.* i. 425; Vespasian passes over from it into Greece, vii. 22; its people descended from Javan, *A.* i. 124; subjugated by Alexander the Great, xi. 305; xvi. 15; its Jews appeal to Agrippa, xvi. 27; its Jews given citizenship by Alexander's successors, *Ap.* ii. 39
Ionian Sea, *B.* i. 183; *A.* xiv. 123; xv. 350
Ionians, agitate against Jews, *A.* xii. 125-126
Iordan. See Iardan
Ios, high priest, son of Joramos, *A.* x. 152
Ira (Bibl. Jerah), son of Joktan, *A.* i. 147
Irad. See Jarad
Irenaeus, advocate of Antipas,

his eloquence relied on by Antipas, *B.* ii. 21; encourages Antipas to seek throne, *A.* xvii. 226
Irene (Ithaca), favourite concubine of Ptolemy Physcon, urges him not to injure Jews, *Ap.* ii. 55
Irenes (Bibl. Eri), son of Gad, *A.* ii. 182
Iron mountain, stretches into Moab, *B.* iv. 454
Isaac, son of Abraham, *A.* i. 191; his birth, i. 213-215; is about to be sacrificed, i. 222-236; marries Rebecca, i. 242, 255-257; buries his father, i. 256; begets twins, i. 257; makes a pact with Abimelech, i. 259-264; disapproves of Esau's Canaanite wives, i. 265-266; his old age, i. 267-277; consents to Jacob's marriage, i. 278; i. 289, 295; his death, i. 345-346; ii. 1, 213, 229; iii. 87; vii. 333; God cherishes his memory, xi. 169
Isaiah (Grk. Esaias), Hebrew prophet, foretells building of temple in Egypt, *B.* vii. 432; *A.* ix. 276; foretells defeat of Assyrians, x. 12, 16; foretells Hezekiah's recovery from illness, x. 27-28; foretells Babylonian exile, x. 32; foretells Cyrus' ending of Jewish captivity, xi. 5-6; Onias encouraged by his prophecy that a temple is to be built in Egypt by a Jew, xiii. 64; prophesies temple in Egypt, xiii. 68, 71
Isakos. See Isokos
Isamach (Bibl. Ahisamach), father of Oholiab, *A.* iii. 105
Isana (1) (Bibl. Jeshanah), Jeroboam's city, north of Jerusalem, plundered by Abijah, *A.* viii. 284; xiv. 458
Isana (2). See Cana (2)
Isebos (Bibl. Jashobeam), son of Achemaios, one of David's warriors, *A.* vii. 308
Ishbak. See Lousoubak(os)
Ishbi-benob. See Akmon

267

GENERAL INDEX

Ish-bosheth. See Jebosthos

Ishmael (1), son of Abraham, *A.* i. 190-192; is thirteen when circumcised, i. 193, 214; sent away by Sarah, i. 215-219; his sons, i. 220; buries his father, i. 256; Esau marries his daughter, i. 277; Abraham bequeaths land of Arabia to him, ii. 213

Ishmael (2). See Ismaelos

Ishmael (3), high priest, son of Phabi, *A.* iii. 320; appointed high priest by Valerius Gratus, xviii. 34; made high priest, xx. 179; delegate to Nero, xx. 194, 196

Ishmael (4), high priest (possibly Ishmael son of Phiabi), beheaded in Cyrene, *B.* vi. 114

Ishmaelites, descendants of Ishmael (1), *A.* ii. 32

Ish-tob. See Istobos

Ishvah. See Isousi(os)

Ishvi (1). See Eioubes

Ishvi (2). See Jesus (2)

Isis, Egyptian goddess, temple of, *B.* vii. 123; her priests trick Paulina into having intimate relations with Decius Mundus, *A.* xviii. 65, 70, 79-80; appears to King Amenophis of Egypt in his sleep, *Ap.* i. 289, 294, 298

Ismaelos (Bibl. Ishmael), wicked and crafty Jew of the royal family, *A.* x. 160; slays Gedaliah, x. 164, 166-171; his captives released, x. 173-175

Isokos (Asochaeus, Isakos, Susakos; Bibl. Shishak), king of Egypt, captures Jerusalem, *B.* vi. 436; carries wealth from Jerusalem, *A.* vii. 105; Jeroboam flees to him, viii. 210; invades Palestine, viii. 253-254; sacks Jerusalem, viii. 255, 258, 263

Isousi(os) (Bibl. Ishvah), son of Asher, *A.* ii. 183

Israel (1), Jacob so named by angel, *A.* i. 333

Israel (2), name for Jews generally, *A.* iii. 189; iv. 50; blessed by Moses before his death, iv. 180;

v. 316; punishment promised if they sin, viii. 127

Israel (3), kingdom established by Jeroboam, *A.* viii. 224; ruled by Baasha, viii. 298; viii. 306; divided into factions after Zimri's death, viii. 311; viii. 314, 316; ix. 20-21, 218, 243; with Syria attacks Judah, ix. 244; attacked by Judah, ix. 246; releases captives from Judah, ix. 250; ix. 258; makes alliance with Egypt, ix. 277; defeated and exiled by Assyrians, ix. 278, 280

Israelite(s), name for Hebrews generally, oppression of them, *A.* ii. 202-206; Egyptians condemn to destruction all of their offspring, ii. 215; attacked by Og, iv. 96; eager for battle, iv. 100; iv. 102, 104, 106, 124, 126, 236; forbidden to use poison, iv. 279; v. 22, 36, 50, 64, 72; defeat Zebekenians (Bezekenians), v. 121-122; relax in struggle against Canaanites, v. 132; become corrupt with riches and relax in fight against Canaanites, v. 134; declare war against Benjamin, v. 150, 155, 158, 160-161, 163-164; v. 168, 174, 176; contaminated by vices of Canaanites, v. 179; saved by Kenaz, v. 182; attacked by Moabites, v. 185; saved from Moabites, v. 187; defeat Moabites, v. 195-196; defeated by Canaanites, v. 198-199; defeat Sisera's army, v. 206; v. 209; attacked by Midianites, v. 210-212; promised victory over Midianites, v. 214; v. 220-221, 227-228; terrorized by Abimelech, v. 251; v. 254, 261; conquered by Philistines, v. 275; v. 318, 350; defeated by Philistines, v. 352; no longer invaded by Philistines, vi. 29; at peace with remnant of Canaanites, vi. 30; informed of the plight of the Gileadites, vi. 73; under Saul fight the Amalekites, vi. 134; challenged by Goliath, vi. 170; vi. 325;

GENERAL INDEX

GENERAL INDEX

273

GENERAL INDEX

GENERAL INDEX

GENERAL INDEX

66; xiv. 477; xv. 318;
Lower City, *B.* i. 39; ii. 422;
iv. 581; v. 11, 137, 140, 253;
vi. 363; *A.* vii. 62, 66; xii.
252; xiv. 477; New Town
(New City; see Bezetha), *B.*
ii. 530; v. 246, 260, 331, 504;
Tyropoeon (see Cheesemakers,
Valley of); Market-place (agora), *B.* i. 251; *A.* xiv. 335;
Upper Market (agora), *B.* ii.
305, 315, 339; v. 137; Timber
Market, *B.* ii. 530; clothes-
market, *B.* v. 331; Gates: of
Essenes, *B.* v. 145; of Gennath, *B.* v. 146; near Helena's
monument, *B.* v. 55; near
Hippicus' tower, *B.* v. 284,
304; Upper Gates, *B.* v. 336;
above the Xystus, *B.* vi. 191,
325; walls: the great wall,
B. v. 252; the old wall, *B.* v.
252; mines, *B.* vi. 370, 371,
392, 402, 429, 433; vii. 26, 27,
215; caverns, royal, *B.* v. 147
Jerusalem, monuments; ar-
chives, *B.* ii. 427; vi. 354;
council-chamber, *B.* v. 144;
vi. 354; hippodrome, *B.* ii.
44; *A.* xvii. 255; the Xystus,
B. ii. 344; vi. 191, 325, 377;
A. xx. 189; bridge, *B.* i. 143;
ii. 344; vi. 377; *A.* xiv. 58;
Palaces: of David, *A.* vii. 66;
of Solomon, *A.* viii. 130-140;
of Hasmonaeans, *B.* ii. 344;
A. xx. 190 (see also *B.* i. 143,
253; *A.* xiv. 59, 388); of
Herod, *B.* i. 402; ii. 44, 301,
312, 320, 429, 431, 530, 557;
v. 176-183, 245; *A.* xv, 292,
318; xvii. 255; *V.* 46; of
Grapte, *B.* ii. 567-569; of
Agrippa and Bernice, *B.* ii.
426; *A.* xx. 189; of Helena,
B. v. 253; vi. 355; of Monobazus, *B.* v. 252; Towers: see
Hippicus, Mariamme, Phasael,
Psephinus, Women's; sepul-
chral monuments: of Alexander Jannaeus, *B.* v. 304; of
Ananus the high priest, *B.* v.
506; of Herod, *B.* v. 108,
507; of John the high priest,
B. v. 304, 356-358, 468; pools:

Amygdalon, *B.* v. 468; Solo-
mon's, *B.* v. 145; Struthion,
B. v. 467
Jerushah. See Jerase
Jeshanah. See Isana
Jeshimon. See Simon (29)
Jeshua (1). See Jesus (4)
Jeshua (2). See Jesus (5)
Jesse, son of Obed, father of Da-
vid, *A.* v. 336; vi. 157; pre-
sents his sons to Samuel, vi.
158, 161-162; vi. 164, 167-169,
175, 236, 252, 255, 298, 315; vii.
278
Jesus (1). See Joshua
Jesus (2) (Bibl. Ishvi), son of
Saul, *A.* vi. 129
Jesus (3). See Abiezer
Jesus (4) (Bibl. Jesuha), son of
the high priest Jozadak, *A.* xi.
73, 75, 79; rejects offer of Samaritans to help build the temple, xi. 84, 86; xi. 90, 121; his
descendants send away foreign
wives, xi. 151; his return from
Babylon, xx. 234
Jesus (5) (Bibl. Jeshua), son of
Joiada, brother of Johanan, *A.*
xi. 298; quarrels with Johanan, xi. 299; killed by Johanan, xi. 299; xi. 300; Bagoses
makes the Jews suffer seven
years for his death, xi. 301
Jesus (6), high priest, son of Simon, *A.* xii. 238; changes name
to Jason, xii. 239; contends
with Menelaus for high priesthood, xii. 239-240; removed
from high priesthood by Antiochus Epiphanes, xv. 41
Jesus (7), high priest, son of
Phabes, removed from high
priesthood by Herod, *A.* xv.
322
Jesus (8), high priest, son of Seē,
replaces Eleazar as high priest,
A. xvii. 341
Jesus (9), called the Christ, *A.*
xviii. 63-64; his brother
James stoned, xx. 200
Jesus (10), son of Damnaeus,
becomes high priest replacing
Ananus, *A.* xx. 203; deposed
as high priest, xx. 213
Jesus (11), son of Gamaliel,

279

GENERAL INDEX

281

GENERAL INDEX

son of Ahaziah, king of Judah,
hidden by Jehosheba, *A.* ix.
142 ; his reign, ix. 156-158 ;
renovates the temple, ix. 161-
165 ; his degeneration, ix.
166-169 ; pays tribute to
Hazael, ix. 170 ; his death, ix.
171-172 ; ix. 173 ; avenged by
his son, ix. 186

Joas (2) (Bibl. Joash, Jehoash),
son of Jehoahaz, king of Israel,
succeeds Jehoahaz, *A.* ix. 177 ;
defeats Ben-hadad, ix. 184 ; his
death, ix. 185 ; ix. 186 ; challenged by Amaziah, ix. 196-198 ;
takes Jerusalem, ix. 199-202 ;
ix. 205

Joash (1). See Joas (1)

Joash (2). See Joas (2)

Joash (3). See Jas

Joates (Bibl. Joah), keeper of the
records of King Josiah, *A.* x. 55

Joazanias (Bibl. Jezaniah), Jewish leader at time of Gedaliah,
A. x. 160

Joazar (1), son of Boethus,
appointed high priest by Herod,
A. xvii. 164 ; removed from
high priesthood, xvii. 339 ;
urges Jews to comply with
Quirinius' assessment of property, xviii. 3 ; deposed as high
priest, xviii. 26

Joazar (2) (var. Jozar), Jewish
priest sent with Josephus and
Judas to Galilee, *V.* 29 ; (63,
73, 77)

Joazar (3). See Jozar (1)

Joazos (Bibl. Jehoahaz), son and
successor to Jehu, King of
Israel, *A.* ix. 160 ; defeated by
the Syrians, ix. 173-176 ; his
death, ix. 177

Jobab. See Jobel (3)

Jobak. See Jabacchos

Jobel (1), Hebrew name for
fiftieth year of jubilee, *A.* iii.
282-283

Jobel (2) (Bibl. Jabal), son of
Lamech and Adah, *A.* i. 64

Jobel (3) (Bibl. Jobab), son of
Joktan, *A.* i. 147

Job(os) (Bibl. Iob), son of Issachar, *A.* ii. 178

Jochabad. See Jochabel(e)

Jochabel(e) (Jochabad ; Bibl.
Jochebed), wife of Amram,
mother of Moses, *A.* ii. 217 ;
iii. 86

Jochabes (Bibl. Ichabod), son of
Phinehas, *A.* v. 360

Jochebed. See Jochabel(e)

Jodamos (Bibl. Jehoiada), leader
of Levites paying homage to
David, *A.* vii. 56

Jodas (1) (Bibl. Jehoiada), high
priest, husband of Jehosheba,
A. ix. 141 ; plots against
Athaliah, ix. 143-144 ; proclaims Joash king, ix. 145-149 ;
has Athaliah put to death, ix.
150-152 ; administers oaths
to people, ix. 153-155 ; ix. 157 ;
collects half shekel for the
temple, ix. 161, 164-165 ; his
death, ix. 166 ; his son
Zechariah stoned to death, ix.
168, 171

Jodas (2) (Bibl. Joiada), high
priest, son of Eliashib, his
death, *A.* xi. 297

Joel. See Iulus

Joesdrus. See Jozar (1)

Johanan. See Joannes (1), (3),
and (4)

John (1) (Joannes, Gaddes,
Gaddis), son of Mattathias,
(Joannes) called Gaddes, *A.*
xii. 266 ; called Gaddis, is
murdered by sons of Jambri,
xiii. 10-11 ; xiii. 19, 21

John (2) the Baptist, put to
death by Herod the tetrarch,
A. xviii. 116-119

John (3), father of John (4), *A.*
xx. 14

John (4), son of John, envoy
from Jerusalem to Claudius,
A. xx. 14

John (5) of Gischala, son of Levi,
fortifies Gischala on the instruction of Josephus, *B.* ii.
575 ; his character, ii. 285 ;
his antagonism to Josephus,
ii. 590-594 ; instigates mob
against Josephus, ii. 599 ; his
antagonism against Josephus,
ii. 614-632 ; his character, iv.
85 ; imposes upon Titus, iv.
98-105 ; flees to Jerusalem,

GENERAL INDEX

GENERAL INDEX

GENERAL INDEX

of Jehoshaphat, viii. 37; ix.
83, 159, 235; scene of defeat
of Scopas by Antiochus the
Great, xii. 132; xii. 222, 229,
233, 335, 348; xiii. 9, 12, 14,
338, 356, 398; xiv. 277, 417;
xv. 147; its source, xv. 364;
xvii. 171, 277; xviii. 28;
Theudas' adherents follow him
to it, xx. 97; *V*. 33; Jeremiah,
commander under Josephus, is
entrenched near it, 399;
squadron of Sulla's cavalry
placed in ambush beyond it, 405
Jordan (2), Lesser (Little), *A*. v.
178; (Little Jordan) course of
Jordan north of modern lake of
Huleh, near site where Jeroboam builds shrine, viii. 226
Jordan (3), Little. See Jordan
(2), Lesser
Josadakes. See Josadakos
Josadakos (Josedekos, Josadakes;
Bibl. Jehozadak, Jozadak, Josedech), high priest, son of Se-
raiah, carried off in chains to
Babylon, *A*. x. 150; son of
Azariah (presumably Josephus'
error), taken captive to Babylon, x. 153; (Josedekos)
father of Jesus the leader of
exiles who returned to Jerusalem, xi. 73; (Josadakes)
taken prisoner by Nebuchadnezzar, xx. 231; (Josedek[os])
father of Jesus the high priest
who returned from Babylonian
captivity, xx. 234
Josaphat (1) (Bibl. Jehoshaphat),
son of Ahilud, keeper of records
for King David, *A*. vii. 110, 293
Josaphat (2) (Bibl. Jehoshaphat),
son and successor of King Asa
of Judah, *A*. viii. 315; his
reign, viii. 393-396; allies
himself with Ahab against
Syrians, viii. 398-400, 402, 405,
411-413; his reforms, ix. 1;
defeats Ammonites, ix. 8, 14;
his alliance with Ahaziah, ix.
16-17; his alliance with Jehoram against Moabites, ix.
30-31; consults Elisha, ix. 33,
35; his death, ix. 44
Josedech. See Josadakos

Josedek(os). See Josadakos
Joseph (1), son of Jacob and
Rachel, *A*. i. 308; beloved by
his father and envied by his
brothers, ii. 9-10; his dreams,
ii. 11-16; his brothers resolve
to kill him, ii. 17-20; ii. 26,
28; sold to Arabs, ii. 33; ii.
34; his brothers dip his tunic
in blood and tell Jacob he was
killed, ii. 35-38; sold to
Potiphar, ii. 39; solicited by
Potiphar's wife, ii. 42-53; flees
from Potiphar's wife, ii. 54;
accused by Potiphar's wife, ii.
55; thrown into prison, ii.
59; endures prison, ii. 60; ii.
61; interprets butler's dream,
ii. 64-69; interprets baker's
dream, ii. 70-73; forgotten by
butler, ii. 74; remembered by
butler, ii. 76-77; brought
before Pharaoh, ii. 79; interprets Pharaoh's dream, ii.
84-86; tells Pharaoh how to
avoid famine, ii. 87-88; appointed minister by Pharaoh,
ii. 89-90; his marriage and
his children, ii. 91; ii. 93;
sells grain to the Egyptians,
ii. 94; ii. 95; his brothers
seek his permission to buy
grain, ii. 96; ii. 103, 105, 107,
108; weeps at his brothers'
distress, ii. 109; ii. 118, 120;
meets Benjamin, ii. 121-122;
entertains his brothers, ii.
123; ii. 128; accuses Benjamin of stealing cup, ii. 136;
ii. 137; offers to keep Benjamin in custody and let the
other brothers go, ii. 138;
ii. 147, 159; reveals himself
to his brothers, ii. 160-167;
ii. 168, 169, 171, 174, 175, 177;
his sons, ii. 180; greets his
father in Egypt, ii. 184 (*bis*);
asks Pharaoh to allow his
family to be shepherds, ii. 185-
186; sells corn to Egyptians,
ii. 189; returns land to Egyptian inhabitants after famine,
ii. 192-193; praised by his father, ii. 195; buries his father,
ii. 196; buried in Canaan, ii.

GENERAL INDEX

200 ; receives oath from his descendants that he will be buried in Canaan, ii. 200 ; forgotten by Egyptians after his death, ii. 202 ; his bones taken out of Egypt, ii. 319 ; iii. 87, 288 ; common ancestor of Cuthaeans (Samaritans) and Jews, ix. 291 ; ancestor of Samaritans, xi. 341 ; tells king of Egypt that he is a captive, brings his brethren to Egypt, *Ap.* i. 92 ; sacred scribe, one of leaders of afflicted persons expelled from Egypt by King Amenophis, according to Chaeremon, i. 290 ; associated by Chaeremon with Moses, i. 299

Joseph (2), tribe of, Jeroboam given command over it, *A.* viii. 206

Joseph (3) the Tobiad, upbraids Onias, *A.* xii. 160 ; goes to Ptolemy Epiphanes as envoy of Jews, xii. 164-174 ; buys the right to collect taxes from Ptolemy, xii. 176 ; uses force to collect taxes in Palestine, xii. 180, 182 ; begets Hyrcanus, xii. 187-189 ; tests Hyrcanus, xii. 190 ; sends Hyrcanus to, Alexandria, xii. 198-201 ; xii. 217 ; angry at Hyrcanus for his lavishness, xii. 221 ; his death, xii. 224, 228

Joseph (4), son of Zacharias, one of Judas the Maccabee's generals, *A.* xii. 333 ; defeated by Gorgias, xii. 350, 352-353

Joseph (5), son of Matthias Curtus and father of Matthias, grandfather of Josephus, *V.* 5

Joseph (6), husband of Herod's sister Salome, *B.* i. 441-443 ; left in charge of Judaea, *A.* xv. 65 ; reveals Herod's instructions concerning Mariamme, xv. 68-69 ; plans to flee with Alexandra and Mariamme, xv. 72 ; accused by his wife, Salome, xv. 81-82, 86 ; executed by Herod, xv. 87, 168 ; instructions to him concerning Mariamme, xv. 204 ; put to death by Herod, xv. 254

Joseph (7), steward of Herod, *A.* xv. 185

Joseph (8), son of Antipater, brother of Herod, *B.* i. 181 ; joins Herod, i. 266 ; at Masada, i. 286-288 ; i. 303 ; his death, i. 323-324 ; outrage to his corpse, i. 325 ; i. 328, 342 ; *A.* xiv. 121, 361 ; defends Masada successfully, xiv. 390, 392 ; guards Herod's interests in Idumaea, xiv. 413 ; remains with Machaeras, xiv. 438 ; his death in battle, xiv. 448-450 ; xviii. 134

Joseph (9), nephew of King Herod and cousin of Archelaus, *B.* i. 562 ; ii. 74 ; *A.* xvii. 20 ; son of Herod's brother Joseph, xvii. 294 ; husband of Olympias, xviii. 134

Joseph (10), son of Ellemus, serves as high priest for a day, *A.* xvii. 166

Joseph (11), called Caiaphas, appointed high priest, *A.* xviii. 35 ; removed from high priesthood, xviii. 95

Joseph (12), son of Camei, appointed high priest, *A.* xx. 16 ; removed from high priesthood, xx. 103

Joseph (13), surnamed Kabi, son of the high priest Simon, appointed high priest, *A.* xx, 196 ; removed from high priesthood, xx. 197

Joseph (14), chief priest, escapes to the Romans, *B.* vi. 114

Joseph (15), son of Gorion, Jewish general against the Romans, *B.* ii. 563

Joseph (16), son of Simon, Jewish commander at Jericho in war against the Romans, *B.* ii. 567

Joseph (17), father of Gorion, Jewish leader in Jerusalem, *B.* iv. 159 (probably identical with Joseph [15] son of Gorion)

Joseph (18), leader of Gamala, *B.* iv. 18, 66

Josephus (1), domestic (private) life : his ancestry and personal background, *B.* i. 3 ; marries

287

GENERAL INDEX

praised by Moses, iii. 59; (Jesus) iii. 308-310; appointed to succeed Moses, iv. 165; iv. 171, 186, 311, 315; accompanies Moses before his death, iv. 324; iv. 326; sends scouts to Jericho, v. 1; v. 15; leads Hebrews across Jordan, v. 17; builds altar of stones, v. 20; besieges Jericho, v. 22, 24; rewards Rahab, v. 30; delivers booty of Jericho to priests, v. 32; establishes camp at Gilgal v. 34; attacks Ai, v. 35; prays after his defeat at Ai, v. 38, 42; discovers Achar as source of pollution, v. 42; conquers Ai, v. 45-48; v. 49; makes pact with Gibeonites, v. 51-57; defeats the league of Canaanite kings, v. 58, 60-61; v. 62; defeats host of Canaanites and Philistines, v. 64-67; erects tabernacle, v. 68; addresses people at Shiloh, v. 71-72; sends men to measure the country, v. 76; measures land, v. 78; divides land among tribes, v. 80, 88; sets up cities for Levites, v. 90; v. 103, 114; addresses people before his death, v. 115; his death (v. 117); his burial (v. 119); v. 121; vi. 84; apportioned Jerusalem to the Israelites 515 years before David captured it, vii. 68; vii. 294; ix. 207, 280; xi. 112

Josiah (Josias), king of Judah, son of Amon, (Josias) prophecy concerning him, A. viii. 232; x. 48; his pious deeds, x. 50-56; is spared exile, x. 61; burns bones of false prophets, x. 66; x. 67; reforms Israelites who escaped captivity, x. 68; his death, x. 73, 75; x. 80; his death, x. 81

Josias. See Josiah

Jotapata, village in Galilee, B. ii. 573; attacked by Placidus, iii. 111-114; invested by Vespasian, iii. 141-339; iii. 405-406, 432, 438; iv. 1, 4, 624; v. 544; fortified by

Josephus, V. 188; forty furlongs from Chabolo, whither Josephus goes with his army, 234; authors of revolt against Josephus are sent there in chains by him, 332; captured by Romans, 350; Josephus besieged there, 353; details of its siege by Romans unknown to Justus of Tiberias, 357; Josephus withdraws to it after engaging Vespasian in battle at Garis, 412; Josephus captured there but receives every attention, 414

Jotape (1), daughter of Sampsigeramus, wife of Aristobulus, A. xviii. 135

Jotape (2) daughter of Aristobulus the brother of Agrippa I, B. ii. 221; A. xviii. 135

Jotape (3), daughter of Antiochus the king of Commagene, A. xviii. 140

Jotbah. See Jatabate

Jotham(os) (1) (Bibl. Uzzi), son of Bukki, father of Meraioth, member of family of Phinehas, A. viii. 12

Jotham (2), son and successor to Uzziah as king of Judah, A. ix. 227, 236-238; his death, ix. 243

Jothamos (3), high priest, son of Juelos, father of Urias, A. x. 153

Jotham (4), son of Gideon, escapes death from Abimelech, A. v. 234; tells people of Shechem parable of trees, v. 235-239; v. 253

Jotham(os) (5) (Bibl. Gatam), son of Eliphaz, A. ii. 5

Jovan. See Javan

Jozadak. See Josadakos

Jozar (1) (Joazar, Joesdrus), Jewish notable, (Joesdrus) B. ii. 628; Pharisee, priest, member of deputation sent by high priest Ananus to seek to depose Josephus from command of Galilee, V. 197 ff.; invited, by a ruse, by Josephus to divide command of Galilee with him, suspects a plot and remains behind, 324-325; dismissed by

GENERAL INDEX

Josephus to Jerusalem, 332 (possibly identical with Joazar, former colleague of Josephus)

Jozar (2). See Joazar (2)

Juba, king of Libya, marries Glaphyra the daughter of Archelaus, *B*. ii. 115, *A*. xvii. 349

Jubal, son of Lamech and Adah, inventor of harps and lutes, *A*. i. 64

Jubel (Bibl. Tubal-cain), son of Lamech and Zillah, invents forging of metal, *A*. i. 64

Jubilee (Year), according to Jewish law, *A*. iii. 281-285

Juctas (Bibl. Joktan), son of Eber, *A*. i. 146-147

Jucundus (1), officer of Herod, *B*. i. 527; Herod's bodyguard, *A*. xvi. 314

Jucundus (2), cavalry commander in Caesarea, *B*. ii. 291

Jucundus (3), Aemilius. See Aemilius Jucundus

Juda, son of, variant for Julius, commander of Roman legion, *A*. xv. 72

Judadaeans, people of western Ethiopia, founded by Judadas (Dedan), *A*. i. 135

Judadas (Bibl. Dedan), son of Raamah, founder of the Judadaeans, a people of western Ethiopia, *A*. i. 135

Judaea (Judaeans), *B*. i. 22, 32, 37, 41, 49, 51, 61, 98, 103, 105, 127, 129, 134, 138, 157, 160, 174, 180, 183, 199, 201, 225, 231, 240, 244, 249, 288, 291, 309, 323, 327. 360, 362, 364, 365, 371, 445, 499, 513, 532, 604, 606, 659, 660; ii. 16, 43, 65, 85, 90, 96, 116, 169, 184, 186, 202, 247, 252, 265; iii. 1, 48; description of, iii. 51-58; iii. 143, 409; iv. 406-409, 473, 502, 545, 550, 657; v. 41; vi. 7, 238, 313; vii. 163, 252, 253, 301; settled by Canaan, *A*. i. 134; name for Canaan, i. 160; (Judaeans) vi. 324; vi. 361; vii. 101; viii. 188; ten tribes of Israel emigrate from there, ix. 280; ravaged by Babylonia, x. 40; spared by

Nebuchadnezzar in return for tribute, x. 86; ravaged by Babylonia, x. 110; x. 163; deserted for seventy years, x. 184; x. 237; xi. 4, 60; Xerxes authorizes Jews to supervise their own affairs there, xi. 124; Nehemiah in Susa meets strangers from there, xi. 160; its affairs settled by Alexander the Great, xii. 1; Jews taken from there by Ptolemy Soter and brought to Egypt, xii. 7; xii. 28, 97, 114; annexed by Antiochus the Great, xii. 131; its timber used to restore the temple, xii. 141; given to Cleopatra as dowry, xii. 154; xii. 175, 233; taken by Antiochus Epiphanes, xii. 245; xii. 265, 289, 293; Antiochus Epiphanes orders that it be subdued, xii. 296; attacked by Ptolemy, Nicanor, and Gorgias, xii. 298; invaded by Lysias, xii. 313; xii. 315, 329, 333, 345, 349, 351, 353, 394; makes treaty with Rome, xii. 416; attacked by Bacchides, xii. 420-421; its cities fortified by Bacchides, xiii. 15; sons of its chief men taken as hostages by Bacchides, xiii. 17; fortified by Bacchides, xiii. 22; xiii. 24, 33, 42; its taxes eased by Demetrius, xiii. 50; wooed by Demetrius, xiii. 54; xiii. 62, 75, 121, 125; gains three districts from Samaria, xiii. 127; xiii. 133, 155; defended by Jonathan against invasion by Demetrius II, xiii. 174; its fortresses strengthened by Simon, xiii. 180; attacked by Tryphon, xiii. 196; invaded by Tryphon, xiii. 203; xiii. 204; attacked by Antiochus VII, xiii. 225; invaded by Antiochus VII, xiii. 236; xiii. 246, 270; exploited by Hyrcanus, xiii. 273; xiii. 284, 318, 336; invaded by Ptolemy Lathyrus, xiii. 345; ravaged by Ptolemy Lathyrus, xiii. 348; xiii. 384; invaded by Antio-

GENERAL INDEX

chus Dionysus, xiii. 389;
invaded by Aretas, xiii. 392;
threatened by Tigranes, xiii.
419; xiv. 9, 15, 17, 29, 34, 35,
47, 49, 80; overrun by Alexander, son of Aristobulus,
xiv. 82; its ruined cities rebuilt by Gabinius, xiv. 87; xiv.
92, 97, 105, 113, 118; invaded
by Cassius, xiv. 120; xiv. 124,
139, 143; order restored there
by Antipater, xiv. 156; xiv.
163, 184; heavily taxed by
Cassius, xiv. 272; xiv. 277,
279; kingship over it promised
to Herod by Cassius, xiv. 280;
xiv. 290, 294; Antigonus
driven therefrom by Herod,
xiv. 299; marched upon by
Parthians and Antigonus, xiv.
332-333; invaded by Par-
thians, xiv. 364; xlv. 365,
379; invaded by Ventidius,
xiv. 392; xiv. 395, 447, 448;
sizable part of it rebels against
Herod, xiv. 450; xiv. 458;
ruled by Herod, xv. 2; arrival
there of Hyrcanus from Parthia, xv. 21; xv. 25, 39;
sought by Cleopatra, xv. 79;
Herod returns there, xv. 80;
coveted by Cleopatra, xv. 92;
visited by Cleopatra, xv. 96;
suffers earthquake during reign
of Herod, xv. 121; Herod
returns there from his meeting
with Octavian, xv. 198; xv.
350; governed by Cuspius Fadus, xv. 406; visited by Marcus
Agrippa, xvi. 13; xvi. 86, 130,
132, 270; pillaged by bandits
from Trachonitis, xvi. 275;
xvi. 297; xvii. 82; designs of
Sabinus on it, xvii. 221-222; disturbances there, xvii. 269-270;
brigandage there after Herod's
death, xvii. 285-286; xvii.
297; given to Archelaus by Augustus, xvii. 319; given to Archelaus as ethnarchy, xvii. 339;
xvii. 344, 348; assessment of
property there by Quirinius,
xviii. 2; xviii. 29; its procurators, xviii. 35; xviii. 55;
Marcellus appointed its pro-

curator, xviii. 89; visited by
Vitellius, xviii. 90; bypassed
by Vitellius in his march
against Aretas, xviii. 121;
Agrippa I arrives there, xviii.
147; Cypros returns there,
xviii. 160; xviii. 196, 237;
Petronius arrives there, xviii.
261; insolence of Gaius Caligula towards its inhabitants,
xix. 1; confirmed as Agrippa's
kingdom by Claudius, xix. 274;
xix. 343; included in Agrippa's
kingdom, xix. 351; Cuspius
Fadus appointed procurator
over it, xix. 363; xix. 366;
arrival there of Fadus as
procurator, xx. 2; purged of
robber bands, xx. 5; xx. 97;
famine there, xx. 101; census
taken there by Quirinius, xx.
102; xx. 105, 107; infested
with brigands, xx. 124; xx.
128; Felix appointed procurator over it, xx. 137; xx.
142; brigands there put down
by Felix, xx. 160, 162; overrun
by brigands, xx. 185; appointment of Albinus as procurator
over it, xx. 197; xx. 228; *V.*
13, 87, 422, 425, 427, 429;
care in marriages of priests
there, *Ap.* i. 32; Hycsos build
city there called Jerusalem,
according to Manetho, i. 90;
i. 179; its extent and beauty,
according to Hecataeus of
Abdera, i. 195; occupied by
Jews upon their being driven
from Egypt, according to
Manetho, i. 228; reached by
impure Egyptians led by
Moses, according to Lysimachus, i. 310; reached by
fugitives from Egypt in six
days, according to Apion, ii.
21, 25

Judah (1), son of Jacob. See
Judas (1)

Judah (2) (Judas), tribe of,
kingdom of, *A.* iii. 105; Caleb's
tribe, iii. 308; Achan's tribe,
v. 33; v. 43, 91, 120; wars on
the Canaanites, v. 128; v.
136; its cities captured by

291

GENERAL INDEX

Canaanites, v. 177; v. 182; Ibzan's tribe, v. 271; vi. 78, 134, 249, 367; vii. 7; chooses David king, vii. 8; vii. 9; engaged by army led by Abner, vii. 10; pays homage to David, vii. 55, 58; vii. 260; makes peace with David, vii. 262; welcomes David, vii. 263-264; joined to David's force, vii. 275; reproached by others for currying David's favour, vii. 276-277, 279-280; its number, vii. 320; not in Adonijah's plot, vii. 347; increases in number during Solomon's rule, viii. 38; remains loyal to Rehoboam, viii. 221; fortified by Rehoboam, viii. 247; viii. 291; contributes to army of Jehoshaphat, viii. 397; Zebadiah's tribe, ix. 6; compelled by Jehoram to transgress, ix. 99; raises army against Amalekites, ix. 188; ix. 247; its people taken captive by Israel, ix. 249; its leaders return to Jerusalem, xi. 8; returns to Judaea, xi. 69, 73; xi. 84; gathers in Jerusalem, xi. 148; name "Jews" derived from it, xi. 173

Judah (3), area held by tribe of, its territory, *A.* v. 81, 87; territory where Etam is, v. 297; territory belonging to tribe of, v. 318; Beth-shemesh a village there, vi. 14; David flees there, vi. 247; David lives there in Hebron, vii. 7; David king of it alone for seven years, vii. 65; Solomon declared king over it, vii. 356; ruled by David, vii. 389; viii. 126; Mareshah located there, viii. 292; Beersheba on its furthest boundary, viii. 348; ruled by Joash, ix. 177; ruled by Amaziah, ix. 186; ruled by Jotham, ix. 236; its cities captured by Sennacherib, x. 1

Judaica. See Josephus (1), works: *Bellum Judaicum*

Judaism, conversion of Izates to it, *A.* xx. 41

Judas (1) (Bibl. Judah), son of Jacob and Leah, *A.* i. 304; counsels brothers to sell Joseph to Arabs, ii. 32-33; persuades Jacob to let Benjamin go to Egypt, ii. 116; pleads for Benjamin's life and offers himself instead, ii. 139-159; his sons, ii. 178; announces Jacob's arrival in Egypt, ii. 184; vii. 372

Judas (2), tribe of. See Judah (2), tribe of

Judas (3), son of Henadad, brother of Kadmiel, *A.* xi. 79

Judas (4) Maccabaeus, eldest son of Matthias (Mattathias) priest of Modin, *B.* i. 37; makes alliance with Romans, i. 38; recovers and cleanses temple, i. 39; battles with Antiochus V at Bethzacharia, i. 41-42; is defeated, i. 45; his death, i. 47; *A.* xii. 266; appointed commander by Mattathias, xii. 284; takes over command, xii. 285; drives enemy out of country, xii. 285-286; defeats Apollonius, xii. 287; defeats Seron, xii. 288-290, 292; encourages his troops, xii. 300-305; defeats Gorgias' army, xii. 307, 309, 311-312; fights Lysias, xii. 314; purifies the temple, xii. 316; celebrates Hanukkah, xii. 323; fortifies Jerusalem, xii. 326; is victorious over surrounding nations, xii. 327; orders Simon to help Jews of Galilee, xii. 330-331; his victories in Gilead, xii. 335; defeats Timotheus, xii. 339, 343-344; xii. 350; his instructions disobeyed, xii. 352; victorious in Idumaea, xii. 353; besieges citadel of Jerusalem, xii. 363, 365; fights Antiochus Eupator at Bethzacharias, xii. 369-370, 372; retires to Jerusalem, xii. 374; accepts Antiochus' proposals of peace, xii. 382; accused by Alcimus to Demetrius, xii. 391, 392; attacked by Bacchides, xii. 393-394; opposes Alcimus-

GENERAL INDEX

xii. 399-401 ; escapes Nicanor's plot, xii. 402-405 ; kills Nicanor, xii. 406, 408, 410 ; given high priesthood, xii. 414 ; seeks treaty with Rome, xii. 416 ; high priest, xii. 419 ; defeated by Bacchides, xii. 422-423, 428-429, 431-433 ; his death, xiii. 1-2 ; his companions persecuted, xiii. 4-5 ; xiii. 7, 46 ; his place taken by Simon, xiii. 201

Judas (5), son of Chapsaios, commander under Jonathan the son of Mattathias, remains loyal to him, A. xiii. 161

Judas (6) the Essene, seer who predicts Antigonus' death, B. i. 78 ff. ; his prophecy, A. xiii. 311-313

Judas (7), also called Aristobulus, high priest, successor to Hyrcanus, first to hold both high priesthood and kingship, A. xx. 240-241 ; see also Aristobulus (2)

Judas (8), son of Sepphoraeus, expert in Jewish law, urges the pulling down of Herod's golden eagle from the temple, B. i. 648-650, 655 ; urges destruction of golden eagle, A. xvii. 149, 151 ; captured by Herod, xvii. 157 ; his death lamented by Jews, xvii. 214

Judas (9), son of Ezechias, brigand-chief, B. ii. 56 ; plunders Galilee, A. xvii. 271-272

Judas (10) the Galilaean (Gaulanite), incites revolt against Romans, B. ii. 118, 433 ; vii. 253 ; cause of troubles that overtook the Jews, A. xviii. 4-10 ; founds fourth philosophy, xviii. 23-25 ; his sons crucified, xx. 102

Judas (11), Jewish priest sent with Josephus and Joazar to Galilee, V. 29, (63, 73, 77)

Judas (12), son of Jonathan, envoy of Jews besieging Romans in Herod's palace, B. ii. 451, 628

Judas (13) (Judes), son of Ari, brave Zealot, (Judes) B. vi. 92 ; vii. 215

Judas (14) (Judes), son of Merton, brave soldier in division of Simon the son of Gioras, B. vi. 92

Judas (15) (Judes), son of Mareotes, in party of Simon the son of Gioras, B. vi. 148 (perhaps identical with Judas [14])

Judes (1) (Bibl. Ehud), son of Gera, daring youth, kills Eglon, A. v. 188, 191-193 ; v. 194 ; honoured with governorship, v. 197

Judes (2), son of Chelcias, joins Eleazar's faction, B. v. 6

Judes (3), son of Judas, general of Simon the son of Gioras, B. v. 534-540

Judes (4), father of Judes the general of Simon the son of Gioras, B. v. 534

Judes (5). See Judas (13) and (14)

Judges, period of, A. xx. 261

Juelos, high priest, son of Sudalos, A. x. 153

Julia (1) (Livia), wife of Augustus Caesar, B. i. 566, 641 ; ii. 167 ; A. xvi. 139 ; urges Salome to marry Alexas, xvii. 10 ; Acme the Jewess her slave, xvii. 141 ; beneficiary in Herod's will, xvii. 146, 190 ; Salome's bequest to her, xviii. 31 ; mother of Tiberius Nero, xviii. 33

Julia (2), daughter of Augustus, B. ii. 25, 168 ; A. xvii. 229 ; city named for her by Philip the tetrarch, xviii. 28

Julia (3), sister of Gaius Caligula, A. xix. 251

Julianus (1), Marcus Antonius, procurator of Judaea, B. vi. 238

Julianus (2), Bithynian centurion, B. vi. 81-91

Julias (1). See Betharamphtha

Julias (2). See Bethsaida

Julius (1), commander of Roman legion, A. xv. 72

Julius (2) Alexander. See Alexander (19), Marcus Julius

Julius (3) Antonius. See Antonius (5), Julius

Julius (4) Archelaus. See Archelaus (4), Julius

293

GENERAL INDEX

GENERAL INDEX

Labimus (Bibl. Lehabim), son of Mizraim, *A.* i. 137

Labina (Lobane ; var. Tomane, Tomiane ; Bibl. Libnah), region or city in Palestine, *A.* ix. 98 ; (Lobane) x. 81

Laborosoardoch. See Labosordachos

Labosordachos (Laborosoardoch; var. Labrosodachos), king of Babylonia, son of Nergalsareser, *A.* x. 231 ; (Laborosoardoch) is assassinated, *Ap.* i. 148

Labrosodachos. See Labosordachos

Lacedaemon (Lacedemon,Sparta) (Lacedaemonians, Spartans), *B.* i. 425, 513, 515, 532 ; ii. 359, 381 ; vii. 240, 243 ; letter of Areios, its king, to Onias, *A.* xii. 225-228 ; xiii. 164, 165 ; (Spartans) letter of Jonathan to them, xiii. 166-170 ; (Lacedaemonians) make alliance with Jews, xiii. 170 ; xvi. 301, 310 ; reviled by Polycrates, *Ap.* i. 221 ; (Lacedaemonians) bravest of the Greeks, their calamities, ii. 130 ; (Lacedaemonians) their education practical, not verbal, ii. 172 ; unduly admired, ii. 225-231 ; (Lacedaemonians) expulsion of foreigners by them, ii. 259-262 ; (Lacedaemonians) condemn their own constitution, ii. 273

Lacedemon. See Lacedaemon

Lacheis (Lacheisa ; Bibl. Lachish), city in Palestine, *A.* viii. 246 ; (Lacheisa) ix. 203

Lacheisa. See Lacheis

Lachish. See Lacheis

" Ladder of the Tyrians," coastline between Tyre and Ptolemais, *B.* ii. 188 ; *A.* xiii. 146

Lagus, father of Ptolemy I (Soter), *A.* xii. 2, 3 ; *Ap.* i. 183, 185, 210 ; ii. 37, 44

Laish. See Dan (3) ; Lisos

lake (1), near Solymian hills, cited by Choerilus, identified by Josephus with Dead Sea, *Ap.* i. 173

Lake (2) of Gennesar. See Gennesar, Lake of

Lamech, son of Methuselah, *A.* i. 63, 65, 79, 86-87

lamps, lighting of by Jews, imitated by non-Jews, *Ap.* ii. 282

Land of Gold. See Gold, Land of

Landing-place, place where Noah landed after flood, *A.* i. 92

Laodice, queen of Samenians, *A.* xiii. 371

Laodicea, city on coast of Syria, captured by Crassus, *B.* i. 231 ; aqueduct in it given by Herod, i. 422 ; letter of its magistrates to Gaius Rabirius, *A.* xiv. 241 ; captured by Cassius, xiv. 289 ; Antony goes there, xv. 64

Larcius Lepidus, Roman commander under Titus, *B.* vi. 237

Lasthenes the Cretan, probably governor of Coele-Syria, *A.* xiii. 86, 126-127

Lathyrus, surname for Ptolemy VIII, *B.* i. 86 ; *A.* xiii. 278, 285, 328, 370

Latin, Caesar's decrees concerning Jews written in it, *A.* xiv. 191, 197 ; edict of Antony to Tyre inscribed in it, xiv. 319 ; Gaius' proficiency in it, xix. 208

Latousim(os) (Bibl. Letushim), son of Dedan, *A.* i. 238

" law," the word, nowhere employed by Homer, *Ap.* ii. 154-155

Law (laws) of Moses, septennial reading of, *A.* iv. 209-211 ; xiii. 297 ; copy of produced, *V.* 134 ; the five books, *Ap.* i. 39 ; degree of Jewish reverence for them, i. 43 ; Jewish observance of them, i. 60 ; willingness of Jews, according to Hecataeus of Abdera, to face death in defence of them, i. 190-191 ; Jewish observance of them, i. 212 ; given on Sinai, ii. 25 ; translated during reign of Ptolemy Philadelphus, ii. 45 ff. ; Jewish faithfulness to them, ii. 82 ; provisions therein concerning vessels in the temple, ii. 106 ; alleged by Apion to be unjust, ii. 125 ;

GENERAL INDEX

GENERAL INDEX

GENERAL INDEX

Lycus, river in Assyria, *A*. xiii. 251

Lydda, city and district on western frontier of Judaea, *B*. i. 302 ; ii. 242, 244, 515, 567 ; iii. 55 ; iv. 444 ; district given to Jewish nation by Demetrius II, *A*. xiii. 127 ; xiv. 208, 275 ; Antigonus' army quartered there, xiv. 412 ; xx. 130

Lydia, *A*. xi. 305 ; revolts against Antiochus the Great, xii. 147, 149

Lydians, *A*. i. 144

Lyons, city in Gaul, *A*. xviii. 252

Lysanias, son of Ptolemy the son of Mennaeus, *B*. i. 248, 398, 440 ; ii. 215, 247 ; becomes ruler of Chalcis in Lebanon and forms pact of friendship with Antigonus, *A*. xiv. 330-332 ; killed by Cleopatra, xv. 92 ; his domain leased by Zenodorus, xv. 344 ; his tetrarchy given to Agrippa I, xviii. 237 ; ruler of Abila, xix. 275 ; his tetrarchy granted to Agrippa II, xx. 138

Lysias (1), noble of high rank, left in command by Antiochus Epiphanes, *A*. xii. 295-315 ; xii. 361 ; commands Antiochus Eupator's army, xii. 367 ; makes peace with the Jews, xii. 379-381 ; urges Antiochus to slay Menelaus, xii. 384 ; xii. 387 ; killed by Demetrius, xii. 390 ; general of Antiochus Eupator, xx. 235

Lysias (2), fortress in Lebanon, *A*. xiv. 40

Lysimachus (1), rules Hellespont after Alexander the Great, *A*. xii. 2

Lysimachus (2), brother of Apollodotus, general of Gazaeans, *A*. xiii. 361

Lysimachus (3), son of Pausanias, envoy from Hyrcanus to Roman Senate, *A*. xiv. 222 ; envoy of Jews to Antony, xiv. 307

Lysimachus (4), friend of Herod, killed by him, *A*. xv. 252 ;

accused by Salome of plotting against Herod, xv. 260

Lysimachus (5), Alexandrian writer, his account of the exodus criticized by Josephus, *Ap*. i. 304-320 ; on date of Jewish exodus from Egypt, ii. 16 ; on number of fugitives driven from Egypt, ii. 20 ; his attacks on Moses and Jewish code, ii. 145 ; reprobate sophist, ii. 236

Lyssa (Frenzy), deified by Greeks, *Ap*. ii. 248

MAACAH. See Machaia ; Machame ; Machane ; Machas ; Micha

Maachah. See Machaia ; Machame ; Machane ; Machas

Maalon. See Malaon

Maaphe. See Mella

Maaseiah. See Amasias (3) and (4)

Mabartha, Jewish name of Neapolis (mod. Nablus), *B*. iv. 449

Maccabaeus (the Maccabee), surname of Judas, son of Mattathias, *A*. xii. 266

Maccabee. See Maccabaeus

Macchida (Bibl. Makkedah), site of cave in Palestine, *A*. v. 61

Macedon (Macedonia, Macedonians), *B*. i. 53 ; ii. 360, 365, 387 ; Macedonian Jews, ii. 488 ; *A*. i. 80, 138 ; ii. 311, 348 ; iii. 201, 239, iv. 84, 327 ; their months, viii. 61, 100 ; their months, xi. 107, 109, 148 ; xi. 286 ; Philip, king of, xi. 304 ; xi. 313, 315-317, 326, 334 ; xii. 1 ; falls to share of Cassander after Alexander the Great's death, xii. 2 ; (Macedonians) Jews in Alexandria given equal rights with them, xii. 8 ; (Macedonians) Jews in Antioch share citizen rights with them, xii. 119 ; xii. 248 ; their garrison stationed in Jerusalem, xii. 252 ; xii. 319 ; (Macedonians) fulfil Daniel's prophecy, xii. 322 ; xii. 354, 412, 434 ; (Macedonians) subjugate Judaea, xiii. 1, 3 ; xiii. 7, 29, 43, 62, 121, 185 ; (Macedonians)

GENERAL INDEX

Judaea liberated from their rule, xiii. 213 ; (Macedonians) rebellion against them by Hyrcanus, xiii. 273 ; xiv. 187, 310, 386 ; Macedonian inhabitants of Seleucia, xviii. 372 ; (Macedonians) their king Philip assassinated on the very same day as Gaius Caligula, xix. 95 ; xix. 298 ; (Macedonians) found Antioch, xx. 68 ; (Macedonians) their war against Hasmonaeans, xx. 238 ; xx. 260 ; left by Stratonice, who goes to Syria, *Ap.* i. 206 ; (Macedonians) privileges of Jews in Alexandria on par with them, ii. 35-36 ; (Macedonians) ancestors (ironical) of Apion, ii. 48 ; (Macedonians) sedition among them in Alexandria, ii. 69 ; (Macedonians) strength of their character, ii. 70 ; (Macedonians) Egyptians as their slaves, ii. 133 ; (Macedonians) not indignant at slaughter of domestic animals, ii. 138
" Macedonians " (1), bodyguard of Antiochus Epiphanes, *B.* v. 460-465
" Macedonians " (2), name of local tribe of Jews in Alexandria, *Ap.* ii. 36
Machaeras, Roman leader sent by Ventidius to aid Herod ; *B.* i. 317-320, 323, 326, 334 ; sent to aid Herod, *A.* xiv. 434 ; hurts rather than helps Herod, xiv. 435-436, 438 ; xiv. 448 ; fortifies Gittha, xiv. 450 ; fights Pappas, xiv. 457
Machaerus, strategic position adjacent to Arabian Mountains, fortified by Alexander son of Aristobulus, *B.* i. 161 ; surrendered by Alexander, i. 167 ; i. 171-172 ; ii. 485-486 ; iii. 46 ; iv. 439, 555 ; vii. 164-168, 170 ; description of, vii. 171-189 ; siege of, vii. 190-209 ; vii. 210 ; *A.* xiii. 417 ; xiv. 83, 89, 94, 96, 111-112, 119
Machaia (Bibl. Maacah, Maachah), mother of Asa, *A.* viii. 286
Machame (Bibl. Maacah, Ma-

achah), wife of David, daughter of Talmai, *A.* vii. 21
machanases (Heb. *miknesaim*), breeches worn by Jewish priests, *A.* iii. 152
Machane (Bibl. Maacah, Maachah), daughter of Tamar, wife of Rehoboam, *A.* viii. 249-250
Machas (Bibl. Maacah, Maachah), son of Nahor, *A.* i. 153
Macheilos. See Seidos
Macheiros (Bibl. Machir), raises Jonathan's son, *A.* vii. 113 ; chief of Gilead, vii. 230
Machir. See Macheiros
Machma (Bibl. Michmash), city near Jerusalem, *A.* vi. 98, 103 ; xiii. 84
Machon, Syrian city, *A.* vii. 105
Macro, successor of Sejanus, *A.* xviii. 196 ; arrests Agrippa I, xviii. 189-191 ; grants concessions to Agrippa, xviii. 203-204
Macrones, neighbours of Syrians, mentioned by Herodotus, *Ap.* i. 170
Madaeans, race descended from Madai son of Japheth, called Medes by the Greeks, *A.* i. 124
Madai. See Mados
Madan(es) (Bibl. Medan), son of Abraham and Keturah, *A.* i. 238
Madian (Midian), country east of Palestine, *A.* vi. 140
Madian(e) (Bibl. Midian), town near Red Sea, *A.* ii. 257
Madianites (Bibl. Midianites), *A.* iv. 101-103, 105 ; entreat Balaam to curse Israelites, iv. 105, 107 ; iv. 120, 123 ; their women seduce Hebrew youths, iv. 126-140 ; iv. 141, 156-157 ; their defeat, iv. 159-164 ; v. 127 ; attack Israelites, v. 210, 212 ; v. 218 ; defeated by Gideon, v. 229 ; their kings put to death by Gideon, v. 229
Mados (Bibl. Madai), son of Japheth and eponymous ancestor of Medes, *A.* i. 124
Maecian tribe, in Rome, *A.* xiv. 220

301

GENERAL INDEX

Maeotis, Lake (modern Sea of Azov), *B.* ii. 366 ; vii. 244

Magadates. See Bagadates

Magaddatus, father of Archelaus the Jewish deserter, *B.* vi. 229

Magassarus, soldier of King Agrippa II and henchman of Mariamme the sister of Agrippa II, *B.* v. 474

Magedo (Mageddo ; Bibl. Megiddo), city in Palestine built by Solomon, *A.* viii. 151 ; (Mageddo) ix. 121

Mageddo. See Magedo

Magi, fail to tell Nebuchadnezzar his dream, *A.* x. 195, 198-199, 203 ; fail to interpret Nebuchadnezzar's second dream, x. 216 ; unable to interpret handwriting on the wall, x. 234, 236 ; xi. 31

Magnus. See Pompey

Magog, son of Japheth, founder of Scythians, *A.* i. 123

Magogians, founded by Magog, *A.* i. 123

Mahalalel. See Malael

Mahalath. See Basemath

Mahanaim. See Manalis

Mahlon. See Malaon

Mahol. See Hemaon

Makkedah. See Macchida

Malachias, soldier of Simon's division, *B.* vi. 92

Malael (Bibl. Mahalalel), son of Cain, *A.* i. 79, 84

Malaon (Maalon ; Bibl. Mahlon), son of Abimelech and Naomi, *A.* v. 318 ; marries Ruth, v. 319, 333

Malatha, city in Idumaea, *A.* xviii. 147

Malchiel. See Melchiel(os)

Malchus (1) the Arab, tutor to Antiochus VI, *A.* xiii. 131-132

Malchus (2), king of Arabs, *B.* i. 274-276, 278, 286, 360, 440 ; declines to aid Herod, *B.* i. 370-375 ; xiv. 390 ; his aid enlisted by Hyrcanus against Herod, xv. 167-168, 171-173, 175

Malchus (3), king of Arabs, *B.* iii. 68

Malchus (4). See Cleodomus

Malichus, Jewish noble, enemy of Antipater, *B.* i. 162, 220, 222-224 ; poisons Antipater, i. 226 ; Herod's revenge on him, i. 227-237 ; *A.* xiv. 84, 273, 276 ; plots against Antipater's life, xiv. 277-279 ; poisons Antipater, xiv. 280-284 ; tries to keep Herod out of Jerusalem, xiv. 285-287 ; killed by Herod, xiv. 288-293 ; xiv. 296

Malla. See Mella

Mallius (1), Lucius, of Menenian tribe, father of Lucius Mallius, *A.* xiii. 260

Mallius (2) (var. Mannius), Lucius, of Menenian tribe, son of Lucius Mallius, *A.* xiii. 260

Malthace, wife of Herod, *B.* i. 562 ; her death, ii. 39 ; Archelaus' mother, her death, *A.* xvii. 250

Mambres (Bibl. Mamre), comrade in arms of Abraham, *A.* i. 182

Mamre. See Mambres

man (1), Hebrew word for " what is this ? ", *A.* iii. 32

man (2). See *manna*

Manaemos (1) (Bibl. Menahem[1]), king of Israel, *A.* ix. 229, 232-233

Manaemos (2). See Manaemus

Manaemos (3). See Menahem (3)

Manaemus (Heb. Menahem), an Essene, predicts that Herod will be king, *A.* xv. 373-378

Manalis (Bibl. Mahanaim), city in Transjordan, *A.* vii. 10

Manasseh (1). See Manasses (1)

Manasseh (2) (Manasses), tribe of (Manassites), awarded their part of land, *A.* iv. 166 ; iv. 174 ; v. 3, 80 ; territory of the half-tribe, v. 83 ; erects altar, v. 100 ; Gideon's tribe, v. 213 ; Jair's tribe, v. 254 ; pays homage to David, vii. 57, 59 ; their land ravaged by Syria, ix. 159 ; many of tribe converted to piety in days of King Hezekiah, ix. 267

Manasseh (3), son of Hezekiah, king of Judah, *A.* x. 37 ; captured by Babylonians, x. 40 ; repents, x. 41-46

302

GENERAL INDEX

303

GENERAL INDEX

443, 451, 480, 521, 563, 566, 586; ii. 222; *A.* (xiv. 300, 353, 467;) xv. 23; her beauty praised to Antony, xv. 25; urges Herod to restore high priesthood to her brother,˙ xv. 31; discovers Herod's secret instructions concerning her, xv. 65, 68; xv. 73; Herod's jealousy of her, xv. 81-84; rebukes Herod for his instructions concerning her, xv. 85; placed in Alexandrion by Herod, xv. 185; doubts Herod's love for her, xv. 202-216; distrusted by Herod, xv. 218-231; put to death, xv. 232-236; her character, xv. 237-239; her death arouses remorse in Herod, xv. 241-246; ruined by calumnies, xvi. 8; her sons distrusted by Herod, xv. 79, 85, 88; xvi. 133; calumniated by Nicolas the historian, xvi. 185; her sons pushed aside by Antipater, xvi. 192; her sons hated by Salome, xvi. 201, 203; xvii. 335; her daughters, xviii. 130; marries Herod, xx. 248

Mariamme (3) II, daughter of Simon the high priest, wife of Herod, *B.* i. 562, 573, 588, 599; *A.* (xv. 320); xviii. 136

Mariamme (4), wife of Herod, king of Chalcis, *B.* ii. 221; *A.* xviii. 134

Mariamme (5), wife of Archelaus the ethnarch, *B.* ii. 115; divorced by Archelaus, *A.* xvii. 350

Mariamme (6), daughter of Aristobulus and Berenice, *B.* i. 552 (perhaps identical with [5])

Mariamme (7), daughter of Agrippa I and Cypros, *B.* ii. 220; xv. 474; *A.* xviii. 132; xix. 354-355; married to Julius Archelaus the son of Helcias, xx. 140; leaves Archelaus and marries Demetrius, xx. 147

Mariamme (8), tower of, in palace enclosure of Herod the Great in Jerusalem, *B.* ii. 439; v. 170; vii. 1

Marion, despot of Tyre, *B.* i. 238-

239; invades Galilee, xiv. 297-299

Marisa (1). See Arydda

Marisa (2) (Bibl. Mareshah), city in Palestine near Eleutheropolis, captured by John Hyrcanus,ᶜ *B.* i. 63; liberated from Jews by Pompey, i. 156; rebuilt by Gabinius, i. 166; i. 269; *A.* viii. 246, 292; ravaged by Judas Maccabaeus, xii. 353; captured by John Hyrcanus, xiii. 257; xiii. 275, 396; xiv. 75, 88; destroyed by Parthians, xiv. 364

Marmaridae, African tribe, *B.* ii. 381

marriages, those forbidden by Jewish law, *A.* iii. 274-275; Jewish laws of, iv. 244-259; of Jewish priests, scrutiny of, *Ap.* i. 31-36; Jewish laws concerning, ii. 199-203; Spartan contempt for, ii. 273

Marsuan (Heb. Marheshwan), Hebrew month, *A.* i. 80

Marsus, governor of Syria, *A.* xix. 316; informs Claudius of Agrippa I's fortification of walls of Jerusalem, xix. 326; orders Agrippa to depart from Tiberias, xix. 340-342; his quarrel with Agrippa, xix. 363; succeeded by Cassius Longinus as governor of Syria, xx. 1

Marsyas, Agrippa I's freedman, attempts to raise funds for him, *A.* xviii. 155-157; xviii. 204; informs Agrippa of Tiberius' death, xviii. 228-230

Maruel (Bibl. Mehujael), son of Irad, *A.* i. 63

Marullus, appointed commander of Roman cavalry in Judaea by Gaius Caligula, *A.* xviii. 237

Mary, daughter of Eleazar, eats her own child, *B.* vi. 201-213

Masada, fortress on western shore of Dead Sea, *B.* i. 237-238, 264, 266; besieged by Antigonus, i. 286; i. 292; its siege relieved by Herod, i. 293-294; i. 303; ii. 408, 433, 447, 653; iv. 399-404, 504, 506, 516, 555; vii. 252, 275;

304

GENERAL INDEX

description of, vii. 280-303 ; besieged and captured by Romans, vii. 304-406 ; guarded by Malichus' brother, *A.* xiv. 296 ; Herod leaves his family there, xiv. 358, 361 ; besieged by Antigonus, xiv. 390 ; Herod rescues his relatives from there, xiv. 396-397, 400, 413 ; Herod places his family there, xv. 184

Masbalus, father of Ananias the Jewish priest, *B.* v. 532

Mash. See Mesas

Masmas (Bibl. Mishma), son of Ishmael, *A.* i. 220

Masmes (Bibl. Massa), son of Ishmael, *A.* i. 220

masnaephthes, turban of Jewish priests, *A.* iii. 157

Maspha. See Masphath(e)

Masphate. See Masphath(e)

Masphatha. See Masphath(e)

Masphath(e) (Maspha, Masphate, Masphatha ; Bibl. Mizpah), city in Palestine, *A.* v. 261 ; vi. 22, 60 ; viii. 306 ; city where Jeremiah dwells, x. 158 ; x. 159, 168, 172-173

Massa. See Masmes

massabazanes, tunic of Jewish priests, *A.* iii. 156

Massagetae, a people living beyond the Araxes River, with whom Cyrus warred, *A.* xi. 20

Massam (Bibl. Mibsam), son of Ishmael, *A.* i. 220

Master of the horse, probably a reference to Mark Antony, *A.* xiv. 210

Masthera, a pass in Palestine, *A.* vi. 291

Mathan (Bibl. Mattan), priest of Baal, *A.* ix. 154

Mathousalas (Bibl. Methushael), son of Mehujael, *A.* i. 63

Mathuel (Bibl. Kemuel), son of Nahor, *A.* i. 153

Mathusalas (Bibl. Methuselah), son of Enoch, *A.* i. 79 ; lives 969 years, i. 86

Matri. See Matris

Matris (Bibl. Matri), name of Saul's family, *A.* vi. 62

Mattan. See Mathan

Mattathias. See Matthias (1)

Matthias (1) (Mattathias), son of Asamonaeus, priest of village of Modein, slays Bacchides, *B.* i. 36 ; *A.* xii. 265 ; urges his sons to defy Antiochus Epiphanes, xii. 267 ; defies Antiochus' decrees, xii. 268-270 ; urges Jews to fight back on Sabbath, xii. 275-278 ; his death, (xii. 279-285) ; xii. 305, 433

Matthias (2), son of Absalom, commander of army of Jonathan Maccabaeus, *A.* xiii. 161

Matthias (3), father of Josephus the historian, *B.* i. 3 ; ii. 568 ; (v. 533) ; *V.* 5 ; distinguished for his upright character, 7 ; warns Josephus of plot, (204)

Matthias (4), high priest, son of Boethus, *B.* iv. 574 ; v. 527-531 ; vi. 114

Matthias (5), son of Margalus, expert in Jewish law, urges Jews to pull down golden eagle from the temple, *B.* i. 648-650, (655) ; urges Jews to destroy golden eagle built by Herod, *A.* xvii. 149, 151 ; captured by Herod, xvii. 157 ; burned alive by Herod, xvii. 167 ; lamented by Jews, xvii. 206, 214

Matthias (6), son of Theophilus, succeeds Jesus as high priest, *A.* xx. 223

Matthias (7), high priest, *B.* vi. 114

Matthias (8), son of high priest Simon Psellus, said to be son of Ephaeus, *V.* 4

Matthias (9), surnamed Curtus, son of Matthias (son of Simon Psellus), *V.* 4

Matthias (10), son of Ananus, appointed high priest by Agrippa I, *A.* xix. 316, 342

Matthias (11), son of Theophilus, appointed high priest by Herod, *A.* xvii. 78 ; deposed by Herod, xvii. 164-166

Matthias (12), brother of Josephus, his education, *V.* 8

Matthis. See Thatis

GENERAL INDEX

Mauretania, region in North Africa, *A.* i. 133

Maurians, African tribe, *B.* ii. 381

Mazaca, city of the Meschenians (later called Cappadocians), *A.* i. 125

Mechônôth, Hebrew name for bases of lavers in temple in Jerusalem, *A.* viii. 85

Medaba. See Medabe

Medabe (Medaba ; Bibl. Medeba), city east of Dead Sea, captured by John Hyrcanus, *B.* i. 63 ; (Medaba) *A.* xiii. 11, 19 ; (Medaba) captured by Hyrcanus, xiii. 255 ; (Medaba) xiii. 397 ; (Medaba) xiv. 18

Medan. See Madan(es)

Medeba. See Medabe

Medes. See Media

Media (Medes, Median Empire), *B.* i. 13, 50, 62 ; iv. 176 ; vii. 245-246 ; *A.* i. 124 ; place to which Damascenes are transported by Tiglath-Pileser, ix. 253 ; Israelites exiled there, ix. 278 ; destroy Assyrian empire, x. 30 ; attacked by Egypt, ix. 74-75 ; their defeat of Babylonia prophesied, x. 113 ; Cuthaeans (Samaritans) come from its interior, ix. 184 ; x. 226, 232 ; their conquest of Babylonia foretold by Daniel, x. 244 ; Daniel taken from there by Darius, x. 249 ; x. 264-265, 272 ; Samaritans come from there, xi. 19 ; xi. 33, 37 ; Cuthaeans (Samaritans) come from there, xi. 85 ; location of Ectabana, xi. 99 ; letter of Xerxes sent to Jews there, xi. 131 ; xi. 203 (var.), 338 ; xii. 257 ; xviii. 48 ; given to Pacorus, xx. 74, 86 ; their domination of Asia, *Ap.* i. 64 ; successfully attacked by Egyptian king Sethosis (Ramesses II), i. 99 ; wife of Nebuchadnezzar brought up there, i. 141

medimni (*medimnoi*), Attic measure, *A.* iii. 321 ; xv. 314

medimnoi. See *medimni*

meeir, tunic of Jewish high priests, *A.* iii. 159

Megalopolis (Megalopolitan), city in Greece, *A.* xii. 135 ; Polybius from there, xii. 358-359, *Ap.* ii. 84

Megasthenes, author of *History of India*, *A.* x. 227 ; compares Nebuchadnezzar with Heracles, *Ap.* i. 144

Megiddo. See Magedo ; Mende

Mehujael. See Maruel

Meirus, son of Belgas, Jewish hero, is consumed with the temple, *B.* vi. 280

Meisa (Bibl. Mesha), Moabite king, *A.* ix. 29

Melas, prince of Cappadocia, *A.* xvi. 325, 328

Melcha (1) (Bibl. Milcah), daughter of Haran, married to Nahor, *A.* i. 151 ; her children, i. 153

Melcha (2) (Melchale, Michaal, Michale ; Bibl. Michal), daughter of Saul, *A.* vi. 129 ; marries David, vi. 204 ; helps David to escape from Saul, vi. 215-220 ; vi. 309 ; returns to David, vii. 25 ; reproaches David for dancing before ark, vii. 85, 87 ; vii. 89

Melchale. See Melcha (2)

Melchiel(os) (Bibl. Malchiel), son of Asher, *A.* ii. 183

Melchis (Bibl. Melchishua), son of Saul, *A.* vi. 129, 369

Melchisedek (Bibl. Melchizedek), king of Solyma (Salem), called " Righteous King," (*B.* vi. 438 ;) *A.* i. 180-181

Melchishua. See Melchis

Melchizedek. See Melchisedek

Melitene, district beside the Euphrates on confines of Armenia and Cappadocia, *B.* vii. 18

Mella (var. Maaphe, Malla), city in Judaea, *A.* xii. 340

Melos (Melians), island in Aegean Sea, *B.* ii. 103, 105, 110 ; its Jews welcome false Alexander, *A.* xvii. 327, 338 ; Diagoras from there, *Ap.* ii. 266

Memmius Regulus, Roman consul, *A.* xix. 9

Memnon (1), tomb of, near city of Ptolemais, *B.* ii. 189

Memnon (2), son of Aristides,

GENERAL INDEX

priest in Halicarnassus, *A.* xiv. 256

Memphibosthos (Bibl. Mephibosheth), son of Jonathan, *A.* vii. 113-116, 205-206 ; excuses his conduct to David, vii. 267-271 ; erroneously called Jebosthos, vii. 296

Memphis, city in Egypt, *B.* i. 190 ; iv. 530 ; vii. 426 ; *A.* ii. 240 ; viii. 155, 157 ; xii. 170 ; captured by Antiochus Epiphanes, xii. 243 ; xiv. 132 ; residence of Salitis, first Hycsos king, *Ap.* i. 77 ; Amenophis, king of Egypt, returns there with his army, i. 246

Memucan. See Muchaios

Menahem (1). See Manaemos (1)

Menahem (2). See Manaemus

Menahem (3), son of Judas the Galilaean, Jewish revolutionary leader, slain by partisans of Eleazar, *B.* ii. 433-449 ; put to death with chieftains of brigands, *V.* 21 ; is prevented from slaying Philip son of Jacimus, 46-47

Menander (1), translator of Tyrian records from Phoenician into Greek, mentions Hiram, *A.* viii. 144-146 ; viii. 324 ; ix. 283-287 ; records events of each reign in both Greek and non-Greek countries, *Ap.* i. 116-120

Menander (2) (var.) of Athens, father of Eucles, of Aithalidean deme, *A.* xiv. 150

Menander (3). See Ampius (2)

Menas, Appius. See Appius Menas

Mende (Bibl. Megiddo), city in Josiah's empire, *A.* x. 75

Mendesian canton, nome in Egypt of which Mendes was capital, *B.* iv. 659

Menedemus, philosopher, admires Jewish elders who are about to produce Septuagint, *A.* xii. 101 *see* Septuagint, *A.* xii. 101

Menelaus, name adopted by Onias, son of Simon the high priest, *A.* xii. 239-241, 383 ; executed by Antiochus Eupa-

tor, xii. 384-385, 387 ; surname of Onias, xx. 235

Menenian (Mentina, Tromentina), Roman tribe, *A.* xiii. 260 ; xiv. 220

Menes. See Minaias

Mennaeus (1), father of Ptolemy who was king of Chalcis in Lebanon region, *B.* i. 103, 185 ; *A.* xiii. 392, 418 ; xiv. 39, 126, 297, 330

Mennaeus (2), a Jew, father of Josephus the envoy of Hyrcanus to Mark Antony, *A.* xiv. 307

Menollus. See Euonymus

Menophilus, president of Ephesus *A.* xiv. 262

Mentina. See Menenian

Mephibosheth. See Memphibosthos

Mephramouthosis, Egyptian king, son of Mephres, *Ap.* i. 95

Mephres, Egyptian king, son of Queen Amesses, *Ap.* i. 95

Merab. See Merobe

Meraioth. See Maraiothos

Merari. See Marair(os)

Merbal, king of Tyre, *Ap.* i. 158

meridarch(es), governor of a district, office held by Apollonius, *A.* xii. 261, 264 ; xv. 216

Mero. See Meroth

Merobe (Bibl. Merab), daughter of Saul, *A.* vi. 129

Merodach-baladan. See Baladas

Meroe, Ethiopian city formerly called Saba, *A.* ii. 249

Meroth (Ameroth, Berothe, Mero), village in Upper Galilee, fortified by Josephus, (Mero) *B.* ii. 573 ; iii. 40 ; (Berothe) *A.* v. 63 ; (Ameroth) *V.* 188

Mersaeans (var. Mestraeans ; Bibl. Mizraim), another name for Egyptians, *A.* i. 132

Mersaeus (var. Mestramus ; Bibl. Mizraim), son of Ham, *A.* i. 133 ; his descendants, i. 136

Merse (var. Mestre), another name for Egypt, *A.* i. 132

Merton, father of Judas, Jewish hero, perhaps identical with Mareotes, *B.* vi. 92

Mesanaeans, founded by Mash the son of Aram, *A.* i. 145

307

GENERAL INDEX

Mesas (Bibl. Mash), son of Aram,
A. i. 145

Meschenians, now called Cappadocians, *A.* i. 125

Meschos (Bibl. Meshech), son of
Japheth, *A.* i. 125

Mesha. See Meisa

Meshach. See Misaelos

Meshech. See Meschos

Meshullam. See Messalamus ;
Mosollamus

Meshullemeth. See Emaselme

mesiltayim. See *kymbala*

Mesopotamia (Mesopotamian[s]),
B. iv. 531 ; Charran located
there, *A.* i. 152 ; its people, i.
157 ; i. 187, 244, 276 ; Jacob
sets out for there, i. 278 ; i.
281, 285, 341, 342 ; ii. 173,
177, 213 ; ally with Ammanites
against David, vii. 121 ; surrender to David, vii. 129 ;
viii. 61 ; some of its Jews sent
to Phrygia, xii. 149 ; xii. 393 ;
xiii. 184 ; massacre of Jews
there, xviii. 310 ; controlled by
Asinaeus and Anilaeus, xviii.
339

Mesopotamians. See Mesopotamia

Messala Corvinus, Valerius, Roman orator and patron of literature, *B.* i. 243, 284 ; *A.* xiv.
325, 384

Messalamus (var. Messalomos ;
Heb. Meshullam), father of
Andronicus, *A.* xiii. 75

Messalina, wife of Claudius, *B.* ii.
249 ; put to death by Claudius,
A. xx. 149

Messalomos. See Messalamus (1)

Messiah, Jesus as the, *A.* xviii.
64

Mestraeans. See Mersaeans

Mestramus. See Mersaeus

Mestre. See Merse

Metellus (1), Quintus, Roman consul, surnamed Creticus, *A.* xiv.
4

Metellus (2), Pompey's legate, *B.*
i. 127 ; *A.* xiv. 29

Methusastartus, son of Deleastartus, gains kingship of Tyre
by conspiring against Abdastratus, *Ap.* i. 122

Methuselah. See Mathusalas

Methushael. See Mathousalas

Metilius, Roman commander, *B.*
ii. 450-455

Metten, king of Tyre, son of Balezor, *Ap.* i. 125

Mia. See Zia

Miamoun. See Harmesses Miamoun

Miarus, father of Herod the
leader of a pro-Roman Jewish
faction at Tiberias in 66, *V.* 66

Mibsam. See Massam

Micah. See Michaias

Micha (1) (Bibl. Maacah), region
north-east of Lake Huleh, *A.*
vii. 121

Micha (2). See Michanos

Michaal. See Melcha (2)

Michaiah. See Michaias

Michaias (Bibl. Micah, Michaiah),
Hebrew prophet, rebukes Ahab,
A. viii. 389-392 ; son of Imlah,
viii. 403-410 ; prophesies Ahab's
doom, viii. 412, 417 ; x. 92

Michal. See Melcha (2)

Michale. See Melcha (2)

Michanos (Bibl. Micha), son of
Memphibosheth, *A.* vii. 116

Michmash. See Machma

Middle, God the, of all things,
Ap. ii. 190

Midian. See Madian ; Madian(e)

Midianites. See Madianites

miknesaim. See *machanases*

Milcah. See Melcha (1)

Milesius, delivers up Damascus
to Antiochus Dionysius (Antiochus XII), *A.* xiii. 388-389

Miletus, city in Asia Minor, *A.*
xiv. 244 ; Cadmus of, *Ap.* i. 13

Minaias (=Menes), Egyptian
king, *A.* viii. 155 ; builder of
Memphis, viii. 157

Minni. See Minyas

Minnith. See Maniath(e)

Minos, Greek legislator, *Ap.* ii.
161

Minucianus. See Vinicius, Marcus

Minyas (Bibl. Minni), district in
Armenia, *A.* i. 95

Miriam. See Mariam(e)

Misaches. See Misaelos

Misaelos (Bibl. Mishael), called
Misaches (Bibl. Meshach) by

GENERAL INDEX

King Nebuchadnezzar, *A.* x. 188-189

Misenum, maritime city in Italy, bridge built there by Gaius Caligula, *A.* xix. 5

Mishael. See Misaelos

Mishma. See Masmas

Misphragmouthosis, Egyptian king, defeats Hycsos, *Ap.* i. 86; father of Thoummosis, i. 88

Mithridates (1), treasurer of Cyrus, *A.* xi. 11, 13, 14, 92

Mithridates (2) Sinakes, holds Demetrius Akairos captive, *A.* xiii. 384-386

Mithridates (3) (VI Eupator), king of Pontus, *B.* i. 138; *A.* xiii. 421; his death, xiv. 53; xiv. 112-114; Mithridatic war, xvi. 18

Mithridates (4) (III of Parthia), fugitive from Parthia, *B.* i. 178; *A.* xiv. 103

Mithridates (5) of Pergamus (Pergamum), *B.* i. 187-192; *A.* xiv. 128-136, 138-139, 193

Mithridates (6), king of Parthia, *A.* xvi. 253

Mithridates (7), Parthian leader, captured and released by Anilaeus, *A.* xviii. 353-360; defeats Anilaeus, xviii. 362-363, 365-366

Mitylene (Mytilene), city on the island of Lesbos, *A.* xv. 350; xvi. 20

Mizpah. See Masphath(e)

Mizraim. See Mersaeans; Mersaeus

Mnaseas, disciple of Eratosthenes, *A.* i. 94; testifies to antiquity of the Jews, *Ap.* i. 216; cited by Apion for story of theft of ass's head by an Idumaean dressed as Apollo, ii. 112

Moab (1), born of Lot and his daughter, *A.* i. 205

Moab (2) (Moabites), *B.* i. 89; iii. 47; iv. 454; descended from Moab (1), inhabit Coele-Syria, *A.* i. 206; iv. 85, 102, 130; attack Israelites, v. 186; v. 187, 196; defeated by Israelites, v. 197; v. 198, 318-319; vi. 90, 129; shelter David, vi. 248; defeated by David, vii. 98; vii.

315; attack Jehoshaphat, ix. 7; revolt against Ahaziah, ix. 19; attacked and defeated by Jehoram and Jehoshaphat, ix. 29-43; ix. 46; defeated by Nebuchadnezzar, x. 181; send letter to Cambyses, xi. 21; hear of building of walls of Jerusalem, xi. 174; subdued by Alexander Jannaeus, xiii. 374; xiii. 382, 397

Mochus, Phoenician historian, *A.* i. 107

Modai. See Modein

Modaiei. See Modein

Modeei. See Modein

Modeeim. See Modein

Modeein. See Modein

Modein (Modai, Modeein, Modeei; var. Modiaiei, Modeeim, Modin), village near Lydda, home of Maccabees, *B.* i. 36; (Modai) *A.* xii. 265, 268; (Modal) Mattathias is buried there, xii. 285; (Modeein) Judas is buried there, xii. 432; (Modeei) Jonathan buried there, xiii. 210

Modin. See Modein

Modius, Aequus, sent by Agrippa II to replace Varus, *V.* 61; shuts up Jews of Caesarea Philippi, 74; commander of force sent by Agrippa II to destroy fortress of Gamala, 114; friend and comrade of Philip son of Jacimus, 180-181

Moesia, region (modern Serbia and Bulgaria), *B.* iv. 619, 633, 643; vii. 92-95, 117

Molon, Apollonius, on date of Jewish exodus from Egypt, *Ap.* ii. 16; his calumnies about the temple in Jerusalem, ii. 79; his attacks on Moses and on Jewish code, ii. 145; his contradictory attacks on Jews, ii. 148; a reprobate sophist, ii. 236; a crazy fool, ii. 255; condemns Jewish exclusiveness, ii. 258; his ignorance of Athenian intolerance, ii. 262; has high opinion of Persians, ii. 270; his lies, ii. 295

GENERAL INDEX

Monobazus (1), surnamed Bazaeus, king of Adiabene, brother
and husband of Helena, father
of Monobazus and Izates, *A.*
xx. 18 ; his death, xx. 24, 26
Monobazus (2), king of Adiabene,
brother of Izates, *B.* ii. 520 ;
v. 252-253 ; *A.* xx. 20 ; appointed trustee of realm after
his father's death, xx. 32-33 ;
converts to Judaism, xx. 75 ;
succeeds Izates, xx. 93, 95-96
Monobazus (3), kinsman of
Monobazus king of Adiabene,
distinguished for valour on
side of Jews in war against
Romans, *B.* ii. 520
Mopsuestia, place in Cilicia, *A.*
xiii. 368
Mordecai (1). See Mardochaios
(1)
Mordecai (2) (Grk. Mardochaios),
one of chief men among Jews,
Esther's uncle, *A.* xi. 198 ;
moves from Babylon to Susa,
(xi. 204 ;) discovers plot against
King Ahasuerus, xi. 207 ; his
name noted in archives, xi.
208 ; refuses to bow before
Haman, xi. 210 ; Haman
seeks revenge against him, xi.
211 ; learns of edict against
the Jews and mourns, xi. 221 ;
xi. 222, 224 ; urges Esther to
intercede in Jews' behalf, xi.
225-228 ; leads fast of people,
xi. 229 ; shows Haman no
honour, xi. 244 ; xi. 246, 249,
251 ; Haman ordered to
honour him, xi. 255-256 ;
changes into regal clothing,
(xi. 258 ;) xi. 259 ; cross set up
for him, xi. 261 ; receives
king's ring, xi. 269 ; receives
Haman's possessions, xi. 270 ;
xi. 278, 284 ; feared by rulers,
xi. 287 ; writes to Jews in
kingdom of Ahasuerus, xi. 293 ;
a great man, xi. 295
Morian Mount, place where
Abraham is commanded to
sacrifice his son, *A.* i. 224
Mosaic code (Jewish law), *A.* iv.
199 ; holy city, iv. 200-201 ;
blasphemy, iv. 202 ; three

annual pilgrim festivals, iv.
203-204 ; tithes, iv. 205 ;
wages not to be expended on
sacrifices, iv. 206 ; foreign
cults, iv. 207 ; forbidden
clothes, iv. 208 ; septennial
reading of the Laws, iv. 209-
211 ; daily prayer, iv. 212-213 ;
administration of justice, iv.
214-218 ; witnesses, iv. 219 ;
undetected murder, iv. 220-
222 ; laws pertaining to kings,
iv. 223-224 ; laws pertaining
to land and agriculture, iv.
225-230 ; rights of poor, iv.
231-232 ; rights of animals, iv.
233 ; rights of poor, iv. 234-
240 ; ceremony of tithes, iv.
241-243 ; laws of marriage,
iv. 244-259 ; rebellious children, iv. 260-265 ; usury, iv.
266 ; loans and pledges, iv.
267-270 ; theft, iv. 271-272 ;
slavery, iv. 273 ; lost property,
iv. 274 ; assistance to people
and beasts in distress, iv. 275-
276 ; respect for blind, iv. 276 ;
damages, iv. 277-284 ; depos-
its, iv. 285-287 ; wages, iv.
288 ; individual responsibility,
iv. 289 ; eunuchs, iv. 290-291 ;
provisions for war and prayers
for peace, iv. 292-300 ; costumes of the sexes, iv. 301
Moses (see also Law), teacher of
God's works to the Jews, *A.*
iv. 18, 21, 26, 29, 33-34, 81, 95 ;
length of his life fixed as limit
for man, i. 152 ; i. 240 ; found
by Pharaoh's daughter, ii. 225 ;
derivation of his name, ii. 228 ;
raised in Pharaoh's palace, ii.
231-238 ; appointed general of
Egyptian army, ii. 241-242 ;
defeats Ethiopians, ii. 243-
251 ; marries Ethiopian princess Tharbis, ii. 252-253 ; flees
to Midian, ii. 254-257 ; helps
daughters of Jethro, ii. 260-
261 ; sees the burning bush and
is commanded to lead Hebrews
out of Egypt, ii. 264-276 ;
convinces the Hebrews by
performing miracles, ii. 280 ;
goes before Pharaoh and is

rebuked, ii. 281-288; blamed by Jews for their increased hardships, ii. 289; his words disdained by Pharaoh, ii. 293-294; asks Pharaoh to let Hebrews go and is refused, ii. 298, 302, 307-310; instructs Hebrews to prepare Paschal lamb, ii. 311-312; ordered by Pharaoh to take Hebrews out of Egypt, ii. 314; is eighty years old when exodus takes place, ii. 319; ii. 320; reasons for route taken by him out of Egypt, ii. 322; blamed by Hebrews for leading them out of Egypt, ii. 326; exhorts Hebrews to have faith in God and not fear Egyptians, ii. 329-333; prays to God to save Hebrews from pursuing Egyptians, ii. 334-337; first to cross Red Sea, ii. 339; composes song of thankfulness to God, ii. 346; collects armour of the Egyptians from Red Sea, ii. 349; makes water of Marah drinkable, iii. 5; blamed by the mob for their distress, iii. 12; promises Hebrews deliverance from their distress, iii. 24; thanks God for succouring the Hebrews, iii. 25; iii. 26, 31; blamed by the Hebrews for their distress at Rephidim, iii. 33; brings forth water out of the rock, iii. 35-38; leads the Hebrews to victory over the Amalekites, iii. 43-54; collects armour of the Amalekites, iii. 59; iii. 61; welcomed by his father-in-law, iii. 63; iii. 65; advised by Reuel, iii. 66-74; ascends Mt. Sinai, iii. 75-82; descends from Mt. Sinai and addresses the people, iii. 83-88; inscribes tablets of stone, iii. 90; iii. 93; reascends Mt. Sinai for forty days, iii. 95-98; builds tabernacle, iii. 103-108, 115-137; iii. 156, 181; appoints Aaron high priest, iii. 188; makes protective coverings for tabernacle, iii. 193; imposes contribution of one

shekel for each man, iii. 195-196; consecrates tabernacle, iii. 204-211; devotes self to service of God and writes out laws, iii. 212; iii. 214; compiles laws, iii. 222; iii. 244; consecrates tribe of Levi, iii. 258; iii. 265; teaches people laws concerning purity, iii. 273; teaches people law about Sabbatical year and Jubilee, iii. 280-286; makes silver trumpets, iii. 291; keeps the Passover for the first time in the wilderness, iii. 294; reproached by the multitude for their trials, iii. 295-297; promises to procure meat for Hebrews, iii. 298; leads Hebrews up to frontier of Canaan and sends out scouts, iii. 300-303; blamed by Hebrews for leading them out of Egypt, iii. 307; iii. 310; announces that Hebrews must wander in desert for forty years, iii. 311-316; his commandments obeyed to this day, iii. 318-319, 322; defied by the Hebrews, iv. 1-5; leads Hebrews into desert, iv. 9; Jews revolt against him, iv. 12-13; his authority challenged by Korah, iv. 14-34; iv. 35-36; opposed by Dathan and Abiram, iv. 37-39; iv. 54, 57-58; quells sedition of Korah, iv. 60-66; assigns cities to Levites, iv. 67; iv. 74; is refused passage through Edomite land, iv. 76-77; purifies people after death of Miriam, iv. 78-81; reveals to Aaron that his death is near, iv. 83; leads people toward land of Amorites, iv. 85-87; leads Hebrew army against Amorites, iv. 87; overruns realm of Og, iv. 97; pitches camp opposite Jericho, iv. 100; attacks Midianites, iv. 101; remonstrates with Zimri about Midianite women, iv. 141-142; defied by Zimri, iv. 145; (iv. 152;) attacks Midianites, iv.

GENERAL INDEX

156 ; records prophecies of
Balaam, iv. 157 ; attacks
Midianites, iv. 159 ; iv. 162 ;
divides spoils of Midianites,
iv. 164 ; appoints Joshua to
succeed him, iv. 165 ; awards
lands to tribes, iv. 166, 171 ;
builds ten cities of refuge, iv.
172-173 ; decides law of inheritance, iv. 174-175 ; addresses
Hebrews before his death, iv.
176-193 ; iv. 194-197, 243 ;
delivers the laws to the people,
iv. 302 ; iv. 306, 308, 311-312 ;
his last words, iv. 320 ; his
death, iv. 323 ; iv. 330-331 ;
v. 1, 4, 39, 40, 69, 89-91, 96, 98,
117, 126-127, 262 ; vi. 84, 86,
89, 93, 133, 140 ; vii. 91 ; his
injunction ignored by David,
vii. 318 ; vii. 338 ; his descendants, Levites, honoured by
David, vii. 367 ; vii. 379, 384 ;
Solomon sacrifices on his
bronze altar, viii. 22 ; lamp-
stands in the temple made
according to his command-
ment, viii. 90 ; viii. 92 ; the
temple built according to his
commandment, viii. 93-94 ;
viii. 101, 104, 120 ; his laws
disregarded by Solomon, viii.
191 ; viii. 349 ; his laws kept
by Jehoshaphat, viii. 395 ; ix.
2, 153, 187 ; x. 43 ; his sacred
book found in days of King
Josiah, x. 58 ; x. 59 ; his laws
publicly read by Josiah, x. 63 ;
x. 72 ; xi. 17, 76, 108 ; his
death, xi. 112 ; his laws
known by Ezra, xi. 121 ; his
laws read by Ezra, xi. 154 ;
xiii. 74, 79, 297 ; xvii. 159 ;
xviii. 81 ; is said to have
deposited holy vessels in
Samaritan territory, xviii. 85 ;
xx. 44, 115, 225, 228, 230 ;
copy of his laws held by Jesus,
son of Sapphias, in speech to
instigate Jews of Tarichaeae to
punish Josephus, V. 134 ; his
five books, *Ap.* i. 39 ; his
death as terminus beginning
prophetic books, i. 40 ; Berosus' account of flood similar to

his, i. 130 ; called a native of
Heliopolis by Manetho, (i. 238 ;)
name adopted by Osariph,
Egyptian priest of Heliopolis,
according to Manetho, i. 250 ;
Manetho's account of him contradicted by Josephus, i. 253 ;
name adopted by Osariph, i.
265 ; Manetho's account of
him criticized by Josephus, i.
279 ff. ; etymology of his
name : " one saved out of the
water," i. 286 ; called Tisithen
by Chaeremon, i. 290 ; associated by Chaeremon with
Joseph, i. 299 ; leader of unclean Egyptians, according to
Lysimachus, i. 309 ; called a
native of Heliopolis by Apion,
ii. 10 ; Apion on prayer-houses
and sundials erected by him,
ii. 10-14 ; refutation of Apion's
statement that he was a
Heliopolitan, ii. 13 ; leads
Jews in exodus, according to
Apion, ii. 15 ; ascends Mt.
Sinai, according to Apion, ii.
25 ; Apion's account of him,
ii. 28 ; attacks on him by
Apollonius Molon and Lysimachus, ii. 145 ; most ancient
of legislators, ii. 154-156 ; his
work as a general, ii. 157-158 ;
his constitution, ii. 159-175 ;
his influence on Greek philosophers, ii. 168 ; Greek philosophers as his disciples, ii. 281 ;
his merits, ii. 290
Mosollamus (Heb. Meshullam),
Jewish archer, participates in
campaigns of Alexander the
Great and of his successors,
Ap. i. 200-204
mou, Egyptian word for water,
Ap. i. 286
Muchaios (var. Amuchaios ; Bibl.
Memucan), interpreter of Persian laws, *A.* xi. 193
Mucianus, Roman governor of
Syria, *B.* iv. 32, 495, 605, 621,
624, 632, 654 ; v. 43 ; *A.* xii.
120
Muia (Fly-god), *A.* ix. 19
Mundus, Decius, has intimate
relations with Paulina by

312

GENERAL INDEX

assuming guise of the god Anubis, *A.* xviii. 67-77 ; exiled by Tiberius, xviii. 80

Munychion, Macedonian month, *A.* xiv. 150

Muppim. See Nomphthes

Murcus, Roman governor of Syria, *B.* i. 217, 219, 224-225 ; *A.* xiv. 270 ; supports Cassius, xiv. 272 ; xiv. 279 ; makes Herod governor of Coele-Syria, xiv. 280

murder, undetected, Jewish law on, *A.* iv. 220-222

Myrrha, character in play *Cinyras*, *A.* xix. 94

Mysia, region in Asia Minor, *B.* i. 425

mysteries, Greek, *Ap.* ii. 189 ; of Athenians, jeered at by Diagoras of Melos, ii. 266 ; of foreign gods, Ninus the priestess put to death for allegedly initiating people into them, ii. 267

Mytilene. See Mitylene

Myttyn, judge of Tyre, *Ap.* i. 157

NAAMAH. See Noema ; Nooma

Naaman. See Neeman(es)

Naamis (Bibl. Naomi), wife of Abimelech, *A.* v. 318 ; returns home, v. 320 ; takes Ruth with her, v. 322 ; v. 323, 326-328, 336

Naas (Naases ; Bibl. Nahash), king of Ammanites, *A.* vi. 68 ; harasses Israelites and neighbouring people, vi. 73 ; killed by Saul, vi. 79 ; (Naases) vii. 117

Naases. See Naas

Naba (Bibl. Nob), city near Jerusalem, *A.* vi. 242, 254 ; its inhabitants slain by Saul, vi. 260

Nabad (Bibl. Nadab), son of Aaron the brother of Moses, *A.* iii. 192 ; burnt to death, iii. 209

Nabadath. See Nabatha

Nabados (var. Nadabos ; Bibl. Nadab), Jewish king ; son and successor of Jeroboam, *A.* viii. 287 ; his death, viii. 298

Nabaioth(es) (Bibl. Nebaioth), son of Ishmael, *A.* i. 220

Nabal, wealthy Jew, refuses to give presents to David, *A.* vi. 296-299 ; vi. 300, 302-303, 305 ; his death, vi. 306-307

Naballo. See Dabaloth

Nabaloth. See Dabaloth

Nabataeans (Nabatene), Arab tribe, *B.* i. 178 ; (Nabatene) *A.* i. 221 ; xii. 335 ; xiii. 10-11 ; attacked by Jonathan, xiii. 179 ; xiv. 31, 46, 48, 103

Nabataeus of Adiabene, his son boldly attacks Romans, *B.* v. 474

Nabataios (Bibl. Nebat), father of Jeroboam, *A.* viii. 205 ; ix. 109

Nabatene. See Nabataeans

Nabatha (var. Nadabath, Nabadath, Gabadan), Arab city *A.* xiii. 18

nabla (Bibl. *nêbel*) twelve-note Hebrew musical instrument, *A.* vii. 306 ; viii. 94

Naboandelos (Nabonnedus), another name for Belshazzar. *A.* x. 231 ; succeeds Laborosoardoch as king of Babylon, *Ap.* i. 149 ; defeated by Cyrus, i. 151-152 ; humanely treated by Cyrus, i. 153 ; his death, i. 153

Nabonnedus. See Naboandelos

Nabopalasaros (Nabopalassar ; var. Nabuchodonosoros), father of Nebuchadnezzar, *A.* x. 220-221 ; (Nabopalassar) king of Babylon and Chaldaea, *Ap.* i. 181 ; (Nabopalassar) sends his son Nebuchadnezzar to put down rebellion of satrap in charge of Egypt, Coele-Syria, and Phoenicia, i. 135 ; (Nabopalassar) his death, i. 136

Nabopalassar. See Nabopalasaros

Nabosaris, Babylonian commander assigned to sack of Jerusalem, *A.* x. 135

Naboth, killed through Jezebel's plot and his vineyard taken by Ahab, *A.* viii. 355-361 ; viii. 407 ; Jehoram of Israel is killed in his field, ix. 118-119

Nabro. See Hebron

313

GENERAL INDEX

Nabrodes. See Nebrodes

Nabuchodonosor. See Nebuchadnezzar

Nabuchodonosoros I. See Nabopalasaros

Nabuchodonosoros II. See Nebuchadnezzar

Nabuzardanes (Bibl. Nebuzaradan), Babylonian general, *A.* x. 144-149; appoints governor of Judaea, x. 155; x. 158-159, 172

Nacatelas. See Cathlas

Nachon. See Cheidon

Nachor(es) (1) (Nahor), son of Serug, *A.* i. 148-149

Nachor (2) (Bibl. Nahor), son of Terah, brother of Abraham, *A.* i. 151; his children, i. 153; grandfather of Rebecca, i. 242; i. 252, 289

Nadab (1). See Nabad

Nadab (2). See Nabados

Nadabath. See Nabatha

Nadabos. See Nabados

Naera, village in Judaea, *A.* xvii. 340

Nahash. See Naas

Nahor. See Nachor (1) and (2)

Nahum. See Naum

Naia (var. Aia, An[n]a; Bibl. Ai) (Naietans), Canaanite city attacked by Joshua, *A.* v. 35; (Naietans) defeat Hebrews, v. 35; (Naietans) defeated by Joshua, v. 48; v. 49

Naietans. See Naia

Nain (var. Ain), Idumaean village, *B.* iv. 511, 517

Naioth. See Galbouath

Nakebos, Arab leader, captured by Herod, *A.* xvi. 284; killed by Herod, xvi. 288; xvi. 350

Naomi. See Naamis

Naphais (Bibl. Naphish), son of Ishmael, *A.* i. 220

Naphes, son of David, *A.* vii. 70

Naphish. See Naphais

Naphtali. See Nephthali

Naphtuhim. See Nedemus

Narbata, Jewish district sixty furlongs from Caesarea, *B.* ii. 291

Narbatene, toparchy bordering on Caesarea, *B.* ii. 509

Nasamons, African people unable to defeat Rome, *B.* ii. 381

Nathan (1), son of David, *A.* vii. 70

Nathan (2), Hebrew prophet, tells David not to build the temple, *A.* vii. 91-92; his parable of the poor man's lamb, vii. 147, 150, 153; vii. 158; his prophecy fulfilled, vii. 214; opposes Adonijah, vii. 346-347; warns Bathsheba, vii. 348-349; warns David, vii. 351, 353; anoints Solomon king, vii. 354-355; prevents David from building the temple, vii. 371

Nathanael (1) (Bibl. Nethanel), son of Jesse, brother of David, *A.* vi. 161

Nathanael (2), father of Dorotheus (the bearer of a letter from the Emperor Claudius to the Jews of Jerusalem), *A.* xx. 14

Naue. See Nauekos

Nauechos. See Nauekos

Nauekos (Naue, Nauechos; Bibl. Nun), father of Joshua, (Naue) *B.* iv. 459; *A.* iii. 49; (Nauechos) iii. 308

Naum (Bibl. Nahum), Hebrew prophet, prophesies against Nineveh, *A.* ix. 239

Nazirites, *A.* iv. 72; xix. 294

Neapolis, city in Judaea, *B.* iv. 449

Neapolitanus, tribune, investigator sent by Cestus, *B.* ii. 335-341 (perhaps identical with Neopolitanus, *V.* 120-121)

Nearda (var. Neerda; = Talmudic Nehardea) (Neardaeans), treasure-city of Jews in Babylonia, *A.* xviii. 311, 314, 369; refuse to deliver up Anilaeus to Mithridates, xviii. 369; haven for Jews, xviii. 379

Nebaioth. See Nabaioth(es)

Nebat. See Nabataios

Nebedaeus. See Nedebaeus

nĕbel. See *nabla*

Nebrodes (Nabrodes; Bibl. Nimrod), son of Cush, builds tower of Babel, *A.* i. 113, 115; (Nabrodes) i. 135

Nebron. See Hebron

314

GENERAL INDEX

Nebuchadnezzar (Nabuchodonosor; = Nabuchodonosoros [II]), king of Babylon, defeats Egypt, marches against Jehoiakim, *A.* x. 84-87; (x. 101;) besieges Jerusalem, x. 116-135; captures Zedekiah, x. 138; destroys Jerusalem, x. 146; captures Egypt, exiles Judah, x. 181-183; his treatment of Jewish captives, notably Daniel, x. 186-216; his dream, x. 195-211; his death, x. 219-229; x. 233, 237, 242, 248; xi. 2, 10; vessels taken by him are returned by Cyrus to the temple, xi. 14; xi. 58, 91-92; takes vessels from the temple to Babylon, xi. 100; exiles Jewish people, xx. 231; (Nabuchodonosor) suppresses Jewish revolt, burns the temple in Jerusalem, transports entire Jewish population to Babylon, *Ap.* i. 131; (Nabuchodonosor) puts down rebellion of satrap in charge of Egypt, Coele-Syria, and Phoenicia, i. 135 ff.; (Nabuchodonosor) his death, i. 146 (Nabuchodonosor) devastates the temple in Jerusalem, i. 154; (Nabuchodonosor) besieges Tyre under King Ithobal, i, 156; (Nabuchodonosor) begins siege of Tyre, i. 159

Nebuzaradan. See Nabuzardanes

Nechao (var. Nechos; Bibl. Necho), king of Egypt, *A.* x. 74-76; (x. 82;) Egyptian king defeated by Nebuchadnezzar, x. 84-85

Nechaos (1) (= Necho), Egyptian Pharaoh, carries off Sarah, wife of Abraham, *B.* v. 379

Nechaos (2). See Nechao

Necho (1). See Nechao

Necho (2). See Nechaos

necropolis, region of Alexandria, *Ap.* ii. 36

Nedebaeus (var. Nebedaeus), father of Ananias the high priest, *A.* xx. 103

Nedemus (Bibl. Naphtuhim), son of Mizraim, *A.* i. 137

Neeman(es) (Bibl. Naaman), son of Benjamin, *A.* ii. 180

Neerda. See Nearda

Nehardea. See Nearda

Nehemiah, Jewish cupbearer to King Xerxes, *A.* xi. 159; cries over countrymen's misfortunes, xi. 162; king sees his gloomy face, xi. 164; asks to go to Jerusalem, xi. 165-167; arrives in Jerusalem, xi. 168; summons people to Jerusalem, xi. 168; attempt to kill him, xi. 174; not deterred by hostile neighbours, xi. 176; orders arming of workers, xi. 177; sacrifices to God, xi. 180; urges people to move to the city, xi. 181-182; his death, xi. 183

Nehushta. See Nooste

Nemesaios (var. Amases; Bibl. Nimshi), father of Jehu, *A.* viii. 352; ix. 105

Neopolitanus, commander of a squadron of horse, ravages district of Tiberias, is halted by Josephus, *V.* 120-121 (perhaps identical with Neapolitanus, *B.* ii. 335-341)

Nephthali(s) (1) (Bibl. Naphtali), born to Bilhah and Jacob, *A.* i. 305; ii. 181

Nephthali(s) (2), tribe of, its territory, *A.* v. 86; city of, v. 91; tribe of Barak, v. 201; pays homage to David, vii. 58; Hiram, the Tyrian craftsman, descended therefrom, viii. 76

Ner, uncle of Saul, father of Abner, *A.* vi. 130; vii. 9, 386

Neraiah. See Neros

Neregalsaros (var. Regalsaros), Babylonian commander assigned to sack of Jerusalem, *A.* x. 135

Nergal-sareser. See Neriglisar

Nerias, high priest, son of Uriah, *A.* x. 153

Neriglisar (Eglisaros; var. Iglisaros, Niglisaros; Bibl. Nergalsareser), assassinates Evilmerodach, his brother-in-law, whom he succeeds as king of Babylon,

315

(Eglisaros) *A.* x. 231 ; *Ap.* i. 147

Nero (Caesar), Roman Emperor, *B.* i. 5, 20-21, 23 ; ii. 248-249 ; his accession and character, ii. 250-251 ; enlarges Agrippa II's kingdom, ii. 252 ; appoints Felix procurator of rest of Judaea, ii. 253 ; ii. 270, 284, (294) ; makes Alexander governor of Egypt, ii. 309 ; ii. 342, (352), (403), (406), (415), 490, 555, 558 ; receives news of Roman reverses in Judaea, iii. 1-4 ; iii. 7-8, 339, 398, 401, 540 ; iv. 440 ; his death, iv. 491-493 ; iv. 497, 623 ; vi. 337, 341, 422 ; during his reign height of temple of Herod is raised, *A.* xv. 391 ; makes Tigranes king of Armenia, xviii. 140 ; adopted by Claudius, xx. 150 ; proclaimed emperor, xx. 152 ; murders his mother, xx. 153 ; attitudes of historians toward him, xx. 154-155 ; xx. 158-159, 162 ; cancels Jewish rights in Caesarea, xx. 182-184 ; supports inhabitants of Jerusalem in their quarrel with Agrippa over temple wall, xx. 194-195 ; (xx. 197 ;) Caesarea Philippi renamed Neronias in his honour, xx. 211 ; appoints Florus as successor to Albinus, xx. 252 ; xx. 257, 259 ; priests sent in bonds by Felix to render an account to him, *V.* 13 ; has a special favourite, the Jewish actor Aliturus, 16 ; hands over Tiberias as a present to Agrippa the Younger, 38 ; does not have audience with Philip son of Jacimus because of prevailing disorders and civil war, 408-409

Neronias, name given to Caesarea Philippi by Agrippa II, *A.* xx. 211

Neros (Bibl. Neraiah), father of Baruch, *A.* x. 158

Nethanel. See Nathanael (1)

Netiras, Galilaean Jewish hero, *B.* iii. 233

Neus, high priest, *B.* ii. 566

New City. See Jerusalem, topography

New Town. See Jerusalem, topography

Nicanor (1), officer of Ptolemy Philadelphus, *A.* xii. 94

Nicanor (2), royal agent in Jerusalem of Antiochus Epiphanes, *A.* xii. 261-262 ; sent against Judas, xii. 298

Nicanor (3) (perhaps same as Nicanor [2]), attempts to capture Judas by deceit, *A.* xii. 402-405 ; threatens Jews of Jerusalem, xii. 406 ; killed by Judas at Adasa, xii. 407, 409 ; his death, xii. 420

Nicanor (4) of Ephesus, *A.* xiv. 262

Nicanor (5), tribune of Titus, speaks to Josephus, *B.* iii. 346-355 ; iii. 392 ; v. 261

Nicator. See Seleucus Nicator

Nicodemus, envoy of Aristobulus the son of Alexander Jannaeus, *A.* xiv. 37

Nicolas of Damascus, historian, friend of Herod, *B.* i. 574, 629, 637-638 ; friend of Archelaus, ii. 14, 21, 34-35, 92 ; *A.* i. 94, 108 ; tells story of Abraham, i. 159 ; vii. 101 ; advocate for Jews of Asia Minor, xii. 126-127 ; xiii. 250, 347 ; apologits for Herod, xiv. 9 ; xiv. 68, 104 ; addresses Marcus Vipsanius Agrippa on behalf of Ionian Jews, xvi. 29-58 ; his partiality to Herod, xvi. 183-186 ; is sent by Herod on mission to Rome, xvi. 299 ; envoy to Augustus, xvi. 333 ; reconciles Augustus with Herod, xvi. 335-355 ; advises Herod not to punish his sons rashly, xvi. 370-372 ; accuses Syllaeus before Augustus, xvii. 54 ; accuses Antipater, xvii. 99 ; denounces Antipater, xvii. 106-121, 127 ; accompanies Archelaus to Rome, xvii. 219 ; brother of Ptolemy, xvii. 225 ; defends Archelaus before Augustus, xvii. 240-248 ; defends

GENERAL INDEX

317

GENERAL INDEX

GENERAL INDEX

244, 280; iv. 402; v. 99; vi. 290, 421, 423; when and how celebrated, *A.* iii. 248-251; kept by Joshua and people, v. 20; festival of unleavened bread, ix. 263-264; celebrated by Josiah, x. 70-71; disturbances in the temple during it, xvii. 213; disturbance during it caused by Samaritans, xviii. 29; xviii. 90; uprising of Jews during it, xx. 106

Pathrusim. See Pethrosimus

Patrocles, son of Chaireas, envoy from Hyrcanus to Roman Senate, *A.* xiv. 222

Paulina, noble Roman lady, beloved by Decius Mundus, tricked into having relations with him disguised as the god Anubis, *A.* xviii. 66-77

Paulinus (1), tribune under Vespasian, *B.* iii. 344

Paulinus (2), successor of Lupus in Alexandria, *B.* vii. 434

Paulus Arruntius. See Arruntius, Paulus

Pausanias (1), father of Lysimachus who was envoy of Hyrcanus the high priest, *A.* xiv. 222, 307

Pausanias (2), slayer of Philip the king of Macedonia, *A.* xi. 304; xix. 95

Peace, Temple of, erected by Vespasian in Rome, *B.* vii. 158

Pedanius (1), Roman legate, *B.* i. 538

Pedanius (2), Roman trooper, *B.* vi. 161-163

Pegae, city northeast of Joppa, restored to Jews by Rome, *A.* xiii. 261

Peitholaus, commander of Jewish troops, *B.* i. 162, 172; his death, i. 180; leader of the Jews, *A.* xiv. 84, 93; killed by Cassius, xiv. 120

Pekah. See Phakeas (2)

Pekahiah. See Phakeas (1)

Peleg. See Phaleg

Peleth. See Phalaus

Pella, city in Transjordan, *B.* i. 104, 134; liberated by Pompey, i. 156; sacked by parties

of Jews, ii. 458, iii. 46-47, 55; part of Jewish territory under Alexander Jannaeus, *A.* xiii. 397; Pompey passes through it to get to Coreae, xiv. 49; Pompey restores it to its own inhabitants, xiv. 75

Pelusium, city in Egypt, *B.* i. 175; the Pelusian Frontier, i. 187; i. 189-190, 278, 362, 395; iv. 610, 660, 661; *A.* vi. 140; x. 17-19, 86; xii. 243; xiv. 99, 128, 130, 375; site in Egypt where King Sethosis (Ramesses II) returns to recover his kingdom, *Ap.* i. 101; son of Amenophis (actually Amenophis himself) marches to it, i. 274; place where afflicted persons expelled from Egypt meet persons left there by Amenophis, i. 291; place where Egyptian cripples join 380,000 persons left there by King Amenophis, i. 297; 380,000 persons there join lepers, i. 302

Peniel. See Phanuel

Peninnah. See Phenanna

Pentapolis, Libyan, group of five of the chief cities of Cyrenaica on the northern coast of Africa (Apollonia, Arsinoë, Berenice, Cyrene, and Ptolemais), *B.* vii. 439

Pentecost, Jewish holiday, *B.* i. 253; ii. 42; vi. 299; referred to as "Weeks," *A.* iii. 252; xiii. 252; xiv. 337; fight between Romans and Jews thereon, xvii. 254

Pentephres (1) (var. Petephres; Bibl. Potiphar), an Egyptian, *A.* ii. 39, 40; Joseph falsely accused before him by his wife, ii. 54-58; ii. 78

Pentephres (2) (Bibl. Poti-phera), priest of Heliopolis, ii. 91

Peraea (Peraeans), region in Palestine, *B.* i. 586; ii. 43, 57, 59, 95, 168, 247, 252, 520, 566, 567; description of, iii. 44-47; iv. 413, 439, 450; vi. 209, 274; *A.* v. 255; xiii. 50; xv. 294; bequeathed by Herod as tetrarchy to Antipas, xvii. 188;

323

GENERAL INDEX

273; writes to Gaius, advocating Jewish request, xviii. 276, 284, 286, 288; ordered to set up statue of Gaius in the temple, xviii. 297; ordered by Gaius to desist from setting up statue, xviii. 300, 302; incurs Gaius' wrath, xviii. 303, 305-307; saved by the providence of God, xviii. 308-309; rebukes people of Dora for setting up statue of emperor in synagogue, xix. 301, 303, 312; succeeded by Marsus, xix. 316

Petronius (2), prefect of Egypt, supplies Herod with provisions to relieve starvation, *A.* xv. 307

Pettius, Lucius, member of Pergamum Council (or perhaps member of a Commission of the Roman Senate), *A.* xiv. 251

Phabes (var. Phoabis, Foavis, Faves, Phiabi), father of Jesus (7), *A.* xv. 322

Phabi, father of Ishmael the high priest, *A.* xviii. 34; xx. 179

Phaedra, wife of Herod, *B.* i. 563; *A.* xvii. 21

Phakeas (1) (Bibl. Pekahiah), son and successor of Menahem, king of Israel, *A.* ix. 233

Phakeas (2) (Bibl. Pekah), slayer of Pekahiah, king of Israel, son of Remaliah, *A.* ix. 234, 244; his death, ix. 258

Phalaus (probably Bibl. Peleth; perhaps Bibl. Pallu), one of the eldest members of the tribe of Reuben, *A.* iv. 19

Phaleg (Bibl. Peleg), son of Eber, *A.* i. 146, 148-150

Phalek, Hebrew word meaning division, from which Peleg gets his name, *A.* i. 146

Phalerum, port of Athens, Demetrius of, *Ap.* ii. 46

Phallion, Antipater's brother, *B.* i. 130; *A.* xiv. 33

Phalnagres, son of David, *A.* vii. 70

Phalti. See Pheltias

Phaltiel. See Pheltias

Phalus (Bibl. Pallu), son of Reuben, *B.* ii. 178

Phanasus. See Phanni

Phanni (Phanasus; var. Phenasus, Phineesus, Finasus), son of Samuel, last high priest, *B.* iv. 155; (Phanasus) *A.* xx. 227

Phanuel (Bibl. Peniel), place near river Jabbok where Jacob wrestled with the angel, *A.* i. 334; city where Jeroboam constructed palace, viii. 225

Pharaó, Egyptian word for "king," *A.* viii. 155

Pharaoh. See Pharaothes (2)

Pharaothai, titles of Egyptian kings starting with Minaias, *A.* viii. 155, 157, 159

Pharaothes (1), first Egyptian king in period before Minalas, *A.* viii. 155

Pharaothes (2) (Pharao, Pharaoh), title of Egyptian kings, king of Egypt when Abraham goes there, elsewhere identified by Josephus with Nechaos, *A.* i. 163; king of Egyptians, ii. 39; dreams, ii. 75; appoints Joseph minister in charge of distributing grain, ii. 89; (Pharaoh) ii. 117; greets Jacob, ii. 187, 271; his death, ii. 277; refuses to let Hebrews leave Egypt, ii. 299-310; asks Hebrews to leave Egypt, ii. 313-314; iv. 44; Solomon marries his daughter, viii. 21; viii. 159; (Pharao) captures Gezer and gives it to Solomon, *A.* viii. 151; (Pharao) viii. 155; (Pharao) receives Hadad kindly, viii. 200, 202-203

Pharatho(n) (Bibl. Pirathon), city in Judaea, *A.* v. 273-274; (Pharatho) fortified by Bacchides, xiii. 15

Phares, word written on Belshazzar's wall, interpreted as "a break" by Daniel, *A.* x. 244

Phares(os) (Bibl. Perez), son of Judah, *A.* ii. 178

Pharisee(s), rise of their power and influence, *B.* i. 110-114; i. 571; ii. 119; described, ii. 162-164; ii. 166, 411; one of the three Jewish schools of thought, *A.* xiii. 171; their attitude towards Fate, xiii.

325

GENERAL INDEX

Herod's youngest brother, *B.* i. 181, 308; offers to redeem brother's head, i. 325; i. 342, 475, 483, 485-487, 498, 502, 504-508, 538, 545, 554, 557, 559, 561, 565, 567-572; his death, i. 578-581; i. 582-583, 585, 586, 589-593, 595-596, 601, 609, 638; ii. 99; *A.* xiv. 121, 419; ransoms Joseph's severed head, xiv. 450; receives head of Pappas, xiv. 464; Herod entrusts his affairs to him, xv. 184, 186; receives tetrarchy, xv. 362; stirs up Herod's distrust of his sons, xvi. 68, 73; quarrels with Herod, xvi. 194-200; incites Alexander, Herod's son, against Herod, xvi. 206-212; distrusted by Herod, xvi. 213-219; accuses Salome of licentiousness, xvi. 223, 226; marries his son to Herod's daughter (Salampsio), xvi. 227-228; accused by Alexander, xvi. 256; reconciled with Herod by Archelaus, xvi. 267, 269; xvii. 321; his daughter promised in marriage to son of Alexander, xvii. 14, 16, 18; refuses to marry Herod's daughters, xvii. 22; comes under influence of Antipater, xvii. 33-35; his wife pays the fine for Pharisees, xvii. 42-43; his wife accused by Herod, xvii. 46, 48-51; his dismissal to his tetrarchy and his death, xvii. 58-59, 61; circumstances of his death revealed, xvii. 62-67, 68-70, 73-74, 76; his death, xvii. 79; his death reported to Antipater, xvii. 85; xvii. 121; his sons married to Herod's daughters, xvii. 322

Phiabi. See Phabes

Phiale, one of sources of Jordan, *B.* iii. 509, 511, 513

Phichola, village from which Joseph the Tobiad came, *A.* xii. 161

Phicol. See Philoch

Phideas, high priest, son of Axioramos, *A.* x. 153

Phidias of Athens, sculptor of Olympian Zeus, *A.* xix. 8

Philadelphia (Philadelphians), city in Transjordan, *B.* i. 60, 129, 380; ii. 458; iii. 46-47; *A.* xiii. 235; their dispute with Peraean Jews, xx. 2-3

Philadelphus (1). See Antiochus (11)

Philadelphus (2). See Philip (4)

Philadelphus (3). See Ptolemy (2)

Philhellene, title of Aristobulus, *A.* xiii. 318

Philip (1), of Macedon, son of Amyntas, *B.* ii. 360; king of Macedon, his death, *A.* xi. 304; xii. 354; his assassination on same day as that of Gaius Caligula, xix. 95

Philip (2), father of Perseus, conquered by Rome, *A.* xii. 414

Philip (3), of Persia, appointed regent of Seleucid kingdom, *A.* xii. 360; threatens Antiochus Eupator, xii. 379-380

Philip (4), Epiphanes Philadelphus, rules part of Syria, *A.* xiii. 369, 371; brother of Demetrius, xiii. 384, 386; xiii. 387, 389

Philip (5), father of Sosipater the Jewish envoy to Rome, *A.* xiv. 249

Philip (6), son of Herod and Cleopatra of Jerusalem, *B.* i. 562, 602, 646, 668; ii. 14, 83; made tetrarch, ii. 94; his tetrarchy, ii. 95; ii. 167-168; his death, ii. 181; ii. 247; iii. 512; *A.* xvii. 21; succeeds to kingship of Jews and subjects Bathyra to taxation, xvii. 27; denounced by Antipater to Herod, xvii. 80; Herod's hatred for him, xvii. 146; Herod's bequests to him, xvii. 189; regent during Archelaus' visit to Rome, xvii. 219; xvii. 303; receives a portion of Herod's kingdom from Augustus, xvii. 318-319; builds cities, xviii. 27-28; brother of Herod the tetrarch, his death, xviii. 106-108; xviii. 114; tetrarch of Trachonitis, married to Salome, xviii.

327

GENERAL INDEX

Romans, *V.* 34; father of Justus, 36; eager to desert Josephus and join John of Gischala, 88; held as prisoner by Josephus, sups with Josephus, 175-178; father of Justus, 390

Placidus, Roman tribune, *B.* iii. 59, 110-114, 144, 325; at Mt. Tabor, iv. 57-61; in Peraea, iv. 419-439; preparations for engagement with him feigned by Josephus, sent by Cestius Gallus to burn Galilaean villages, declines battle with Josephus, *V.* 213-214; meditates incursion into Galilee, is watched by Josephus, 227; commander of garrison given to Sepphorites, 411

Plain (1), the Great, of Asochis, *V.* 207

Plain (2), the Great, of Esdraelon, *B.* ii. 188, 232, 595; iii. 39, 48, 59; iv. 54, 455-458; *A.* iv. 100; v. 83; viii. 36; xii. 348; xiv. 207; xv. 294; xviii. 122; xx. 118; entrusted to decurion Aebutius, *V.* 115; crossed by wife of Ptolemy, overseer of Agrippa II, and her baggage plundered, 126; situated on the confines of Galilee, reached by Jonathan's party on way from Tiberias to Jerusalem, 318

plain (3), royal. See " royal plain "

Plancinus (1), Marcus Quintus, father of Marcus, of the Pollian tribe, *A.* xiv. 220

Plancinus (2), Marcus Quintus, son of Marcus, of the Pollian tribe, present at promulgation of decree of the Roman Senate confirming Julius Caesar's decisions regarding the Jews, *A.* xiv. 220

Plataea, city in Greece, *B.* ii. 359

Platana, Sidonian village, *B.* i. 539; *A.* xvi. 361

Plato, Greek philosopher, similar to Moses in his view of God's nature, *Ap.* ii. 168; his ideal constitution ridiculed by statesmen, ii. 223-224; criticism of his dialogues, ii. 225; excludes

poets from the republic, ii. 256; follows Moses' example in prescribing study of laws and in preventing foreigners from mixing at random, ii. 257-261

Plautius (1), Publius, father of Publius Plautius, of Papirian tribe, *A.* xiv. 220

Plautius (2), Publius, Roman of Papirian tribe, present during promulgation of decree of Roman Senate regarding Jews, *A.* xiv. 220

pledges, Jewish law on, *A.* iv. 267-270

Pleiades, stars, *A.* xiii. 237

Plinthine, Libyan frontier of Egypt, *B.* iv. 610

" Plowland." See Arura

Polemo (1), king of Pontus, entertained by Agrippa I at Tiberias, *A.* xix. 338

Polemo (2), king of Cilicia, marries Berenice, *A.* xx. 145-146

Poliorcetes. See Demetrius (2)

Pollian tribe, a Roman tribe, *A.* xiv. 220

Pollio (1). Herod's friend, presumably Asinius Pollio. See Asinius Pollio

Pollio (2), Rufrius, praetorian prefect under the Emperor Claudius, *A.* xix. 267

Pollion the Pharisee, honoured by Herod, *A.* xv. 3-4; Herod tries to persuade him to swear loyalty to him, xv. 370

Polybius of Megalopolis, Greek historian, corroborates Josephus' account of Jews' aid to Antiochus the Great, *A.* xii. 135-137; xii. 358-359; cited on Antiochus Epiphanes' motive in plundering the temple in Jerusalem, *Ap.* ii. 84

Polycrates, Greek writer, reviles Lacedaemon, *Ap.* i. 221

Polydeuces, slave of Claudius, *A.* xix. 13

Pompedius, Roman of senatorial rank, accused of insulting Gaius Caligula, *A.* xix. 32-33, 36

Pompeius (1), Titus, father of Pompeius (2) Longinus, *A.* xiv. 229, 238

GENERAL INDEX

Pompeius (2) Longinus, Titus, legate, present when Lentulus promulgates decree exempting Jewish citizens of Ephesus from military service, *A.* xiv. 229, 238

Pompeius (3), Gaius, father of Gaius Pompeius of Sabatine tribe, *A.* xiv. 239

Pompeius (4), Gaius, Roman, of Sabatine tribe, present when Lentulus promulgates decree exempting Jewish citizens of Ephesus from military service, *A.* xiv. 239

Pompeius (4), Silvanus. See Silvanus

Pompey. *B.* i. 19, 127-128, 131 ; conducts war against Aristobulus, i. 133-154 ; reinstates Hyrcanus as high priest, i. 153 ; redistributes territory of the Jews, i. 155-158 ; i. 160, 179, 183-185, 187, 195-196, 201, 216, 343 ; ii. 356, 392 ; v. 396, 408-409, 506 ; vi. 329, 436 ; forces Aretas to raise siege of the temple, favouring Aristobulus, *A.* xiv. 29 ; receives gifts from Jews at Damascus, xiv. 34 ; hears charges of Jews against Hyrcanus and Aristobulus, xiv. 41-46 ; orders Aristobulus to yield, xiv. 48-52 ; arrests Aristobulus, xiv. 55-57 ; invades Jerusalem, xiv. 58-59 ; besieges the temple, xiv. 60-61 ; xiv. 68 ; respects sanctity of the temple, xiv. 72 ; restores cities of Coele-Syria to their inhabitants, xiv. 76 ; takes Aristobulus to Rome as captive, xiv. 79 ; xiv. 82, 104-105, 123-125 ; defeated by Julius Caesar, xiv. 127 ; xiv. 144, 156, 268 ; his strategy copied by Herod, xiv. 466 ; Herod and Sossius capture Jerusalem on the same day (of the Fast) that he did, xiv. 487 ; restores high priesthood to Hyrcanus, xv. 180 ; xix. 228 ; restores high priesthood to Hyrcanus, xx. 244 ; his invasion of Judaea,

Ap. i. 34 ; occupies the temple in Jerusalem, ii. 82 ; Judaea free until his time, ii. 134

Pomponius Secundus, Quintus, Roman consul, declares war on Claudius, *B.* ii. 205 ; opposes Claudius, *A.* xix. 263-264

Pontifex Maximus, Julius Caesar's title, *A.* xiv. 190, 192

Pontius, father of Marcus Junius Brutus, *A.* xiv. 263

Pontus (see also Euxine), country in north-eastern Asia Minor, *B.* ii. 366 ; *A.* ix. 17 ; xiv. 53 ; xvi. 21, 23 ; ruled by Polemo, xix. 338 ; xix. 365

poor, rights of, according to Jewish law, *A.* iv. 231-232, 234-240

Poplas, friend of Archelaus, *B.* ii. 14 ; called Ptollas, *A.* xvii. 219

Poppaea, wife of Nero, intercedes on behalf of Jews of Jerusalem, *A.* xx. 195 ; xx. 252 ; Nero's consort, aids Josephus in securing liberation of Jewish priests in Rome, *c.* 61, and gives large gifts to Josephus in Rome, *V.* 16

population, vast Jewish, *Ap.* i. 194 ; of Jerusalem, 120,000, i 197

Porcius Festus. See Festus

pork, Jewish abstention from it denounced by Apion, *Ap.* ii. 137 ; abstention from it by Egyptian priests, ii. 141

Port of Augustus. See Sebastos

porters of the temple, not to be taxed, *A.* xi. 128 ; come to Ezra, xi. 134

Poseidon, Greek god, brother of Zeus, conspires against him, (*Ap.* ii. 241) ; hired as builder, (ii. 247)

Posidonius, philosopher and historian, his calumnies about the Jewish temple, *Ap.* ii. 79

Potiphar. See Pentephres

Pouthod(os) (Bibl. Ohad), son of Simeon, *A.* ii. 178

Praetor, Julius Caesar's title, *A.* xiv. 213

prayer, prescribed by Jewish Law, *A.* iv. 212-213 ; proper

332

GENERAL INDEX

(put to death by Cleopatra), *A.*
xv. 92 (identified by Niese
with Ptolemy [14])

Ptolemais (Bibl. Accho), city in
north-western Palestine, *B.* i.
49, 116; admits Pacorus, i.
249; i. 290, 394, 422; ii.
67-68, 187; description of, ii.
188-191; ii. 192, 201, 459,
477, 501-507; iii. 29, 35, 38,
53, 64, 110, 115, 409; *A.* xii.
331, 334, 350; xiii. 35, 37,
81-83, 106, 123, 190-192, 203,
268; besieged by Alexander
Jannaeus, xiii. 324-326, 328-
329; xiii. 330, 332-333; attacked by Ptolemy Lathyrus,
xiii. 336; captured by Ptolemy
Lathyrus, xiii. 347; besieged
by Cleopatra, xiii. 350, 353;
xiii. 419, 421; admits Pacorus,
xiv. 333; Herod collects large
army there, xiv. 394; xiv.
452; Herod receives Octavian
there, xv. 199; xvii. 287-288;
occupied by Vitellius, xviii.
120; xviii. 155, 262-263;
borderland where Jesus the
brigand chief was active, *V.*
105; its borders reached by
Josephus after stopping troops
of Aebutius, 118; its frontier
has village named Chabolo,
213; its neighbourhood ravaged by Placidus, who refuses
to leave his post there, 214-215;
Vespasian there is pressed to
punish Justus of Tiberias, 342;
Vespasian receives remonstran-
ces there from the leaders of
the Syrian Decapolis against
Justus of Tiberias, 410

Ptolemies, name of kings of
Egypt, *A.* vii. 102; viii. 156;
testimonials to Jews by them,
Ap. ii. 62

Ptolemy (1) I (Soter), son of
Lagus, takes Egyptian part of
Alexander the Great's empire,
A. xii. 2; called Soter (Saviour),
xii. 3; seizes Jerusalem, xii.
6; brings Jewish captives to
Egypt, xii. 7; his liberality to
the Jews, xii. 9; length of his
reign, xii. 11; Hecataeus of

Abdera associated with him,
Ap. i. 183; defeats Demetrius
in battle of Gaza and becomes
master of Syria, i. 184-186;
his humanity, i. 186; captures
Jerusalem on Sabbath, i. 210;
his letter bestows rights on
Jews of Alexandria, ii. 37;
honours Alexandrian Jews, ii.
44

Ptolemy (2) II (Philadelphus),
arranges to have Jewish law
translated, *A.* i. 10; his reign,
xii. 11; has Jewish law translated, xii. 13; his letter to
Eleazar the high priest, xii. 45;
has Jewish law translated, xii.
51; his gifts to the high priest
Eleazar, xii. 58-85; welcomes
the seventy Jewish elders, xii.
86; elders pay their respects
daily to him, xii. 106; honours
translators of the law, xii. 118;
requisitions Jewish deputies to
interpret Scriptures to him,
Ap. ii. 45-47

Ptolemy (3) III (Euergetes), *A.*
xii. 158 (var.); offers sacrifice
in Jerusalem, *Ap.* ii. 48

Ptolemy (4) (Philopator), defeated by Antiochus the Great,
A. xii. 130-131

Ptolemy (5) (Epiphanes), defeated by Antiochus the Great,
A. xii. 130-131; xii. 135;
marries Cleopatra, Antiochus'
daughter, xii. 154; angered by
Onias, xii. 158; receives
Joseph the Tobiad as envoy of
Jews, xii. 165-174; grants
Joseph the Tobiad tax-farming
rights, xii. 178, 182; a son is
born to him, xii. 196; sends
for Hyrcanus, xii. 205-207;
impressed by Hyrcanus' lavishness, xii. 219; his death, xii.
234; xii. 242

Ptolemy (6) VI (Philometor),
disputes with Antiochus Epi-
phanes the suzerainty of Syria,
B. i. 31-33; vii. 423-424, 426;
A. xii. 235; circumvented by
Antiochus, xii. 243; receives
Onias IV with honour, xii. 387;
xiii. 62-63, 65; allows Onias

334

GENERAL INDEX

i. 153; meets servant of Abraham, i. 242-243, 245-251; introduces servant to parents, marries Isaac, i. 252-255; bears twins, i. 257-258; helps Jacob receive blessing, i. 269; urges Isaac to go to Mesopotamia, i. 276; i. 290-292, 294-299; her death, i. 345

Rebilus, Gaius Caninius, Roman senator, *A.* xiv. 220

Rechab. See Thaenos

Red Sea (Erythraean Sea), *B.* ii. 382; iv. 608; *A.* i. 39, 221, 239; ii. 257, 315; vi. 140; Solomon builds his fleet there, viii. 163; where Elath is, ix. 217, 245; Aelius Gallus leads troops there, xv. 317; incident of Mosollamus on march toward there, *Ap.* i. 201

refugees, treatment of by Josephus, *V.* 113, 149 ff.

Rega, town of the Philistines, *A.* vi. 325

Regalsaros. See Neregalsaros

Regeb. See Ragaba

Reginians, Greek name for Aschanaxians, *A.* i. 126

registers, Jewish public, *V.* 6

Regulus, Aemilius. See Aemilius Regulus

Rehob. See Araos

Rehoboam. See Roboamos

Rehoboth. See Rooboth

Rehum. See Rathymos

Rekem, king of Midianites, *A.* iv. 161

Rekeme (called Arce, *A.* iv. 82), Arabian city called Petra by the Greeks, *A.* iv. 161

Remaliah. See Romelias

Rephaim (1). See Giants

Rephaim (2), Valley of. See Giants, Valley of the

Rephidim. See Raphidin

Republic of Plato, ridiculed by statesmen, *Ap.* ii. 223-224

Respha (Bibl. Rizpah), Saul's concubine, *A.* vii. 23

Reu. See Reus

Reuben. See Rubel

Reuel. See Raguel; Rauel(os)

Reumah. See Ruma (1)

Reus (Rumus; var. Ragauos;

Bibl. Reu), son of Peleg, *A.* i. 148; (Rumus) i. 149

reward for good deeds, according to Jewish law, *Ap.* ii. 217-219

Rezin. See Arases

Rezon. See Razos

Rhaëpta, Arab fortress captured by Herod, *A.* xvi. 283, 288

Rhegium, Italian harbour city, *A.* xix. 205

Rhesa (Oresa; var. Thresa; Bibl. Horeshah), Idumaean fortress where Herod meets Joseph, *B.* i. 294; recovered by Herod, i. 294; *A.* xiv. 361, 400

Rhine, river-boundary of Roman Empire, *B.* ii. 371, 377; iii. 107

Rhinocorura (Rhinocoroura), maritime town between Egypt and Palestine, Herod learns of brother's death there, *B.* i. 277; Titus stops there on way to Caesarea, iv. 662; *A.* xiii. 395; (Rhinocoroura) xiv. 374

Rhoa (Bibl. Rimmon), a rock of the desert near Gibeah, *A.* v. 166

Rhodes, island in Aegean Sea, Herod welcomed there by Ptolemy on way to Rome, *B.* i. 280; Herod presents himself there to Caesar, i. 387; supported by Herod, i. 424; vii. 21; Herod arrives there, *A.* xiv. 377; Herod meets Octavian there, xv. 187; xvi. 17; Herod's benefactions for it, xvi. 147

Riblah. See Amathe; Arablatha

riddles, exchanged by Hiram of Tyre and Solomon, *Ap.* i. 114-115

Rimmon. See Eremmon; Rhoa

Riphataeans, nation founded by Riphath, descendant of Japheth, *A.* i. 126

Riphath. See Riphathes

Riphathes (Bibl. Riphath), son of Gomer, *A.* i. 126

Rizpah. See Respha

Robees (Bibl. Reba), king of Midianites, *A.* iv. 161

Roboamos (Bibl. Rehoboam), grandson of David, *A.* vii. 105,

GENERAL INDEX

GENERAL INDEX

Antipater, xvii. 6-7; gives
Ulatha as dwelling place to
band of Babylonian Jews, xvii.
24; xvii. 57; relieved of
governorship of Syria and
succeeded by Quintilius Varus,
xvii. 89

Saturninus (2), husband of
Paulina, noble Roman lady,
A. xviii. 66

Saturninus (3), husband of Fulvia
the Jewish proselyte in Rome,
A. xviii. 83

Saturninus (4), Gnaeus Sentius,
Roman consul, *B.* ii. 205; his
speech in the Roman Senate
after assassination of Gaius
Caligula, *A.* xix. 166-185

Saul (1), son of Kish, first Jewish
king, *A.* vi. 46; seeks Samuel,
vi. 47; meets Samuel, vi. 50-
52; anointed by Samuel, vi.
54-57; vi. 58; chosen king by
lots, vi. 62; hides when chosen
as king, vi. 64-65; vi. 67;
defeats the Ammonites, vi.
74-75, 80-81; vi. 82; again
proclaimed king, vi. 83, 94;
prepares for war against Philistines, vi. 95; vi. 98-99;
performs sacrifice contrary to
Samuel's injunction, vi. 100-
101, 103; defeated by Philistines, vi. 105-106; father of
Jonathan, vi. 107; vi. 112;
victorious over the Philistines,
vi. 115-116; invokes curse on
any Hebrew who should partake of food before nightfall,
vi. 118; builds altar, vi. 121;
vi. 123, 126; his children and
relatives, vi. 129-130; wipes
out Amalekites, vi. 131, 134-
135, 138; his conquests, vi.
140; incurs anger of God, vi.
141, 143-145; begs forgiveness,
vi. 151-152; vi. 154, 156;
takes David as his musician,
vi. 166-169; vi. 170; challenged by Goliath, vi. 172, 174;
vi. 175; allows David to fight
Goliath, vi. 179, 181, 184;
slays Philistines after Goliath's
death, vi. 191; vi. 192; envious of David, vi. 193; sets

conditions for David's marriage
to Michal, vi. 196, 199-200,
203-204; plots against David's
life, vi. 205; persuaded by
Jonathan to do no wrong to
David, vi. 209, 212; hurls
spear at David, vi. 213-214;
tries to capture David, vi. 215,
218; vi. 219-220; pursues
David, vi. 221-223; vi. 224,
226; attacks Jonathan as
David's accomplice, vi. 237-
238; vi. 244-245, 247, 250;
orders priests slain, vi. 255,
259-261; vi. 262, 268-269;
attempts to capture David at
Keilah, vi. 272-274; vi. 275,
277, 279; diverted by Philistines from pursuit of David,
vi. 281-282; his life spared by
David, vi. 282, 284-285;
reconciled with David, vi.
290-291; vi. 294, 309; his life
spared again by David, vi. 310-
314, 316, 319; vi. 320; consults witch of Endor, vi.
327-337; fed by witch of
Endor, vi. 339-340; eulogized
by Josephus, vi. 343-350; vi.
352; his death in battle, vi.
368, 371-373; his burial, vi.
374, 376, 378; his death
reported to David, vii. 1-6;
his burial, vii. 8; vii. 9, 18;
his son Ish-bosheth engaged in
civil war with David, vii. 20;
vii. 22-25, 32, 46, 48, 50, 53,
55-56, 79, 85, 87, 89, 111-112;
his property given by David to
Memphibosheth, vii. 114-115;
vii. 117, 151, 199, 205-207, 263,
267; his family punished for
his slaying of Gibeonites, vii.
294, 296; x. 143; xi. 112

Saul (2), member of Jewish royal
family, is sent to ask Agrippa II
to crush Jewish revolt against
Romans, *B.* ii. 418, 556, 558;
brother of Costobar, *A.* xx. 214

Saul (3), brother of Simon the
renegade, *B.* ii. 469

"Saul's hill" (Gabath Saul),
village near Jerusalem, *B.* v. 51

Scaurus, Roman general, *B.* i.
127-129, 132; becomes gover-

352

nor of Syria, i. 157; invades
Arabia, i. 159; relieved by
Gabinius, i. 160; *A*. xiv. 29,
33, 37; becomes ruler of
Syria, xiv. 79; reconciled with
Aretas by Antipater, xiv. 80-81
Scipio (1) Africanus, Roman
general victorious over Hannibal, *B*. ii. 380
Scipio (2), Q. Caecilius Metellus,
father-in-law of Pompey and
governor of Syria, *B*. i. 185,
195; executes Alexander the
son of Aristobulus, *A*. xiv. 125;
xiv. 140, 142, 185
Scopas, general of Pompey, *A*.
xii. 131-133, 136
Scopus, mountain near Jerusalem,
B. ii. 528, 542; v. 67, 106,
108; called " Lookout," *A*. xi.
329
scribes, of the Jews not to be
taxed by Persian satraps, according to King Xerxes' letter,
A. xi. 128
Scripture(s), Holy (" sacred
books," Bible), Josephus' mas-
tery of, *A*. xx. 261, 265; copy
of them presented by Titus to
Josephus, *V*. 418; the *Antiquities* based on them, *Ap*. i. 1;
care bestowed on them, i. 29 ff.;
consist of twenty-two books, i.
37-41; Jewish veneration for
them, i. 42-43; the *Antiquities*
based on them, i. 54; their
chronology of destruction and
reconstruction of the temple,
in agreement with Berosus, i.
154; agree with books of
Chaldaeans and Tyrians on
chronology of the temple, i.
160; unknown to Greek
writers, i. 217-218; interpreta-
tion of them by Jewish deputies
requisitioned by Ptolemy Philadelphus, ii. 45-47 (*cf.* also
Law)
Scythians, tribe inhabiting region
of Black Sea, *B*. vii. 89-90,
244; formerly Magogians, *A*. i.
123; known to Greeks through
navigators of the Black Sea,
Ap. i. 64; their intolerance of
foreign customs, ii. 269

Scythopolis (Beth-shean, Bethesana, Bethsan, Bethsane, Beth-
shan; Bibl. Beth-shan), (Scythopolitans) city in Judaea, *B*.
i. 65-66, 134; freed by Pompey, i. 156; rebuilt by
Gabinius, i. 166; ii. 458;
(Scythopolitans) their perfidy
to Jewish allies, ii. 466-468;
ii. 470-472, 477; iii. 37, 412,
446; iv. 54, 87, 453; vii. 364;
formerly Bethesana, *A*. v. 83-
84; formerly Bethsan, vi.
374, 376; city from which
Joseph the Tobiad collected
taxes, xii. 183; Greek name
for Bethsane, xii. 348; Greek
name for Bethsan, xiii. 188;
xiii. 277, 280, 355, 396; xiv.
49, 75, 88; its natives compel
their Jewish residents to fight
against Jewish invaders, after
which they massacre them, *V*.
26; scene of raids by Justus of
Tiberias and his followers, 42;
place to be protected by Neopolitanus, 121; on side of
Agrippa, 349
Seba (1). See Sabas
Seba (2), son of David, *A*. vii. 70
Sebaios. See Saraios
Sebaste (1), Samarian city,
founded by King Herod, besieged by Aristobulus and
Antigonus, the sons of John
Hyrcanus, *B*. i. 64-65; i. 118;
built by Herod, i. 403; i. 551;
ii. 97, 288, 292, 460; name for
Samaria, *A*. xiii. 275, xv. 246;
name given Samaria by Herod,
xv. 293; adorned by Herod,
xv. 296; built by Herod, xv.
342; Herod entertains Agrippa
there, xvi. 13; Aristobulus and
Alexander are killed there, xvi.
394; made subject to Archelaus by Augustus, xvii. 320;
rejoices at death of Agrippa I,
xix. 356, 361; rebuked by
Fadus, xix. 365; xx. 176
Sebaste (2), island off Cilicia in
Asia Minor, formerly Elaeusa,
A. xvi. 131
Sebastenians, troops drafted in
region of Sebaste (Samaria),

353

GENERAL INDEX

354

GENERAL INDEX

Sellius. See Gellius (1) and (2)

Semachonitis. See Semechonitis

Semechonitis (Semachonitis), Lake, north of Sea of Galilee, *B.* iii. 515; iv. 2-3; (Semachonitis) *A.* v. 199

Semegaros, Babylonian assigned to sack of Jerusalem, *A.* x. 135

Semelios (Bibl. Shimshai), Samaritan scribe, writes letter to Cambyses, *A.* xi. 22, 29

Semiramis, Assyrian who, according to Greek historians, founded Babylon and erected its marvellous buildings, *Ap.* i. 142

Sempronius (1), Gaius, Roman, of Falernian tribe, father of Gaius Sempronius, *A.* xiii. 260

Sempronius (2), Gaius, Roman praetor, son of Gaius Sempronius, *A.* xiii. 260

Sempronius (3) Atratinus, L. See Atratinus, L. Sempronius

Senaar (Bibl. Shinar), plain where sons of Noah settled after flood, *A.* i. 110; place where sacred vessels of Zeus were brought, i. 119

Senacheirimos (var. Senacheiros, Sennacheribos; Bibl. Sennacherib), king of Assyria, (*B.* v. 387); exacts tribute from King Hezekiah, *A.* x. 1-2, 6; his death foretold by Isaiah, x. 14; withdraws from Egypt, x. 18, 20-21; his end, x. 23

Senacheiros. See Senacheirimos

Senate, Roman, *B.* i. 174, 284, 298, 346; ii. 205-214; iv. 506, 600; *A.* xii. 416-417; xiii. 164-165; renews treaty with Hyrcanus, xiii. 259-260; restores cities to Jews, xiii. 261-262; renews treaty with Jews, xiii. 265-266; releases Aristobulus' children from captivity, xiv. 97; xiv. 123; honours Antipater and Hyrcanus, xiv. 144-148; passes decrees favourable to Jews, xiv. 189; confers high priesthood on Hyrcanus, xiv. 199; xiv. 207-208, 217-222, 233; makes treaty with Jews guaranteeing their rights against Antiochus

the son of Antiochus, xiv. 249, 251-252; its decrees favourable to Jews, xiv. 252-253, 260, 264; xiv. 315; Herod presented to it, xiv. 384-385, 388; encourages Herod against Antigonus, xiv. 407; decrees that Herod be king, xiv. 469; xiv. 489; confers privileges on Jews, xiv. 207, 209-210, 212, 217, 219, 221, 233; grants rights to Ionian Jews, xvi. 48; honours Antipater, xvi. 53; xix. 2; engages in perfunctory investigation of murderers of Gaius Caligula, xix. 158; xix. 161; scene of Sentius Saturninus' tirade against tyrants, xix. 166; xix. 185; urges Claudius to submit to it, xix. 227-230; xix. 235; Claudius about to yield to it, xix. 238; urged by Agrippa I to send a deputation to Claudius to persuade him to lay down his office, xix. 239-244; its confusion recounted to Claudius by Agrippa, xix. 245; Claudius promises it to behave with propriety, xix. 246; meets in Temple of Jupiter Victor but is helpless in the face of the soldiers, xix. 248-263; xix. 264; Claudius is urged by Agrippa to spare its members, xix. 265-266; its decrees attest services of Jews to Julius Caesar against Egyptians, *Ap.* ii. 61; its testimonials to Jews, ii. 62

Senate-house, scene of Julius Caesar's assassination, *A.* xiv. 270

Sennabris (Ginnabris), village near Taricheaee, *B.* iii. 448; (Ginnabris) iv. 455

Sennacherib. See Senacheirimos

Sennacheribos. See Senacheirimos

Sentius (1), Gaius, father of Gaius Sentius (2), *A.* xiv. 229

Sentius (2), Gaius, Roman present during promulgation of decree of Lentulus exempting Jews of Ephesus from military service, *A.* xiv. 229 (identified

355

GENERAL INDEX

Publius Servilius Strabo, *A.*
xiv. 239

Servilius (7) Strabo, Publius, son
of Servilius (6), present at
promulgation of decree of
Lentulus exempting Jewish
citizens of Ephesus from
military service, *A.* xiv. 239

Servius (var. Papinius) Sulpicius
Quintus, Roman of Lemonian
tribe, present at promulgation
of decree of Roman Senate
confirming Julius Caesar's decisions regarding the Jews, *A.*
xiv. 220

Sesostris, mythical king of Egypt,
A. viii. 253 ; said to have
blinded Apion, *Ap.* ii. 132.

Sestius, Publius. See Serrius,
Publius

Seth (1), son of Adam, *A.* i. 68-
69 ; in genealogy of Noah, i.
79, 83

Seth (2), father of Ananus the
high priest, *A.* xviii. 26

Sethos(is) (1), Egyptian king, also
called Ramesses (II), son of
Amenophis III, suppresses revolt against him by his brother
Harmais, *Ap.* i. 98-102 ; known
as Aegyptus, expels his brother
Hermaeus (Harmais), i. 231 ;
i. 245

Sethos (2) (Josephus' error for
Amenophis), son of Amenophis,
flees upon attack of Jerusalemites, *Ap.* i. 274

Sethroïte, Egyptian nome containing city of Auaris, *Ap.* i.
78

Seventy, council of, Galilaeans,
V. 79

sexes, interchange of costumes of,
forbidden by Jewish law, *A.* iv.
301

Sextus Caesar, kinsman of Julius
Caesar, governor of Syria, *B.* i.
205 ; interferes in Herod's
trial, i. 211 ; i. 212 ; appoints
Herod governor of Coele-Syria
and Samaria, i. 213 ; his death,
i. 216 ; *A.* xiv. 160, 170, 178,
180, 268-270

Sextus Calvarius. See Calvarius,
Sextus

sexual relations, solely for pro
creation, according to Jewish
law, *Ap.* ii. 199 ; Jewish laws
regarding them, ii. 234

Shadrach. See Ananias (1)

Shallum (1). See Sallumos (1)

Shallum (2). See Sellemos

Shalmaneser. See Salmanasses

Shamgar. See Sanagar

Shammah (1). See Sabaias

Shammah (2). See Samal

Shaphan. See Sapha

Shaphat. See Saphates (1)

Sharezer. See Seleukaros

Shaul. See Saar(as)

Shavsha. See Se sa

Shealtiel. See Salathielos

Sheba (1). See Sabaeus

Sheba (2). See Sabaios

Sheba (3). See Sabakin(es)

Sheba (4). See Sabas

Sheba (5). See Saphas

Shebna. See Subanaios

Shechaniah. See Achonios

Shechem (1) (Sikim, Sikima,
Sichem) (Shechemites, Sikimites), city in Palestine, (Sichem) captured by John
Hyrcanus, *B.* i. 63, 92 ;
(Sikimites) *A.* i. 337 ; (Sikimites) slain by Jacob's sons, i.
340 ; (Sikim) Cananaite city,
i. 337, 342 ; (Sikima) place
where Joseph's brothers tend
their sheep, ii. 18 ; (Sikima) iv.
305 ; (Sikima) v. 69 ; (Sikima)
declared city of refuge, v. 91 ;
(Sikima) place where Joshua
lives in his old age, v. 115 ; v.
233, 235 ; (Shechemites) expel
Abimelech from city, v. 240 ;
(Shechemites) v. 243 ; (Shechemites) their city and rock destroyed by Abimelech, v. 248,
250-251 ; (Shechemites) v.
253 ; (Sikimites) vi. 140 (Josephus' error for Kenites) ;
(Sikima) viii. 212 ; (Sikima)
city where Jeroboam made his
dwelling, viii. 225 ; xi. 340,
342, 345 ; (Shechemites) quarrel with Jews in Egypt, xii. 10 ;
xii. 258, 262 ; captured by
Hyrcanus, xiii. 255 ; xiii. 377

Shechem (2). See Sychem

357

GENERAL INDEX

GENERAL INDEX

his wife from captivity, iv.
503-544; iv. 556, 558, 564; in
Jerusalem, iv. 573-584; v. 11-
12, 21, 23, 104, 169, 248, 252,
266-267, 278, 304, 309, 322,
358, 423, 440, 455, 473;
murders Matthias, his former
patron, and others, discovers
plot to surrender Jerusalem,
v. 527-540; vi. 72, 92, 114,
148,. 191, 227-229, 326, 360,
377, 380, 433; vii. 25; is
captured, vii. 26-36; vii. 118;
his death, vii. 154; vii. 265
Simon (25), son of Arinus, one of
Zealot chiefs, B. v. 250; vi.
92, 148
Simon (26), son of Hosaias, brave
Jewish hero, in party of Simon
the son of Gioras, B. vi. 148
Simon (27), son of Esron, joins
party of Eleazar the son of
Simon, B. v. 6
Simon (28). See Atomus
Simon (29) (Bibl. Maon or, perhaps, Jeshimon), name of a
wilderness in Judah, A. vi. 280
Simonias, village on frontier of
Galilee, V. 115
Simonides, surnamed Agrippa,
younger son of Josephus by his
third wife` (who came from
Crete), V. 427
Simueis. See Samuis
Sin (perhaps Wilderness of Zin
is meant), mountain where
Miriam is buried, A. iv. 78
Sinai, mountain where Moses saw
burning bush, A. ii. 264; ii.
283-284, 291, 323, 349; iii. 1;
Hebrews reach it, iii. 62;
ascended by Moses, iii. 75-76;
iii. 95, 100, 212, 222, 286;
Hebrews depart from there,
iii. 295; iv. 43; viii. 104;
Elijah makes his abode there
in a cave, viii. 349; mountain
between Egypt and Arabia
ascended by Moses, Ap. ii. 25
Sinakes, cognomen of Mithridates, governor of Parthians.
See Mithridates (2)
singers of hymns. See hymns,
singers of
Sinite. See Seinaeus

Sinope, city in Pontus in Asia
Minor, where Herod meets
Agrippa, A. xvi. 21
Sisares (Bibl. Sisera), Canaanite
general, A. v. 199, 204; flees
from battle, v. 207
Sisenna (1), Roman general, B.
i. 171; A. xiv. 92
Sisenna (2), father of Jonathan,
who is sent by John of Gischala
to Jerusalem, V. 190
Sisera. See Sisares
Sisines (Bibl. Tatnai), governor
of Syria and Phoenicia, A. xi.
12, 89; decides to continue
building of the temple, xi. 95;
his letter read by Darius, xi.
98; written to by Darius, xi.
104; learns king's wishes,
xi. 105
Sisyphus, mythological figure allegedly punished in Hades, B.
ii. 156
Sitnah. See Stena
slavery (slaves), Jewish law on,
A. iv. 273; penalty prescribed
by Jewish law for abuses of
them, Ap. ii. 215
Sleep, book by Clearchus, is
quoted, Ap. i. 176-182
So. See Soas
Soaemus (1), powerful Arab in
Petra, B. i. 574; A. xvii. 54
Soaemus (2), king of Emesa, B.
ii. 481, 483, 500; iii. 68;
vii. 226
Soar(os) (Bibl. Zohar), son of
Simeon, A. ii. 178
Soas (Bibl. So), king of Egypt,
A. ix. 277
Soba (Bibl. Zobah), kingdom
north-east of Palestine, A. vi.
129
Sobacches. See Sabreches
Socho. See Sochus
Sochoh. See Sochus
Sochus (Socho; Bibl. Sochoh,
Soco), town in south-western
Palestine, A. vi. 170; (Socho)
viii. 246
Soco. See Sochus
Socrates, Greek philosopher, men-
tioned as genius by Apion, Ap.
ii. 135; charges against him
by Athenians. ii. 263-264

361

GENERAL INDEX

Sodom (Sodomites), city near Dead Sea, *B.* iv. 453, 483-485 ; v. 566 ; Lot settles near there, *A.* i. 170 ; i. 171 ; their war with Assyrians, i. 172-175 ; freed by Abraham from captivity, i. 176-179 ; i. 182 ; incur God's anger, i. 194-196 ; burned, i. 198-203 ; i. 206 ; on border of territory of Judah, v. 81

Soemus (1), father of Ptolemy the ruler of Syria, *A.* xiv. 129

Soemus (2), tetrarch in Lebanon, ancestor of Varus (probably identical with Soemus [1]), *V.* 52

Soemus (3) the Ituraean, placed in charge of Herod's wife Mariamme and her mother Alexandra by Herod, *A.* xv. 185 ; his favour courted by Mariamme, xv. 204-207, 216 ; accused of intimacy with Mariamme, xv. 227-229

Soganae, village in Lower Galilee, fortified by Josephus, *V.* 188

Soganaea (Sogane), village in Gaulanitis, *B.* ii. 574 ; iv. 2, 4 ; (Sogane) its Jews capture Gischala and are then defeated by John of Gischala, *V.* 44-45 ; (Sogane) fortified by Josephus, 187 ; (Sogane) Josephus sends counter-embassy to Jerusalem from there, 265 ff.

Sogane. See Soganaea

Sohaemus, brother of Azizus, succeeds him as overlord of Emesa, *A.* xx. 158

Solomon, son of David, Hebrew king, *B.* v. 137, 143, 185 ; vi. 269 ; *A.* v. 362 ; vii. 70 ; kingdom promised to him by God in vision to Nathan, vii. 93 ; vii. 106 ; his birth, vii. 158 ; vii. 190, 244 ; instructed concerning the building of the temple, vii. 337-342 ; plotted against by Adonijah, vii. 347-348, 350, 352 ; is promised kingdom by David, vii. 353 ; is anointed king, vii. 355 ; vii. 356-357 ; forgives Adonijah, vii. 360-362 ; army ordered by

David to attend him, vii. 368 ; commended by David to the people, vii. 372-373 ; is given plans of the temple, vii. 375-376 ; prayed for by David, vii. 381 ; anointed again, vii. 382 ; receives David's dying charge, vii. 383 ; buries David, vii. 392 ; his accession as king, viii. 2 ; Adonijah seeks from him permission to marry Abishag, viii. 4, 6, 8 ; orders Joab killed, viii. 13, 15 ; confines Shimei in Jerusalem, viii. 18 ; marries daughter of Pharaoh, viii. 21 ; asks God for wisdom, viii. 23-25 ; judges dispute between two women, viii. 26-34 ; father of Basmath, viii. 36 ; his chariots, viii. 41 ; his great wisdom and proverbs, viii. 42-49 ; receives greetings from king of Tyre, viii. 50 ; requests trees from Tyre, viii. 54 ; sends gifts to king of Tyre, viii. 57-58 ; builds the temple, viii. 61-62, 76, 95 ; prays at dedication of the temple, viii. 107 ; is blessed by people, viii. 124 ; description of his palace, viii. 133-140 ; his exchange of gifts with Hiram, viii. 141-143 ; poses riddles to and receives them from Hiram, viii. 143, 146, 148-149 ; marries Pharaoh's daughter, viii. 152 ; viii. 155, 159 ; reduces Canaanites to slavery, viii. 160 ; builds fleet, viii. 164 ; visited by Queen of Egypt and Ethiopa (Sheba), viii. 165, 168, 175 ; receives costly gifts from kings everywhere, viii. 182 ; his foreign wives, viii. 193 ; punished by God, viii. 198 ; rebelled against by Hadad, viii. 199 ; suffers for unlawful acts, viii. 203 ; suffers rebellion of Hadad, viii. 204 ; rebelled against by Jeroboam, viii. 205 ; punished by God by having his kingdom split, viii. 207-208 ; rebelled against by Jeroboam, viii. 209-210 ; his death, viii. 211-212 ; viii. 222, 246, 259, 278, 287 ;

GENERAL INDEX

131, 133, 157, 160, 176, 179-180, 183, 188, 194, 201, 204-205, 218, 224-225, 236, 239, 248, 259, 288, 324, 327, 346, 360, 394, 398-399, 425, 433, 538, 543, 554, 577, 617; ii. 16, 39-40, 91, 97, 186, 239; they oppose Jews at Caesarea, ii. 266-267; ii. 268, 280, 458, 462-463; general rising there against the Jews, ii. 477-478; ii. 506, 591, 625; iii. 7-8, 29, 35, 57, 66; slingers from there repel Jewish assaults, iii. 211; iii. 416; iv. 32, 38, 501, 609, 620, 662; v. 1, 42, 384, 520, 550-551, 556; vi. 54, 317; vii. 18, 43, 46, 59, 96, 220, 367, 423; occupied by Ham and his sons, *A.* i. 130; (Syrians) Greek name for Aramaeans, i. 144; ravaged by Assyrians, i. 174; ii. 32; vi. 244, 254; fight along with Philistines against David, vii. 74; their king defeated by David, vii. 100-101, 104; vii. 124-125; join Ammanites against David, vii. 127; ruled by Solomon, viii. 39; Solomon founds a city there, viii. 154; its king receives a chariot from Solomon, viii. 189; viii. 203-204, 260, 262; Hazael appointed king of Damascus there, viii. 352; its king, Ben-hadad, besieges Ahab, viii. 363-364, 368, 374; defeated by Ahab, viii. 377-378; defeated again by Ahab, viii. 382-385, 388; Ahab and Jehoshaphat ally against it, viii. 398-401, 403; their victory over Ahab prophesied, viii. 404; Ahab goes out against them, viii. 409; oppose Ahab, viii. 411; defeat Ahab, viii. 413, 416; alliance of Ahab and Jehoshaphat against Ben-hadad its king, ix. 1; their plot against Jehoram foiled, ix. 51; trapped by Elisha, ix. 57-59; attack Jehoram, ix. 61; flee before four lepers, ix. 76, 79, 82; ix. 92; ruled by Hazael, ix. 93;

attacked by Jehoram of Israel, ix. 105-106; wars on Israelites, ix. 159; exact tribute from Joash, ix. 170-171; defeats Jehoahaz, king of Israel, ix. 174; their defeat by Joash prophesied by Elisha, ix. 179, 181; defeated by Jeroboam, ix. 206-207; with Israel attacks Judah, ix. 244-245; ix. 246; defeated by Tiglath-Pileser, king of Assyria, ix. 252-254; their gods worshipped by Ahaz, ix. 255; invaded by Assyrians, ix. 283; x. 82; occupied by Nebuchadnezzar, x. 84, 86; x. 110, 149-150, 222; xi. 12; sends letter to Cambyses, xi. 21-22; xi. 60, 88; Sheshbazzar its eparch and governor, xi. 101; xi. 122; its treasurers written to by Xerxes, xi. 127; xi. 129; Addaios its eparch, xi. 167; its nations hear of building of walls of Jerusalem, xi. 180; xi. 317, 332; taken over by Ptolemy, son of Lagus, after Alexander the Great, xii. 3; script of Jews similar to their (Aramaic) writing, xii. 15; xii. 28; governed by Mucianus, xii. 120; xii. 169; angered at Ptolemy Epiphanes' favourable reception of Joseph the Tobiad, xii. 174; Joseph the Tobiad collects taxes there, xii. 180, 182; celebrates birth of son to Ptolemy Epiphanes, xii. 196; Joseph the Tobiad collects money there, xii. 201; xii. 212; its taxes controlled by Joseph the Tobiad, xii. 224; xii. 234; routed by Judas the Maccabee, xii. 292; xii. 299, 385, 389, 408; invaded by Alexander Balas, xiii. 35; xiii. 58; ruled by Alexander Balas, xiii. 80; xiii. 103, 116, 144, 148, 154, •186, 213 (*bis*); ruled by Demetrius, xiii. 253; invaded by Hyrcanus, xiii. 254; hostile to Demetrius, xiii. 267; ruled by Antiochus Grypus, xiii. 270; xiii. 272, 275, 329,

367

GENERAL INDEX

conquered by Ptolemy Euergetes, ii. 48

Syria, Lower, *A*. xii. 119

Syria, Upper, Solomon advances into it, *A*. viii. 153 ; xiii. 223

Syros (1), Greek island in the Aegean Sea. birthplace of Pherecydes, *Ap*. i. 14

Syros (2) (Bibl. Aram Beth-Rehob, Aram Naharaim ; Josephus has mistaken an ethnic for a personal name), king of Mesopotamia, *A*. vii. 121 ; wages war with David, vii. 124

Syrtes, African tribe, *B*. ii. 381

TAAU (Bibl. Tahash), son of Nahor, *A*. i. 153

Tabai (Bibl. Tebah), son of Nahor, *A*. i. 153

tabernacle, Jewish, building of, *A*. iii. 102-114 ; its exterior, iii. 115-121 ; its interior, iii. 122-124 ; its curtains, iii. 123-133 ; its ark, iii. 134-138 ; table there, iii. 139-143 ; its candelabrum, iii. 144-146 ; its altars, iii. 147-150 ; its symbolism, iii. 179-183 ; erected by Moses, has no images, *Ap*. ii. 12

Tabernacles, Jewish holiday, *B*. i. 73 ; ii. 515 ; vi. 300 ; regulations in Torah concerning it, *A*. iii. 244-247 ; iv. 209 ; viii. 100 ; celebrated in the new temple, viii. 123 ; viii. 225 ; (viii. 230 ;) celebrated by Zerubbabel, xi. 77 ; celebrated by Jews returning from Babylonia to Jerusalem, xi. 154 ; xiii. 46, 241, 372 ; xv. 50

Tabor (Itabyrion), Mount, town and mountain in Palestine, *B*. i. 177 ; (Mt. Itabyrion) ii. 573 ; iv. 1 ; captured by Vespasian, iv. 54-61 ; (Mt. Itabyrion) on border of Issachar's territory, *A*. v. 84 ; (Mt. Itabyrion) v. 203 ; (Mt. Itabyrion) its governor under Solomon, viii. 37 ; xiii. 396 ; xiv. 102 ; village in Lower Galilee, fortified by Josephus, *V*. 188

Tachmonite. See Achemaios

Tadmor. See Thadamora

Taganas (perhaps Bibl. Tatnai), eparch of the Samaritans, written to by King Darius, *A*. xi. 118

Tahash. See Taau

Tahpenes. See Thaphine

Talmai. See Tholomaios

Tamar (1). See Thamara (1)

Tamar (2). See Thamara (2)

Tanais, river (the modern Don), *B*. vii. 244 ; furthest point in Asia where sons of Japheth settled, *A*. i. 122

Tanis (Bibl. Zoan), city in Egypt, *B*. iv. 660 ; *A*. i. 170

Tantalus, mythological figure, said to undergo punishment in Hades, *B*. ii. 156

Taos (var. Daos), Apollonius. See Apollonius (2) Taos

Tappuah. See Tochoa

Tarentum, city in Italy, *B*. i. 609 ; *A*. xii. 18 ; xvii. 85

Tarichaeae (Tarichaeans), city in Lower Galilee, *B*. i. 180 ; ii. 252, 573, 596-597, 599, 602, 606, 608-609, 634-635, 641 ; iii. 445, 457 ; taken by Romans, iii. 462-504 ; iii. 532 ; iv. 1-2 ; *A*. xiv. 120 ; given to Agrippa II by Nero, xx. 159 ; refuge reached by Josephus after escape from Tiberias, *V*. 96-97 ; place to which highwaymen of Dabaritta bring goods plundered from wife of Ptolemy, Agrippa II's overseer, 127 ; its Jewish inhabitants urge Josephus' bodyguards to leave him, 132 ff. ; its people express gratitude to Josephus, 143 ; house of Agrippa II's noble vassals there assaulted by some Tarichaeans, 151 ; fortified by Josephus, 156 ; Josephus sees Roman cavalry on road to it, 157 ; Josephus' soldiers there dismissed to go to their homes for Sabbath, 159 ; its people not permitted by Josephus to sack Tiberias, 162 ; friends of Josephus posted at gates there, 163 ; ten leaders of Tiberias kept under arrest there by Josephus, 168-

368

GENERAL INDEX

by Antiochus because of his
impecuniosity, ii. 84; rules
concerning admission to its
courts, ii. 102-104; other rules
concerning it, ii. 105-109;
dimensions of its gates, ii. 119;
purpose and description of
sacrifices there, ii. 193-198

temples (1) of Egyptians, razed
by Persian invaders, *Ap.* ii. 129

temples (2) of Greeks, old and
new, *Ap.* ii. 254

ten words (commandments). See
Decalogue

Tephthaeus. See Gephthaeus

Terah. See Therrus

Terebinths of Mamre. See Ogyges

Terentius Rufus, commander of
Roman forces which capture
Simon ben Giora, *B.* vii. 31

Teresh. See Theodestes

Teretine tribe, Roman tribe, *A.*
xiv. 220, 229, 238

terpole ("delight"), name of
golden vine given as gift by
Aristobulus to Pompey, *A.* xiv.
35

Tertius (1), Aulus Furius. See
Furius (2)

Tertius (2), Aulus Furius. See
Furius (3)

Tethmosis (Thoummosis), son of
Misphragmouthosis, (Thoummosis) besieges Hycsos, concludes treaty with them, *Ap.* i.
88; expels Hycsos from Egypt,
i. 94, 231, 241; king of Egypt
during Jewish exodus, ii. 16

Teutius (1), Gaius, father of Gaius
Teutius (2), of Aemilian tribe,
A. xiv. 238

Teutius (2), Gaius, of Aemilian
tribe, Roman military tribune
(identified by Niese's index
with Gaius Sentius), *A.* xiv.
238

Thaceas. See Cathlas

Thadal (Bibl. Tidal), Assyrian
commander, *A.* i. 173

Thadamora (Bibl. Tadmor), city
in Upper Syria built by Solomon, called Palmyra by the
Greeks, *A.* viii. 154

Thaenos (var. Thaunos, Thannos;
Bibl. Rechab), son of Rimmon

and slayer of Ish-bosheth, *A.*
vii. 46

Thaglathphallasar(es) (Bibl. Tiglath-Pileser), king of Assyria,
A. ix. 235; (Thaglathphalla-
sares) bribed by Ahaz to attack
Israel, ix. 252

Thaiman (Bibl. Tema), son of
Ishmael, *A.* i. 220

Thainos (Bibl. Toi), king of Hamath, makes alliance with
David, *A.* vii. 108

Thales, among first Greek astro-
nomers and theologians, *Ap.* i.
14

Thamanaios (Bibl. Tibni), candidate of one party in Israel for
kingship, is killed to allow
Omri to rule, *A.* viii. 311

Thamara (1) (Bibl. Tamar),
daughter of David, *A.* vii. 70,
162, 178

Thamara (2) (Thamare; Bibl.
Tamar), daughter of Absalom,
A. vii. 243; (Thamare) mother
of Maachah, viii. 249

Thamare. See Thamara (2)

Thamna (1) (Bibl. Timnath-
serah), city in Judaea, *B.* ii.
567; iii. 55; iv. 444; Joshua
is buried there, *A.* v. 119; xiv.
275 (perhaps to be identified
with Thamna [2])

Thamna (2) (Bibl. Timnah)
(Thamnites), Philistine town,
A. v. 286; (Thamnites) v.
289; v. 296 (perhaps to be
identified with Thamna [1])

Thamnae (Bibl. Timna), concubine of Eliphaz, *A.* ii. 5

Thamnatha (prob. Bibl. Timnath-
serah), city in Judaea, fortified
by Bacchides, *A.* xiii. 15

Thannos. See Thaenos

Thaphine (Bibl. Tahpenes), sister
of wife of Pharaoh, wife of
Hadad, *A.* viii. 201

Thapsa (Bibl. Tiphsah), city in
Palestine, *A.* ix. 229, 231

Tharabatha. See Arabatha (2)

Tharata (Bibl. Tartan), Assyrian
commanding officer, *A.* x. 4

Tharbis, daughter of Ethiopian
king, marries Moses, *A.* ii.
252

GENERAL INDEX

Thargelion, Delian month, *A.* xiv. 231

Tharsale. See Tharse

Tharse (var. Tharsale ; Bibl. Tirzah), city in kingdom of Israel, *A.* viii. 299 ; Baasha buried there, viii. 307 ; captured by Omri, viii. 310 ; viii. 312 ; ix. 229

Tharsians, name given to his subjects by Tharsos, son of Javan, is ancient name of Cilicia, according to Josephus, *A.* i. 127

Tharsikes (Bibl. Tirhakah), king of Ethiopia, comes to aid Egyptians, *A.* x. 17

Tharsos (Bibl. Tarshish), son of Javan, *A.* i. 127

Thathis. See Thatis

Thatis (var. Thathis, Matthis), nickname of Simon the son of Mattathias, *A.* xii. 266

Thaumastus, slave of Gaius Caligula, freed by him, *A.* xviii. 192, 194

Thaunos. See Thaenos

Thea Musa. See Thesmusa

theatres, tortures and deaths of Jewish prisoners there, *Ap.* i. 43

Thebae. See Thebes (2)

Thebaid. See Thebes (1)

Thebes (1) (Thebaid), city in Egypt, *B.* vii. 416 ; (Thebaid) *A.* xi. 345 ; (Thebaid) its kings revolt against Hycsos, *Ap.* i. 85

Thebes (2) (Thebae ; Bibl. Thebez), town north-east of Shechem, besieged by Abimelech, *A.* v. 251 ; (Thebae) vii. 142

Thebes (3), city in Greece, reviled by author of *Tripoliticus*, *Ap.* i. 221 ; homosexuality rampant there, ii. 273

Thebez. See Thebes (2)

Thebuthi, father of the priest Jesus (deliverer of sacred treasures of the temple to Titus), *B.* vi. 387

theft, Jewish law on, *A.* iv. 271-272 ; *Ap.* ii. 208 ; penalty for it prescribed by Jewish law, ii. 216

Theires (Bibl. Tiras), son of Japheth, *A.* i. 125

Theirians, nation founded by Theires, called Thracians by Greeks, *A.* i. 125

Thekel, one of the words (meaning " weight ") written on Belshazzar's wall, *A.* x. 244

Thekoa. See Thekoue

Thekoe. See Thekoue

Thekoue (Thekoa, Th koe ; Bibl. Tekoa, Tekoah), city near Bethlehem in Palestine, *B.* iv. 518 ; (Thekoe) fortified by Rehoboam, *A.* viii. 246 ; (Thekoa) ix. 12 ; (Tekoa) village investigated by Cerealius and Josephus as a suitable place for camp for Titus, *V.* 420

Thella, village near Jordan River, *B.* iii. 40

Theman(os) (Bibl. Teman), son of Eliphaz, *A.* ii. 5

Themasios. See Rabezakos

Theobel (Bibl. Tubal), son of Japheth, *A.* i. 124

Theobelians, people founded by Theobel, later called Iberians, *A.* i. 124

theocracy, Jewish constitution a, *Ap.* ii. 165-167

Theocritos, Greek equivalent of Dan. *A.* i. 305

Theodectes, Greek tragic poet, afflicted with cataracts when about to mention Biblical matters in one of his dramas, *A.* xii. 113

Theodestes (var. Theodosites ; Bibl. Teresh), plots against Ahasuerus, *A.* xi. 207 ; mentioned in records, xi. 249

Theodorus (1), son of Zeno(n), owner of precious possessions in Amathus beyond the Jordan, which were captured by Alexander Jannaeus, *B.* i. 86-87, 89, 104 ; *A.* xiii. 356, 394

Theodorus (2), father of Alexander the envoy of the high priest Hyrcanus to Rome, *A.* xiv. 222, 226, 307

Theodorus (3), Jewish legate of Hyrcanus, *A.* xiv. 252, 254

Theodorus (4). See Diodorus (2)

GENERAL INDEX

tions to Gaius, xviii. 292, 294;
his relationship to Gaius, xix.
209

Tiberius (3) Claudius Caesar.
See Claudius

Tiberius (4) Gemellus, son of
Drusus the Younger, grandson
of Tiberius Caesar, *A.* (xviii.
166 :) xviii. 187-188, 191 ; surnamed Gemellus, xviii. 206;
xviii. 213 ; not selected to succeed Emperor Tiberius, xviii.
215, 219-221; put to death by
Gaius, xviii. 223

Tibni. See Thamanaios

Tidal. See Thadal

Tigellinus, Sophonius, appointed
by Nero praetorian prefect, *B.*
iv. 492

Tiglath-Pileser. See Thaglath-
phallasar(es)

Tigranes (1), son of Glaphyra and
of Alexander the son of Herod
the Great, *B.* i. 552; *A.* xviii.
139-140

Tigranes (2), king of Armenia, *B.*
i. 116, 127, 363; *A.* xiii. 419-
421; xiv. 29; father of Artabazes, xv. 104

Tigranes (3), son of Alexander (9)
the son of Alexander, *A.* xviii.
140

Tigranes (4) III, restored to Armenian throne, *A.* xv. 105

Tigris (Bibl. Hiddekel), river in
Mesopotamia, called Diglath,
i.e. " narrowness," " rapidity "
(in Aramaic), *A.* i. 39

Timaeus, Greek historian, exposes
mendacity of Ephorus, his own
mendacity exposed by later
writers, *Ap.* i. 16; as historian
of Sicily disagrees with Antiochus. Philistus, and Callias, i.
17; abuses Athens, Sparta, and
Thebes, i. 221

Timagenes, Greek historian, *A.*
xiii. 319, 344; cited on Antiochus' motive in plundering the
temple in Jerusalem, *Ap.* ii.
84

Timber Market, part of Jerusalem,
B. ii. 530

Time, personified, witness of
excellence of Moses' laws, *Ap.*

ii. 279-280; witness of Moses'
merits, ii. 290

Timidius, accuses Pompedius to
Gaius Caligula, *A.* xix. 33-34

Timius of Cyprus, married to
Alexandra the daughter of
Phasael and Salampsio, *A.*
xviii. 131

Timna. See Thamnae

Timnah. See Thamna (2)

Timnath-serah (1). See Thamna
(1)

Timnath-serah (2). See Thamnatha

Timotheus, leader of Ammanites,
A. xii. 329-330; besieges Jews
in fortress of Dathema, xii.
337, 339; defeated by Judas
the Maccabee, xii. 341, 343

Tiphsah. See Thapsa

Tiras. See Theires

Tirathana, Samaritan village, *A.*
xviii. 86, 88

Tirhakah. See Tharsikes

Tiridates, king of Armenia,
brother of Vologeses, *B.* vii.
249; given Armenia, *A.* xx.
74

Tiro, old soldier in Herod's army,
expresses indignation at Herod's
condemnation of his sons
Alexander and Aristobulus, *B.*
i. 544, 546; is accused by
Trypho the barber, i. 547; is
tortured, i. 548; is beaten to
death at instigation of Herod,
i. 550; rebukes Herod for his
treatment of his sons, *A.* xvi.
375, 379-386; is accused of plotting to kill Herod, xvi. 387-391;
is killed by the mob at Herod's
instigation, xvi. 393

Tirzah. See Tharse

Tishbi. See Thesbone

Tishri. See Thisri

Tisithen, Egyptian name for
Moses, *Ap.* i. 290

Titans, mythological giant divini-
ties, (var. *A.* vii. 71); chained
in Tartarus (*Ap.* ii. 240);
chained in prison (ii. 247)

tithes, Jewish law on, *A.* iv. 205,
241-243; *V.* 63, 80; *Ap.* i. 88

Titius (1). See Tedetius

Titius (2), governor of Syria,

reconciled with Archelaus by Herod, *A.* xvi. 270

Titus (1) Caesar, Roman commander at Jerusalem and emperor, attests to fact that civil strife ruined Jews, *B.* i. 10 ; i. 25, 27, 28, 29 ; iii. 8, 64, 110, 238 ; captures Japha, iii. 298-307 ; iii. 324, 396, 399, 408, 446 ; at Tarichaeae, iii. 471-504 ; iv. 32, 70-71, 87 ; ʌt Gischala, iv. 92-120 ; iv. 130, 498, 501, 597, 627, 658 ; v. 1 ; advances on Jerusalem, v. 40-53 ; is cut off and his life imperilled, v. 54-66 ; saves legion, v. 81-97 ; v. 159 ; at Jerusalem, v. 106-135 ; v. 258, 281, 289, 292, 295, 303, 310, 316, 319-320, 324-325, 346, 356, 360, 408-409, 422, 446, 450, 455, 463, 486, 491, 519, 522, 530, 540, 553 ; vi. 33, 54, 82, 93, 118, 124, 130, 146, 163, 228, 230 ; holds staff meeting, vi. 236-243 ; vi. 249, 251, 254, 316, 321, 323, 327 ; his speech to John and Simon, vi. 328-350 ; vi. 352, 356, 362, 378, 380, 409, 418, 440 ; vii. 21, 23, 37, 63, 75, 96, 100, 104-105, 111, 119, 124, 128, 152, 308, 450 ; maintains Jewish privileges in Antioch, *A.* xii. 121-122, 128 ; xx. 144 ; captures the temple, xx. 250 ; author of *Commentaries* on Jewish War, *V.* 358 ; conducts Jewish war, 359 ; Josephus presents to him his account of the Jewish war, 361 ; affixes signature to Josephus' *History of the Jewish War* and orders its publication, 363 ; is sent to siege of Jerusalem, with Josephus accompanying him, 416 ; is constantly besought by Romans to punish Josephus as their betrayer, 416 ; represses Roman soldiers' outbursts against Josephus, 417 ; urges Josephus to take whatever he wishes from wreck of Jerusalem, 417 ; is requested by Josephus to free some Jews,

gives Josephus some sacred books, 418 ; is petitioned by Josephus for his brother and fifty friends, permits Josephus to enter the temple, 419 ; sends Josephus to prospect whether Tekoa is suitable for a camp, 420 ; orders, upon Josephus' request, that three of Josephus' crucified friends be taken down, 420-421 ; gives Josephus parcel of ground in the plain to replace his lands in Jerusalem, 422 ; as emperor shows high esteem for Josephus, 428 ; keeps Josephus as prisoner under surveillance, *Ap.* i. 48 ; is sent, accompanied by Josephus, from Alexandria to siege of Jerusalem, i. 48 ; commander-in-chief in Jewish war, used as witness by Josephus for his account of Jewish war, i. 50 ; Josephus presents the volume of his *Jewish War* to him, i. 51 ; occupies the temple in Jerusalem, ii. 82

Titus (2) Phrygius. See Phrygius, Titus

Tityus, Greek mythological figure, *B.* ii. 156

Tobias, father of Joseph the Tobiad, *A.* xii. 160

Tobias, sons of (Tobiads), *B.* i. 31-32 ; support Menelaus, *A.* xii. 239-240

Tochoa (Heb. Tappuah), city in Judaea, fortified by Bacchides, *A.* xiii. 15

Togarmah. See Thugrames

Tol. See Thainos

Tola. See Thoulas

Tomane. See Labina

Tomiane. See Labina

Tongius (1), Titus, Roman, father of Titus Tongius (2) of Crustuminian tribe, *A.* xiv. 229

Tongius (2), Titus, Roman of Crustuminian tribe, present when Lentulus issues decree exempting Jewish citizens of Ephesus from military service, *A.* xiv. 229, 238

toparchy, division of a political district, *B.* ii. 98, 167, 252, 509,

567, 652; iii. 48, 54-55; iv. 444, 504, 511, 551; *A.* viii. 35; xiii. 102; xvii. 25

Trachon. See Trachonitis

Trachonitis (Trachon) (Trachonites), region in Coele-Syria south of Damascus, added to Herod's realm, *B.* i. 398; i. 400; inherited by Philip, i. 668; its archers, ii. 58; ii. 95, 215, 247, 421; iii. 56, 510, 512, 542; founded by Uz, *A.* i. 145; xiii. 427; given to Herod by Augustus, xv. 343-345; on border of Zenodorus' territory, xv. 360; (Trachon) its people revolt against Herod, xvi. 130; rebels against Herod's rule, xvi. 271, 273; subdued by Herod, xvi. 276, 285; its people resort to brigandage, xvi. 292; its brigands flee to Arabia, xvi. 347; (Trachonites) Herod attempts to free himself from their danger to him by settling Babylonian Jews in Batanaea nearby, xvii. 23, 25-26; bequeathed by Herod as tetrarchy to Philip, xvii. 189; given to Philip by Augustus, xvii. 319; ruled by Philip the tetrarch, xviii. 106; xviii. 137; granted to Agrippa II, xx. 138; joins Varus, viceroy of Agrippa II, in attack on "Babylonian Jews" in Ecbatana, *V.* 54; forcible circumcision of two nobles from there is prevented by Josephus, 112-113

Trajan, Roman commander of tenth legion, captures Japha, *B.* iii. 289-307; iii. 458, 485; iv. 450

Tralles, city in Asia Minor, Jews' rights there reaffirmed, *A.* xiv. 242; xiv. 245

Transjordan, *A.* xvii. 254

Treasury, in Rome, depository of decrees of the Senate, *A.* xiv. 219, 221; at Palatine, xix. 223

Trebellius Maximus, Roman, smashes image of Gaius Caligula in Sentius Saturninus' ring, *A.* xix. 185

tribal chief. See phylarch

Tripolis, city in Syria, aided by Herod, *B.* i. 422; *A.* xii. 389; xiii. 279; xiv. 39

Tripoliticus, pamphlet attacking Athens, Sparta, and Thebes, not written by Theopompus, *Ap.* i. 221

Troglodytis (Troglodytes), name of Arabian shore of Red Sea, *A.* i. 239; bequeathed to descendants of Keturah, ii. 213; (Troglodytes) their women customarily take charge of flocks, ii. 259

Trojan War, warriors in it were ignorant of writing, *Ap.* i. 11-12; nearly a thousand years later than Hycsos, i. 104

Tromentina. See Menenian

Trypho (1), Herod's barber, accuses Tiro of plotting to kill Herod, *B.* i. 547-548, *A.* xvi. 387; (xvi. 393)

Trypho (2) (Tryphon), Diodotus, guardian of young Antiochus, *B.* i. 49-51; general of Alexander Balas, xiii. 131-132; xiii. 143-144, 147, 186; his plot against Jonathan, xiii. 187-190; captures Jonathan by treachery, xiii. 191-193; marches on Judaea, xiii. 196-197; xiii. 202; his treachery toward the Jews, xiii. 202-208; kills Jonathan, xiii. 209; kills Antiochus VI and claims throne, xiii. 218-222; defeated by Antiochus VII, xiii. 223; his death, xiii. 224; kills Jonathan the high priest, xx. 239

Tryphon (1). See Trypho (2)

Tryphon (2), jester of Ptolemy Epiphanes, *A.* xii. 212-213

Tryphon (3), son of Theudion, Jewish envoy to Emperor Claudius, *A.* xx. 14

Tubal. See Theobel

Tubal-Cain. See Jubel

Tullius Cicero, M. See Cicero, M. Tullius

Tusculum, city in Italy, *A.* xviii. 179

Tutimaeus, Egyptian king, over-

GENERAL INDEX

thrown by Hycsos invaders, *Ap.* i. 75

Typhon, Egyptian god to whom city of Auaris is dedicated, *Ap.* i. 237

Tyrannius Priscus. See Priscus (2)

Tyrannus, officer of Herod, *B.* i. 527; Herod's bodyguard, *A.* xvi. 314; killed at Antipater's prompting, xvi. 327

Tyre (1) (Tyrians), city in Phoenicia, *B.* i. 147, 231, 238, 245, 249, 275, 361, 422, 543; ii. 239, 459, 478, 504, 588; iii. 35, 38-39; iv. 105; sends gift of cedar wood to David, *A.* vii. 66, 335; their king sends greetings to Solomon, viii. 50; viii. 55, 57, 62; sends craftsmen to build the temple, viii. 76; Hiram its king, viii. 141-142; their records translated into Greek, viii. 144; Abdemon one of their citizens, viii. 149; viii. 163; Solomon marries their women, viii. 191; viii. 317; Jezebel builds temple to one of their gods, viii. 318; viii. 320; Ithobalos its king, viii. 324; worship Baal, ix. 138; their archives, ix. 283; ix. 285-286; their archives, ix. 287; besieged by Nebuchadnezzar, x. 228; xi. 317, 319-321, 325; attacks Jews, xii. 331; xiii. 154; Demetrius II put to death there, xiii. 268; xiv. 62, 120; Julius Caesar's decrees about Jews inscribed there, xiv. 197; xiv. 288, 290, 297-298, 305; commanded to restore possessions to Jews, xiv. 313; its Jews given privileges by Antony, xiv. 314; commanded by Antony to return Jewish possessions, xiv. 319; xiv. 327; exclude the Parthian Pacorus, xiv. 333; Antony refuses to give it to Cleopatra, xv. 95; xv. 169; xvi. 370; xviii. 150; xx. 125; its Jews capture Gischala in 66, but are then defeated by John of Gischala, *V.* 44-45; 372; Ves-

pasian arrives there accompanied by Agrippa II, 407; reprimanded by Vespasian for insulting Agrippa II, 408; bitterest enemies of Jews among the Phoenicians, *Ap.* i. 70; its archives record that Solomon built the temple 143 years before foundation of Carthage, i. 107-108; Hiram its king, i. 109; temple of Zeus there, i. 113; evidence of Menander of Ephesus concerning its kings, i. 117; temple of Zeus there, i. 118; Philostratus mentions its siege, i. 144; besieged by Nebuchadnezzar, i. 156; its kings enumerated, i. 156-159; its siege begun by Nebuchadnezzar, i. 159; their books agree with Jewish Scripture and Chaldean books on chronology of the temple, i. 160; their laws prohibiting use of foreign oaths cited by Theophrastus, i. 167

Tyre (2), city in Transjordan near Heshbon built by Hyrcanus, *A.* xii. 233

Tyrian (1) coin, *B.* ii. 592

Tyrian (2) purple, *A.* viii. 185

"Tyrians (Tyre), Ladder of the," mountain range north of Ptolemais in Galilee, *B.* ii. 188; *A.* xiii. 146

Tyropoeon. See Cheesemakers, Valley of

Tyrrhenians, Italian people (Etruscans), given citizenship by Romans, *Ap.* ii. 40

ULATHA, village in Syria, given to Herod, *A.* xv. 360; xvii. 25

Unleavened Bread, Festival of. See Passover

Upper City. See Jerusalem, topography

Ur (1), Chaldaean city where Haran died, *A.* i. 151

Ur (2) (Bibl. Hur), husband of Miriam, *A.* iii. 54

Ures (1) (Bibl. Hur), Midianite king, *A.* iv. 161

Ures (2) (Bibl. Ben Hur), governor of Ephraim under Solomon, *A.* viii. 35

GENERAL INDEX

Uri, father of Bezalel, *A.* iii. 105
Uriah, husband of Bath-sheba, *A.* vii. 131; his death planned by David, vii. 134-140; his death reported to David, vii. 141, 144; vii. 146, 153-154, 391
Urias (1), father of Hiram the Tyrian craftsman, *A.* viii. 76
Urias (2), high priest, son of Jothamos, *A.* x. 153
Urus (Bibl. Hul), son of Aram the son of Shem, founder of Armenia, *A.* i. 145
Uses (Bibl. Uz), son of Aram the son of Shem, founder of Trachonitis and Damascus, *A.* i. 145
usury, Jewish law on, *A.* iv. 266
Utica (Uticans, Itykaians), city in northern Africa, north-west of Carthage, (Itykaians) Hiram's successful campaign against them, *A.* viii. 146; successful campaign against it by Hiram, *Ap.* i. 119
Ux (Bibl. Uz), son of Nahor, *A.* i. 153
Uz (1). See Uses
Uz (2). See Ux
Uzal, son of Joktan, *A.* i. 147
Uzzah. See Ozas
Uzzi (1). See Jotham(os) (1)
Uzzi (2). See Ozis
Uzziah. See Ozias

VALE, the, region beginning at Carmel, won by tribe of Asher, *A.* v. 85
Valens, Fabius, general of Vitellius, *B.* iv. 547
Valerianus, decurion sent by Vespasian to Tiberias with peace proposals, *B.* iii. 448-452
Valerius (1) Asiaticus, Roman consul, *A.* xix. 102, 159; claimant to the empire after Gaius' death, xix. 252
Valerius (2). See Gratus (2)
Valerius (3). See Messala
Valerius (4), Lucius, father of Lucius Valerius (5) the praetor (or consul), *A.* xiv. 145
Valerius (5), Lucius, Roman praetor (or consul), *A.* xiv. 145

Valley of Antiochus. See Antiochus, Ravine (Valley) of
"Valley of Blessing." See "Blessing, Valley of"
Valley of Cheesemakers. See Cheesemakers, Valley of
Valley of the Cilicians. See Cilicians, Valley of the
Valley of the Fountain. See Siloam
Valley of the Giants. See Giants, Valley of the
Valley of Kings. See "royal plain"
Vardanes, son of Artabanus, succeeds his father as king of Parthia, contemplates war against the Romans, *A.* xx. 69, 71; his death, xx. 73
Varro, Roman governor of Syria, *B.* i. 398; *A.* xv. 345
Varus (1), Quintilius, Roman governor of Syria, *B.* i. 20, 617-618, 620, 622, 625, 627-628, 636, 639-640; ii. 16-18, 25, 39-41, 45, 54; marches to aid Sabinus, ii. 66-75; quells Idumaean revolt, ii. 76-79; ii. 80, 83; *A.* xvii. 89; hears Herod accuse Antipater, xvii. 91, 93, 118, 120; hears Antipater's defence, xvii. 127; his advice to Herod, xvii. 131-133; prevents Sabinus from taking Herod's property, xvii. 221-222, 229; puts down revolt in Judaea, xvii. 250-252; called to aid Sabinus in putting down revolt of Jews, xvii. 256, 268; comes to aid of Sabinus and subdues revolt, xvii. 286, 288-300; urges Philip to go to aid of Archelaus, xvii. 303; invades Judaea, *Ap.* i. 34
Varus (2) (Noarus), friend of Agrippa II, (Noarus: identified by Schürer with Varus) *B.* ii. 247; (Noarus) relative of King Soaemus of Emesa, *B.* ii. 481-483; viceroy of Agrippa, receives letter from Philip son of Jacimus, *V.* 48-49; slays envoys from Philip, 50, 52; slays many Jews to ingratiate

GENERAL INDEX

380

GENERAL INDEX

Zambrias (2) (Bibl. Zimri), commander of horsemen under Elah king of Israel, slays Elah, *A.* viii. 307-308 ; becomes king of Israel, viii. 309 ; his death, viii. 310-311

Zaraios (Bibl. Zerah), king of Ethiopia, attacks Asa, *A.* viii. 292 ; defeated by Asa, viii. 293

Zarasa (var. Gazasa, Gazaga ; Bibl. Zeresh), wife of Haman, *A.* xi. 245 ; advises Haman to crucify Mordecai, xi. 246

Zarephath. See Sarephtha

Zarmunes (Bibl. Zalmunna), chief of Midianites, *A.* v. 288

Zealots, *B.* ii. 651 ; iv. 160-161, 302-310, 490, 514-558 ; v. 3, 5, 7, 101-103, 250, 358, 528 ; vi. 92, 148 ; vii. 268

Zeb (Bibl. Zeeb), king of Midianites, killed by Israelites, *A.* v. 227

Zebadiah. See Zabadias

Zebah. See Zebes

Zebedee (Bibl. Zabdi), father of Achan, *A.* v. 33

Zebes (Bibl. Zebah), chief of Midianites, *A.* v. 228

Zebeke (Bibl. Bezek) (Zebekenians), city in Canaan, *A.* v. 121 ; (Zebekenians) v. 121

Zebinas, Alexander. See Alexander (3) Zebinas

Zebudah. See Zabuda

Zebul. See Zabul

Zebulun. See Zabulon

Zechariah (1), prophet, encourages Jews, *A.* xi. 96, 106

Zechariah (2). See Zacharias (3)

Zedekiah (1). See Sacchias

Zedekiah (2). See Sedekias (1)

Zeeb. See Zeb

Zelophehad. See Solophantes

Zelpha. See Zelphah

Zelphah (Zelpha ; Bibl. Zilpah), handmaid of Leah, concubine of Jacob, *A.* i. 303 ; (Zelpha) gives birth to two sons, i. 306 ; her children, ii. 182

Zemaraim. See Samaron, Mt.

Zemarite. See Samaraeus

Zembran(es) (Bibl. Zimran), son of Abraham and Keturah, *A.* i. 238

Zena. See Zeus

Zeno (1). See Zenodorus

Zeno (2) (Zenon), surnamed Cotulas (Cotylas), *B.* i. 60 ; despot of Philadelphia, father of Theodorus, i. 86 ; ruler of Philadelphia, surnamed Cotylas, *A.* xiii. 235 ; xiii. 356, 393

Zeno (3), Greek Stoic philosopher, mentioned as genius by Apion, *Ap.* ii. 135

Zenodorus (Zeno), leases domain of Lysanias, *B.* i. 398-399 ; his death, i. 400 ; (Zeno) ii. 95 ; loses his territory of Trachonitis to Herod, *A.* xv. 344-345, 349 ; stirs up Arabs against Herod, xv. 352, 355 ; his death, xv. 359 ; his territory given to Herod, xv. 363 ; Trachonitis taken from him and given to Herod, xvi. 271 ; a portion of his domain given to Philip by Augustus, xvii. 319

Zenon. See Zeno (2)

Zephaniah. See Sephenias

Zephathah. See Saphatha

Zepho. See Sophous

Zephyrion, place in Cilicia in Asia Minor, *B.* i. 456

Zerah (1). See Zaraios

Zerah (2). See Ezele(os)

Zeresh. See Zarasa

Zerubbabel. See Zorobabelos

Zeruiah. See Saruia

Zetho. See Berzetho

Zeugma, city on right bank of upper Euphrates in region of Samosata, *B.* vii. 105

Zeus (Zena), Enyalius (" the Warlike "), his sacred vessels taken by priests from Tower of Babel to Senaar in Babylonia, *A.* i. 119 ; his temple in Tyre, viii. 145 ; his temple in Tyre adorned by Hiram, viii. 147 ; (*Zena*) accusative case of Zeus, identified by Aristaeus with Jewish God, xii. 22 ; (Zeus Hellenios) Samaritan temple to him, xii. 261, 263 ; (" Zeus "), statue, called Olympian, ordered brought to Rome by Gaius Caligula, xix. 8 ; Gaius Caligula's audacity towards

35°

SEA

E.

33°

PTOLEM.
(Acch

MOU

Dora

32°
30' CAESAREA
(Strato's Tower)

DS 1408   35

GALILEE & SURROUNDING DISTRICT (c. 40 B.C. – 70 A.D.)

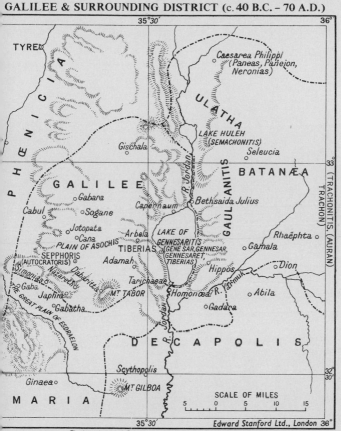

The boundaries of Galilee represent the greatest extent of that
territory during the reign of Herod the Great.

SCALE OF MILES
5   0   5   10

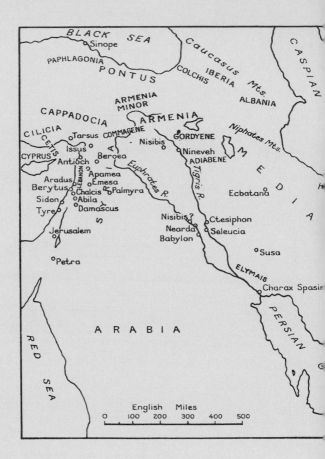